ADOLESCENT PSYCHIATRY

VOLUME I

DEVELOPMENTAL AND CLINICAL STUDIES

Editorial Board

Annals of the American Society for Adolescent Psychiatry

ADOLESCENT PSYCHIATRY

VOLUME I

DEVELOPMENTAL AND CLINICAL STUDIES

EDITED BY

SHERMAN C. FEINSTEIN
PETER L. GIOVACCHINI
ARTHUR A. MILLER

BASIC BOOKS, INC., PUBLISHERS

NEW YORK   LONDON

IN MEMORIAM

WILLIAM A. SCHONFELD, M D.

William A. Schonfeld died at the age of sixty-four in New York City on September 21, 1970. In May 1969, at the First Scientific Meeting of the American Society for Adolescent Psychiatry, he was awarded the Distinguished Service Award for his outstanding efforts in behalf of Adolescent Psychiatry and in recognition of his role as founder and first president of the Society. His energy and vitality were a wonder to all who worked with him and his death is an enormous loss.

After his graduation from the University and Bellevue Hospital Medical College in 1931, he was trained in child psychiatry and pediatrics and was certified as a Diplomate of the American Boards of Psychiatry, Child Psychiatry and Pediatrics. He was on the faculty of the College of Physicians and Surgeons, Columbia University, and on the staffs of the Vanderbilt Clinic of the Columbia-Presbyterian Medical Center, New York State Psychiatric Institute, Morrisania City Hospital and Mount Sinai Hospital.

William A. Schonfeld was President of the New York Society for Adolescent Psychiatry in 1961. He represented the position of adolescent psychiatry on the Committee on Child Psychiatry of the American Psychiatric Association from 1963–1966 and was instrumental in its change of name to the Committee on the Psychiatry of Childhood and Adolescence. He was to be a Delegate to the 1970 White House Conference on Children and was on the executive committee of the Council of National Organizations for Children and Youth. He had served at the 1950 and 1960 White House Conferences.

He sensed the need for a national organization as groups were forming in Philadelphia, Chicago, and Los Angeles following the lead of New York. In 1967 in Detroit, his proposal was accepted and the American Society for Adolescent Psychiatry was formed with William A. Schonfeld as the first President. He served for two years with creative leadership and saw groups in Maryland, New Orleans, the Carolinas, and North Texas join the Society.

In 1968 he lectured in South America and as a result of his efforts the Argentina Society of Psychiatry and Psychology of Childhood and Adolescence was formed with whom ASAP will hold a joint meeting in January 1971.

William A. Schonfeld was devoted to his family, his practice of child and adolescent psychiatry, and the general psychiatric community. He made great contributions in scientific research, teaching and promoting the communication of knowledge about the children and adolescents he knew and loved so well. We mourn the loss of a dear friend and colleague.

SHERMAN C. FEINSTEIN

FOREWORD

BY WILLIAM A. SCHONFELD

THE AMERICAN SOCIETY FOR ADOLESCENT PSYCHIATRY

1958–1970

It was early in 1958 that a group of child and adult psychiatrists mutually interested in adolescents first met in New York City to discuss the feasibility of an organization, and in October 1958 established the Society for Adolescent Psychiatry of New York. The basic aims of the Society were to provide a forum for the exchange of psychiatric knowledge about the adolescent, to encourage the development of adequate training facilities for adolescent psychiatry, to stimulate research in the psychopathology and treatment of adolescents, and to foster the development of adequate adolescent services.

The Philadelphia Society for Adolescent Psychiatry was subsequently organized in 1962, the Chicago Society in 1964, the Southern California Society in 1967, the Maryland Society in 1968, the New Orleans Society in 1969, and the Carolinas and North Texas Chapters in 1970.

The first recognition given to the organization was by the Executive Committee of the American Psychiatric Association in 1962, requesting that the New York Society sponsor a Round Table on Adolescent Psychiatry. In 1963, a representative was appointed as a member of the APA committee on Psychiatry in Childhood and Adolescence, and since then other members of the Society have served.

On May 9, 1967, a confederation of local societies formed the American Society for Adolescent Psychiatry. The first officers elected were: William A. Schonfeld, New York, President; Sheldon Selesnick, Los Angeles, Vice President; Sherman C. Feinstein, Chicago, Treasurer; Herman Staples, Philadelphia, Secretary. Because it is a federation of local societies, there is no direct membership in the American Society for Adolescent Psychiatry; membership is attained through joining one of the local societies. The Council of each SAP appoints delegates to the annual meeting and decisions are based on a unit vote.

We have established liaison relationships with the American Orthopsychiatric Association, the National Association of Private Psychiatric Hospitals, the American Medical Association, and the American College Health Association, and participate in joint sessions at their annual meetings. We are active members of the Council of National Organizations for Children and Youth, and participated in planning for the 1970 White House Conference for Children and Youth. We are also an affiliate association of the International Association for Child Psychiatry, and took part in their International Congress on the "Family" in 1970 in Israel.

With the founding of the Society, committees were appointed to study pertinent problems of adolescence. The Annual Scientific Meetings of 1969 and 1970 and the Conference on Training of November 1969 received reports of these studies and some of these findings are reported in this volume. Distinguished Service Awards have been presented to Peter Blos, William A. Schonfeld, and Irene Josselyn for their outstanding contributions to adolescent psychiatry.

This volume is our Society's official publication and is our attempt to reach and communicate to our colleagues the exciting and stimulating work being done with our youthful population.

We now have over 900 members from 30 states, District of Columbia, Puerto Rico, Canada, Venezuela, and Argentina. Our members are among the leaders in the development of adolescent psychiatry in the country. Practically every director of an adolescent psychiatry service in the United States is a member of ASAP, and many of our members hold professorial ranks at major universities. In the short existence of our Society we have succeeded in establishing an identity as a national organization without losing, but rather enhancing, the identity and individuality of the constituent societies. But this is only the beginning.

WILLIAM A. SCHONFELD

THE AUTHORS

BRAHM BAITTLE is Assistant Clinical Professor of Psychiatry at the Abraham Lincoln School of Medicine, the University of Illinois College of Medicine. He is an Attending Psychiatrist at the Institute for Psychosomatic and Psychiatric Research and Training of Michael Reese Hospital and Medical Center, Chicago, Illinois.

JULIAN I. BARISH is formerly Director of the Psychiatric Treatment Center and Chief, Four Winds Hospital Adolescent Service. He is President of the New York Society for Adolescent Psychiatry.

BRUNO BETTELHEIM is the Stella M. Rowley Distinguished Service Professor of Education, Departments of Psychology and Psychiatry and Director, Sonia Shankman Orthogenic School of the University of Chicago.

PETER BLOS is a Faculty Member and Supervisor of Child and Adolescent Analysis at the New York Psychoanalytic Institute. He is President (1970–1972) of the American Association for Child Analysis. He received the 1969 Distinguished Service Award of the American Society for Adolescent Psychiatry.

GENE H. BOROWITZ is Associate Professor of Psychiatry and Director of Psychiatric Residency Training at the University of Illinois School of Medicine, Chicago, Illinois.

L. BRYCE BOYER is in the private practice of psychiatry and psychoanalysis in Berkeley, California. Formerly Research Associate in the Departments of Anthropology at the University of California and New Mexico, he is currently Psychiatric Consultant to the Alta Bates Hospital and Herrick Hospital.

FREDERICK WILLIAM COONS is an Assistant Professor in the Department of Psychiatry, Indiana University Medical School, and Director of the Psychiatric Division of the Indiana University Student Health Service.

ALFRED FLARSHEIM is Clinical Assistant Professor of Psychiatry at the University of Illinois College of Medicine. He is a member of the Group for the Advancement of Psychiatry Committee on the College Student and Psychiatric Consultant to the North Shore Country Day School, Winnetka, Illinois.

DANIEL X. FREEDMAN is Louis Block Professor of Biological Sciences and Chairman, Department of Psychiatry, Pritzker School of Medicine, University of Chicago. He is Editor of the Archives of General Psychiatry and Chairman of the American Psychiatric Association Task Force on Drug Abuse in Youth.

PETER L. GIOVACCHINI is Clinical Professor of Psychiatry at the University of Illinois College of Medicine and in private practice of psychoanalysis. A managing editor of this volume, he has edited and authored many books and articles. He is a past President of the Chicago Society for Adolescent Psychiatry.

ROY R. GRINKER, SR., is Director of the Institute for Psychosomatic and Psychiatric Research and Training and Chairman Department of Psychiatry Michael Reese Hospital and Medical Center and Professor of Psychiatry, Pritzker School of Medicine, University of Chicago. Formerly Editor of the Archives of General Psychiatry, he was the 1970 Benjamin Rush Lecturer at the Annual Meeting of the American Psychiatric Association.

IRENE M. JOSSELYN is Training Analyst at the Southern California Psychoanalytic Institute and Clinical Professor of Child Psychiatry at the University of Southern California. Formerly Chairman of the Committee on Child Analytic Training and Training Analyst at the Chicago Institute for Psychoanalysis as well as Editor of the Journal of the American Academy of Child Psychiatry, she now resides in Phoenix, Arizona where she served as President of the Arizona Psychiatric Society (1967–1968). Dr. Josselyn received the 1970 Distinguished Service Award from the American Society for Adolescent Psychiatry.

KENNETH KENISTON is Professor of Psychology, Department of Psychiatry and Director, Behavior Sciences Study Center, Yale University School of Medicine. He is a member of the Carnegie Commission on

Higher Education and the Task Force on Adolescents and Youth of the Joint Commission on Mental Health of Children.

MALVINA W. KREMER is a Training Analyst in the Comprehensive Course in Psychoanalysis, New York Medical College, Assistant Clinical Professor of Psychiatry and Psychiatrist-in-Charge of the Adolescent Clinic at Metropolitan Hospital. She is Associate Clinical Professor of Psychiatry at New York University School of Medicine, past President of the Society for Adolescent Psychiatry and the Society of Medical Psychoanalysts.

LAURENCE LOEB is Assistant Clinical Professor of Psychiatry at the Cornell University Medical College. Formerly Psychiatrist to Briarcliff College, he is President-Elect of the Psychiatric Society of Westchester. He is coeditor (with Leopold Bellak) of the *Schizophrenic Syndrome*.

LEONARD NEFF is Clinical Professor of Psychiatry at New York University School of Medicine and Assistant Visiting Psychiatrist at the New York University-Bellevue Medical Center. He is past President of the New York Society for Adolescent Psychiatry.

KENNETH NEWMAN is Director of Adolescent Services and Associate Attending Psychiatrist at the Institute for Psychosomatic and Psychiatric Research and Training, Michael Reese Hospital and Medical Center, Chicago, Illinois.

DANIEL OFFER is Associate Director of the Institute for Psychosomatic and Psychiatric Research and Training of Michael Reese Hospital and Medical Center and Associate Professor of Psychiatry at the Pritzker School of Medicine, University of Chicago. He is Secretary of the American Society for Adolescent Psychiatry and a past President of the Chicago Society for Adolescent Psychiatry.

ROBERT PORTER is an Associate Clinical Professor of Child Psychiatry at Mount Sinai School of Medicine and Chief of Pediatric Psychiatry liaison. He is President-Elect of the New York Council on Child Psychiatry and a past President of the New York Society for Adolescent Psychiatry.

DONALD B. RINSLEY is Director, Children's Section, Topeka State Hospital and member of the Executive and Training Faculty in Child Psychiatry, Menninger School of Psychiatry. He is Associate Clinical Professor of Psychiatry, University of Kansas School of Medicine.

GILBERT J. ROSE is Associate Clinical Professor, Department of Psychiatry, Yale University School of Medicine and Instructor, Western New England Institute for Psychoanalysis, New Haven, Connecticut.

WILLIAM A. SCHONFELD is Assistant Clinical Professor of Child Psychiatry at the College of Physicians and Surgeons, Columbia University. He is on the attending staff of the New York State Psychiatric Institute and Columbia Presbyterian Hospital and was formerly Chief of the Adolescent Research Unit in the Department of Psychiatry at Columbia-Presbyterian Medical Center. He is past President of the American Society for Adolescent Psychiatry and was recipient of the society's first Distinguished Service Award (1969).

MAX SUGAR is Clinical Associate Professor, Department of Psychiatry and Behavioral Sciences, Louisiana State University. He is President of the New Orleans Society for Adolescent Psychiatry.

PAUL H. TOLPIN is Attending Psychiatrist at the Psychosomatic and Psychiatric Institute of Michael Reese Hospital and Medical Center. He is Psychiatric Consultant to the Illinois State Psychiatric Institute and a faculty member of the Chicago Institute for Psychoanalysis.

M. ROBERT WILSON is consultant in Child and Adolescent Psychiatry at the Mayo Clinic, Rochester, Minnesota. He is Professor of Psychiatry, Carleton College, Northfield, Minnesota and Instructor in Psychiatry at the Mayo Graduate School of Medicine.

D. W. WINNICOTT practices child psychoanalysis in England where he was a physician on the staff of Paddington Green Children's Hospital. He is a past President of the British Psycho-Analytical Society and was formerly Chairman of the Medical Section of the British Psychological Society and President of the Paediatric Section of the Royal Society of Medicine.

ERNEST S. WOLF is Assistant Professor of Psychiatry and Director, Mental Health Section, Student Health Service, Northwestern University. He is on the Faculty of the Chicago Institute for Psychoanalysis and a past President of the Chicago Society for Adolescent Psychiatry.

PREFACE

This volume, sponsored by the American Society for Adolescent Psychiatry, reflects the increasing interest in adolescence as a stage of life. This interest stems from several sources. As a clinical challenge adolescence demands the utilization of specialized techniques. As a period of life adolescence may be of great importance in the general understanding of development and psychopathology. Beyond the individual, adolescence is also a social phenomenon. The adolescent needs to be understood for his influence on values and social institutions.

Psychoanalysis has provided us with a dynamic theoretical system in which the personality has been depicted in terms of conflicting inner forces. Developmental factors are also important and the experiences of the first years of life, the first year especially, have been assigned considerable significance in determining the eventual outcome of psychic integration. Thus, the interplay of constitutional endowment and the nurturing infantile environment during which early object relations are established leads to a sequence of developmental stages resulting in the structuring of the ego.

The longitudinal observational approach has confirmed the etiological importance of infancy on normal emotional development and the genesis of psychopathology. The oedipal period, during which the identificatory processes receive their greatest stimulation, continues to affect developmental growth. However, there is a growing conviction that adolescence as a developmental stage may be more important than has been recognized. It may achieve the same degree of significance as an etiological precursor of later development as has been assigned to the infantile period.

If adolescence has formative potential for future development, then it represents a phase of life in which there is a possibility of a "second chance," one that might undo the harmful effects of a traumatic infancy. Possibly many of the disruptive and peculiar aspects of adolescence are examples of both successful and unsuccessful attempts to effect a reorientation that will rectify the distorted direction of previous development. Adolescent behavior, moratoriums, and other actions gain another perspective if they are seen as adaptations designed to achieve characterological stability.

Adolescence is also a period in which experiences have far-reaching consequences in the synthesis and stabilization of character formation. The adolescent suffering from a character disorder has general adjustment difficulties rather than discrete symptoms. This group is not easily conceptualized in a psychodynamic frame of intrapsychic conflicts, but is more easily understood in ego-psychological or behavioral terms with the sources of the tensions in adolescence itself. Concentration on this stage of life then becomes especially important when dealing with patients suffering from characterological problems rather than the rarely seen classical psychoneuroses.

This does not necessarily mean that adolescence is the crucial developmental phase and that childhood experiences recede into the background. It may mean that infancy will recede into the background insofar as adolescence is the time when major characterological formations occur. However, infantile factors continue exerting their effects; the importance of one phase does not exclude the other.

The whole world is in a ferment that has affected values and social institutions. The industrialization and computerization of society has led to basic changes in child-rearing techniques and attitudes. Adolescence has been extended as children are kept in a dependent position for a longer period while being stimulated sexually and intellectually earlier. This demands that any examination of adolescence includes the biological, anthropological, sociological, as well as the psychological approach.

The purpose, therefore, of a publication such as this one is to explore adolescence as a process. We hope to enter challenging and exciting areas that may have profound effects on our basic concepts. Though our focus will be clinical and developmental, we recognize that creative ideas come from many areas and can become clinically valuable even if they do not seem to directly contribute to our needs at the moment.

This volume was designed with a twofold purpose. It can stand on its own as a contribution to adolescent psychiatry. However, we hope that it will be the first volume of a series that will provide a forum for the expression of ideas and problems that plague and excite so many of us working in this enigmatic but fascinating field.

SHERMAN C. FEINSTEIN
PETER L. GIOVACCHINI
ARTHUR A. MILLER

CONTENTS

xvii

PART III

EFFECTS OF EARLY OBJECT RELATIONS ON ADOLESCENT CHARACTER STRUCTURE

PART IV

TRAINING IN ADOLESCENT PSYCHIATRY

Contents

PART V
PSYCHOTHERAPY OF ADOLESCENCE

PART I

ADOLESCENCE: GENERAL CONSIDERATIONS

INTRODUCTION

Today, as in no other time in history, adolescence has taken over the center stage. This curious time in a human's life has suddenly attracted the attention of the entire world. Its idealism and concrete truthfulness have embarrassed and challenged all the professions to describe, analyze, tolerate, and treat the various manifestations of this process.

Part I of this volume contains essays that give a general feeling for adolescent activity at this time in history. Peter Blos discusses the generation gap. As the first essay, it is significant on many levels. It was presented as the first Distinguished Service Award lecture at the first scientific meeting of the American Society for Adolescent Psychiatry. Blos, who has done so much to clarify adolescence as the "second separation-individuation process," sees two extremes of the generational conflict; from a prolonged distancing device used as a defense against maturational failure to an individuating and differentiating device where resolution of adolescence is finally achieved.

Bruno Bettelheim is deeply concerned with the alienation of youth through automation and feels that personal importance is being robbed. Youth is kept dependent too long, is forced to go on with his education when he has little interest or ability, and therefore his youth is obsolete in terms of providing him with adequate experiences in character formation. D. W. Winnicott has contributed a most hopeful essay on the doldrums of adolescence. The cure for adolescence is the passage of time and gradual maturation. The adolescent does not want to know that he is an adolescent and must experience the vicissitudes. Society must tolerate these doldrums as part of the normal adolescent process.

Ernest Wolf presents a retrospective concept of adolescence by his examination and translation of Freud's adolescent-age letters to Emil

3

Fluss. The revelation of his identifications being formed and thinking processes becoming synthesized give insight into the resolution processes of adolescence and some indications of the early development of Freud's creativity as a scientist.

Kenneth Newman reviews the recent film *Bonnie and Clyde* and sees it illuminating the "here and now" in society in regard to the deep disturbances in its individuals and institutions. He also sees in the character development of Bonnie and Clyde examples of pathological narcissism and faulty self-esteem regulation and speculates on the developmental causes as well as the adolescent processes these defenses illustrate.

Two important chapters on the current drug problem focus on the aspect of ego impact from usage of hallucinogens and from complications of various prescribed chemicals. Daniel X. Freedman reviews the use and abuse of hallucinogens and attempts to definitively answer the questions about their use as a therapeutic agent, as a stimulant to creativity and most important, how we can best use them in the study of the mind. Leonard Neff presents an important related phenomenon to the impact of drugs on the ego with a discussion of the profound alterations from medically or self-prescribed drugs. The reactions were correlated with the phases of adolescent development and interesting correlations were seen in the disruptions and subsequent development.

1] THE GENERATION GAP:

FACT AND FICTION

PETER BLOS

From time to time, new terms make their appearance in our language and, insidiously, acquire a life of their own; they become overextended and overused. In this process they come to serve as convenient labels and ready explanations for whatever appears similar; in short, they become separated from their context of origin. At this point, they say either more or less than was intended when they first sprang from some creative tongues. "Generation gap" is such a term. It is in the process of acquiring the status of an eternal truth and reality, similar to a newly discovered star in outer space. The generation gap is an epochal phenomenon that arouses our analytic curiosity. In order to assign to this new word its proper reference, I shall delineate it from a term often used as a synonym, namely, "generational conflict."

The formation of a conflict between generations and, subsequently, its resolution is the normative task of adolescence. Its importance for cultural continuity is evident. Without this conflict no adolescent psychic restructuring will occur. This is, of course, not contradicted by the obvious fact that adolescent behavior contrasts, universally and radically, with that of the preceding years of childhood. We must not forget that, for example, sexual maturation or puberty progresses independently from psychological development. Therefore, all kinds of infantile drives and needs can find their expression and gratification in genital activity. We know from our clinical work that genital sexual behavior is a most unreliable indicator for the assessment of psychosexual maturity; no direct correlation exists between genital activity and genitality. Pres-

Distinguished Service Award lecture presented at the Annual Meeting of the American Society for Adolescent Psychiatry, May 4, 1969, Miami, Florida.

ent-day emphasis on sexual, that is, genital, freedom prompted me to emphasize this differentiation at the outset, because it can be argued on solid clinical grounds that precocious adultomorphic behavior as such, the sexual one in particular, often impedes rather than promotes progressive development. In saying this, I imply that progressive development can only be appraised if conceptualized in terms of internal changes or in terms of internal cathectic shifts. These internal processes are not necessarily noticeable, externally, by the environment and yet, revolutionary dislocations take place intrapsychically, replacing old regimes by new ones. The intensity of observable signs, or the "public noise" if you will, rarely tell us reliably what kind of psychic accommodation the adolescent is initiating or consolidating.

The revolutionary psychic changes seldom proceed in the secret depth of the soul without giving rise to excesses in action and thought, to turbulent manifestations, to ideational iconoclasm, to special forms of group behavior and social styles. None of these has ever failed to be noticed as the typical phenomenology of the transition from childhood to adulthood.

I will now set down some passages that were written sometime ago by an observer of human nature. About adolescence he had the following to say:

Young men have strong passions, and tend to gratify them indiscriminately. Of the bodily desires, it is the sexual by which they are most swayed and in which they show absence of self-control. They are changeable and fickle in their desires, which are violent while they last, but quickly over—bad temper often gets the better of them, for owing to their love of honour they cannot bear being slighted, and are indignant if they imagine themselves unfairly treated. While they love honour, they love victory still more; for youth is eager for superiority over others, and victory is one form of this. —Their lives are mainly spent not in memory but in expectation; for expectation refers to the future, memory to the past, and youth has a long future before it and a short past behind it:—their hot tempers and hopeful dispositions make them more courageous than older men are; the hot temper prevents fear, and the hopeful disposition creates confidence; we cannot feel fear so long as we are feeling angry, and any expectation of good makes us confident.—They have exalted notions, because they have not yet been humbled by life or learnt its necessary limitations; moreover, their hopeful disposition makes them think themselves equal to great things—and that means having exalted notions. They would always rather do noble deeds than useful ones: their lives are regulated more by moral feeling than by reasoning; and whereas reasoning leads us to choose what is useful, moral goodness leads us to choose what is noble. They are fonder of their friends, intimates, and companions than older men are, because they like spending

6

their days in the company of others. All their mistakes are in the direction of doing things excessively and vehemently. They love too much and hate too much, and the same with everything else. They think they know everything, and are always quite sure about it; this, in fact, is why they overdo everything. If they do wrong to others, it is because they mean to insult them, not to do them actual harm.—They are fond of fun and therefore witty, wit being well-bred insolence (Aristotle, *Rhetoric*).

This attests to the fixity of developmental stages which are timed and determined by biological processes of maturation; these processes are species bound. In contrast, the forms by which psychobiological processes are translated into psychosocial expressions, have changed widely and endlessly over historical times. Generational conflict is essential for the growth of the self and of civilization.

We can say with confidence that the conflict between generations is as old as generations themselves. This could hardly be different, because the child's physical and emotional immaturity determines his dependence on the family (nuclear or extended) and, consequently, lays down the essential models of object relations. The psychic institutions (ego, superego, ego ideal) take their origin from the internalization of object relations and, in fact, demonstrate these origins, when adolescent individuation sets in. Then, the conflicts aroused by regressive and progressive adaptations confront the maturing child with overwhelming challenges and alternatives. There lies the conflict between the generations. In essence, it is aroused by the emotional disengagement from the old and by the beckoning of the new that can only be reached via the gradual elaboration of compromise. Both these developmental achievements stabilize self-esteem in consonance with physical status, with cognitive competence, and with a value system that transcends the family ethics by seeking a broader base for its realization in society and in humanity.

The generational conflict has been conceptualized around various nodal issues of psychic differentiation: Anna Freud (1958) speaks of the "loosening of the infantile object ties," Erikson (1956) of the "identity crisis," whereas I have described the same processes in terms of the "second individuation process of adolescence." All these formulations have in common the one basic assumption that only through conflict can maturity be attained. We might carry this statement one step further and say that developmental conflict never appears without an affective correlate, such as tension, generally, and, more specifically, anxiety and depression. The tolerance for these painful affects cannot be acquired in

7

adolescence, just as one accomplishes nothing by running to the store to buy a fire extinguisher when the house is aflame. Our genetic way of thinking tells us that the developmental stage for acquiring these essential faculties is the latency period. It is at this stage that so much of adolescent trouble is brewed in blissful oblivion.

Before I continue I must define the position from which I look at disaffected youth. The fact that we live in the midst of a social revolution is not the doing of youth at all, even though youth is a carrier of the momentum to effect change. The adult state of mind has to be juxtaposed to that of youthful disaffection. Much of today's adult position is reminiscent of Voltaire's Doctor Pangloss. As you will remember, Pangloss, the all-knowledgeable tutor of Candide, sent off his bright and inquisitive charge on travels through a world of dubious human excellence. With never failing sophistry and verbosity (hence his name), Pangloss replies to Candide's intelligent questions about the absurdities of human conduct with the monotonous phrase that the world we live in is—in spite of the appearance to the contrary—"the best of all possible worlds."

It remains a deplorable fact that only through violence are the responsible institutions of society awakened and moved to change. This fact does not, in my mind, grant young people the exalted privilege to employ violence whenever something displeases them or causes them hardship. I fully appreciate the place for violence in the desperate search for a way out of the social morass of our time. I am cognizant of these issues which should not be simplified by attaching them to the generation gap. It is rather the other way round, namely, that the generation-gap-minded youth attaches itself to these broader social issues and thus imbues his sense of personal separateness and cultural discontinuity with a viable ideology and an emotional reference.

In order to continue with my topic I must narrow it down to manageable proportions and forgo the dubious courage of advancing between the crossfire of the various disciplines such as sociology, education, political theory, and history, which all contribute their share to an understanding of the youth situation today. I am no Lord Raglan, eager to fight the battle of Balaklava over again. I rather note my clinical observations as far as they relate to the generation gap issue. I make these remarks because I want the reader to know that I am cognizant of the fact that my presentation is not relevant to the total youth upheaval of today, but focuses on one form of deviant adolescent development familiar to all of us. A few clinical vignettes shall clarify this further.

Recently I had a conversation with a seventeen-year-old college freshman who had been suspended after his participation in the occupation of a building, a sit-in, and vandalism. He explained to me that the university "separated emotion from action" by substituting "action and thought." He had expected that college would give him "something like meaning and relevancy." He did not find it. He then described to me at great length the endless chain of recriminations between "us" and "them." Finally, I interrupted his reportage by reminding him of our telephone conversation at the time he made an appointment with me. I had told him then that I knew his mother had suggested that he talk with me but that I wanted to know why *he* wanted to see me. He had answered, "I have a problem of communication with my father." When I now brought this telephone conversation to his attention, he told me of a letter he had written to his father from college, asking him to "just let me be, not argue any more, but understand that I have to do what I am doing." I said at this point, "I see—you come from a very close family," whereupon his eyes watered, and he replied, "Yes, my mother always told me that I have a very good mind, that I have the germ of a book in my head." What this boy expected from college was to receive "meaning and relevancy" as a direct continuation of parental support, or, in other words, he wished that college would release him from the bondage of his childhood, just as he had wished his father could spare him the agony of the generational conflict. His life had been laid out for him at home in the friendliest of terms, but it had ceased to be his own. Being forced to leave college gave him a sense of freedom, independence, and identity which enabled him temporarily to bear his sense of guilt.

A college girl described the exquisite feeling of elation while participating in a sit-in. The great disappointment came when the administration decided not to expel the rebellious students. Said the girl to me, "I wish they had expelled me. I hate college." My reply, "Can't you leave college on your own?" was quickly answered by her saying, "Oh, no— that would disappoint my mother, and I could never do that."

A nineteen-year-old girl who had to leave college on account of anxiety symptoms settled down with her boyfriend in an apartment. Coming from a "good" middle-class family, she felt quite exceptional among her peers for living with her boyfriend; it afforded her a sense of maturity, superiority, and independence. Through her boyfriend she found herself in a group of radicals whom she idealized as the heroic protagonists in the creation of a new world. However, she never could quite trust their

9

sincerity nor her own. Being a radical offered her the opportunity to be pugnacious and hateful, both of which made her feel "good" and "real." Her boyfriend's irregular work habits pleased her because it provided her with constant companionship. Money, of course, she accepted off-handedly from her parents. It took arduous analytic work for her to admit that she is revolted by sexual intercourse. What made her submit to sex was fear of abandonment and her incapacity to be alone. This girl had possessed only one friend all through childhood and adolescence, namely, her mother. A powerful regressive pull to the preoedipal mother was counteracted by heterosexual displacement and surrender. The seeming emancipation concealed the perpetuation of infantile dependency.

All three adolescents came from white, affluent, middle-class, child-centered homes. Families like these always do things together, share their feelings freely with one another, and discuss their problems rationally. The parents are, often uncannily, attuned to their child's needs way beyond early childhood, indeed all through adolescence. They badly tolerate their child's anger, anxiety, and guilt. Tension, failure, and disappointment, which no child can be spared, become readily neutralized by a constant flow of stimulation and encouragement. One might think that such an abundance of appreciation as the immediate environment provides ought to last for a lifetime. Actions of revolt or independence, from civil disobedience to sexual freedom, often appear on closer inspection to be owing to violent ruptures of dependencies rather than to conflictual elaborations. Of course, these three adolescents had rejected their families as hopelessly out of step with the times, as lacking any insight into their children's motivations and unable to say anything relevant to their offspring. They keenly felt the generation gap. The subjective feeling of the gap is owing to its nature as a distancing device in which spatial and ideological separations are substituted for inner conflicts and emotional disengagement. The result is an arresting on the adolescent level owing to conflict avoidance; consequently, the maturation owing to conflict resolution is forfeited. This must not be true for all who take this path because, for many, it is an obligatory stance they must take in order to remain part of the group they cherish; they accept the group code only with inner reservations and temporarization.

I hinted earlier at the fact that children from such middle-class, usually liberal or progressive, homes are burdened with family ties that are difficult to alter gradually. These affectionate ties find unceasing expression from early childhood till puberty in demonstrative closeness

10

and readily available need gratification. Such upbringing, which is often recommended by the expert or by popularized and misunderstood expert opinion, interferes with normal latency development. The advances of the ego, characteristic for this stage, never become sufficiently detached from object relations and, therefore, never acquire essential autonomy. In other words, object relations are not given up and replaced by identifications (A. Freud, 1958), at least not to the extent that renders the onrush of puberty drives less devastating or disorganizing. Such children are totally unprepared to deal with adolescent regression and live in deadly fear of regressive engulfment. They have no other choice but total rupture with the past, spatial self-exile and oppositional absolutism. Drugs and sexual freedom acquire an important function in this developmental impasse by staving off regressive personality dissolution. The inability to regress prevents the rectification of infantile remnants of maldevelopment and renders the adolescent process incomplete. The sense of a generation gap and of alienation represents the subjective awareness of this impasse as an unbridgeable abyss. Ironically, this impasse has become a mark of distinction among the young. Erik H. Erikson told me not so long ago of a conversation with a student who stopped him in Harvard Yard. The student led up to the fact that he is in search of his identity. Erikson asked him: "Are you complaining or are you boasting?" We see so many young people today who carry their identity crisis like a badge of honor that should entitle them to diplomatic immunity in the foreign territory of their elders.

This brings me to another aspect of the generation gap, namely, the role of the adult society and its institutions in contributing its share to the erosion of generational bonds.

Last summer I walked into the country house of an old friend whose sixteen-year-old generation-gap-minded son greeted me heartily. I waved his greetings aside in mock disgust and said, "I don't talk to anybody under thirty." He was quick with his reply. "Ah," he said, "so you are envious of us!" This little anecdote shall serve to tell us of the motives that, so the young suspect, govern the adults' attitudes toward them. We cannot deny that there is a great deal of truth in it. The adults' obsession with youthfulness, the commercial exploitation of clothing styles the young have created, the popularization and merchandising of their "thing," all rob the young people of their rightful monopoly.

Adults gaze with fascinated attention at the young, ready to imitate them, marginally, of course, in order to evade getting older. One can observe the reciprocal role of alienated youth and disquieted adults: one

11

the performer and the other the spectator. There exists a compelling need in the young to arouse the attention of the adult world, the Establishment in all its forms and shapes. And conversely, there exists a compelling wish of the youth-minded adult to show understanding of the young by acquiescing in the face of the most outrageous insults. The most disconcerting situation presents itself if some young generation gap rebel is met by a truly fair-minded and dialogue-ready adult. What is wanted from the stereotyped adult is his admission to his wrongdoing, to his selfishness, and to his incompetence. How many times have we not heard in our consulting room the adolescent rage against his parents and say, "If they only would *admit* that they were wrong!" Of course, all this holds true only for that section of young people who, by definition, experience the generation gap owing to their incapacity to experience generational conflict. This definition restricts the use of the term "generation gap" because it attaches certain developmental preconditions to it and, therefore, gives it psychological meaning. Looking at the problem as I do, namely, psychologically, I cannot possibly be a wholesale apologist for and admirer of all youthful liberators and iconoclasts.

Much is written today about youth by adults who can only see the visionary, reformist, and liberating effects of youth on society. Such apotheosis or idolatry of youth remains a highly personal matter, and such enthusiastic embraces conceal, like most generalizations, the contradictory and heterogeneous elements at work. You must have realized that I do not attempt to encompass in my exposition the total condition of today's youth, but that I directed my effort toward a definition of terms and, consequently, toward the delineation of a psychological type. This type—"the generation gap youth"—constitutes, no doubt, a minority; but, then, has not our profession always turned its attention to minorities and to the maladaptive ways of life?

Within the definitions I have advanced it might be possible to summarize the thesis that I have laid before you. When the generation gap establishes itself as a prolonged distancing device in terms of a wholesale disaffection from the individual's background, there the generational conflict is feeble, without structure and elaboration. On the other hand, where generational conflict asserts itself, working toward individuation and differentiation, there the generation gap as a way of life will find no fertile ground on which it can grow and sustain itself. Under these conditions it remains transient and self-liquidating. The extremes of both categories are easily recognizable, whereas the in-between stages, containing ingredients from both quarters, often shake our clinical assessment with doubt and uncertainty. It might be helpful to have the extremes defined in order to recognize the approximations. It is only by this laborious process of assessment that we can gauge our usefulness to the generation-gap-minded adolescent. When we are able to decipher the message that lies embedded in his actions, then we can entertain the reasonable hope that he will comprehend what we are saying to him.

REFERENCES

Erikson, E. H. (1956). The problem of ego identity. Journal of the American Psychoanalytic Assn, 4:56–121.
Freud, A. (1958). Adolescence. Psychoanalytic Study of the Child, vol. 13. New York: International Universities Press.

2] OBSOLETE YOUTH:
TOWARD A
PSYCHOGRAPH OF
ADOLESCENT REBELLION

BRUNO BETTELHEIM

"Call me Ishmael," is how *Moby Dick* begins. So we know at once that Ishmael is not the hero's true name, that his true name has no meaning because he has no true identity, and the stage is set for a novel about the struggle to gain an identity. But "Ishmael" told the reader much more at a time when everyone was familiar with the Bible. For the Bible says of Ishmael that "his hand will be against every man and every man's hand against him." He is the outsider par excellence, and this is how Melville describes his state of mind:

> Whenever I find myself growing grim about the mouth; whenever it is a damp, drizzly November in my soul; whenever I find myself involuntarily pausing before coffin warehouses, and bringing up the rear of every funeral I meet; and especially whenever my hypos get such an upper hand of me, that it requires a strong moral principle to prevent me from deliberately stepping into the street and methodically knocking people's hats off—then, I account it high time to get to sea as soon as I can. This is my substitute for pistol and ball.

This, more than 100 years ago, is how Melville saw the adolescent in crisis—saw the inner pressure to turn either toward senseless violence or to self-destruction. The only means he saw of avoiding one or the other was to change the environment *in toto*—to "escape the Establishment," as we now say. For Melville, the path to solutions was not to drop out or to attack—though the pressure to do one or the other was intense, then as now. His way was to temporarily leave the Establish-

Reprinted from *Encounter,* September 1969.

ment and, in desperate struggle with the elements and moral issues, to test his ability to be a man. In his day this was still possible on many frontiers: One could go West, go to sea, even go native in the tropics. In any case, the goal was not to break up the established order, but to return to it from one's wanderings, find one's rightful place in society and improve it by virtue of the manhood one had gained.

These, then, are the great differences between Melville's time and our own. What have changed are neither the adolescent turmoil nor the social and psychological pressures, but the ways of resolving these and the ultimate goals. These differences also constitute our problem today. For example, though history does not repeat itself (and America today is vastly different from pre-Hitler Germany), there are some striking similarities between the present student rebellion and what happened in the German universities to spearhead the rise of Hitler. Then, as now, we see the same lumping together of all facets and institutions of society into one defamatory image. This is meant to symbolize a reality so monolithic that it becomes out of the question to improve one or another part of it at a time. No need, then, for any reasonable assessment of differing merits for all the many and so different features of "the establishment"—or, in Nazi terminology, *das System.* Having decided a priori that no improvement is possible, it follows that the only thing left is to bring down the whole system. With society so rotten, it can neither reform itself nor be reformed, but can only be reborn through violent revolution. Goering's "When somebody mentions culture (or appeals to reason) I reach for my revolver" reappears today in the Black Panther slogan—"1968—The Year of the Pig, the Death of the Ballot, the Birth of the Bullet." And Tom Hayden gives it symbolic expression when he ends an impassioned appeal for revolution by going off stage to return brandishing a rifle.

This fascination with violence and the intoxication with repetitious exaggerations to demonstrate the validity of assertions have their counterpart in the familiar antiintellectual stance. One hammers home a simplistic reduction of complex issues, unwilling to consider reasonable arguments because these are only efforts to confuse the cause and divert the movement. The reliance is on inspiration because "gut" reactions, according to which the cause "feels" right, will prove its correctness. Because everything is based on felt, rather than thought-out, convictions, there is no program for what is to be done once the revolution succeeds. In short, these are "true believers," as were the German students before them, convinced that theirs is the only moral position.

Their moral absolutism gives them the right to destroy what they judge to be amoral—the right to break up and take over meetings, shout down or physically assault those not in full agreement with them. Indeed such militance is not only felt to be right, but obligatory.

In pre-Hitler Germany, of course, student rebels came from the extreme Right whereas now they are from the extreme Left. Then the new philosophy that won a mass following for the faithful was racist, was directed against a discriminated minority (the Jews), whereas now the avowed intention of radical students is to help a discriminated minority. Though this is an important difference, it does not change the essential parallel that, in each case, universities were coerced into procedures mapped out by the true believers—even to making appointments, in each case, on the basis of racial origin. To use only one example, German universities began to cave in when students coerced faculties to appoint professorships in *Rassenwissenschaft* (courses on the special history, merits, and achievements of one race apart from all others) instead of focusing all teaching on contributions to knowledge, whatever the origin of the scholar.

I stress the parallels because they seem to me to be characteristic of the violent, antiintellectual youth movements of our age. Still, the social and economic realities of pre-Hitler Germany and of America and Western Europe today are so vastly different that one may hopefully expect a far different outcome.

What social or psychological changes, what present-day constellations can explain the different ways of Melville's time and our present adolescent revolt? About the climate of student revolt, I can offer no deeper insight than Melville's description of Ishmael's state of mind. All too many of our late adolescents are choosing "pistol and ball" as an answer: That is, with no frontiers left for flight or for conquest some try to evade and escape an inner conflict they find unbearable by dropping out—today more and more often through the slow suicide of LSD or Speed. Such persons, even if they escape killing themselves, destroy their autonomous selves through a delusional life of nonexistence. Others "step out into the street," to use Melville's phrase (it is as though he had foreseen the adolescent itch to confront for the sake of confrontation). They are convinced that they are struggling actively for personal autonomy, but they are in fact destroying it as radically as those others who withdraw into solipsistic isolation.

Nevertheless today, just as in pre-Hitler days, rebellious students are pictured as the brave new generation, disgusted with the complacency of their parents, battling courageously for a better world. In what were

16

then the mass media, they were seen as idealists, young persons concerned with the real issues of society—the "wave of the future," as they came to be known. But during 1968 Left student activists burned books they disliked in the same manner and place (Berlin) that Hitler's youthful followers burnt them during 1933.

If I read the signs of our own times correctly, I do not think our student rebels, in and by themselves, are a serious political danger—though I deem them a real threat to the universities and the intellectual life of our society.

What I fear is rather the opposite: that the provocative behavior of a very small group of students will arouse a dangerous counterreaction. Their fascism of the Left (particularly when, as in the United States, it is combined with a black fascism such as that of the Black Panthers, whom they have been trying to annex) may bring on a Right backlash that could indeed strangle the democratic order. This is what I hold to be most menacing about the student attempts to create chaos: The democratic process could prove to be quite ineffectual in containing them. Clearly such demonstrations undermine trust in the democratic way and lead their opponents toward extreme solutions of their own. If this happens it could indeed swell the ranks of the still insignificant fascists of the right, give them a mass following that would constitute a very real danger. In desperation, and in order to prevent chaos, repressive measures might then be taken that would seriously threaten democratic institutions. The tactics of the New Left radicals, designed as they are to test and exhaust the patience of what they call the Establishment (or the System, or the Structure), do create desperation, particularly in that the student movement has no comprehensive positive program of its own and in that revolution without a definite picture of what the future would be like when the revolution is over can only contribute to the creation of well-founded anxiety. It is because of this danger that I believe we must deal with student rebellions. How else can this be done constructively than by dealing with the deep-seated causes of widespread unrest among academic youth?

The Age Groups of Anxiety

In order to understand the discontent, one has to begin by asking: "What do the dissenting youth, all round the globe, have in common?" In the United States students point first to Vietnam and the Negro problem. Because of the first, they say, we have "no future" and no possibility of a "relevant" education; because society has failed to solve the problem of war and peace it should be "destroyed." Even if some do not go quite so far, they distrust a society that (they say) does nothing to end violence, racial injustice, urban decay, air and water pollution, and so on. But in Germany there is no Negro problem; in Japan there is no Vietnam; in Italy and France no one threatens to make nuclear war. What, then, is common to so wide a cross-section of world youth? One thing they do share is that all are "against the Americans"— presumably because of the magnitude of their military establishment, and especially the bomb. But Soviet Russia has an even larger standing army, relies just as much on atomic weapons, not only represses small nations but grants her own population, including her young people, considerably less freedom. Why, then, the concerted anger against the United States.

I believe that there are sound psychological reasons for this anger against the United States and for the indifference to suppression by the even larger, more powerful, military-industrial complex that rules Soviet life. I am convinced that Vietnam and the bomb serve youth as a screen for what really ails them.[1] I refer to their feeling that "youth has no future" because modern technology has made them obsolete—that they have become socially irrelevant and, as persons, insignificant. This is not because their future is bleak with prospect of a nuclear holocaust (as George Wald told MIT students and for which they gave him a standing ovation [2]), but because they feel that nobody needs them, that society can do nicely without them. This is the even bleaker anxiety behind their feeling that youth has no future. If a young man does not feel it is he who will be building the future, and is genuinely needed to bring it about, then the feeling is that he has no future. That is why, in hopes of denying such an anxious conviction, youth insists that its mission is to build a "wholly new and different" future. The anxiety of the young is not (as they claim) about an impending atomic war. It is not that society has no future. Their existential anxiety is that they have no future in a society that does not need them to go on existing.

It is modern technology—with its automation and computerization —that seems to make man and his work obsolete, to rob him of his personal importance in the scheme of things. Because America's technology is the most advanced, it is the Americans who become the main target, whatever they do or do not do. This may also explain the lack of ire against Soviet Russia's imperialism and atomic weaponry. Young

18

Russians are still very much needed. They may lack freedom of expression and thought, but there is no question in their minds that their society needs them for its future. Deep down, what youth is fighting against is not so much the war in Vietnam or the global balance, but an America whose technology seems to have robbed them of any place in the real work of the world.

It makes sense, then, that so much of their battle is fought in and around schools—in the United States in the grammar and high schools where Negroes are concerned, or the colleges and universities where both whites and blacks are concerned. (Actually, I believe, the problems of black students are entirely different from those of white students, but this is a subject for another discussion.) For it is education that prepares us for our place in society. And if education today prepares us only to be replaceable items in the production machine, or to be program assistants in its computer systems, then it seems to prepare us not for a chance to emerge in importance as persons, but only to serve the machine better. The battle against the "war machine" serves more readily than most to disguise how much the battle is really a hatred of machines altogether for seeming to dominate the whole of life. Essentially—as for the nineteenth-century Luddite—the machinery, and what it appears to do to human beings, is the true enemy. And because youth does not trust the human intellect to find ways out of the impasse to which modern technology has brought us, it becomes antiintellectual. Even the outcry against research, and in favor of teaching, bespeaks youth's conviction that intellectual labors are not the answer. Instead, it pins its hopes on the personal relation, which gives it, temporarily, the feeling that for at least as long as the personal interaction lasts, the individual is important to someone.

Behind this feeling lie even more fundamental reasons why adolescent malaise grows so widespread. These begin to emerge, in my view, when we look in quite another direction: when we recognize that adolescent revolt is not a stage of development that follows automatically from our natural makeup. What makes for adolescent revolt is the fact that a society keeps the next generation in a state of dependence, too long, in terms of mature responsibility and a striving for independence, of a sense of place that one has personally striven for and won. This, I believe, is the common denominator of the various new movements of student power and youthful revolution. And that they occur only where affluence exists, only in the modern industrial state, is merely this common denominator as seen from the outside.

Years ago, when schooling ended for the vast majority at fourteen or fifteen (and thereafter one became self-supporting, got married, had children) there was no need for adolescent revolt. Puberty is a biological fact, but adolescence as we know it, with its special identity crisis, is not. All children grow up and become pubertal. They do not all become adolescents. To be adolescent means that one has reached (and even passed) the age of puberty, is at the very height of one's physical development—healthier, stronger, even handsomer than one has been, or will be, for the rest of one's life—but must nevertheless postpone full adulthood till long beyond what any other period in history has ever considered reasonable.

Unlike Melville's time, there are no more open frontiers. With such escape routes now closed, our society has no special place for adolescence—with the single exception of our colleges and universities. To compound matters, nowadays we push our young people toward maturity even while overextending the years of their dependence. We start them sooner and sooner in school and make a farce of graduations (even from kindergarten now!) until school becomes a rat race with never a home stretch in sight. And so, by the time they get to college, they have "had it." I for my part, doubt whether life was ever less of a rat race than today. But it only became a senseless rat race when more and more people came to feel that they were racing after goals that were not really worthwhile or urgent, because survival seemed so assured by the affluent state.

At the same time, only a small minority of youth emerges from the educational experience today (whether in the home or the school) well prepared for such a prolonged waiting, for controlling their angry impatience. Here we should not overlook the symbolic meaning of the student invasions of the office of the president or dean. Big in size and age, those who sit-in feel like little boys with a need to "play big" by sitting in papa's big chair. They want to sit in the driver's seat, and they want to have a say in how things are run, not because they feel competent to do so, but because they cannot bear to feel incompetent a single moment longer.

The Desperate Search

I think it is unnatural to keep a young person in dependence for some twenty years of school attendance. This may be a bearable way of life for that small elite that would always have chosen it in the past. There were always those who could go to school for twenty years, but they were never more than a small percentage of the population—even of the university population, which included those attending as a matter of caste. The tremendous push now on everyone to "go to university" has brought incredibly large numbers to the academic life who do not find their self-realization through study or the intellectual adventure—or not at that point in their lives. What they still want urgently, however, is to find their manhood.

To make matters worse, our institutions of higher learning have expanded too fast. Under public pressure for more education for all, they have steadily increased enrollment without the means to make parallel adjustments in the learning situation. One result is far too large classes; another is the anonymity, the impersonal nature of student-faculty contacts against which students rightly complain. Too many classes in our large universities are taught by teaching assistants (some of whom share the same dilemma as the students, and hence tend to side with the rebellion). So, once again, the students feel cheated.

Professor Allan Silver (1969) of Columbia University has put his finger on what to me seems the real problem when he says, "Their attack on the university—whether as surrogate for society's sins, or for its own peculiar failings—has something to do with the desperate search for a livable home in America. . . ." Most of all (one is tempted to add), they search for a home in which one is finally the master in his own house. Such students want, essentially, those group therapeutic experiences that will help them feel that they have at long last come of age. But colleges are simply not mass therapeutic institutions, and hence they must inevitably disappoint the students where their greatest need lies.

It is, thus, the waiting for things—waiting for the real life to come —that creates a climate in which a sizable segment of students are chronically seduced into following the militant lead of a small group of zealots. In the words of Jerry Rubin (1969) the yippie organizer: "Who the hell wants to 'make it' in America any more? The American economy no longer needs young whites and blacks. We are waste material. We fulfill our destiny in life by rejecting a system which rejects us."

Campus rebellion seems to offer youth a chance to short-cut the time of empty waiting and to prove themselves real adults. This can be seen from the fact that most rebellious students, on both sides of the Atlantic, are either undergraduates or those studying the social sciences and humanities. There are precious few militants among students of medicine, chemistry, engineering, the natural sciences. To dismiss this as self-selection would be oversimplifying. It is true that those who come to the university and who are already deeply dissatisfied with themselves and society tend to study psychology, political science, philosophy, sociology. Such students even choose psychology in the hope that to study it will add to self-knowledge (which it can) and will solve their psychological problems (which it cannot). Feeling lost in themselves, they also feel lost with others and come to think that by studying society they will feel more at home in the world, and hence with themselves. But when the study of these and related subjects fails to solve their inner difficulties, or the various problems they have in relating to others, they come to hate the university whose teaching disappoints them. They are convinced that the teaching is "irrelevant"—as indeed it is when it comes to solving deep-seated emotional problems of long standing, because it was never designed to that end.

Another and even more widespread disenchantment derives from what I have discussed earlier: the need of late adolescents to feel that their labors make a difference in the world, and the depressing conviction that they do not. For it is hard to see how the average social science student or the student of humanities can get a sense of importance from his studies until such time as he is deeply immersed in them—and this takes effort and concentration. Even then, the feeling may be somewhat esoteric. But what swifter and surer way to feel active than to become an activist? On the other hand, as Michael Beloff (1968) has pointed out, "Student power has no meaning in the laboratory; no one doubts the need for leadership by the more experienced of the less experienced . . ." Though one can easily convince oneself that one knows precisely what's wrong with society, particularly if one's friends all agree, it is impossible to fool oneself that one knows what went wrong in the cancerous cell or of how easy it would be to "create a new system" in the sciences. One has to try to test one's conviction about shortcomings in science through experiment, and if poorly thought out experiments fail, one must study to see why they failed. It may seem easy to believe one can create "a better world" without working things out in detail, but it is impossible to claim solution for a prolem in chemistry without the experiment to prove it, and this takes real work.

The medical student who is confronted with cancerous tissue cannot believe that what he is doing, or the discipline it demands, is "irrelevant." This may explain the large number of clinical psychology students (those studying emotional disturbance in the vain hope that this

22

will cure their own) among campus dissenters, and the near total absence among them of students of experimental or physiological psychology.

Those who cannot find themselves in their studies or their work are hence the most vocal in finding the university irrelevant. Typically, the militant finds his largest following among the newcomers, those with least time or chance as yet to find a place for themselves at the university. Some try to find this place instantly, by plunging into active, even violent battle against the existing order. Yet, if they should win they would be changing the university into an institution that no longer serves inquiry and study, into a belligerent political workshop for the reshaping of society. And it is exactly this that the militant personality wants to be "part of"—not inquiry and study but *la lutte finale*.

I do not mean to say that political change is not needed, but to insist that the campus is not the pertinent arena, for the purpose of the academic inquiry is to search for proper avenues of reform, not to drop the inquiry in order to carry the gun.

Freudian Ambiguities

I should like to speak briefly of the small group of leaders of the radical Left, whom, during recent years, I have come to know well for one reason or another. In most cases, it has seemed to me, their intellect was developed at much too early an age, and at the expense of their emotional development. Though exceedingly bright, some remained emotionally fixated at the age of the temper tantrum. It is this discrepancy between great intellectual maturity and vast emotional immaturity that is so baffling—often even to the professors and university administrators who fail to see, behind the obvious intelligence, the inability to brook delay or to think rationally or to act responsibly. This blind spot is an occupational hazard of the academic mind. Committed as academicians to the intellect as the highest of values, they are so captivated by the intelligence of student rebels that they are ready to excuse, or overlook, the cult of open contempt for reason-based action.

One other personal impression: Practically all those who have investigated the phenomena of student revolts and the related upsurge of beatniks and hippies have been struck by the dominance among the leadership of the children of enlightened, upper-middle-class parents.

Nothing is so illuminating as to listen to what these students tell us when they are asked why they feel the Establishment has to be "smashed" down, why they feel this society, of which they are such obviously privileged members, is not worth being preserved or improved. As one Harvard senior reported: "Time after time SDS members respond to questions about their views on the sickness of society with, 'Well, take my father for example. . . .' " Just as often, in my own experience, I received this answer. And it is indeed in the new ways of rearing children in the upper-middle-class home that we have to look for some additional answers.

What is wrong? First, because of the ways we bring them up as infants and children, we send many youngsters into adolescence ill prepared for the kind of identity crisis I have just described—the one caused by a prolonging of adolescence beyond all reasonable limits. Second, many adults do not want to recognize the adolescent's experiment with extremes as being exactly that. Many among the intelligentsia are well aware that, for sound or understandable psychological reasons, adolescents may have to experiment in their own minds with extreme and nonviable solutions. But too many who should know better are suddenly calling them potentially viable solutions—ones that should, therefore, get serious consideration. Thus, when we adults fail to take a stand from which adolescents can sort out for themselves which ideas are suitable for experiment in thought only, youth is left without any clear directions. They come to believe that whatever can be experimented with in thought is also suitable to be tried in reality.

Much adult inconsistency comes of a misapplication of psychoanalytic insights and procedures. This can be illustrated by the question of violence and the learning of controls. Psychoanalysis has certainly suggested that we should not suppress our inner rages but should face them. But we are only expected to face them in thought, and only in the safely structured treatment situation. This has been misapplied by large numbers of the educated middle classes to mean that aggression should always be expressed, and not just in thought. Accordingly, many children today do not learn to repress aggression, to express it in thought and not in violence. They do not internalize superego controls over their rages. Consequently, when adolescent pressures flood them with aggression, they have no built-in ways to control it or restrict it to thought only. What Freud taught us about the crippling effects of an over-repression of emotions (because that was where the shoe pinched in his day) has been wrongly extended to mean it is all right to discharge emotions in action, including rage, without control of the discharge by fear or by rational reflection.

I speak of fear because of a related misunderstanding of Freud: the vague feeling among parents and educators that children should never be made to feel frightened at breaking a moral command. Not only are our children ill prepared to brook delay, they have also been confronted with a morality whose basic motivation we have done our best to remove. We want to remove fear from the life of the child, but we want him to curb his own tendencies toward violence as if we had not. Yet for children, the earliest controls of violence rest on fear and are largely irrational; they come from the moral commands of adults. On the basis of fear, not of rational judgment, the child is told what he "must do" and "must not do." Only later does the mature ego apply reason to these do's and don'ts and then slowly subject them to critical judgment. Only as maturity grows can we slowly free ourselves of fear and begin to question its absolute tenets.

What was wrong, then, with old-fashioned, authoritarian education was not that it rested on fear. On the contrary, that is what was right with it. What was wrong was that it disregarded the need to modify the fear in a continuous process so that irrational anxiety would steadily give way to more rational motivation. Today many parents are no longer willing to take displeasure from their children by imposing controls. But neither are they willing to invite the child to join in the troublesome search for alternatives whenever frustration occurs. To such parents, modern psychology seems a way out.

Because Freud showed them the evil effects of too much fear, of too much Victorian repression—because he concentrated on what most plagued the middle classes then—our own middle classes (to paraphrase Schiller) learned carefully how their master coughed and spit in order to totally disregard what he taught. Freud certainly knew that without strong inner controls (preferably conscious ones) man would sink back into barbarism. If he stressed it less, it was because the dominant pathology in his day came of too much, not too little, control. But with both teachings available, many middle-class families chose to follow Freud where it suited their convenience and were as demanding of conformity as the worst Victorian parent where it did not. In either case, they evaded their adult responsibility. Whereas the old way of repression was at least all of a piece, the modern way is one of contradictions. Some instinctual tendencies are still repressed as before, whereas others are directed toward discharge without intervening thought and rational control. This makes no sense at all, and it is a major source of the youthful cry that our society seems senseless. Even worse, the decisions as to what to repress and what to discharge are based not on the interests of the child but on the convenience of adults. This arbitrariness, in my view, is where the fatal error lies, and it constitutes what most outrages youth. That is, instinctual pleasure was not given so the child could begin life by enjoying his own body and, hence, the world, but as a bribe held out so the child would become more proficient at making his parents feel good about themselves. Sufficient reason then, for such youngsters to make a farce of permissiveness by asking for everything, with no sense of obligation to give in return.

When I see some of these way out or unwashed and unkempt students (though, of course, nothing I say here is true for all of them) I cannot help thinking: "There goes another youngster who, as an infant, was practically scrubbed out of existence by his parents in the name of good hygiene and loving care." Any look at their manner of dress or hairdo should demonstrate how they revolt against parents who told them they could dress as they liked, provided they came out looking exactly as pleased the parent's pride, and not the child's convenience. Yet, in a strange contradiction—and I talk of the inner contradictions that tear the extremist apart and mark all his outer behavior, his hatred of self and society, and of all adults over thirty—he only seems to reverse, or compensate for, what his parents did to him. He seems, on the surface, to be doing "the opposite"; he believes that in his manner of dress he is defying his parents; yet, deep down, he is still copying their behavior. He mistreats the legitimate needs of his body just as much as his parents did, only this time not by scrubbing, but by neglect. Having been pushed out of infancy and childhood toward higher maturity in one area, and indulged or overstimulated in others, he finds himself in a crisis that can only tear him to pieces.

As these children strive for independence from their parents, how natural it is that some drop out whereas others furiously resent the professors (those parental figures, once removed). That the academic faculty is resented for some of the reasons I have mentioned, may be inferred from the angry charges of students that "professors care more for their research than for teaching," as though the search for and transmission of knowledge were not all of a piece. True, a lot of pedantic research goes on at universities (though, too, a lot of pedants who have never done a stitch of research teach). But, in general, I have found those who combine teaching with a meaningful search for knowledge the more inspiring teachers.

The contradictory rearing I speak of would still be manageable (as parental contradictions always were) if, as the youngster approached adulthood, he could begin at last to arrange for what to him was a meaningful life of his own. Failing that, all he can do to reassert his independence is to reverse parental standards in his style of living, of dress, of sexual behavior. And this is where he collides head-on with the final contradiction that, in my opinion, provokes student revolt. Because deep down he knows these are empty postures, that it is only making a show of self-determination when to be sustained by his parents (or the taxpayers) at college disproves it. All of his life, up to now, he has been told that he must learn to be a self-directing person. Now at last, when the pressures are overwhelming to do and to be just that, he is told to go on being dependent, beholden to the grown-ups for his livelihood, to follow directions, to study hard, and to submit to examinations where others will decide whether and what he has achieved.

The "scene" where this happens for millions of students is the university, and it is the university at which he lashes out—though the university cannot end a war, dismantle a military-industrial complex, or achieve for him the personal independence he craves. Because he does not know (or does not dare to know) what his deepest longing and deepest rages are, he does not take them where they belong. He does not burn down his parents' home, or even the Capitol. What he threatens to burn down is the university. It is the university, he believes, that is keeping him from manhood.

Psychologically I found most student extremists hating themselves as intensely as they hate the Establishment—a self-hatred they try to escape from by fighting any establishment. Here, again, this is not to say an established social order is not always due, and sometimes overdue, for reform. But, I maintain that despite the high-sounding moral charges against its sins, those sins (in the hearts and minds of youth) are not "the destruction of youth in Vietnam" but the neglect of youth on the home front: They think they have been classified as "waste material," and they feel compelled to "reject a system that rejects us."

Paranoia and Politics

I have worked professionally with some militant leaders for years, and I know that student revolt permits the social isolate to believe temporarily that he is "part of a community," and offers an opportunity for the paranoid person to act out his own paranoia as could happen in no other niche of society. I have found it all too understandable that so many extreme isolates and paranoids have quickly flocked to the ranks of extremism. Unfortunately, most nonprofessionals do not know how persuasive paranoiacs can be in their unconscious appeal to the vague and fleeting paranoia of the immature and disgruntled. Paranoiacs are always persuasive in their appeal to any group of the population that rightly or wrongly feels persecuted. They seek out such groups as most likely to take their paranoia for a true understanding of the particular dilemma of a group's grievances.

Political activity for such persons enables them to escape a complete break with reality. They may interpret reality in line with their delusions, but at least they remain in touch with isolated aspects of reality, and the support and admiration of their followers is another, though most tenuous, contact.

I know one student who took part in every demonstration he could, because while they lasted they gave him a temporary feeling of being "close to others." For the same reason he pressed for as many (and as drawn-out) demonstrations and sit-ins as he could. Or, as Silver (1969) has described the climate inside the four occupied buildings at Columbia University during the spring of 1968:

> An intense communal life emerged, in which students at last enjoyed [a] shared commitment and purpose. . . . This enjoyment became one of the chief purposes of the uprising, something that could not easily be bargained or negotiated away.

But then one day, the student I have referred to was on one of his marches, and the instruction was given that each one should hold someone's hand. It so happened that he found himself without anyone holding his. It was after this experience that he also began to take drugs to escape his personal misery, until eventually he entered psychiatric treatment. Much later, recalling the incident in therapy, he still remembered with tears: "No one held mine."

To embrace the extreme position, then, can actually be an ego defensive action. It succeeds because the discharge of rage and violence drains off the aggression that would otherwise destroy whatever paranoid defenses remained working. Typical of such persons is the quasi or openly delusional quality of their beliefs, their inaccessibility to reason while loudly complaining that nobody listens to them, the oversimplification of issues, and the preoccupation with violence and destruction (the imagined destruction of themselves, and the readiness to consider the destruction of their enemies). All this is combined with an absence of, or emotional paucity and flatness in, their personal relations.

For them, an essential purpose of revolt is not to reach a limited or tangible goal, such as an acceptance of some or even all of their demands, but to escape their devastating isolation, or to prove themselves strong, or both. Because the weakness is their own, no achievement of goals will ever satisfy, and this is why negotiated solutions are rejected and the ends always escalate. Such goals as are achieved merely add to frustration. Success merely threatens to make them realize that the goal reached has not in any way relieved the inner sense of isolation or weakness, of being oppressed, and it ends the fleeting relief they enjoyed in the struggle.

The Germans called their own rebellious adolescents the *Halbstarken* "half-strong." In German, the connotation is that they feel their weakness but wish to deny it through a show of great strength. Only it does not "come off," because all their efforts are only (to continue in American slang) "half-assed." [3]

But even if some of these rebellious students are paranoid, and others desperate isolates, both pathologies have existed in all societies, and can hardly explain our problem. Certainly it does not account for the seriousness or the magnitude of the present student revolt. For our real concern is not so much with the activist leaders as with their followers: that larger and ever-changing body of students whom the leaders can attract and enlist once they have set up the confrontation that pits the world of the fathers against the world of the sons.

Just an additional word, however, about the small group of the militant leaders. I find their psychological makeup very different indeed from that of those serious students who are deeply concerned with what is wrong in our universities and in society, who try for improved ways of doing things, but who know that violence only leads to destruction, and who respect themselves and others too much to manipulate them, to push them around or to prevent others from doing their own freely chosen work. The militant leaders have very different motives. Most of them I found to be consumed by a self-hatred from which they try to escape by fighting *any* establishment. Many of these extremists are highly intelligent and very verbal. Unfortunately their claim to act out of high motives, and their occasional on-target attack on real evils, have misled many well-meaning people into overlooking the true motif—hate, not desire for a better world. This is not to say that much in our world is not itself hateful, but only that hatred and the lust for destruction never lead to an improvement of life. Here we should not overlook how many —and for how long!—were taken in by Hitler's emphasis on "the suffering of the people" as a mainspring of his actions; a great many Germans (and not a few Europeans) hoped he would indeed create a new order, overlooking the fact that the real source of his passion for change was an overwhelming *ressentiment*.

It is their hatred of society that makes it so easy for the small group of militant leaders to make common cause with two other small groups that provide temporary leadership for some rebellions: those persons who suffer from extreme isolation and those who are clearly paranoid. I do not believe the number of paranoids among students is greater than their number would be in any comparable group of the population. They become dangerous because their high intelligence makes them so successful at hiding their disturbance from the layman. Recently a former extremist tried to explain to me why he became so engaged.

Instead of my true emptiness and hate, I could, in the movement, claim that I loved man. I could think I was constructive, and not destructive. Because I had no real self, did not feel any understanding for the individual, I had to have group beliefs. When I was able to take my anger out on the System, screaming with others, "Hey, hey LBJ, how many kids have you killed today?" it was both a release and a connection. . . .

After a few years of this existence he came to realize that "it was similar to fascism and that I had gotten involved with an evil, power hungry, manipulating, fascist-type Left. . . . Then I was healthy enough to get out. . . ."

After such knowledge and partings of the ways, we should take very seriously what he now has to say:

I had and still have no respect for our schools because they always thought I was so good and bright [all through school he had been an outstanding student] when I was so sick. The rebelliousness of the extremists is caused by this emotionally starved and contact denied infancy. I was attracted to communism because they have communal nurseries, so that mothers cannot "murder" their infants [as he felt his mother had done]. . . . My Leftist preoccupation was to change the world so that what had happened to me could not and would not happen to any other child.

What he meant was, namely, his exploitation by his parents for their narcissistic needs required that he should be an outstanding academic, that he concentrate on developing his intellect, at the expense of satisfying his most urgent inner needs. Like many other extreme militants, who are often so bright, he was intellectually precocious but emotionally terribly immature.

I was also told this:

One motivation in my politicalization was not in the least political. After having sat inactive, internally and externally—in school and outside—most of my life, I could now picket, distribute leaflets, run off to Washington, work and talk with people all over the country, as if I had a connection to other people. . . . It was either doing that, or remaining what to me seemed an inept, selfish, bored, lifeless, and friendless, in short, a lost, child. I felt if I would stop fighting I would disappear, because my stake and claim to life would disappear with it. But in the movement there was always something new to get involved in, and I couldn't let my involvement stop and be faced with myself. . . .

We had teach-ins. And in protest against the army draft we had a sit-in and a sleep-in. We all slept together, in the president's office, on his rugs. There I met a new boyfriend. Later that week I and a few other members of SDS went to confront the president in his office. I was aware of the fact that with me, and many others on the Left, if we were granted what we said we wanted, we would no longer be happy—for we could no longer protest. We would be useless, we would be nothing, we would have to face ourselves. . . .

My thesis is that more than anything else it is the seeming vacuum to which we graduate so many of our young in the modern industrial state that so convinces them that ours is a society that cannot make sense. This is the ground on which they make common cause with the activist leader; though for the activist, the emotional world his parents fashioned for him made "no sense" from the very beginning. It is on this common evaluation of the present that the many temporarily join ranks against the existing order with the few who lead them. The difference is that for the extremist, the overpowering motive is to uproot, not to reform. For within him is the utter despair that anything could ever be right for him, an outlook bred into him during a lonely and desperate childhood when too much was asked of him and too little was given.

That is why student followers begin to look at things differently once the present becomes more satisfying—thanks to a satisfying sexual relation, a reasonably good marriage, gratifying work, or some other satisfaction. The leaders remain committed to upheaval. Their permanent commitment is again reflected in the lack of designs for a better world to come once the revolution is made. Their unhappy beginnings have been a prologue; the rest of their lives may turn out to be one long epilogue to the rage that overwhelmed them in childhood. They continue to feel helpless to build anything positive in the huge world outside them, the world of their parents. Just as the infant sees his elders as so forbidding that, while they are still around, he can do nothing to better his fate, so it is for these rebellious students who project their past on to present conditions. Until they can be rid of this Establishment they feel they have no chance at all to live their own lives.

The Secret Excitement

We know that each society can raise a new generation in its own way. For example, if a society does not taboo sex, children will grow up in relative sex freedom. But so far, historical experience has indicated that such a society does not create culture or civilization, but remains a primitive society. Without a fair degree of sex repression, no latency period; without latency, no prolonged span of intellectual learning. And the same goes for reasonable (but not overwhelming) fear. Without some fear, no internalization; with too much fear, overwhelming rage or despair. Moderate fear leads to the internalization without which we cannot work for long-range goals, cannot control our instinctual tendencies toward violence or aggression. Too much fear leads to utter withdrawal, or else to violent and destructive enactments. That is why controls will not work when the pressures pushing against them are too heavy—as when youth arrives at coming-of-age and feels it has no place to go.

It may be objected here that psychoanalysis is not responsible for errors in modern child-rearing, any more than nuclear scientists who did not personally work on the bomb were to blame when the knowledge they discovered was destructively used. But once that did happen, they became actively concerned, and their house organ, the *Bulletin of the Atomic Scientists,* stressed a more rational control of their discoveries. My charge, then, against my own profession is that in their formal or informal efforts to educate outside of the treatment room, too little thought is devoted to dangerous misapplications of their findings; nor is there any concerted action to spread awareness of the dangers.

In the case of rebellious youth, our profession bears a second burden of guilt, but this one it shares with the entire literate adult community. We fail these youth if we do not act on our knowledge of what lies behind the grandiloquent way in which they give voice to their confusion and distress. We should know how to interpret their rejection of reason, their reliance on coercion, and ultimately on violence itself.

Lewis Feuer (1969), who has studied (and was himself deeply involved in) the student revolt at Berkeley, has correctly observed: "Because the driving energy of such a movement stems largely from unconscious sources, it has trouble defining what it wants. The ideological consciousness is founded on the emotional unconscious of a generational revolt." To which I would add that even more critical for extremists is the unconscious revolt against how they were brought up by their families.

But to unravel unconscious sources is the task of adults. Despite the present turmoil, these inner causes of outward behavior are not being exposed by us as fearlessly and vigorously as when Freud pulled the veil away from a set of high-sounding moral claims and exposed Victorian sexuality for the sham that it was. We do not, in regard to student excesses, confront with equal vigor the inner anxieties that power the high-sounding moral pronouncements—whether voiced by the leaders of dissent or their adult public supporters. We are so anxious to look progressive that we fail to analyze the unconscious causes for such behavior, though that is the only way we can help them with their inner conflicts.

Beholden as we are to some of the virtues admittedly present among rebellious students—just as there was considerable virtue in Victorian respectability—we refrain on that account from exposing their vices. But to refrain here is as much a betrayal as to deny there is merit to such complaints as may be sound and just.

There are reasons why it is mainly the children of Leftist parents who become hippies or student revolutionaries in American society. The emotional content of student revolt may always be the same, yet its political content depends largely on the belief of the parents. In many ways it is a desperate wish to do better than the parent, especially where the parent seemed weak in his beliefs. This makes it just as desperate a wish for parental approval. But most of all it is a desperate wish that the parent should have been strong in the convictions that motivate his actions. This is why so many of our radical students embrace Maoism, why they chant "Ho Ho Ho Chi Minh" in their demonstrations (with the noise that other generations of students expended at football rallies). They chant of strong fathers with strong convictions who powerfully coerce their children to follow their commands. While consciously they demand freedom and participation, unconsciously their

33

commitment to Mao, and leaders like him, suggests their desperate need for controls from the outside, because without them they cannot bring order to their own inner chaos.[4]

C. P. Snow's *The Sleep of Reason* deals with precisely this issue of adult abdication from the teaching of controls. Two young lesbians (one a leader raised in the new freedom, the other a follower) abduct a small boy. First they torture him, "to teach him obedience," and then they kill him, "to see how it feels." What both girls felt was so missing in their lives they try to recapture through a sexual crime. Snow raises the problem of whether this is what comes of thinking we can raise our children in freedom. He asks: Have we, in our desire for instinctual and political emancipation, so put our reason to sleep that we have brought forth monsters? And a second and even deeper problem he broaches is the secret excitement provided for us by the violent and at times obscene behavior of these, our children.

In my own experience at faculty meetings, and listening to intellectuals talking about the turbulent events, I have come to a sense of how much these movements feed on excitements secretly felt and hidden from oneself. There is abroad in society today a fascination with sex and violence, with drugs and insanity, that student militants exploit to the full. If students protest and do so in orderly fashion, they get little or no public attention. But if they shed all their clothes and walk around naked, this makes news across the nation, whatever the original cause or conflict may have been.

Universities in particular lend a prestige to the claims of revolutionary students they would otherwise never enjoy. For example, there were days when no more than some twenty or thirty students occupied the administration building of the University of Chicago, but they got their daily headlines and were featured prominently in the newscasts of radio and television. If some thirty people had demonstrated anywhere else, such coverage would never have occurred. This the SDS knows, hence their concentration on the universities. The contrast between an institution devoted to the highest achievements of reason and the obscene and violent happenings perpetrated there makes it all the more fascinating. On this fascination, student militants try to build their success.

Erwin Scheuch (1969) has called it the technique of parasitical publicity. An idea in itself, he says, may be next to nothing, but it becomes news by interfering with something else that is considered, for one reason or another, to be of public importance. Thus, in themselves, a couple of hundred demonstrators somewhere in New York or Chicago would mean very little. But, "if you march into a large lecture hall, take control of the podium, and broadcast your own ideas to people who came to hear something quite different, then you have made news. . . . This is where the function of political phraseology becomes operative."

If girls dress up as witches and put a curse on professors (as they did in Chicago), or undress in public and walk around naked (as they did on other campuses) but without reference to the "sickness of society," everyone might well get the impression that it was they, poor souls, who were sick. But if they

do so as a condemnation of the Viet Nam war . . . they have the support of many of the older liberals and enlightened radicals, who will inevitably consider it all to be very socially significant. If you are a teen-ager wrestling with the police and you say you are doing it because of the moral superiority of a future social order, you cannot fail to get the sympathetic attention of the editors of all . . . radio and TV-stations, rather than psychiatrists and youth welfare workers. The ritualistic invocation of ideology is thus both an alibi and a defence.

Recapturing the Initiative

Absurd or not, these rebellions can and do paralyze universities. Not only because classes are interrupted and buildings occupied, not only because the faculty must devote all their energies to calming things down, but because all the time and effort that should go to more lasting achievements are diverted to forestalling the next confrontation.

In our universities today we see faculty members who strive to remain aloof from it all, whereas others try to anticipate even the most radical of student demands in order to avoid confrontations. Unfortunately, too little is done to activate more constructive attempts at reform or to mobilize alternative student groups. Yet what this age group needs and wants is to be active. Even if student representatives were to sit on all faculty committees, take part in all their ponderous deliberations, this is not the active life youth hankers for. Much as they now clamor for it, they would soon enough want "out." Instead of searching, however, for modes of bringing action to student life, university authorities seem to spend their time worrying about what the militants may do next or in anxious efforts to give them no offense. Worst of all, many are so intimidated that they cave in before the students have even begun to exert pressure. All this has been sapping the universities of their

35

strength to the point of paralysis. This anxious avoidance of taking a firm stand gives militants—but also many noncommitted students—the feeling that they have the faculty on the run. What spectacle could be more irresistibly attractive?

If the colleges and universities felt sure of their values, took a determined stand against coercive intimidation—while open to and inviting reasonable discussion of any and all relevant improvements—I believe student rebellions would cease to be a threat. And here, I believe, lies the true challenge to our universities—the opportunity to give a lead to intellectual life, and beyond that to society in general.

The liberal mind in America and elsewhere has made all too much of a fetish out of formal democratism. They are so afraid they may be thought to be "unpopulistic" that they have become helpless when faced by the threats of mob rule. True, no system of government is more vulnerable than a democratic framework of civil liberties. If it should ever lose its ability to right itself by adapting to emergencies without losing its democratic way, it would indeed perish: destroyed either by an authoritarianism of the Right or the Left or by its own defensive recourse to repressions. The alternative to being destroyed from without by revolution, or from within by suppression, is to win back the consensus that protects it without the need for repressive extremes. So far the universities have done a poor job of protecting themselves; they have been vacillating between repression and surrender.

But the day seems gone when we could rely on our institutions remaining unchallenged because those who had a voice in them were part of a once broad consensus, part of the only establishment that counted and ran things. From now on, all institutions will be questioned—through force and intimidation, if the challengers can get away with it, through superior reasoning, if we are strong enough to permit nothing less. The more we invite and take advantage of sound reasons for and against change, and the more firmly we protect ourselves from coercion, the better off everyone will be.

At this moment in history both seem equally needed. If proposed changes are bad they should be rejected, violence or no. If they are better than what exists, why should they have to be dragged into being under duress, and thus legitimize the effectiveness of violence? On both counts it would seem the better part of valor for universities to recapture the vital thing they have lost—the initiative for change.

I think it should be obvious by now what I believe some of these much-needed improvements might be. First, all too many who now go to university have little interest, ability, or use for what now constitutes higher education. They would be better off with a high-level education in the professions and the services, closely linked to a work program. This would give scope to their need to be active, while enjoying tangible achievement in the immediate present. Their complaint is that "nobody needs" them. Because they feel themselves to be parasites of society, they come to hate a world that gives them such a feeling. But nothing so balances the uncertain sense of being an apprentice as already to be actively serving in the profession one is beginning.

Here we should not be above learning from the communist countries where study is combined with work in the factory and field (particularly if we include the service occupations). I believe this to be a much better arrangement for those who feel no deep commitment to study and research—and those who do will always be a relatively small part of this age group. I would even suggest a youth service program of a few years' duration (something on the order of a civilian peace corps) in which young people could work on socially relevant projects while earning pay, and getting higher professional training as they do. After this period, only those would go to universities who really wanted to. By that time most of them would probably have acquired a real stake in society because they had been helping to shape it. At the very least, they would be better prepared for permanent jobs because of the training received.

So long as the need for any army draft in the United States continues, civilian service could be an alternative choice. Only those young Americans who preferred it would serve in the armed forces, making it a voluntary army. I am convinced that if every able-bodied person had to serve two years in one program or the other there would be no scarcity of those with a preference for two years of military service. This would further do away with the special draft exemption of U.S. college students that provokes so much unrest. Because if I am exempt from serving in Vietnam when others are not, I can only live in peace with myself by believing it an amoral war. (As if there was ever a moral war!)

As for the extreme elements in the "groupuscules" who lead the student rebellion, I have little to add here. Without the current widespread discontent among youth, they would find scant enough following, which might force them to do something constructive for themselves. How could one assist in providing for them those emotional experiences that would help them out of their desperate isolation? For some, this could be provided most effectively by psychotherapy. If some others did seriously break the law they could, without followers, readily be contained. It is the mass support they arouse because of the general unrest among youth that alone makes them dangerous. I think it would be wrong to concentrate, in our thinking and planning for youth, in or out of college, on these very few. Our focus belongs on how to provide our young people with the real life experiences and the emotional satisfactions they need, for these are very different from those toward which their largely unconscious motives will go on pushing them for want of better direction.

N O T E S

1. I note that the presidents of three American universities (Michigan, Brandeis, San Francisco State) agreed that if the war in Vietnam were to end tomorrow, it would do little or nothing to end the student revolt (CBS, 1970).

2. In his speech (widely reprinted all over the United States) Professor Wald quoted a U.S. senator who remarked on the floor of the Senate that if it came to nuclear war he would prefer that the survivors be Americans. Many (including me) would take exception to such a statement. But Professor Wald called it "criminally insane," and said he called it that speaking as a "Nobel Laureate" (in biology), a reliance on titular authority he would normally shun when not speaking as a "true believer." Because a criminally insane person should be locked up, Wald's remark suggests that the senator be denied free speech. It is examples such as this—where illustrious faculty members would deny freedom of speech to those they disagree with on grounds of their own higher truth—that disruptive students emulate when they deny the right to speak to those with whom they disagree.

3. This, according to *The Dictionary of American Slang*, means: "Ignorant of a specific field of endeavour or pertinent facts; without full or proper plans, experience, knowledge or understanding. . . ."

4. There is another reason why rebellious youth has put Castro and particularly Che Guevara in its pantheon of heroes: the romantic appeal of the man who leaves the city culture and goes out into the wilderness (as did Ishmael, and the early explorers and pioneers). This shows how little they have outgrown childhood identifications with archaic culture heroes, how little they have accepted the ego ideals of maturity in our time—those of the scientist or political leader who attempts to ameliorate an imperfect industrial society, not those who try to escape or destroy it. Both Cuban guerrillas represent an image of individual man living a primitive life outside of a hated society. It is again the premachine age that is being extolled. They feel it is modern technology that robs them of the chance to be strong, to be men. Like Che Guevara they choose a quixotic battlefield and certain defeat with the poor—to whom they romantically ascribe all the attributes of Rousseau's noble savage, though the poor want nothing more than to enjoy, at long last, all the material advantages that only a highly industrialized society can provide.

REFERENCES

Beloff, M. (1968). October for the rebels. Encounter. (October)

CBS. (1970). The college turmoil. News special.

Feuer, L. S. (1969). Conflict of generations. New York: Basic Books.

Rubin, J. (1969). An emergency letter to my brothers and sisters in the movement. The New York Review of Books. (February 13)

Scheuch, E. K. (1969). The liberation from right reason. Encounter. (April)

Silver, A. (1969). Who cares for Columbia? The New York Review of Books. (January 30)

] ADOLESCENCE: STRUGGLING THROUGH THE DOLDRUMS

D. W. WINNICOTT

There is at present a world-wide interest in adolescence and the problems of the adolescent. In almost all countries there are adolescent groups that make themselves evident in some way or other. Many studies of this phase of development are being made, and there has arisen a new literature, either of autobiography written by the young or of novels that deal with the lives of teenaged boys and girls. It is safe to assume that there is a connection between this development in our social awareness and the special social conditions of the times we live in.

One thing that must be recognized at the start by those who explore in this area of psychology is the fact that the adolescent boy or girl does not want to be understood. Adults must hide among themselves what they come to understand of adolescence. It would be absurd to write a book for adolescents on adolescence because this period of life is one that must be lived, and it is essentially a time of personal discovery. Each individual is engaged in a living experience, a problem of existing.

Cure for Adolescence

There exists one real cure for adolescence, and only one, and this cannot be of interest to the boy or girl who is in the throes. The cure for

Reprinted from D. W. Winnicott, *The Family and Individual Development*. London: Tavistok, 1965.

adolescence belongs to the passage of time and to the gradual maturation processes; these together do in the end result in the emergence of
the adult person. This process cannot be hurried or slowed up, though
indeed it can be broken into and destroyed, or it can wither up from
within, in psychiatric illness.

We do sometimes need to remind ourselves that though adolescence
is something that we have always with us, each adolescent boy or girl
grows up in the course of a few years into an adult. Parents know this
better than some sociologists do, and public irritation with the phenomenon of adolescence can easily be evoked by cheap journalism and by
the public pronouncements of persons in key positions, with adolescence referred to as a problem, and the fact that each individual adolescent is in process of becoming a responsible society-minded adult left
out of the argument.

Theoretical Statement

There is a considerable measure of agreement among those concerned
with dynamic psychology with regard to a general statement of adolescence in terms of the emotional development of the individual.

The boy or girl in this age phase is dealing with his or her personal
puberty changes. He or she comes to the developments in sexual capacity and to secondary sexual manifestations with a personal past history,
and this includes a personal pattern in the organization of defenses
against anxiety of various kinds. In particular, in health, there has been
in each individual an experience before the latency period of a full-
blooded oedipus complex, that is to say, of the two main positions in
the triangular relationship with the two parents (or parent substitutes);
and there have been (in the experience of each adolescent) organized
ways of warding off distress or of accepting and tolerating the conflicts
inherent in these essentially complex conditions.

Also derived from the experiences of each adolescent's early infancy
and childhood are certain inherited and acquired personal characteristics and tendencies, fixations to pregenital types of instinctual experience, residues of infantile dependence and of infantile ruthlessness; and
further, there are all manner of illness patterns associated with failures
of maturation at oedipal and preoedipal levels. Thus the boy or girl approaches puberty with all patterns predetermined, because of infantile

41

and early childhood experiences, and there is much that is unconscious, and much that is unknown because it has not yet been experienced.

There is room for a great deal of variation in individual cases as to the degree and type of the problem that may result, but the general problem is the same: How shall this ego organization meet the new id advance? How shall the pubertal changes be accommodated in the personality pattern that is specific to the boy or girl in question? How shall the adolescent boy or girl deal with the new power to destroy and even to kill, a power that did not complicate feelings of hatred at the toddler age? It is like putting new wine into old bottles.

THE ENVIRONMENT

The part played by the environment is immensely significant at this stage, so much so that it is best in a descriptive account to assume the continued existence and interest of the child's own father and mother and of wider family organizations. Many of the difficulties of adolescents for which professional help is sought derive from environmental failure, and this fact only emphasizes the vital importance of the environment and of the family setting in the case of the vast majority of adolescents who do in fact achieve adult maturity, even if in the process they give their parents headaches.

DEFIANCE AND DEPENDENCE

A characteristic of the age group under examination is the rapid alternation between defiant independence and regressive dependence, even a coexistence of the two extremes at one moment of time.

THE ISOLATION OF THE INDIVIDUAL

The adolescent is essentially an isolate. It is from a position of isolation that a beginning is made that may result in relationships between individuals, and eventually in socialization. In this respect the adolescent is repeating an essential phase of infancy, for the infant is an isolate, at least until he or she has repudiated the not-me and has become set up as a separated-off individual, one that can form relationships with objects that are external to the self and outside the area of omnipotent control. It could be said that before the pleasure-pain principle has given way to the reality principle the child is isolated by the subjective nature of his or her environment.

Young adolescents are collections of isolates, attempting by various means to form an aggregate through the adoption of an identity of tastes. They can become grouped if they are attacked as a group, but this is a paranoid organization reactive to the attack; after the persecution the individuals return to their state of being an aggregate of isolates.

SEX PRIOR TO READINESS FOR SEX

The sex experiences of younger adolescents are colored by this phenomenon of isolation; and also by the fact that the boy or girl does not yet know whether he or she will be homosexual, heterosexual, or simply narcissistic. In many cases there is a long period of uncertainty as to whether a sex urge will turn up at all. Urgent masturbatory activity may be at this stage a repeated getting rid of sex, rather than a form of sex experience, and indeed compulsive heterosexual or homosexual activities may themselves at this age serve the purpose of a getting rid of sex or a discharge of tensions, rather than of a form of union between whole human beings. Union between whole human beings is more likely to appear, first, in aim-inhibited sex play, or in affectionate behavior with the accent on sentiment. Here again is the personal pattern, waiting to join up with the instincts, but in the long meanwhile there has to be found some form of relief from sexual tension; and compulsive masturbation would be expected in a high proportion of cases if we had an opportunity to know the facts. (A good motto for any investigator of the subject would be this: Whoever asks questions must expect to be told lies.)

It is certainly possible to study the adolescent in terms of the ego coping with id changes, and the practicing psychoanalyst must be prepared to meet this central theme, either manifest in the child's life or displayed cautiously in the material presented by the child in the analytic setting, or in the child's conscious and unconscious fantasy and in the deepest parts of the personal psychic or inner reality. Here, however, I will not pursue this approach, because my purpose is to survey adolescence in another way and to attempt to relate today's urgency of the adolescent theme to the social changes that belong to the past fifty years.

The Time for Adolescence

Is it not a sign of the health of a society that its teenagers are able to be adolescent at the right time, that is to say, at the age that covers pubertal growth? Among primitive peoples either the pubertal changes are hidden under taboos or else the adolescent is turned into an adult in the space of a few weeks or months by certain rites and ordeals. In our present society, adults are being formed by natural processes out of adolescents who move forward because of growth tendencies. This may easily mean that the new adults of today have strength and stability and maturity.

Naturally, there must be a price to pay for this. The many adolescent breakdowns call for toleration and treatment; and also this new development puts a strain on society, for it is distressing for adults who have themselves been defrauded of adolescence to watch the boys and girls in a state of florid adolescence all round them.

Three Social Changes

In my opinion there are three main social developments that have altered the whole climate for adolescents in adolescence:

1. Venereal disease is no longer a bogy. The spirochaete and the gonococcus are no longer (as they were certainly felt to be fifty years ago) agents of a punishing God. Now they can be dealt with by penicillin and by appropriate antibiotics.[1]

2. The development of contraceptive techniques has given the adolescent the freedom to explore. This freedom is very new, the freedom to find out about sexuality and sensuality when there is not only an absence of a wish for parenthood but also, as there nearly always is, a wish to avoid bringing into the world an unwanted and unparented baby. Of course, accidents happen and will happen, and these accidents lead to unfortunate and dangerous abortions or to the birth of illegitimate children. But in examining the problem of adolescence we must accept the fact, I suggest, that the modern adolescent can explore, if he or she has a mind to, the whole area of sensuous living without suffering the mental agony that accidental conception involves. This is only partly true because the mental agony associated with the fear of an accident remains, but the problem has been altered during the course of the last thirty years by this new factor. The mental agony now, we can see, comes from the individual child's innate guilt sense. I do not mean that each child has an innate guilt sense, but I mean that, in health, the child develops in a very complicated way a sense of right and wrong, a sense

of guilt and ideals, and an idea of what he or she wants for the future.

3. The atom bomb is perhaps producing even more profound changes than the two characteristics of our age that I have listed so far. The atom bomb affects the relationship between adult society and the adolescent tide, which seems to be for ever coming in. We have to carry on now on the basis that there is not going to be another war. Now it can be argued that there might be a war at any minute in some place in the world, but we know that we can no longer solve a social problem by organizing for a new war. So there is no longer any basis on which we can justify the provision of strong military or naval discipline for our children, however convenient it might be for us to be able to do so.

Here comes the effect of the atom bomb. If it no longer makes sense to deal with our difficult adolescents by preparing them to fight for their king and country, then that is another reason why we are thrown back on the problem that there is this adolescence, a thing in itself. So now we have got to "dig" adolescence.

The adolescent is prepotent. In the imaginative life the potency of man is not just a matter of the active and passive of intercourse. It includes a man's victory over a man and a girl's admiration of the victor. All this now, I am suggesting, has to be wrapped up in the mystique of the café bar and in the occasional disturbance with knives. Adolescence has to contain itself much more than it has ever had to do before, and itself is pretty violent material—rather like the repressed unconscious of the individual, not so beautiful if opened out to the world.

When we think of the notorious atrocities of modern youth, we must weigh against them all the deaths that belong to the war that is not and that is not going to be and against all the cruelty that belongs to every war that has ever been but is not going to be again. So adolescence is here with us, which is evident, and it has come to stay.

These three changes are having an effect on our social concern, and this shows clearly in the way in which adolescence comes into prominence as something that is no longer to be hustled off the stage by false maneuvers, like conscription.

The Unacceptability of the False Solution

It is a prime characteristic of adolescents that they do not accept false solutions. This fierce morality on the basis of the real and the false belongs also to infancy and to illness of schizophrenic type.

45

The cure for adolescence is the passage of time, a fact that has very little meaning for the adolescent. The adolescent looks for a cure that is immediate, but at the same time rejects one cure after another because some false element in it is detected.

Once the adolescent can tolerate compromise, he or she may discover various ways in which the relentlessness of essential truths can be softened. For instance, there is a solution through identification with parent figures; or there can be a premature maturity in terms of sex; or there can be a shift of emphasis from sex to physical prowess in athletics, or from the bodily functions to intellectual attainment or achievement. In general, adolescents reject these helps, and instead they have to go through a sort of doldrums area, a phase in which they feel futile, and in which they have not yet found themselves. We have to watch this happening. But a total avoidance of these compromises, especially of the use of identifications and vicarious experience, means that each individual must start from scratch, ignoring all that has been worked out in the past history of our culture. Adolescents can be seen struggling to start again as if they had nothing they could take over from anyone. They can be seen to be forming groups on the basis of minor uniformities, and on the basis of some sort of group adherence that belongs to locality and to age. Young people can be seen searching for a form of identification which does not let them down in their struggle, the struggle to feel real, the struggle to establish a personal identity, not to fit into an assigned role, but to go through whatever has to be gone through. They do not know what they are going to become. They do not know where they are, and they are waiting. Because everything is in abeyance, they feel unreal, and this leads them to do certain things that feel real to them and that are only too real in the sense that society is affected.

We do in fact get very much caught up with this curious thing about adolescents, the mixture of defiance and dependence. Those looking after adolescents will find themselves puzzled as to how boys and girls can be defiant to a degree and at the same time so dependent as to be childish, even infantile, showing patterns of the infantile dependence that dates from their earliest times. Moreover, parents find themselves paying out money to enable their children to be defiant against themselves. This is a good example of the way in which those who theorize and write and talk are operating in a layer different from the layer in which adolescents live, and in which parents or parent substitutes are faced with urgent problems of management. The real thing here is not the theory but the impact of the one on the other, the adolescent and the parent.

Adolescent Needs

So it is possible to gather together the needs that adolescents manifest:

1. The need to avoid the false solution.
2. The need to feel real or to tolerate not feeling at all.
3. The need to defy in a setting in which dependence is met and can be relied on to be met.
4. The need to prod society repeatedly so that society's antagonism is made manifest and can be met with antagonism.

Healthy Adolescence and Illness Patterns

That which shows in the normal adolescent is related to that which shows in various kinds of ill person. For example:

1. The need to avoid the false solution corresponds with the psychotic patient's inability to compromise; compare also psychoneurotic ambivalence and the deceptiveness and self-deception of health.
2. The need to feel real or not to feel at all is related to psychotic depression with depersonalization.
3. The need to defy corresponds with the antisocial tendency as it appears in delinquency.

From this it follows that in a group of adolescents the various tendencies tend to be represented by the more seriously ill members of the group. For example, one member of a group takes an overdose of a drug, another lies in bed in a depression, another is free with the flick knife. In each case the aggregate of isolates is grouped behind the ill individual, whose extreme symptom has impinged on society. Yet, for the majority of the individuals who are involved there is not enough drive behind the tendency to bring the symptom into inconvenient existence and to produce a social reaction.

47

THE DOLDRUMS

To repeat, if the adolescent is to get through this developmental stage by natural process, then there must be expected a phenomenon, which could be called adolescent doldrums. Society needs to include this as a permanent feature and to tolerate it, to react actively to it, in fact to come to meet it, but not to cure it. The question is, has our society the health to do this?

Complicating this issue is the fact that some individuals are too ill (with psychoneurosis or depression or schizophrenia) to reach a stage of emotional development that could be called adolescence, or they can reach it only in a highly distorted way. I have not included in this account a description of severe psychiatric illness as it appears at this age level; nevertheless, one type of illness cannot be set aside in any statement about adolescence, namely, delinquency.

ADOLESCENCE AND THE ANTISOCIAL TENDENCY

It is revealing to study the close relationship that exists between the normal difficulties of adolescence and the abnormality that may be called the antisocial tendency. The difference between these two states lies not so much in the clinical picture that each presents as in the dynamic, in the etiology, of each. At the root of the antisocial tendency there is always a deprivation; if it occurs at a difficult moment, it may have a lasting result because it overstrains the available defenses. Behind the antisocial tendency there is always some health and then an interruption, after which things are never the same again. The antisocial child is searching in some way or other, violently or gently, to get the world to acknowledge its debt; or is trying to make the world reform the framework that got broken up. At the root, therefore, of the antisocial tendency is this deprivation. At the root of adolescence in general it is not possible to say that there is inherently a deprivation, and yet there is something the same, but, being less in degree and diffused, it just avoids overstraining the available defenses. So that in the group that the adolescent finds to identify with, or in the aggregate of isolates that forms into a group in relation to a persecution, the extreme members of the group are acting for the total group. All sorts of things in the adolescents' struggle—the stealing, the knives, the breaking out and the breaking in, everything—all these have to be contained in the dynamic of this group, sitting round listening to jazz or having a bottle party. And, if nothing happens, the individual members begin to feel unsure of the reality of their protest, and yet they are not in themselves disturbed enough to do the antisocial act that would make things right. But if in the group there is an antisocial member, or two or three, willing to do the antisocial thing, this makes all the others cohere, makes them feel real, and temporarily structures the group. Each individual member will be loyal and will support the one who will act for the group, though not one of them would have approved of the thing that the extreme antisocial character did.

I think that this principle applies to the use of other kinds of illness. The suicidal attempt of one of the members is very important to all the others. Or one of the group cannot get up; he is paralyzed with depression, and has got a record-player playing very doleful music; he locks himself in his room and nobody can get near. The others all know that this is happening, and every now and again he comes out and they have a bottle party or something, and this may go on all night or for two or three days. Such happenings belong to the whole group, and the group is shifting and the individuals are changing their groups; but somehow the individual members of the group use the extremes to help themselves to feel real, in their struggle to get through the doldrums period.

It is all a problem of how to be adolescent during adolescence. This is an extremely brave thing for anybody to be, and some of these people are trying to achieve it. It does not mean that we grown-ups have to be saying: "Look at these dear little adolescents having their adolescence; we must put up with everything and let our windows get broken." This is not the point. The point is that we are challenged, and we meet the challenge as part of the function of adult living. But we meet the challenge rather than set out to cure what is essentially healthy.

The big challenge from the adolescent is to the bit of ourselves that has not really had its adolescence. This bit of ourselves makes us resent these people being able to have their phase of the doldrums and makes us want to find a solution for them. There are hundreds of false solutions. Anything we say or do is wrong. We give support and we are wrong, we withdraw support and that is wrong too. We dare not be understanding. But in the course of time we find that this adolescent boy and this adolescent girl have come out of the doldrums phase and are now able to begin identifying with society, with parents, and with all sorts of wider groups, without feeling threatened with personal extinction.

49

NOTE

1. I remember clearly a conversation with a girl, sometime after World War I. She told me that it was only the fear of venereal disease that had kept her from being a prostitute. She was horrified at the idea I put forward in a simple conversation that venereal disease might one day be preventable or curable. She said that she could not imagine how she could have gotten through her adolescence (and she was only just coming through it) without this fear, which she had used in order to keep straight. She is now the mother of a large family and would be called a normal sort of person; but she had to come through her adolescent struggle and the challenge of her own instincts. She had a difficult time. She did a bit of thieving and lying, but she came through. But she held on to the venereal disease deterrent.

4] SIGMUND FREUD:
SOME ADOLESCENT
TRANSFORMATIONS OF
A FUTURE GENIUS

"The childhood shows the man, as morning shows the day," John Milton already knew, almost 300 years before Freud laid the cornerstone of a scientific theory for the psychological development of man. As scientists we are very much concerned with theories and observations, with data and statistics, with projects and programs—and very little with poets. Freud himself knew the value of a poetic inspiration. On his seventieth birthday he is quoted (Trilling, 1950) to have said: "The poets and philosophers before me discovered the unconscious; what I discovered was the scientific method by which the unconscious can be studied." He admired the intuitive insights of the great writers, and he used them as a source of creative imaginativeness. Yet we know very little about the influence of the literary background in Freud's education on his creativity as a scientist. This chapter is an attempt to examine some aspects of the early development of Freud's creativity, as an adolescent, and as they are revealed in some early letters (Freud, 1969).

Not only psychoanalysts but historians, philologists, and other students of man are increasingly turning to the study of the life and work of Sigmund Freud. For the great psychologist left us not only a massive opus of scientific writings but also more than 4,000 letters. Much of the material is of only vaguely concealed or even frank autobiographical nature and allows for deeply insightful studies into the processes of creativity and genius. Though Jones (1953) wrote an exemplary biogra-

51

phy and though there have been many other important contributors it seems that the surface has barely been scratched and the definitive study of this creative genius will be a task for future generations of scholars.

One sign of this widening interest is the recent publication by Schoenau (1968) of a thorough examination of Freud's prose style. Schoenau's main concern is with the identification and evaluation of the literary element in Freud's writings. It has long been recognized that Freud wrote prose of a high literary quality. Among the European intelligentsia Freud had a solid reputation as a gifted writer long before his scientific achievements were noticed by the scientific community. Thomas Mann (1953), perhaps the greatest German language writer of this century, spoke about Freud as an artist and about his compositions as part of world literature. In 1930 Freud was honored with the Goethe prize for literature.

Schoenau examines the question of Freud having been an artist who dealt mainly with scientific topics versus Freud having been a scientist who used artistic devices mainly in the services of his scientific purpose, and he firmly takes the position that Freud was first and last a scientist, albeit a scientific genius with unusually remarkable artistic endowments. Freud seems to have been well aware of his literary propensities and used his talents well but always subordinated to his scientific purposes. Decisively, even angrily, he would reject being designated an "artist" because he clearly recognized the danger to psychoanalysis that was hidden beneath some apparently complimentary comments on his work. Replying to Havelock Ellis, who had praised Freud's artistry, Freud said: "We cannot but regard this view as a fresh turn taken by resistance and as a repudiation of analysis even though it is disguised in a friendly, indeed in a too flattering, manner. We are inclined to meet it with a most decided contradiction" (Freud, 1920). However, even Freud acknowledged that his case histories "read like novels" (1898). In his younger preanalytic days Freud (1969) was less reticent in thinking about himself as a poetic writer: In a letter to his friend Emil Fluss on February 7, 1873, he notices that he is "expressing himself poetically . . ." and in another letter he reports with pleasure, "Thus ends my little novel" (September 18, 1872), and on June 16, 1873, he cautions Fluss to save the letters because Fluss is corresponding "with a German stylist," and, well, "one never knows." Ten years later, in a letter (Freud, 1960) to his bride, Martha Bernays, on July 13, 1883, he teases by asking her, "Why didn't I become a gardener instead of a doctor or poet?"

52

Inevitably, as one becomes more familiar with the multifaceted wealth of Freud's work, controversies about the relative primacy of artist or scientist fade into the background and are supplanted by questions about the function of artistic elements in works of science. First, of course, there is the aesthetic function, the use of beautiful phrases and of elegant forms as decorations and to elicit the sense of pleasure that comes with aesthetic experience. More importantly, especially for Freud, there is the function of creating in the reader a sense of conviction by the use of vivid images and metaphors, and by the allusions and associations that are evoked by mottoes and citations derived from the unlimited heritage of the literary tradition. Particularly skillful is Freud's use of fictive dialogue to establish empathic contact with the reader to heighten the reader's participation in an affective experience and to lead the reader to think along the path of conjectures, objections and refutations to arrive at a conclusion. Finally one wonders about the function of metaphor in the process of concept formation. What is the role of the vivid images and analogies in Freud's development of scientific theories and concepts? To what extent is the intense dialogue with the reader an externalization of an internal dialogue through which Freud becomes aware of his preconsciously formed conclusions? Later I shall return to these questions.

Psychological states, like their biological analogues, are usually best understood by retracing the steps leading to their development. Similarly, our understanding of the relationships between artistic and scientific creativity may be enhanced by a closer examination of the formative stages. The recent rediscovery of a number of letters (Freud, 1969) from the sixteen-, seventeen-, and eighteen-year-old Freud to his friend Emil Fluss therefore is an important new source of data about Freud during his adolescence and may yield some clues about the unfolding of his creative powers.

The Fluss family had been friends of the Freud family when the latter were still living in Pribor, the town where Freud was born and from which the family moved when Freud was three years old. During a visit with the Fluss family in the summer of 1872, Freud had rekindled a friendship with his childhood playmate Emil. Following his return to Vienna there ensued a brief but revealing correspondence of seven letters and two postal cards from Freud to Fluss. All but one of these letters had not been published until recently.

Looking at these letters superficially we see Freud reporting on his travels, on his flirtations, on the "Spanish Academy" (his secret society with his friend Eduard Silberstein), on the Twentieth Jubilee of the accession to the throne of Kaiser Franz Joseph I, on his *Matura* (the final examinations before going on to the university), and on the lectures he attended during his first year at the university. Interspersed are perceptive observations of others and especially of himself, and the educated German-speaking reader will be reminded of Goethe's "The Suffering of the Young Werther." However, the tone is not one of suffering but rather ironically distant, critical yet detached. It is aristocratic in the best sense of that word. It is the tone of Horace. Indeed, Freud tells Fluss: "I read Horatian Odes, you live them" (May 1, 1873). We know Freud was intimately familiar with the life and work also of Goethe and probably not unaware of a poem the sixteen-year old Goethe had written on the occasion of his friend F. M. Moors's departure to the university. Goethe had quoted from Horace ("Risum teneatis amici?" 'Can you hold back laughter, friends?') and had ended his poem by writing that he would not like to be forgotten. Similarly Freud admonishes Fluss to preserve the letters—"bind them together—guard them well —one never knows" (June 16, 1873).

Let us pause and see how quickly we have plunged from considering the adolescent Freud's aristocratic tone to tenuous speculations about the influence of Horace and Goethe on the young man's writing. Yet we cannot escape that these letters fairly resonate with citations from and allusions to these two poets. An incomplete survey might include the following intimations of Horace: "The unvarnished truth" (September 18, 1872) alludes to "Nudas Veritas" (Odes I, 24, 7); "similar circumstances produce similar people" (September 18, 1872) alludes to "Fortes creantur fortibus" (Odes IV, 4, 29); "I have lost almost all recollection of the past and like numbed allow everything to happen to me" (September 18, 1872) alludes to "you ask me why a soft numbness diffuses all my innermost senses with deep oblivion" (Epodes II, st. 1). We will return to this particular citation later when we will consider the role of metaphor.

Freud's teacher in the gymnasium had praised Freud's style with the words of the poet Herder as both correct and characteristic, and Freud teases Fluss about exchanging letters with a German stylist (June 16, 1873). There is overwhelming evidence to show the intense involvement of the adolescent Freud with literature.

To start from the surface, there is the sheer quantity, the length of the letters, the obvious love of words and phrases, almost the need to write, coupled with a discerning awareness of the importance of style as shown in the following quotations: "phrases as slippery as an eel" (September 18, 1872) or "to express myself poetically" (February 7, 1873) or "This word is a concession to your style" (February 1, 1873). An example of Freud's pleasure in telling a story is the skillful manner in which he expands a single sentence taken from his friend's letter "Recently I was at the ice [to skate], so was she" (February 7, 1873) into an ironic and imaginative little story. One is reminded of the mature Freud who took a sentence of a letter written to him by Romain Rolland and expanded it into the great *Civilization and Its Discontents* (Freud, 1930).

The frequent citation or allusion to literary references is another important sign of Freud's identification with the classic authors. Earlier I have mentioned Horace and Goethe. We also find Shakespeare: "Sucking melancholy from each event" (May 1, 1873) alludes to "I can suck melancholy out of a song" (*As You Like It*); "more common than elsewhere are blackberries" (May 1, 1873) alludes to "if reasons were as plenty as blackberries" (*Henry IV*); "delicate conscience" (May 1, 1873) alludes to "Conscience, conscience! O, 'tis a tender place" (*Henry VII*); "to be content with cold dishes" (June 16, 1873) alludes to "He receives comfort like cold porridge" (*Tempest*).

The Bible is well represented among the citations: "My cup runneth over" (Psalms) is mirrored in Freud's "made the measure full" (September 18, 1872); similarly we find from Genesis "an angel with a fiery sword" (May 1, 1873), "A Tower of Babylon" (May 1, 1873), "Finds no favor in my eyes" (June 16, 1873) and from Job we find "with fear and trembling" (June 16, 1873).

Heine and Cervantes and the Mass for the Dead reappear but this is not the place to attempt an exhaustive listing. Let it suffice to have documented that the young Freud was a thoroughly literate person.

The most graphic expression of Freud's vivid literary imagination is the pictorial metaphors that illuminate his prose style. One need only think of the comparison of libido to water, of psychoanalytic treatment being like a train ride or like taking a walk with the analyst as guide, or of the psychoanalytic investigator being like an explorer or like an archeologist discovering clues to the past, or of the analytic interpreter of dreams being like the translator of ancient hieroglyphics. Together with numerous other brilliant metaphorical images Freud's opus is thus given an underlying web of interconnected threads that lends it unity and strength underneath the rich texture. It should occasion no surprise, therefore, to discover that the writing of the sixteen-year old Freud already was rich in the metaphorical images that in later years would twine the fabric of his scientific conceptualizations. "With full sails I steer into the future" he writes (September 28, 1872) presaging his love for the nautical metaphor. He later used "Fluctuat nec mergitur" ('Swamped but not sunk') from the insignia of the City of Paris, as his motto for the "History of the Psychoanalytic Movement" (1914) and in *The Interpretation of Dreams* (1900) we find "Flavit et dissipati sunt" ('Wind-blown and scattered'), an inscription from a coin memorializing the defeat of the Spanish Armada. Among Freud's later favorites were also military metaphors which already make their appearance in these early letters: "to continue the reconnaissance" and "to pass in review" (September 18, 1872).

I have already noted Freud's resonance with Horace when on September 18, 1872 he writes: "I have lost almost all recollection of the past and like numbed allow everything to happen to me." Ten days later Freud writes: "I am like a scholar whom you question about the past of the earth. The whole period is as if totally foreign to me however much I once seemed to be at home in it." A vague apprehension associated with the dim past and with a feeling of helplessness has become transformed into a vivid image and the tone is now one of detached contemplation. The image is, of course, one of Freud's key metaphors, the metaphor of childhood as prehistory with the associated simile of the psychoanalyst as archeological rediscoverer. The metaphor recurs in a letter to Fliess (January 16, 1898): ". . . happiness is the deferred fulfillment of a pre-historic wish"; in the next paragraph, apparently talking about something different, Freud goes on to say, "All sorts of other things keep dawning on me and always everything earlier is forgotten" (my translation—E.S.W.). It seems that twenty-six years after Freud first linked a subjective sensation of fading memory to an image of buried prehistory he still unconsciously makes the same association. That same year (Freud, 1898) in his published scientific writings Freud for the first time explicitly compared childhood to prehistory, again in his work on dreams (Freud, 1900) and in his "Three Essays on the Theory of Sexuality" (Freud, 1905), and the last time, the year before his death when he said: "With neurotics it is as though we were in a pre-historic landscape" (Freud, 1938). In another letter to Fliess (January 30, 1899) Freud had mentioned his "preference for the pre-historic in all its human forms" (Freud, 1969).

Returning to the 1872 image we can also discern the idea of not quite involuntary forgetting—the seeds of the later concept of repression. The impression is strong that for Freud metaphorical thinking served not only his aesthetic sensibility to communicate clearly and beautifully but was also a necessary step in his own processes of insight and concept formation.

Adolescence is a time for the recasting of the psychic apparatus. Accompanied by more or less turmoil, archaic imagos are decathected and the freed libido together with accretions of new energies needs to be redistributed into newly altered structures. The vicissitudes of narcissistic as well as of object libido are replayed on the stages of preoedipal and oedipal drama, sometimes with a new and happier ending. Particularly visible are the transformations of narcissism (Kohut, 1966) as the wildly grandiose self is tamed and idealized parental imagos become inspiring ideals in a process of repeated idealizations and disillusionments. Through these adolescent letters we can catch a fleeting glimpse of these processes in the young Freud. The disillusionment erupts in a number of comments typical of an adolescent Jew's need to depreciate his elders and, *pari passu,* himself. More interestingly, in the above cited example of the metaphor of childhood as prehistory I have tried to dimly see traces of erupting anxiety mobilized by a feeling of helplessness and smallness rooted in the once familiar but now foreign past and how through an idealizing identification probably with Horace, Freud achieved a measure of detachment that allowed him to channel what must have been wild imaginings into a vivid image that by way of becoming a metaphor crystallized into a scientific concept.

Arlow (1969) has stated that "metaphor constitutes an outcropping into conscious expression of a fragment of an unconscious fantasy." I would add that the appearance of metaphor is also a concretization of this fragment of unconscious fantasy signifying a newly laid down neutralizing structure. Using the concepts elaborated by Kohut (1966) this could be formulated, particularly, in adolescents, as structure formation through identification with idealized imagos that represent an amalgam of idealized aspects of parental imagos with idealized aspects of a group culture that has become personalized. Some of the only partially neutralized energy with which the adolescent typically deals by acting out thus may be absorbed into and channelled by structures that crystallize around such amalgamized derivatives of narcissistic libido. An amalgam of idealized imagos seems particularly suitable as a seed for such processes of identification because it can be suitably ambiguous, by which I mean neither too much like nor too much unlike the rejected and decathected aspects of archaic parental imagos. Fortunate is the youngster

57

who can partake of the heroes of a noble tradition when he creates a fittingly ambiguous amalgam of idealized imagos with which he then can identify.

We have reached the point where one has to ask why did Freud not become a poet or writer of novels but a scientist? Perhaps the answer is that he became both. In these letters he records this significant turning point in his life. "About me I can report to you news which perhaps are the greatest of my wretched life. . . . but the matter is not yet ripe for decision" (March 17, 1873). Almost certainly Freud was here referring to the fateful lecture by Bruehl at which he was so decisively impressed by hearing Goethe's essay on nature. Six weeks later he can say: "If I lift the veil, will you not be disappointed? Well, try this: I have decided to be a Natural Scientist. I shall gain insight into thousand year old acts of Nature, perhaps even eavesdrop on its eternal processes" (May 1, 1873). This time the idealizing identification crystallized into a life-long identity in response to the stirring model of the unique post-Renaissance example of an artist-scientist—Goethe. An analogous identification with Leonardo da Vinci, perspicaciously pinpointed by Jones, must in part have been based on the latter's similar range of passionate interests. It is intriguing to note from these letters that this consolidation of Freud's identity coincides with his changing the spelling of his given name from Sigismund to Sigmund.

As already noted earlier much of the lucidity and persuasive power of Freud's mature style is the result of the reader becoming engaged in a fictive dialogue that leads him to think along with Freud, who writes with continuous courteous concern for the reader's affective experience. The letters examined here show the young Freud already using this device, even if not with the sure mastery of later years. This finding refutes suggestions that ascribe the fictive dialogue to Freud's experience in the analytical consulting room. Rather, it seems that, analogously to the use of metaphor, fictive dialogue serves not only as a means of effective communication but as the externalization of a necessary internal dialogue that disciplines the unfettered imagination into creative scientific ideas. "What conclusions would you draw from this?" (February 7, 1873) Freud asks Fluss in forcing him to think along with him. With courteous regard he says: "How well I can imagine your feelings" (June 16, 1873). Constantly Freud keeps one eye on the reader, one eye on himself: "As I see I have not spared you my comment even though at first I wanted to" (September 18, 1872). Here in the interested yet detached observation of his friend as well as of himself is the prefigurement of the psychoanalytic attitude.

58

Whereas in fictive dialogue the reader's participation is openly recruited, in nonfictive dialogue the reader's response can be just as powerfully, even though more covertly, elicited by a well-chosen metaphorical image. The effective metaphor creates tension, which should not be too great, as, for example, when the comparison is too far-fetched. Nor should the tension be too small, as, for example, when the parallel is too conventional or too close. Discussing personal style in another context Rosen (1961) stated "Just as ambiguity beyond certain limits disturbs the reception of meaning by offering too great a number of possible interpretations, so too an excessively explicit message limits the recipient's participation in the process to mere registration and excludes him from the creative act of the completion of meaning by the resolution of ambiguity." Optimal ambiguity appears to be the fulcrum on which balances the creative process awaiting completion by the reader. Freud's prose style is characterized by just this ability to construct satisfyingly effective and therefore artistic moments of optimal ambiguity that facilitate the communication and creation of scientific insights. One need think only of that most optimally ambiguous situation, the analytic one. Freud's prescription for interpretation contains the same call for creative completion when he says: "One must be careful not to give a patient the solution of a symptom or the translation of a wish until he is already so close to it that he has only one short step more to make in order to get hold of the explanation for himself" (Freud, 1913). Indeed, this is almost a prescription for artistic creativity as well.

Our examination of the letters of the young Freud has revealed to us some of the roots from which grew the later creative genius. We have glimpsed some of the adolescent transformations that played a role in channeling the unleashed energies of youth into artistic and scientific discipline. Truly, we behold, "The child is father of the man."

REFERENCES

Arlow, Jacob. (1969). Unconscious fantasy and disturbances of conscious experience. Psychoanalytic Quarterly, 38:1–27.
Freud, S. (1895). Studies on hysteria. Standard Edition, 2:160.
———. (1898). Sexuality in the aetiology of the neuroses. Standard Edition, 3:267.
———. (1900). The interpretation of dreams. New York: Basic Books.
———. (1905). Three essays on the theory of sexuality. New York: Basic Books.
———. (1913). On beginning the treatment (Further recommendations on the technique of psycho-analysis, I). Standard Edition, 12:140.

———. (1920). A note on the prehistory of the technique of analysis. Standard Edition, 18:263.

———. (1930). Civilization and its discontents. Standard Edition, 21:64.

———. (1938). Findings, ideas and problems. Standard Edition, 23:299.

———. (1954). The origins of psychoanalysis: Letters to Wilhelm Fliess, drafts and notes: 1887–1902. Edited by Marie Bonaparte, Anna Freud, Ernst Kris. New York: Basic Books.

———. (1960). Letters of Sigmund Freud. Selected and edited by Ernst L. Freud. New York: Basic Books.

———. (1969). Some early unpublished letters of Freud. International Journal of Psycho-Analysis, 50:419–427.

Jones, Ernest. (1953). The life and work of Sigmund Freud. New York: Basic Books.

Kohut, Heinz. (1966). Forms and transformations of narcissism. Journal of the American Psychoanalytic Association, 14:243–272.

Mann, Thomas. (1953). Altes und Neues. Frankfurt a. M.: Fischer.

Rosen, Victor. (1961). The Relevance of "style." International Journal of Psycho-Analysis, 42:447–457.

Schoenau, Walter. (1968). Sigmund Freud's Prosa. Stuttgart: J. B. Metzlersche Verlagsbuchhandlung.

Trilling, Lionel. (1950). The liberal imagination. New York: Viking Press, p. 34.

5] *BONNIE AND CLYDE:*

A MODERN PARABLE

KENNETH NEWMAN

Seldom in recent years has a movie evoked so much controversy and stimulated so much discussion as *Bonnie and Clyde*. Motivated by both my emotional reactions and my intellectual curiosity I have tried to discover what elements in this film activated such intense feelings. The movie will be discussed in three sections. First the focus will be on the film as a valuable work of art and attempts will be made to validate this judgment. In this section the emphasis will be on viewing the movie as a modern parable offering insights into aspects of contemporary society. The second section will be devoted to a study of some of the individual characters and will attempt to show how they may reveal to us vital insights into the problems of the narcissistic personality. In the final section I will endeavor to show how the movie can be enjoyed as a demonstration of some typical adolescent processes. This latter focus may partly explain why this film caused such excitement and a sense of recognition in so many young people. The central themes of depression and narcissistic conflict are universal feelings we all have had to deal with in ourselves, especially as we have attempted to work through our own adolescence.

I

Art, to be psychologically meaningful, should be expressed so that conflicts or unconscious themes being communicated by the artist (Beres, 1957) are experienced or felt by the viewer. The artist through his creative work allows unconscious impulses and their derivatives to enter the preconscious where they are then cathected with more neutralized energy. The creator uses disguises and symbols in a novel or original way so that the audience is provided with a shared aesthetic pleasure. The concrete images that help shape the work should have sufficient distance from the original id impulses so that the art form is not simply a vehicle for the expression of unaltered primary process products. Through this sublimation the audience can enjoy the unconscious and conscious expressed in fantasies without being forced to isolate the emotions activated or else discharge them immediately.

Often creative artists can pick up both unconscious and contemporary themes and skillfully portray these in ways which help us to put words to inner experiences that were previously below our level of awareness. The artist's job is to communicate this, and we as psychiatrists may then try to understand the meaning of the symbols. *Bonnie and Clyde* is an exciting and original way to communicate themes that are germane to the 1960's as well as to the 1930's. On an individual level the themes center around depression, self-esteem regulation and depletion, fragmented ego states and defenses against these conditions such as illusionary omnipotence, magical thinking, and narcissistic fantasies, which stimulate delinquent acting out. On the social level the themes encompass commentary on the breakdown of traditional values and ideals, the failure of institutions to provide models for adequate identification, the bankruptcy behind many cherished illusions, and the feelings of alienation and isolation in many of our young people today. Dramatic and destructive forms of rebellion seen today throughout the country may be the modern counterpart of the gangster of the 1930's expressing dissatisfaction with both inner and outer worlds. The Depression is not only used for setting but it is the dominant mood. We can also see in the movie dramatizations in action of various forms and manifestations of adolescent conflict that are phase appropriate and closer to normal phenomena. Thus my contention is that the creators of this movie have conspired (in spite of their protest) to present us with a mirror of contemporary society with its frightening problems and pathological attempts at solutions.

Two critical concerns have been voiced about the movie. The first is that it glorifies and idealizes violence and sadism, and second that it therefore may stimulate acting out and identification with delinquent heroes. The film as a work of art uses aggression and violence as a motif, but this motif paradoxically is used to portray in a disguised form other conflicts. We have come to realize that perversions, homosexuality, fetishism, and the like frequently have little to do with sexuality per se but represent outward manifestations of severe character disorders, and these symptoms are frequently related to primitive forms of defense against separation and annihilation anxieties. So, too, overt acts of aggression or violence may be viewed as defensive or adaptive manifestations and may be only one expression of a more pervasive problem. Aggression then, can express needs that range from the most primitive to the more structured. Aggressive discharge may represent a quest for tactile stimulation, which affirms the sense of being alive or reaffirms ego boundaries. It may indicate the regressive activation and cathexis of archaic, grandiose, and fragmented body parts which serve then as narcissistic replacements or substitutes for lost external objects and their function in reaction to slight injury or separation from these objects. Action can serve as a defense against boredom: the seeking of external stimulation to ward off painful affects seen particularly in those individuals who have had to repress or decathect fantasies and instincts involving early introjects (Greenson, 1953). The inner tension that results feels like a void or empty sensation and discharge is sought via stimulation from outside sources. Currently we may see this with the widespread use of drugs and promiscuity as well as in delinquent and sadistic activity. In normal adolescence action is frequently used as a discharge and may serve to defend against depression. Also in adolescence it may derive from an ego overburdened with instinctual energy related to revival of earlier conflicts, and the discharge then is seen as an attempt at mastery. Sadism is certainly present in the movie, but consistent with the wider meaning of the film the aggression may be more accurately considered to be symptomatic and not necessarily as primary. For instance, we note that Clyde is bewildered and confused when he realizes that the grocer meant to hit him with a hatchet to keep him from stealing. Not only is this part of his narcissistic character, that is, to fail to be aware of the impact of his actions on others, but it also attests to the fact that sadistic discharge was not his primary motive. When he kills a police officer on the running board he becomes quite disturbed and frightened as if his actions and its effects were not seen as related nor did he wish to kill.

Finally when people argue that the film exploits violence and gratifies a hunger for the sensational in the public, they are confirming an inherent theme of the movie that society and its individuals crave external stimulation and therefore our gratification from the film may parallel the motives of the Barrows gang in seeking action.

From another vantage point the argument that the movie stimulates violence is oversimplified. Let us consider the concept of the aesthetic illusion (Kris, 1952). This concept implies that the audience must be able to maintain the awareness of the separation between fantasy in the film and reality, and it is the artist's job to help maintain this. He does this by ensuring neutralization of drive derivatives so that the viewer is not overwhelmed and there is sufficient distance from the instinctual conflicts for avenues of enjoyment to be possible. If then the undercurrent themes in the movie are indeed quite powerful, how do the filmmakers protect us from excessive stimulation, or, to say it another way, help us resist the breakdown of the aesthetic illusion? There are several ways they do this. First there is the creation of apparent distance in time, in setting, and in character. It is seemingly a story of the Depression and the 1930's set in rural communities and peopled by antiheroes whose stylized behavior, clothes, and mannerisms appear almost as a caricature. How alien their fashions in dress (pin stripe), how quaint but ridiculous the cars, and how foreign their taste in music and radio! (Eddie Cantor singing.) Especially during the first half of the movie there is much that is deliberately comic and not only does this serve as a counterpoint to the building pathos, but the humor also functions to create the feeling of distance and as an antidote to the more threatening evocative feelings. (Of course it should be well recognized that for many, especially youngsters, the capacity to have or maintain the aesthetic illusion is weak or not yet developed.)

One final point to be made in examining the impact of the violence in the film on the younger viewers is with respect to the concept of anonymity. In the movie there is a process of an increasing bond between the audience and the central figures. Despite distance and caricature we begin to identify with them, and at the end we are involved sufficiently so that their death matters. We form a kind of object relatedness and their death brings a sense of momentary personal loss. In contrast, violence done to and by anonymous people on the myriad of cheap television serials or on the news (for example, the films on Vietnam) permits little identification, and a human life has little significance. It is this latter kind of mechanized and utilitarian view of human life and relatedness that has a much more harmful effect on a vulnerable audience. Last, what is there about the actual humdrum life of Bonnie and Clyde that is glorious? The dreams of dining in the Dallas Hotel are actualized as a fried chicken and hamburger dinner eaten furtively in a dingy cabin in Iowa. Their only waltz is a slow agonizing dance of death.

64

Why was this movie so successful or more personally why did it provoke such intense reactions? Actually this movie with its central folk heroes has been made and remade about three times since the 1930's, and apart from the original "Our Life to Live" it has aroused little interest. I believe that this movie is essentially a movie of the here and now and about the deep disturbances in our society—its institutions and its troubled individuals. It might then be viewed as an allegory or as the external representation of an internal state. For example, let us take a person with a borderline personality suffering from a severe underlying depression and conflicts mainly around separations, object constancy, and beset by feelings of deep personal damage and worthlessness. Or, let us take an adolescent experiencing the pain and emptiness of his intrapsychic attempts to decathect old imagos and let us ask these people to describe or picture their internal state or how the world appears to them based on the projection of their internal state. I believe they may describe something very much like a bleak Arkansas town as it appeared by the height of the Depression, impoverished and bankrupt both economically and morally with value systems in disintegration. Their external object world may be divided into the cruel persecutors like the sheriffs, bankers, and rejecting parents of the movie or into fellow sufferers. Note the bond between Bonnie and Clyde and the common people—fellow victims of the Depression.

It is known that even fairly typical adolescents, owing to the intensity of their mood swings, will relate to the external world chiefly as a projection of their internal state. Their hold on or capacity for accurate reality testing may then be quite distorted, and hence they may view it at one time as a source of autoerotic gratification and at another as filled with dangerous attackers (Blos, 1963).

Though this is a highly creative film, it is historically part of a long literary tradition to use the outlawed and alienated as heroes to reflect both an individual and a national mood of confusion and depression as the institutions and value systems are undergoing major upheavals. The modern alienated youth uses drugs, withdrawal, and love-ins as means of dealing with inner tensions, or else he may seek to merge in a mystical all embracing way as in the various popular cults (for example, Great Om), whereas the Barrows gang chose aggressive and delinquent ideals to identify with and stealing as the modus operandi. In a world of poverty and depression, robbing banks may have been one of the few things that seemed to make sense. To many of our current youngsters, drugs, promiscuity, and/or retreat may be the only things that seem to

65

make sense. But both are dealing with the same personal forms of anguish and seeking similar restitutive goals. It may be more than coincidence that as the hippies seek to re-create a family style of life and essentially get the world to feel and care for them, so the Barrows gang too form a family style, aggressively stealing what they passively desire.

II

Theorists and clinicians have fairly exhaustively studied neurotic conflicts and have appropriately used structural and topographical models to delineate clinical phenomena. But when we come to studying many of the disturbed people seen in our offices or portrayed recently on stage and film, the familiar structural conflicts are seen in altered and modified form, and we find problems of self-object confusion, poor ego boundaries, faulty and poorly cathected self-images, and fixations at early symbiotic prestructural object levels. As clinicians we have been struggling of late also to share with one another what we mean when we talk of borderlines, narcissistic characters, and so on. Kohut (1966, 1968), Reich (1960), and Jacobson (1954) have been writing about such problems with increasing refinement and clarification. I shall attempt to view the heroes of *Bonnie and Clyde* as they help to reveal certain aspects of pathological narcissism and faulty self-esteem regulation.

The stress on exhibitionistic strivings is revealed from the very first scene as we see Bonnie—bored and restless—wander to the mirror and then to the window and ostentatiously display herself to Clyde. To Bonnie and Clyde, and later to the whole Barrows gang, the goal of being recognized and admired as the greatest and most notorious of bank robbers is their chief ambition—not money or killing. The main source of gratification comes from the knowledge that they are on every front page; in one touching scene Clyde strides proudly up to a bankrupt tenant farmer and declares, "I'm Clyde B. and this here's Miss Bonnie Parker; we rob banks." Every encounter with those who represent external reality focuses on their wish to impress that they are the famous gangsters. Note too, that in the first confrontation with the sheriff they use the visual—a photograph—to humiliate him. Their intuition that this would be the sheriff's greatest mortification only emphasizes the role of exhibitionism with both its negative and positive valences. To bask in the sunlight, to live out a grandiose fantasy of being the greatest even if it is a delinquent hero, is to elevate to immeasurable heights the feelings of self-esteem. To be portrayed as a failure, to be frustrated in one's exhibitionistic, narcissistic strivings leads to painful states of shame and feelings of inferiority. Throughout the movie there is the repeated expression of the underlying feelings of damage and deficiency in self-feeling. Our first glimpse of Clyde shows him physically crippled and very shortly thereafter we see he is emotionally handicapped and incapable of intimacy. His main preoccupations are with living out his narcissistic fantasy and people are seen as significant only insofar as they serve either to reflect a mirror for his own exalted image or to act in a way to appreciate or admire him. The precarious nature of his self-esteem regulation is vividly illustrated in the scene of his first bank job. It is both humorous and sad as he reacts with anger and shame when he discovers the bank is empty. His narcissistically oriented self image is immediately threatened and he attempts to restore it by forcing the bank clerk at gun point to verify to Bonnie that the bank is indeed bankrupt and he is not a failure.

Developmentally the child's self-image becomes positively cathected and gradually integrated within the relationship with the mother who appropriately responds to the child's needs to be touched, held, and so on and at phase-appropriate times to be admired or to be a gleam in her eye (Kohut, 1966). The normal narcissistic self with its various disparate and grandiose aspects will gradually become modified and wielded into a cohesive self-image. If for some reason there is a disturbance in the parent-child relationship that prematurely injures the child's needs for admiration, there is a danger of repression of the grandiose self so that it continues to exist in its cruder more primitive forms but isolated away from the ego and not subject to modification by reality. We may conceptualize this in a slightly different way (Reich, 1960) if we focus on a pattern of disappointment or loss at a stage that is so traumatic for the child that it leaves him threatened with a constant sense of impending panic (the states of helplessness or overwhelming anxiety). This danger state may lead to a too permanent withdrawal of cathexis onto the self and then to attempts at repair that revolve around the elaboration of the grandiose fantasy (the ideational representative of the narcissistic self). This grandiose fantasy is driven by narcissistic-exhibitionistic ambitions and often features overevaluation of the body or body organs and primitive sexualization of the ideal self and ideal object. The compensatory grandiose strivings are seen as attempts to re-create a perfection originally attributed to the self. This is accomplished intrapsychically by a merging with early omnipotent ego ideals or at least trying to live up to these unrealistic ideals. Thus in their search for fame and admiration through their delinquent acts we may now more appropriately ascribe their motivations as related to attempts to re-create a feeling of perfection. By attempting to merge with their own omnipotent ideals they continually try to restore a sense of wholeness to a badly shattered self-image which is constantly in danger of fragmenting. Public recognition fulfills the regressive wish to be one with the needed object—an object not seen as separate from the self but one originally experienced as part of the self and still needed to perform a function that the self is not yet capable of taking over (Kohut, 1968). Similarly, stealing can be viewed as a wish to gain control over such an object.

If we wish to make some sort of a guess as to what kinds of trauma the heroes were subjected to as children, the scene between C. W. Moss and his father may be used as a representative sample. On returning home with Bonnie and Clyde he proudly displays his tattoo to the father and enthusiastically attempts to bask in the glory of belonging to the Barrow gang. His father instead of responding in the hoped-for way, gives a grunt (Ech!) of disgust at the sight of his son. If with considerable license, this scene can be viewed as a carrier of a whole network or pattern of experiences between C. W. and his parents we may gain some sort of intuitive understanding as to the genesis of this boy's wishes for recognition and admiration and the excessive frustration of these wishes. Furthermore, there are aspects of the body as phallus concepts that are further indicative of the narcissistic erotization of the body. This theme is echoed throughout as we see the stress on photographs and the emphasis on cocky postures and the ever-present gun. But to return momentarily to C. W. and his father we may speculate that his betrayal of Bonnie and Clyde follows this scene, and it may be that his father's depreciation shattered his omnipotent illusions and led to a sudden devaluation of his heroes. Having failed him they are no longer useful as narcissistic supports and now as projected aspects of his own damaged self-image may then become the objects of his aggression.

It is the scenes with parents that serve to heighten our awareness of the fragile human quality of the gang and serve as dramatic juxtaposition to the view of them as comic caricatures. Bonnie's brief reunion with her mother is a haunting one but not simply because of the cinematographic technique. This sequence filmed in a gauzy kind of slow motion style creates a hazy enigmatic and filmy sensation that evokes the elusive feelings and frustration that Bonnie must experience as she too reaches out for her mother. Bonnie has reached a higher level of object relatedness and thus the mother is seen as a separate object. After she realizes there is nothing left for her at home, she develops a depression based on the loss of the love object. The tough little façade of the moll breaks down to a whimpering child with the "blues" after her mother rejects her.

I want to turn now to a consideration of the developmental process in the movie with respect to self-object relations, as it is exemplified through Clyde. His initial relationship to the world as we see it seems to be quite simply a narcissistic one, based on preserving his sense of entitlement and maintaining his illusion of omnipotence. Bonnie is apparently seen as an extension of himself and may also be considered as his wish for a kind of twin, albeit a feminine counterpart. She can reflect back for him in a way that flatters his narcissistically oriented self image. His fear of sexual intimacy with her is probably overdetermined, but one elementary motive may be inferred: To have intercourse with and to need her is to acknowledge her as a real and therefore separate object. The separation problems in such a severe character disorder are so great that he must maintain her in accordance with his projected needs. Also we may speculate that intimacy may be dangerous because of the fear of the release of primitive rage and the danger of the loss of the self based on the fear of fusion. However, a development along the lines of object relations seems to occur. He becomes concerned for her safety after they shoot an officer and later becomes quite frantic when she threatens to leave him to return to her mother. At this point he no longer views her as simply a glorified phallic extension or a mirror image of himself who will serve to gratify his needs for admiration; she has become a separate object. If she is separate then he fears losing her but also values her sufficiently to recognize her own needs and responds by taking her home to Texas. With this obvious increase in differentiation it is now understandable why he would burden himself carrying Bonnie to safety as they elude their pursuers. It is after she has eulogized him in a poem that we may assume that some aspects of his damaged self-image may have been healed and he feels more integrated. Bonnie through her empathic attitude toward Clyde acted to fulfill Clyde's narcissistic self-image through her continued appreciative perception of him (Kohut, 1968). He can then turn to her as an object of gratification who is also partially viewed internally now as partly separate and needed. This represents considerable taming and maturation of

69

his narcissism, a change that goes hand in hand with the emergence of differentiated object relations. As this process has developed first for Bonnie but by the end for Clyde as well, the acting out has become more ego alien. Hence by the end of the film we as an audience no longer conceive of them primarily as bank robbers either.

III

In this last section I shall examine some dramatic representations of conflicts and attempts at solution in the movie which may be viewed as exaggerations of more typical adolescents. Here I am making a shift in emphasis from a view of the characters as reflecting severe pathological traits to seeing them as dramatizing conflicts phase appropriate for normal adolescents. Again I feel it is the universality of the themes and the original creative way they are depicted that makes this valuable for a brief study.

Blos (1963) has pointed out that action in adolescents (and for the sake of explication I am taking the liberty of calling Bonnie and Clyde adolescents) is phase appropriate and is related to two processes. First the rise in and need for discharge consequent to the upsurge in instinctual feelings. Second, as a result of the processes of decathexis of parental imagos and an increase of narcissism and narcissistic conflict there is a vacuum created with a danger of ego impoverishment. This activates a decisive turn to external reality often in a frantic and aggressive manner.

We know that as pregenital impulses are revived along with oedipal conflicts the danger of passivity is great for the adolescent boy. Action may be the prime defense utilized to counteract in an almost magical way the regressive pull. Furthermore not only is there a danger in the passive longings for the father but at times an even greater fear of the preoedipal phallic mother and the threat of submission to her. Delinquency, gang formations, and so on are frequently employed in attempts to deal with such conflicting aims as fear of submission and a longing for an acceptable form of homosexual attachment. Clyde is presented as being crippled, and almost as he introduces his damaged foot he exhibits his gun to Bonnie. The exhibitionistic wish is to impress and shock the woman but ultimately the aim is to deny the feared castration. Throughout the first half of the film we are treated to familiar scenes that cause us rueful laughter as they depict masculine bravado and boyish playfulness in almost a syncopated counterpoint (for example, the scenes with Clyde and Buck and Clyde and C. W.).

For the adolescent girl we are also familiar with the fact that she seeks to emancipate herself from her relationship with the mother. This regressive pull is extremely threatening because of the fear of engulfment, homosexuality, and so on. We are also familiar with girls who struggle to counteract this pull by a sudden bold thrust of activity frequently into promiscuity carried on in an aggressive masculine way. This latter trait attests to the use of the phallic narcissistic identification both to deny passivity and their feminine identification. If the early relationship with the mother has been especially ambivalent this problem of feminine identification is even greater. A further defense is the use of hostility toward other women to further ward off positive feelings. Bonnie is portrayed as struggling with all of these conflicts and utilizes every one of the above defenses. She even dramatizes most beautifully the family style fight as she feels antagonistic to and provokes fights with Buck's wife Blanche from the moment they meet. It may be suggested that it is the presence of this other woman that activates such intense longings for her mother.

To reemphasize, action is frantically sought after by adolescents; it is the magical behavior that denies passivity, castration, anxiety, and helplessness. In this movie a restless driving action is present at all times and is underscored by the dominant role of the automobile and the persistent beat of the country music in the background.

The narcissistic features of the heroes have been stressed from a pathological point of view but normal adolescence is a time when narcissism and its derivatives are phase appropriate. Adolescence revives not only sexual and aggressive conflicts but narcissistic conflicts as well. The adolescent's shame and inferiority reflect fluctuations and vacillations of self-esteem. The shape of the self is still invested with discordant images of smallness and inadequacy as well as wishful images of powerful and glamorous people he wants to be or even feels himself at times to be. Adolescents as a consequence may endeavor to model or imitate various kinds of heroes or pseudoideals expressive of pregenital and phallic-narcissistic goals. Jacobson points out that not rarely does the adolescent indeed glorify prostitutes or gangsters and even join their ranks. "Since wars mobilize sadistic and also narcissistic strivings and permit or even glorify them as long as they are subservient to the national idea, it is not surprising that wars are regularly followed by an increase of juvenile delinquency" (Jacobson, 1954).

The normal adolescent process is characterized by a gradual deca-

71

thexis of the parental imagos. The pain of loss and depression following the separation from these internal object representations is often defended against by acting out. Here delinquent actions may serve a restitutive function. Delinquent behavior attempts to confirm the illusion of omnipotence, the declaration that the self and the needed object are one and therefore separation has not taken place.

Finally the frantic search for motor discharge and excitement may be also related to the need in the adolescent to resist the pull back to infantile objects. The need to repress instinctual needs for the old objects and wishes for reunion with them lead to the creation of a painful void often described as boredom (Greenson, 1953). External stimulation, whether it be drugs, promiscuity, or stealing, serves to avoid the feelings of emptiness.

Bonnie is seen as struggling with both intense passive longings and wishes for reunion and defenses against such impulses. She is introduced to us as a bored girl restless for excitement. The frantic search for this excitement may be viewed as a defense against the inner feelings of emptiness—the emptiness created by the denial of primitive cravings and fantasies for her mother.

Summary

In recent years movies have gained wide acceptance as significant avenues for artistic expression. *Bonnie and Clyde* is one of the most exciting and controversial of the modern films and has provoked intense reactions. This essay contends that the movie has evoked such reactions because it is not only a highly creative film but because it has touched on and communicates powerful themes pertinent to the contemporary human condition. The movie is examined from three different perspectives. First, it is examined as an aesthetic experience to be enjoyed in its own right and also capable of being interpreted as an allegory or commentary on present-day society. The themes and characters have a social and psychological significance reflecting in a disguised form moods and trends relevant to the 1960's. Second, on an intrapsychic level the movie offers a unique opportunity to see illustrations of various aspects of pathological narcissism. No attempt is made to reconstruct a case history of an individual pathology. Instead the emphasis is on Bonnie, Clyde, and C. W. Moss as they reveal, in aspects of their personality structure, manifestations, in terms of drive (narcissistic-exhibitionistic) and defense of problems, that center around narcissistic imbalance and faulty self-esteem regulation. In the final section, a shift is made and the characters are viewed as dramatizing exaggerated forms of solutions utilized by more normal adolescents as they attempt to handle phase-appropriate conflicts. Delinquency and other forms of acting out are seen as major defenses mobilized transiently to defend against passivity, regressive pulls, depression, and states of temporary narcissistic imbalance.

Epilogue

So this is the saga of Bonnie, Clyde, and depression.
I've tried to make sense of excessive aggression.
They lived out their fantasies as long as they lasted,
But unbridled narcissism had to be tasted.
And what of society? I've said it's a parable
Concerning the things, I feel are quite terrible.
Like 'tween rich and poor there's too wide a gap.
And police brutality must come in for a rap.
For parents too there's a lesson to heed
To bask in your sunlight all children need.
I'm ending on one note and that'll close that:
A sound I'll never forget
   and that's rat tat tat tat.

REFERENCES

Beres, D. (1957). Communication in psychoanalysis and in the creative process. Journal of the American Psychiatric Association. 5:408–421.

Blos, P. (1963). The concept of acting out in relation to the adolescent process. Journal of the American Academy of Child Psychiatry. 2:118–136.

Greenson, R. (1953). On boredom. Journal of the American Psychiatric Association. 1:7–21.

Jacobson, E. (1954). The self and the object world. New York: International Universities Press.

Kohut, H. (1966). Forms and transformations of narcissism. Journal of the American Psychiatric Association. 14:243–272.

73

———. (1968). Narcissistic personality disorders. Psychoanalytic Study of the Child. 28:86–113.

Kris, E. (1952). Psychoanalytic exploration in art. New York: International Universities Press.

Reich, A. (1960). Pathologic forms of self-esteem regulation. Psychoanalytic Study of the Child. 15:215–232.

6] ON THE USE

AND ABUSE OF LSD

DANIEL X. FREEDMAN

Though scientists may debate the appropriate use of hallucinogens, history records our unceasing urge to cope with dreary reality or dread with the aid of magic, drugs, drama, festival rites, and (with biological regularity) through dreams. The need to transcend limits also finds a voice in utopian ideologies—be they of the inner world, of this, or the next; the promise of omnipotent mastery is always either implicit or readily inferred. Thus whether it is the proletarian masses, youth mesmerized by mellow yellow banana, or the princes of the land of genital primacy, or the meek—each is promised the inheritance of what probably will be a rather crowded earth. Given the prevalence of these motives it is not surprising that drugs play a role not only in the behavior of individuals but also in social and ideological processes.

With the appropriate motives and occasion, almost any psychoactive drug can provide a brief "ego disruption" producing a moment of being out of it (Barron, Jarvik, and Bunnell, 1964). This disruption in *itself* may promote the release of powerful affects, and this ego state will be

This is an expanded version of a lecture given at the Michael Reese Hospital and Medical Center, June 6, 1967. It is a revision of a paper, "Perspectives on the Use and Abuse of Psychedelic Drugs," published in *Ethnopharmacologic Search for Psychoactive Drugs*, D. H. Efron (editor-in-chief), U.S. Department of Health, Education and Welfare, Public Health Service Publication No. 1645, 1967, with the permission of the editors. Selections on the definition of a "psychedelic" dimension, model psychosis, and the scope of contemporary problems have been extensively revised and that on inherent problems in ethnopsychopharmacology and the use and abuse of conversion omitted. Work with the drug in man and animal over the past ten years has been supported by Public Health Service grants MH-03363, 13186, and Career Investigation Awards M-1204 and K3-18566. Reprinted from *Archives of General Psychiatry*, 18 (March 1968). Copyright 1968 by the American Medical Association.

welcomed for its novel value as a remarkable trip from reality. Etched on it may be the specific pattern of the drug. I believe that the action of drugs such as LSD extend and accent this primary ego state in a salient and sustained way. In any event, scrutiny of the social use of drugs cannot infallibly discriminate the basic patterns of effects. We first have to distinguish the range of effects of ego disruption and what is commonly called the power of suggestion. With this in mind, we can focus on the ways in which hallucinogens do and do not selectively enhance suggestion and various psychological and ideological phenomena.

The reported consequences of drugs such as LSD range from isolated awe or benign or even bored surprise to shifts of values. They range from transient to long-term psychoses to a gamut of confusional states and depression to varieties of religious or aesthetic experience and insight, to clique formation and ritual (Aberle, 1966). There are now conflicting reports of therapeutic effectiveness in alcoholism, depression, character disorders, and severe neurosis (Abramson, 1967; Chandler and Hartman, 1960; Chwelos, Blewett, Smith, and Hoffer, 1959; Leary and Alpert, 1963; Ling and Buckman, 1963; MacLean, MacDonald, Byrne, and Hubbard, 1961; Sandison, Spenser, and Whitelaw, 1954; Savage, Terrill, and Jackson, 1962; Shorvon, 1963; and Smith, 1958). There is also a mushrooming psychedelic culture. This underlies the tribal motions (or brownian movements) of young and aging dropouts, rebels disavowing society's games if not all (nonmusical) instrumental behavior. The paraphernalia of fringe fashions, music, and art comprise the trappings and trippings commercialized as psychedelic go-go. Some serious theologians, some hippies as well as our peripatetic prophets now seek the drugs as promoters of love, of religion, of self-enhancement. Some view the drug as transforming Western society into a Zen elysium. Some are sincere and private in these pursuits, some provocative and evangelistic, and there are variant subgroups whose rapidly evolving habits, ideologies, and behavior are as yet unrecorded.

Of course, gentle and ferocious reformers have often held that special visions were not only their inspiration but their explicit guide. The élite threaten misery for those who do not accurately assess—that is, agree with—their claims of value. Truly dispassionate assessment—the exercise of judgment—may deprive one of access to the mysteries revealed in special states; there is only one way to be in on the truth—*their* way —and if one is in there may be no way out! The only answer to such dilemmas posed by any cult is exposure to experience, to knowledge, and assessment over time—that is, perspective.

The Psychedelic Dimension in Behavior

The recurrent theme in historical records is that certain drugs are compellingly related to learning, to self-revelation, and that they are involved in some mystical, often ritual, use (McGlothlin, 1965). The American Indian often states that "peyote teaches." This major theme does not dominate ordinary accounts of marijuana usage. The potent preparations of cannabis—charas and ganja—are an exception and have been used in India to enhance contemplative states as well as for a high and are not without paranoid and other psychotomimetic effects (Benabud, 1967; Chopra and Chopra, 1957). Apparently, there is a continuum of effects along the dimension of self-revealing and ritual usages.

To the extent that there are classes of agents that reveal normally suppressed components of the mind—exposing these dimensions to our attention—we can say that both use and abuse stem from an amazed response to a drug-induced subjective experience. If this is what Humphrey Osmond meant by the term "psychedelic" (or "mind manifesting"), it is an apt though not novel description. Whatever the outcome, the mode of functioning and experiencing called "psychedelic"—or "psychotomimetic"—reflects an innate capacity (like the dream) of which the waking human mind is capable (Bowers and Freedman, 1966). The fact that a certain class of drugs so sharply compels this level of function (with all the variability inherent in less organized states) and does so for a chemically determined package of time is what so intrigues the biobehavioral scientist.

From our work over the past nine years (Freedman, 1966; Freedman and Aghajanian, 1966; and Giarman and Freedman, 1965), we now know that the indole and catechol derivatives that are psychotomimetic in man can induce a response in the brain of animals, altering brain serotonin metabolism and probably increasing the utilization of norepinephrine. Most of these drugs show cross-tolerance. In contrast, psychotomimetic agents such as atropine or piperidylglycolates (for example, Ditran), which produce amnesia and delirium (Bowers, Goodman, and Sim, 1964; Lebovits, Visotsky, and Ostfeld, 1962; and Wilson and Shagass, 1964), primarily affect brain acetylcholine rather than monoamines

(Giarman and Freedman, 1965). This indicates that we are dealing with agents for which some exquisite molecular (Synder and Merrill, 1965) and biological specificity exists; each of the brain monoamines appears to be lawfully related to specific, largely polysynaptic neural systems, and it is not unlikely that with autoradiography and fluorescence and electron microscopy (Freedman and Aghajanian, 1966; Snyder and Merrill, 1965), our knowledge of the involved neural systems and chemical changes induced by these drugs can be ever more finely specified.

At the behavioral and experiential level this specificity has intrigued many. William James (1916), who had taken mescaline, wrote that there are potential forms of consciousness which with "the requisite stimulus and at a touch . . . are there in all their completeness . . . somewhere (they) have their field of application and adaptation . . . How to regard them is the question . . . *they may determine attitudes though they cannot furnish formulas and open a region though they fail to give a map"* (italics mine—D.X.F.). What about the experience of this region of the mind is so striking? Two features are obvious, the nature of the experience and the contrast with ordinary experience. It is my impression that one basic dimension of behavior latently operative at any level of function and compellingly revealed in LSD states is portentousness—the capacity of the mind to see more than it can tell, to experience more than it can explicate, to believe in and be impressed with more than it can rationally justify, to experience boundlessness and boundary-less events, from the banal to the profound. If we were to relate this to psychoanalytic theory, we would say that an ego (or cognitive) consequence of the primary process and its hypothesized mobility of energies is this dimension of portentousness. Affects are equally mobile; fragmentations and fusions—plasticity—are, as Freud described it for dreams, characteristic.

To this disjointed world of clear perceptions one can react with awe rather than tempered judgment, or even with irrational and boundless affect—ecstasy or terror. The sense of truth is experienced as compellingly vivid but not the inclination to test the truth of the senses. Unlike the sleeping dreamer, the waking dreamer is confronted with the coexistence of two compelling and contradictory orders of reality—with the interface of belief and the orderly rules of evidence.

James saw this as a region of the mind which knows both mysticism and madness; "there seraph and snake abide side by side." But experiences of this realm of the mind cannot be totally disconnected from normal life; how they are connected is the crucial issue. As James remarked, what comes from this inner world must "eventually run the gauntlet of confrontation with reality just as what comes from the outer world of our senses." The trip back to reality after tuning in to this region may be discordant or harmonious; one's sense of both the inner and outer world may be revised in the service of the ego or altered to suit the requirements of irrational needs. There are, then, modal and characteristic forms of mental operations that can underlie behavioral states and experiences of widely different consequence, intent, and meaning; and these modal operations are common both to madness and mysticism, which must be differentiated on other grounds (Prince and Savage, 1966). To summarize, I believe that there are few drugs that can so unhinge us from the constancies that regulate daily life or so clearly present us with unevaluated data from the inside world and from the many normally useless perceptions potentially available to us. It clearly has been tempting to snatch some good from this. It also can do little harm, given such an ample smorgasbord of claims, to seek perspective by concentrating on what—if anything—is common to all of these varied effects of LSD.

What must be described is a multipotential state that, in its most general sense, can underwrite a variety of outcomes: religious feeling and conversions, states of hyperperception leading to inspirational insights, to psychosis, to exalted states, or perhaps to behavior or value change. The more we can grasp some of the intrinsic features of this state, the more we will be able to predict and understand why such drugs can be properly called psychotomimetic, psychedelic, or "cultogenic" agents. It will also be clear that some of the modes of experience—the styles— that characterize the drug experience can be linked to the outcome or to the style of life commonly centered around drug-taking: whether this frequently persistent hangover of drug effects represents new learning, or reinforcement of the ongoing trend of goals and adaptations, or more complex mechanisms is not now known. Beyond impressions which are hardly sanguine about long-term use, evaluated data are still lacking.

Pharmacological Features

The sequence of effects following the usual doses has been described elsewhere (Salvatore and Hyde, 1956). During the first four and one-half hours there is generally a clear-cut self-recognition of effects—an internal television show (marked by shifts of bodily sensations, affect, and perception) followed by another four- or five-hour period in which the subjective sense of change is less marked but during which heightened self-centeredness, ideas of reference, and a certain apartness are observed. At twelve to twenty-four hours after drug there may or may not be some letdown and slight fatigue. There is no craving to relieve this and no true physiological withdrawal.

Contrary to previous myth, the acute stage correlates with the biological half-life of the drug in plasma in rat (Freedman et al., 1964) or man (Aghajanian and Bing, 1964); and the duration of what can be identified clearly as drug related effects is dose dependent, lasting generally 8 to 12 hours. There is a dose-contingent tolerance in both rat and man requiring three or four daily doses for maximum effect and about four days for a loss of tolerance (Freedman et al., 1964a.); with high dosage there is an unexplained cyclicity of tolerance—a sudden loss after eight days and then a gradual build-up with continued dosage (Koella, Beaulieu, and Bergen, 1964). With doses of 200 to 1,000γ there is, with increasing dosage, an increasing loss of autonomy and control of critical and discriminative functions. Usually, one trip produces psychological satiation (McGlothlin, 1965) and is sufficient for most people forever and for others, at least for a few days, months, or years.

The Drug Experience

It is the intense experience without clouded consciousness—the heightened "spectator ego" witnessing the excitement—that is characteristic for these drugs in usual dosages. Thus there is a split of the self—a portion of which is a relatively passive monitor rather than an active, focusing, and initiating force, and a portion of which receives vivid experiences. Some people seem to repeat this long after the drug stage; standing apart from life and its games or relying on the group to direct events, they turn away from the prosaic world—or else are turned away by society. The striking self-centeredness—the experience of the self seeing the self—can be elaborated in a variety of ways, from detachment to symptomatic narcissism. The dominant experience of seeing can be expressed as convictions of revelation—that is, psychological, mystical, aesthetic, or religious insights.

During the drug state, awareness becomes intensely vivid while self-control over input is diminished, fragile, and variably impaired. Thus there is always the lurking threat of loss of inner control—loss of control of integral stability. This is variably experienced and symbolized. At its height, it has been called "dying of the ego" and is often reported in bad trips or in phases of mystical experiences with the drug. For some, such experience is dread transcended; for others, it is unwelcome or denied anxiety and dyscontrol. Many anxious concerns and problems after the drug state center around issues of control, autonomy, self-directedness, and decision-making.

In the drug state, customary boundaries become fluid and the familiar becomes novel and portentous. Any event or category of events that comes to one's attention—sensory, sexual, or cognitive—takes on a trajectory of its own. Qualities become intense and gain a life of their own; redness is more interesting than the object that is red, meaningfulness more important than what is specifically meant. Connotations balloon into cosmic allusiveness. This can be experienced religiously, aesthetically, sensually, or in a variety of clear or confused frames of reference.

After the drug state, we may find pseudoprofundity (Aberle, 1966; Gordon, 1963) or omniscience as well as more tolerance for the novel, the unusual, or the ambiguity. We also can find an associated inability to decide, to discriminate, to make commitments. This occurred as a Rorschach pattern in Indian peyote users (Spindler, 1952). Such a tendency to avoid distinctions could lead to alienation and retreatism, even if these were not preexisting traits (as they often are). For many, the drug experience may represent a beginning—an attempt to feel intensely—which without luck or expertise, cannot easily come to a useful conclusion (just as neurotic acts may be viewed as unguided attempts at self-cure).

Certainly when hidden meanings perpetually contaminate the response to the explicit conventions of everyday life, focus and goal-directed efficiency are impaired. Judgment is not enhanced during the drug state and isolation or apartness bring their own problems: Accordingly persons who continually overvalue the modes experience of the drug state could develop and reinforce poor practical habits. Pseudoprofundity, philosophical naïveté, impractical detachment, and inadequate foresight and judgment or impulsiveness in dedicated users were already evident to an observer of the Harvard scene of 1963 (Gordon, 1963). The consequences of long-term and frequent use of the drug—involving possibly 5 percent to 15 percent of those experimenting with LSD— would probably have to be evaluated in this context.

Immediacy, Novelty, and Creativity with LSD

In the drug stage, the experience of compelling immediacy diminishes the normal importance of past and future. One's organized anticipations of time dissolve and the anticipatory factor, so important in the psycho-physiology of pain, is similarly affected. (This—coupled with effects of suggestion—may be why the drug experience could be reported as re-placing narcotics in dying cancer patients.) Dehabituation (that is, a re-sponse to the familiar as if it were novel) was noted in early studies of the drug in cats (Bradley and Elkes, 1957; Bradley and Key, 1958; Key and Bradley, 1958; Krus and Wapner, 1959; Becker, Appel, and Freedman, 1967; Kohut, 1966; Freud, 1949; Keeler, 1965; Silverman, 1967; Wiener, 1967; Leuner, 1967; Pious, 1961; and Redlich and Freedman, 1966).

The overvaluation of "nowness" is not unrelated to the fickle pursuit of the novel apparent in certain youth subcultures. The ability to see old and familiar events in a new light is also a facet in the poorly un-derstood processes related to creativity. But the impairment of goal-directed efficiency and sustained focused attention carries with it the impairment of integrative and synthetic functions. Thus the more merg-ings of sensory objects (the synesthesias, the plastic rearrangements or the clear focusing on fine details or usually disregarded perceptual ele-ments) or the elisions of thoughts and concepts hardly are the same as an organized building and arrangement in which boundaries and distinc-tions are essential. Sharpened, or heightened, perception and conscious-ness is not equivalent to adaptive perception, nor is abnormal brilliance necessarily to be equated with beauty. Indeed, the primitivization of perception seen in man (Krus and Wapner, 1959) and animal (Becker et al., 1967) suggests vividness more than powerful discrimination of the complex. Creativity requires some facility not only for seeing but for implementing new meanings; but, as we shall stress, it is the need for synthesis—not the ability to synthesize with due account for real limits—that tends to be reinforced in the drug state.

82

Cultogenic Effects of LSD

An important feature of the state is an enhanced dependence on the environment for structure and support as well as enhanced vulnerability to the—now novel—surrounding milieu. With the loss of boundaries, persons or a group are used for such elemental functions as control—for helping one to know what is inside and what is outside, for comfort and for binding and balancing the fragmenting world.

With the fusion of self and surroundings, some of the strain caused by the exertion of personal strivings and their conflict with what is projected as harsh authority, can (for the moment) be transcended or dissolved. At the same time there is a leaning on others for structure and control. Hence, when the drugs are taken in a group setting, the breach with reality can—and must—be filled by the directive mystique and support of the group. This is, in part, why I have termed these drugs "cultogenic."

Many successful self-help groups are peer groups or form around a common flaw. If they are uncritical of weakness, less masking of inadequacy can ensue. With such arrangements, the distance between authority and the miscreant is diminished and so, too, is the inner tension. The cost is a surrender of a certain order of autonomy to the group, a certain passivity, and dependence on the concrete presence of a group to share the burdens of initiative. The surrender of a conflictful autonomy (reflecting a prior instability, isolation, or diffusion) may be preferable to the compensatory delusional autonomy seen in proselytizers who aggressively threaten the establishment with love and drugs. Of course, a compulsive tendency to externalize the conflict with authority can be reinforced by peer-grouping. Nor are all the tribal affiliations we call groups endowed with the competence to guide; many are loose alliances based on the denied mutual despair of their members.

Object Relations and Values

Actual persons in the environment have positive or negative value in terms of quite elemental functions, for example, as threats or as anchors in maintaining a primary self-control (quite as in the so-called psychotic transference) and intensities of affect can mercurially escalate and diminish in the absence of normal boundaries. Persons are self-centeredly seen and used—either to be clung to, or to be contemplated in terms of what essentially is a self-centered sensory, aesthetic, or ideologic frame of reference; they may become vivid objects of highly personal transferences. At best there may be a narcissistic shifting of one's relationship to others and to one's own ambitions which, as Kohut has noted (1966), can lead to outcomes that are socially valued—wisdom, humor, perspective. But such internal syntheses never guarantee socially pleasant behavior, and pathological outcomes are also probable.

Model Psychosis in the Drug Experience

The elements of a model psychosis are present. This does not mean identity; rather it is an approach to certain processes that are variably present in both the drug state and psychoses. The conditions for either state have similarities and obvious differences (just as do dreams and psychosis) (Freud, 1949).

During the first hour after LSD most people refer their altered perceptions and relationships to the body and its parts; this period of changed bodily sensations and perceptions could be called hypochondriacal (with all this connotes as a prodromic symptom) or simply altered body image, depending on the context. The point is that there is a uniform change in the experience of the relationship of the body, the self, and their normal environmental coordinates.

The basis for hallucinations can be analyzed (Keeler, 1965). For example, what is impinging on an ongoing perception is a vivid memory of what has just been perceived; these coexisting images can compete for attention and thus give rise to illusions. (In our laboratories we have observed monkeys under LSD who may respond to serial stimuli as they had been trained to respond to overlapping stimuli.) This is marked usually two to three hours following 200μg. or less of the drug and following the period of altered perceptions referred to the body and its boundaries. With the increasing loss of distance, such illusions can be imaginatively or regressively elaborated into hallucinations. Similarly, memories can emerge as clear images competing for the status of current reality. This failure to suppress the prior perception or memory or

84

thought is reminiscent of what Bleuler called "double registration" in schizophrenia or what, in Rorschach parlance, is called contamination. Similarly the failure of identities and categories to be maintained underlies most of the descriptions of paralogic in schizophrenia.

The capacity selectively and relevantly to direct one's focus is impaired; allocation of the source of a feeling, a sound, a sight, or a thought becomes difficult because the distinction of inside and outside tends to diminish. Accordingly there are frequent mislocations or misconceptions—projections—of motives and sensations. This tendency is reinforced when one must exert energy to account for even slight changes in the environment; slight details not only capture attention but also can gain the patina of portentousness and are linked to the ever-present threats of dissolution. The eventual outcome of this hypervigilance, inefficient scanning (Silverman, 1967; Wiener, 1967), and mislocation is called paranoid behavior.

There is also a remarkably heightened sensitivity to gestures, inflections, and nonverbal sensory-motor cues which normally are in the background; however, the ability accurately to judge these cues and appropriately lodge them in context—just as in schizophrenic sensitivity —is easily impaired. The altered relationship of figure and ground also means that metacommunications fail; the context no longer predicts the relationship of parts to the whole.

Similarly the component affects can be enhanced under the drug state but are difficult to focus on. Thus several contrary feelings coexist, or they fluctuate (just as sensations do); this is reminiscent of ambivalence. Subjects later refer to the total state as a pleasant-unpleasant experience. Those seeking mystical experience speak of heaven and hell. Euphoria mixed with tension may be seen.

Laughing or crying or both during the first three hours are common. With care, one observes that—following the initial perceptual changes referred to the body—there is a primary need for elemental tension discharge—a welling up that requires laughing or crying for relief. Subjects have to laugh or cry, and they then seem to find the appropriate setting to rationalize this.

However these experiences may be represented and symbolized, they are evolved from a groundwork entailing a coexistence, heightening, and fragmenting of component urges and feelings. Thus, changes in ego or organization and capacity seem to occur first; this is usually manifest in the perception of bodily changes. A tension or need for discharge then becomes apparent; perception of affective changes and changes in

85

the self and relationships with objects in the milieu supervene and dominate the experience. These changes during the first three or four hours underlie the varied experiences for "insight." Expectations and preconscious fantasies certainly stamp the content and even influence the capacity to exert control during the drug state, but with the loss of structure a "program" of vulnerabilities and needs seems to be "released" (Leuner, 1967), or compelled, by the drug.

The enhanced value and intense attention placed on the self; the narcissism, ego splits, and regression; the loss of boundaries; the "double registrations"; the ambivalence; the heightened tension; the diminished control and problems of focus (Pious, 1961); the unstable (or inappropriate) affect—all can represent the primary symptoms of a psychosis. Given this state of affairs one can see a variety of psychotomimetic, or psychedelic, phenomena elaborated and expressed—all of which require such basic shifts in ego organization. Whether the observing ego keeps touch with reality may be crucial to outcome, but is irrelevant to the classification of a psychotomimetic state. Catatonic schizophrenics often maintain a silent observing ego monitoring reality during their psychosis (Redlich and Freedman, 1966).

The appearance of peak experiences (or acute psychedelic experiences) in clinical psychosis has long been documented (Maslow, 1962); early phases of acute psychoses often cannot be differentiated from accounts of drug experience (Bowers and Freedman, 1966). During the hours following the acute flux, as adaptations to the first phase begin, we can note the subject's attempts to structure while still impaired by the drug. Where energy for scanning and testing the reality of unwanted input is required, delusional simplifications, ideas of reference, or passionate beliefs occur and provide an economical explanatory anchorage.

We have with these drugs at least a tool with which to study the genesis and sequence of a number of familiar phenomena in psychiatry. Whether it can lead us to a better sorting and description of the varied elements present in the range of clinical disorders is yet unanswered; for example it is obvious that differences in outcome of LSD states depend on specific prior strengths as well as varying circumstances. It is also obvious that a time-bound state such as a drug state cannot demonstrate symptomatic phenomena that develop over time and are embedded in confusing life circumstances (Lidz, Fleck, and Cornelison, 1965). Indeed, the role of these factors in symptomatology could be more readily distinguished by appropriate comparative study of clinical and drug-induced alterations of consciousness. Comparative studies of

86

drug-induced states could also be useful in determining factors and sequences related to outcomes of such a multipotential and fluid state. Finally, it bears on our thinking about any psychosis to recognize that—whatever the role of motivation—primary or secondary shifts in such elemental ego functions as attention and discriminations—the adaptive control of sensory input and perception (Silverman, 1967; Wiener, 1967)—can underlie a range of psychotic symptoms.

Adaptations during the Drug State

Some persons endure all this without evident harm. The spectator ego can simply be interested in the reversal of figure and ground, the visual tricks, or—with higher doses—the spectator is entranced or totally absorbed. But with increasing dosage the experiencing ego can be overwhelmed. At any level, defensiveness can appear; the spectator shuts his eyes and a blind struggle for control may dominate. Basic attitudinal shifts, redirection of attention, projection, denial, displacement, affective explosions, panic, confusion, withdrawal, or magical and delusional syntheses may be seen as persons attempt to cope. Rarely there is an acute loss of judgment or impulsive and primitive thinking manifest in attempts to fly or defy gravity, which results in a concrete and fatal confrontation with the real world. One protection is *not* to fight the experiences during the drug state. An upsurge of the traditional defensive operations requires extra vigilance and may lead to temporary panic even in relatively stable people.

It is striking that when self-examination or confrontation with personal problems is the motive for illicit drug-taking, effects are not infrequently bad. Both licit and illicit drug users note that unstable surroundings or confused motives lead to bad trips. When problems are aptly externalized or shared there is less panic and subsequent upset. Those who are unable to tolerate the flux by shifting attention from it or enduring it (or "guiding" it by delusional, mystical, or aesthetic revisions) may retreat into catatonic-like postures. Thus, a certain yielding and surrender of ambition and personal autonomy helps some individuals to have a good experience; but this requires, if not group support, a certain personal strength, or at least a facility. It also requires stable groups.

Those who are encouraged or equipped to not attend to the frag-

87

mented disparate elements let them flow into the sway of a mystique, steered by latent guiding interests or memories. Thus, all that occurs is given a tone—or a very diffuse direction. With higher dosages and the increasing loss of detailed focusing, the importance of guiding "sets" (music, mystique, affective expectation such as the doctrine of boundless love) is enhanced. Indeed, under LSD it is the positive or negative attitudes and postures toward the ego's varied experiences that are most vulnerable to suggestion. The "maps"—the formulas and specific ideologies supplied by guides—are actively sought because of the vulnerability of the ego and the relative loss of synthetic and higher cognitive functions (such as goal directedness). Accordingly panic states may be guided by redirection of attitudes, or attention, and by provision of structure.

Summary of the Drug State

Thus we may say that in the presence of a heightened sense of awareness, there is a diminished role of the array of functions related to cognitive control and discrimination of complexities. The ego may be said to be less autonomous—less reliable—in the deployment of focused and sustained attention. It is vulnerable to being guided by a widened and more variable range of both internal and external factors. In order to anchor the drug-induced period of flux, direction of attention and basic orienting attitudes can be supplied either by the now impaired ego (with its defenses and prior expectations) or by the setting. Such expectations may be explicit and implicit, conscious and unconscious; accordingly, prediction and control over outcome especially in self-experimentation are inherently unreliable. Similarly, the utility, fittedness, and reliability of the setting will, in fact, vary widely.

The extent to which the experience of a specific trip is related to outcome requires finer study. So, too, does the fact that one good trip does not predict a second. Accurate studies in this area are important to our understanding of outcome. Nevertheless, the primary changes described are the background state from which a number of divergent outcomes and adaptations ensue—adaptations both during and after the drug experience. No doubt the rearrangements of reality that occur during this state produce a memorable experience, but one is reminded of Sidney Cohen's (1964) remark that most people get what they "deserve" or what they are equipped at the time to experience as modified by set, equipment, and setting.

Restoration of Constancies after the Drug

Two realities have been exposed in startling contrast—private and public reality—both of which are a part of experienced reality. Anyone who has experienced this intense episode must come to deal with it; some judgment about the significance and utility of these realms of the mind must be made. Our dreams are an episode in a sequence of states that we usually can somehow integrate into the normal fabric of living; similarly something must now be done to represent and cope with the total drug experience—nightmare, illusion, or ecstasy.

Some borrow stability from ready-made explanations or isolate the experience. Still others will decide that the experience of cosmic comprehension is equivalent to self-mastery. Still others, lacking any other means of mastery, will be compelled repeatedly and unexpectedly to confront what was experienced. We see this in students who come in for help weeks after a trip—experiencing anxieties or brief unwanted trips in the absence of drug (Rosenthal, 1964).

The breakdown of those constancies and habits that normally smooth over the disparate details of our perceptions and actions can persist in frightful but also benign ways. One scientist experienced his peripheral vision to be enhanced during the drug state; it is not uncommon that there is an equivalence of value for what is at the periphery and what is normally perceived at the center of the visual field. He commuted daily, reading during the train trip. For months after the drug, he was bothered by the telephone poles that flashed by his train window. He could no longer suppress what normally is background rather than compelling figure. Similarly, the unconscious background to thoughts, gestures, and feelings can emerge.

There are numerous anticipatory sets or constancies that operate to keep the body oriented in space and ready to meet the environment as we expect to experience it; the mind provides constancy wherever the sense organs deal with variability. We anticipate or correct for the images on our retina to keep the world stable and ordered; the hand stretched eight inches before one may appear small, though on the retina or camera it is large. Coming off a boat one may still waddle, maladaptively anticipating the roll of the ship. Such habits or sets can smooth out our preceptions and actions; but they can persist when they are not useful and lead to inappropriate and confused responses. LSD appears to affect these stabilizing perceptual anticipations. It rearranges and unbalances our ideas of order, whether the self and its defenses or perceptions are a referent.

The Need for Synthesis and Outcome

The intensity of the drug experience manifest in the change of constancies can lead to a number of repetitive behaviors. The search for synthesis may take the form of attempts to reexperience the intensity of elements within the drug experience in order to master it, just as with the traumatic neurosis and its breaching of the stimulus barrier. It is an old theme in psychopathology that in a state of altered consciousness in which control over awareness is diminished, there is no way to bind the intensities experienced and symptoms may ensue. Breuer (and, more reluctantly, Freud) referred to this as the hypnoid state; explanations of the consequences of early pregenital experience to repetitive neurotic symptoms in later development have been placed in this context (Loewald, 1955).

Though bad trips occurring without the drug may be explained in the model of the traumatic neurosis or hypnoid state, it is astonishing to see an entire sequence of heightened sensations as well as altered perceptions occurring with apparent suddenness weeks after the drug. This obviously evokes comparison with psychomotor epilepsy; but this connotation is as yet without foundation in fact. The psychodynamics preceding these lapses from reality also require close scrutiny; yet these reports appear to present us with evidence that the barrier against dereistic thinking and altered states (or the "switch" permitting a shift of mental states) is a factor that in itself merits intensive investigation. There are schizophrenic patients who appear eventually to have learned or discovered that there was some control that they could exert against slipping into such states. Whatever the explanation for either the loss or the mastery of such controls may be, it is evident that the experience of the LSD state with its intense clarity in the presence of diminished control can have a range of consequences that cannot always be anticipated simply by monitoring the apparent intensity of the ongoing drug state.

Repetitive symptoms—such as acting out—may occur. In part, these may be viewed as unsuccessful attempts to restore or find constancies and boundaries. Such behavior, which invites control and guidance, frequently appears as a provocative accusation against authority and—by provocation—preserves a tie with it. Others aggressively and endlessly talk about their experiences as if they were trying to put them together.

For some, reflection about the sharp contrast of drugged and real life may evoke mild or severe rumination and depression—related to an urge to recapture the lost illusionary and brilliant drug world. The extent to which primitive and regressive fusion fantasies will dominate these reactions varies. Conflict and confusion about "what *is* reality" or the experience of normally repressed thoughts and urges by the unprepared ego can lead to mild or severe symptomatic states, perplexity, and disorganization.

In any event, variably determined needs or capacities to cope with the split or breach of normal experience can be expected. This may be a simple sealing over, or even the enlightened and useful thought formation we call insight. Some react with a denial of inadequacy and anxiety about loss of control; borrowing the enhanced omnipotence of the drug state, they show a delusional autonomy. This may lead to various outcomes: that of the benevolent and foolish prophet, or the defensive, alienated therapist, angry at those who prevent his curing the rest of the world. Any threat to the values of the illusory experience of union and omnipotence—such as undrugged reality—could evoke defensive denial and strident proselytizing.

It is interesting that classifications of pathological outcomes of conversion (Clark, 1958)—including irresponsibility and omniscience—startlingly resemble patterns we see with LSD. Indeed, we must seriously wonder why those who find salvation are so implacably generous and so ready to advertise! Implied are unsolved problems with authority figures. Salvation often involves renunciation of previous ties; those who are saved must repetitively convince others in order to diminish their own doubt, isolation, and guilt. At best, they may do this not only to share but in order to reachieve union with those from whom they have been separated by their unique vision and experience and to synthesize these breaches with important others.

The Role of Groups in Outcome

Some kind of continuity with the gap in reality is sought. The bridge may be a book as it was with Huxley, a silent synthesis, or change of values and tastes, or the understanding of a group or person. In the native American church the Indian utilizes religious explanation and adherence, specific ceremonies, and the group with its ideology to integrate the experience which serves a purpose in the total fabric of his life (Aberle, 1966).

There are mixed consequences with the reliance on groups. In some chronic users one sees a bland impulsiveness—an indifference to the habitual and customary that may border on a supercilious posture of superiority. The elect of many cults either assume this attitude or the outsider feels this to be the attitude of those who know something he does not. This benign or irritating posture has also been remarked on in the American Indian peyote users, who are often a subculture not infrequently at odds with established groups. Nevertheless, the observed reliance of drug users on cults can permit at least a measure of authentic self-involvement at a level realistically available to the persons involved. Where these cults are but loosely juxtaposed cliques connected by common rationalizations there is still some comfort and protection from a ruminative self-concern, which is enhanced by isolation.

Mystical or religious representations also are remarkably apt for synthesizing the experience. Religion can relate man to his limits while taking account of his boundlessness which occurs in all aspects of this realm of the mind. It may be that religious symbolism aptly represents the transformations characteristic of this latent part of the mind. Against fragmentation and directionlessness, something coherent lends continuity to experience. Against dread, transcendent love can prevail; loving, like redness, can apparently be enhanced and is remembered. The lovingness and strongness of a parent can be parted from the particular persons and transcendentally represented in various forms of power ascribed to deities.

There are, then, a number of features of this multipotential state related to its intensity, its novelty, its boundlessness that account for some of the expectable occurrences within it and some of the expectable— and observed—dangers and variable outcomes.

LSD in Psychiatry

There are a number of psychotherapists (Tenenbaum, 1961; Lennard, 1956) who have attempted to use the loosening of associations and the intense experiencing produced by the drug in order to influence behavior change in individual as well as group therapy (and the drug obviously is useful for the study of group processes). There are a few ongoing controlled projects and a long history of experience with the use (Abramson, 1967; Cole and Katz, 1964)—and abuse (Grinker, 1964)—of LSD in therapy. During the late 1950's some physicians thought they had discovered a new reality of the mind and were not only struck by the drug-induced phenomena, but apparently addled by them. Perhaps they were simply jealous of the subject when they insisted on taking the drug concurrently with him.

Today, two major serious modes of treatment prevail. That employed by many European workers—called "psycholytic" by Leuner (1967)—represents a method by which certain defenses are breached. With a strong drug-enhanced tie to the therapist, feelings, memories, and transferences are allowed to emerge vividly and unforgettably before the eye of the consciousness and their strength discharged. The events are later worked over with care. Dosages are regulated in part by the capacity of the patient to steer a course between being utterly lost or overly constrained by habitual defenses. A kind of active participation in the presence of a general loosening is sought. As issues in therapy arise, clusters of intense affects directed toward early experiences and objects are encouraged; thus, fantasies involving rebirth, early transference strivings, and trauma can emerge with sensory intensity. The therapist lends support and later interprets.

Certainly, people are initially less guarded under the drug and can experience a range of insights they might normally disown. Yet they also can react quite defensively under the drug when what is seen is, for personal reasons, overly traumatic. To an extent they can ward off self-recognitions with affective outbursts, and they can clearly distort them by basic attitudinal shifts, displacements, redirection of attention and projections, denial, confusion, withdrawal, or magical and delusional syntheses.

For quite vivid self-encounters there is usually no postdrug amnesia.

93

The integration that follows is a collaborative venture requiring the active participation and the output of the patient. During treatments, a sequence of defensive memories, transferences, and distortions commonly arises and requires further drug sessions and work. Illicit drug users also encounter hang-ups but have little guidance to work them through sequentially. The therapists find this absorbing and exhausting; they generally work with inpatients and severely ill or characterologically impaired patients.

In the so-called psychedelic therapies now being tested there is an awareness of an immense amount of preparation, of salesmanship with an evangelical tone in which the patient is confronted with hope and positive displays of it before he has his one great experience with a very high dose of drug. The drug experience is structured by music and by confident good feelings. With the support of the enthusiastic therapist, the patient is encouraged to see his life in a new light, to think of his future accordingly. There now tends to be a rather long period of follow-up and support before the patient is discharged. An earlier mode of intervention attempted to avoid the tangled problems of relationship between therapist and patient (Savage et al., 1962) with but a single high-dose drug session as the chief therapeutic contact; the current approach is more explicitly ritualized (in the model of nativistic movements); the person and attitude of therapist tends not to be analyzed but incorporated. It is speculated that the egocentric problems of the alcoholic may be specifically tailored for this "ego-dissolving, ego-building" technique. Other approaches, for example, employing hypnosis (Ludwig and Levine, 1967), lie somewhere between these two. It is interesting that peyote cultures also report cures of alcoholics but the effects may not persist without sustained group support and leadership (Aberle, 1966). The effectiveness and selectivity of current therapies is far from settled, and research is still ongoing (Abramson, 1967). Obviously, careful follow-up is essential because the immediate glow that occurs with drug-induced personality changes in such contexts can be deceptive. The fact that under LSD the therapist can often readily suggest positive or negative attitudes toward life experiences and promote a state in which struggle may be diminished should arouse our fundamental curiosity not only about LSD therapy and its effectiveness, but about the mechanisms, utility, resistances, and pitfalls in behavioral change achieved through persuasion (Frank, 1961; Laing, 1965).

The Scope and Dangers of Illicit Use

We should recall that the increasing problem of drug abuse in most countries is alcohol, followed by the barbiturates, amphetamines, opiates, and mild tranquilizers. In this context the consequences to national health of hallucinogens are not as yet truly startling—either in terms of the utility of LSD or its harm. In the long run, debates about whether or not to use LSD are hardly as socially consequential as the use of the pill. The agent most frequently used by youth for illicit purposes and with lethal effect is the automobile; and the most faithful monitor of the scope of such social problems is the prevailing high insurance rates for young men. The acturial superego of our society has not yet instituted insurance rate changes for medical, psychiatric, or mortician's coverage in response to these chemicals. This is an interesting generation but they have not as yet gone completely to pot!

Not all users are youth nor are all youthful users initially unconventional and unproductive. A few current illicit self-help groups reportedly employ the drug and religion to achieve a conventional outcome: for example, a group of exconvicts and a group of homosexuals. Several religious and lay groups have set up agencies to be phoned when panics are encountered. We seem to be living in an era when many practices (half-way houses, group therapies, cathartic therapy, confrontation therapy) built into the fabric of psychiatric work are imitated by ever-proliferating self-help groups that frequently tap our society's long tradition of distrust of medical science. Unfortunately, nonscientific searches for cures are too easily dismissed as fanaticism, eccentricity, or ignorant superstition. Yet these social responses in part reflect on the ability of the health professions to deliver relevant services, to treat irrational anxieties, or to be competently aware of and responsive to the issues and consequences of different patterns of drug abuse.

Reliable estimates of the incidence of psychedelic drug use (however defined) are always vulnerable to criticism. They range from 1 percent to 15 percent on certain campuses. Figures higher than 5 percent probably do not distinguish single trials from habitual use nor LSD from other drugs of abuse; proselytizers frequently tell us about the inevitable growing use of "marijuana and LSD." Only a small fraction of persons who have taken the truly potent hallucinogenic drugs could be said to

95

constitute a reliable base for study of long-term users. Groups of persons who drift in and out of the category of users are not easy to identify and are hardly reliable reporters. The problem is that some are always first discovering the drug (available now for twenty years) and acclaiming it while the silent others are experiencing disillusion after a year or two of absorption. Still others actively seek or passively accept one or two self-experiments. We clearly require a study of the fad element in usage; cycles of interest may well be shown to follow certain press releases and to vary sharply with opportunity and the ethos of different settings—for example, hippie centers or campuses or enclaves of middle-aged imitators who mourn their lost youth. Clearly the motives for experimenting, maintaining—or self-regulating—the intake of any drug differ as do the consequences of these varied patterns of use.

Complications for research also arise from sensational publicity. The select as well as the popular press provide a structure for the curious, restless, and lost as they compete to announce or denounce drug usage. The psychedelic hucksters—for a bandwagon effect—confidently announce that growing hordes of youngsters are independently dedicated chronic users. To the mature, their message is that this is a revolution in which adults are helpless; to the young it is a subtle invitation to revolt under the sanction of inevitability. The Establishment then reacts with irritation and fright. As the advertising escalates and the empirical problem indeed grows, the young and their frequently confused and permissive parents must enter the debate and assess the claims of value. Physicians hysterically crying alarm join the melée, lumping all bad reactions into one dire outcome—permanent madness. They can now also cite somatic dangers.

Reports of chromosomal changes in preparations of lymphocytes raised in tissue culture are not identical with genetic damage or clinical disease. Apart from unwarranted biological inferences, the reliability of such findings is not established; nor do we as yet know the relationship to dose, to common stimulants, or to drugs related by structure or behavioral effect. Similarly, a finding of LSD-induced stillbirth or stunted growth in rats is not identical to fetal anomalies or germ cell damage; effects in mice may differ; rodents may differ from man; similar reports of effects of other drugs (including reserpine) should be evaluated prior to sanctioning alarming reports about LSD. Nor does the persistence of hippocampal discharges for several weeks following LSD (in cats trained to avoid shock) indicate long-term brain changes or brain damage in man; reserpine, in fact, produces more dramatic persisting effects in the hippocampus (Adey, Porter, and Walter, 1965) and without the intervention of shock. Neither the history of folk usage of psychedelics nor the past twenty years of medical and lay use of LSD have—as yet —produced clear and reliable evidence of somatically dangerous consequences of the drug in man.

While such important research continues, caution about publicity is warranted on both scientific and humane grounds lest we further panic the susceptible. A single past indiscretion with LSD now leads to serious brooding over the shape of what the young parents fear will be a psychedelic monster. No doubt the social problems presented by LSD could easily be diminished if a clear-cut somatic danger is established; we might, however, have yet to cope with this phenomenon without the aid of such facile warnings!

Psychiatric Complications of LSD

The facts are that dangerous and tragic psychological consequences are now unequivocally established (Cohen, 1966; Cohen and Ditman, 1963; Fink, Simeon, Haque, and Itil, 1966; Frosch, Robbins, and Stern, 1965; Klee and Weintraub, 1959; Ludwig and Levine, 1965; and Ungerleider, Fisher, and Fuller, 1966), and it is just this fact that users deny (as if it were concocted to attack their autonomy and self-esteem). From our own campus experiences it appears that users who end up in hospitals with prolonged and serious psychoses are initially a quite unstable group. They are, in any event, a small group. Suicides and violence are also uncommon. More frequently one sees a transient panic occurring during the drug state from which recovery (without the administration of often complicating phenothiazine medications) occurs within twenty-four hours. If other than supportive and reassuring treatment is required, adequate barbiturate hypnosis or a sedative tranquilizer such as chlordiazepoxide is a simple regimen. A few visits for follow-up can be instituted when required. Others do not require hospitalization but often seek treatment because they are concerned about having taken the drug. They are upset or depressed about some of their thoughts and experiences during the drug state, or about their basic life dilemma—which in many instances is obviously serious. And a few others, as noted, may have serious nondrug-induced panics some weeks after the drug state very much as a bad dream recurs. Occasionally a complicated history of

97

multiple drug intake by a rootless youngster leads to a picture of toxic psychosis.

We must make a distinction between an unpleasant trip—even one that might lead to emergency room referrals—and various psychiatric complications of drug use that may or may not be contingent on a bad episode. Such unpleasant episodes have turned off those who try a casual experiment—a socially valuable response! When patients are brought to physicians by drugged or unstable friends, or in disorganized circumstances, physicians should be aware not only of the role of momentary panic (and the fact that any escalating panic can look like a toxic state) but of the possibility of complicated drug-taking patterns, of prior instability if not mental disorder. Similarly, we should note that classical instances of identity diffusion, of borderline phenomena and adolescent turmoil may—in contemporary life—be associated with LSD; this is hardly a basis for citing the drug as totally causal.

We now see little scare literature presenting an unevaluated snapshot of steroid psychoses because we can now predict with more confidence what the results will be and evaluate the risk. Similarly we should—in time—become familiar with these drugs. The facts are that a fair number of people have had LSD without serious untoward effects. The majority of acute untoward reactions with LSD—though severely troublesome—are not as yet proven to be inevitably permanently crippling. The suggestibility, despair, confusion, and latent disorganization of those who unwisely take LSD is, I believe, as crucial a variable as the chemical that renders them—unexpectedly—vulnerable to more trauma than they can handle. The habitual long-term use of LSD for pleasure or escape produces the possibility for the impairment of good sense and maturation. In this sense, the drug can reinforce a dissociative trend, leading to acute reactions or insidious disorganization and failure successfully to integrate life crises.

The Risk of LSD Trips

Impressions gathered from various observers indicate that the experience—though not necessarily the outcome—of approximately 10 percent of any batch of trips (whether or not it is an initial one) can be potentially upsetting. With skilled guides perhaps many of these potentially unpleasant experiences are warded off or redirected. With skilled therapists, 1 percent or less of drug experiences may be unexpectedly traumatic. Certainly under these circumstances less than 1 percent is traumatic in outcome. With proper immediate follow-up most of these reactions should be therapeutically resolved. This appears to have been the case even though attempts to screen subjects in order to predict reactions have not yielded clear-cut guidelines (Eggert and Shagass, 1966; Pauk and Shagass, 1961); and it has not been established that the drug is necessarily traumatic when given to severely mentally ill persons with the structure and follow-up available in therapeutic settings. In all probability older subjects (past twenty-six years) are less likely to have prolonged reactions linked to a single bad experience.

Though such impressions require research, we can be confident—from the experience at responsible research centers during the 1950's and in European clinics—that the setting and the ability to manage the experience and its aftermath are crucially important. We can also be reasonably certain that the risk differs when the drugs are taken under unsupervised circumstances; or with unwise therapists or guides; or by adolescents attempting self-analysis; or in specifically therapeutic experiences; or in sensibly controlled research conditions. There is no question that good sense and trained skills can help to control bad LSD experiences and outcomes. The inescapable problem is that—excepting within narrow limits—a bad experience and an unwelcome outcome need not be associated and neither can always be predicted.

The Drug Mystique

My current opinion is that the chief abuse of LSD is irresponsible, allurring, and provocative advertising. Havelock Ellis's (1898) enthusiastic report of the effect of mescaline, though evoking alarm about possible abuse (Editorial, 1898), did not flower into a cult or into a topic for the bored mass media. An ideology couched in the language of drugs has been insinuated into youth culture by a band of quite articulate writers and vagrant professionals. These have replaced the old medicine show of yesteryear with an updated campus version complete with readings and tempting arguments if not pills to sell: "tune in, turn on, and dropout." A drug mystique has been welded to the underlyingly serious shifts and strains inherently experienced by the most potentially unstable group of any society—the adolescent and young adult.

99

We need not determine whether this is indeed a "now" generation valuing honesty, love, direct confrontation, and uncomplicated action and avoiding ideologies in favor of simple justice. These values, however germane to the LSD experience, were not born from the drugged mind. The Pied Pipers of LSD, peddling a drug that can enhance poor judgment, would lure youth from the acquisition of competence (or even from the serious study of man's attempts to deal with the two orders of reality in his personal development and in his religious, artistic, philosophical, and scientific endeavors).

If we make the distinction between the psychedelic mystique and issues about the utility of LSD, and if we attempt to account for the fact that the greatest abuse has been among the well-educated—or those who might be—we would in all honesty have to question the strange tolerance for these psychedelic follies in campus cultures. Forgetting both Freud and James, many of our teachers and intellectuals are either entranced or perplexed by stories of LSD-induced revelations. They appear neither to have learned from nor to teach from experience.

We seem to have forgotten that there are trained persons who in fact have more experience than the self-appointed gurus in coping with adolescent turmoil and the more serious dysfunctions. There are scholars and disciplines knowledgeable about man's attempts to understand subjective experience and its manifold aesthetic, literary, and intellectual expressions. The social psychology of groups, cults, conversion, enthusiasm, and utopias is hardly a new discipline. None of this seems to have crucially permeated our campus cultures in terms of new curricula or opportunities for both confrontation and reflection. In brief, much of this advertising may take because in exploring new frontiers we have lost confidence in our traditions and seem to have avoided dealing both with the rationalizations and the honest probings of the drug cultists and other youth on campus. In any event it is clear that education of the drug-prone young will require more than a troop of physicians. Some sophistication about the vicissitudes of man's gullibility might render our institutions less vulnerable to sophistry.

The psychedelic apologists insist they have the civil right to take any agent that does not harm others. It is, of course, hardly a private matter (and it is a civil matter) when irresponsible proselytizing—born from the spirit of oedipal revenge—leads to a number of drug-related cases in children and young adults requiring psychiatric care for either brief or long periods of time. It is often forgotten that the real momentum for such claims arose when a few psychologists who peddled the drug resented the notion that medical training was required for the responsible administration of potentially toxic agents. The problem, of course, is that the psychedelic gurus—while promoting frenetic advertisements for themselves—are not in a position to manage the consequences of their ideological schemes. When they do admit the drug might be dangerous, they do so by insisting that only the very courageous should take it! The rationalizations that prevail among those who experiment with LSD are often borrowed from these various preachings.

Motives for Use

The motives for LSD use are varied. Sociologists refer to problems of commitment and alienation and at least add thereby to the younger generation's verbal mythology. We might remember that wild analysis and "psyching"—probing into one another's supposedly unconscious motives—characterized youth of previous generations, as did self-experiments with hypnosis even during the nineteenth century. Curiosity about the mind, about what can be experienced, about who one is and is to be can be expected. All the crises of adolescence (Blos, 1962)—the fluidity, shift of primal objects, narcissism, somatic changes, inexperience, and identity issues—play into the drug-taking culture.

Of the college users I have studied, a "need to feel"—to gain access to themselves and others—a pervasive sense of being constricted seem characteristic. In a recent report of a group in which Rorschach and other studies were available, this theme dominated even though outcomes sharply differed: These ranged from psychosis, to instability, to a reaction of bemused enlightenment (Bowers, Chipman, Schwartz, and Dann, 1967). One wonders whether the consequences of a boundaryless or destructively permissive upbringing leads to a lack of distinctions, a deficient recognition of self-experience especially when drugs or authoritarianism (masked as rebellion) are common ways to achieve feeling and a sense of distinctiveness.

Some college students clearly tried the drug as part of clique activity; taking the drug puts the student one up—he has "been there." This is a challenge evoking interest among friends and can provide the basis for a loose group cohesion. For this group, magical transformation of reality, omniscient union rather than painful confrontation of separateness and effort is a lure. Old limits can be dissolved and—with a single gulp—

philosophical infants are transformed into sages. The frustration of years of inexperience are replaced by an intense arcane experience; it is as if the secrets of the parental bedroom are instantly transcended by the mysteries of the drug! The tables are turned as the young turn on; now it is the parents who stand by in perplexed, uncomprehending, and fascinated impotence.

Others sincerely feel they should confront an experience advertised to be so important. They can be dared by accounts of pleasant or assertedly profound experiences. They see the drug as an emotional fitness test, somewhat analogous to physical fitness. The issue for many is "control." They experiment with the right to drink and test their ability to stop. At this age they are often doing the same with cigarette smoking, studying, or masturbation. In general, they are rehearsing their strength and autonomy at a time when their lives are largely unwritten. Many behaviors of this age constitute a probing for consequences—an impatient attempt to leap the barriers of time, to come to grips with life and seize the fruits and risks promised in the future, the threshold of which is now just barely visible. This underlies many of the grimmer statistics of the eighteen to twenty-five age group, including accidents and suicide. One wonders if these represent the inevitable costs of learning the lesson of consequences, of limits, of mortality.

Summary and Conclusions

With respect to the LSD experience, we know that many serious persons have reported some transient or even long-term value in it. There is some objective evidence that aesthetic appreciation can be enhanced; for example, an LSD group bought significantly more records for a period of six months (McGlothlin, Cohen, and McGlothlin, 1964). If, though, we search for major productions of art, letters, music, or visionary insight few clear-cut monuments to the drug are available. Related to creativity, the effects of the drug do not seem to have compelled it. Huxley's greatest output preceded his mescaline states; he thereafter, as I read him, tended to write about drugs, not to create with them. If we ask whether there have been cultures that have eradicated mental disorders and disease with these drugs, or groups that have seen the dissolution of deviant behavior, we find some slight association but no clear-cut over-all differences that I know of in the general titer of human misery. In fact, the extensive use of these drugs is often associated with some form of psychosocial deprivation—an equivalent form of which is marked privilege (as in Brahmins and college students). That private satisfactions might have been achieved, that groups with the presence of these plants and chemicals could have attained some spiritual equilibrium seems apparent, but whether no alternative means exist within a culture is another question. That startling examples of new learning or even conversion can occur cannot be denied, but that we can as yet control and systematically reinforce drug-induced insights is uncertain.

We must ask whether a stable person is really under sufficient control of his motives and shifting circumstances let alone the dosage to take these drugs as a civil right for whatever personal reasons he wishes (Scher, 1966). If so, who has to care for the consequences of his misjudgments? How can the stability of religious custom protect drug-takers who have little authentic orientation to religion and unstable groups and barely reliable leaders on whom to lean. If we learn from the effects of drugs on much simpler biological systems, some side effects of any chemical cannot be avoided. Few of the advocates of unsupervised use seem to appreciate how difficult it often is to assess risk and value in drug administration—even in the best practice of medicine and psychiatry.

We should not forget to assess the cost of sustained euphoria or of pleasure states. We can seriously wonder if man is built to endure more than a brief chemically induced glimpse of paradise. Many authors have stressed that we are endowed with mechanisms with which to filter input and structure and use the fluid and irrational components of behavior. Heinrich Kluver (1966) concluded his systematic and pioneering series of neuropsychological studies of mescaline with speculations about the drug's differential action on those vast subcortical areas characterized by emotionality and variability and those anchoring sensori-motor systems that aid in constancy. The question is perhaps not so much expanding the mind—it is expanded enough—but to see if there are drugs (or developmental experiences) that can enhance a better and more creative coordination among these so-called regions.

Thus, etched on the variabilities of culture and personality are drugs with a certain skew toward that mystical realm of the mind that knows both psychosis and religion, both heightened and useful self-insight and impaired and distorted judgment about both the drugged and everyday world. Perhaps similarities and differences of these various chemicals and their effects could—if analyzed (Snyder and Merrill, 1965)—

reveal means for finer control of these experiences—at least in terms of their intensities. The possibility or impossibility of such manipulations are questions of basic importance to our notions of how neurobehavioral mechanisms are intrinsically related and the extent and means by which they can selectively be dissociated and controlled (Freedman, 1966; Rosenbaum, Cohen, Luby, Gottlieb, and Yelen, 1959; and Elkes, 1966).

In general, then, it seems that we have been more awed than aided by our experience with these drugs. They still remain agents that reveal but do not chart the mental regions; to chart these we must employ our mental faculties available in the undrugged state. Accordingly we should do better than simply be amazed, repeating thereby the ontogeny of past encounters with mind-revealing drugs. With these drugs we could learn to analyze how behavior is organized, disrupted, and influenced and see what nature can teach us about the ways in which the chemical organization of the brain is related to the dimensions of experiencing and behaving that comprise—to use an archaic term—the study of the mind.

REFERENCES

Aberle, D. F. (1966). The Peyote religion among the Navaho. Chicago: Aldine.
Abramson, H. A., ed. (1967). The use of LSD in psychotherapy and alcoholism. Indianapolis: Bobbs Merrill.
Adey, W. R., Porter, R., and Walter, D. O. (1965). Prolonged effects of LSD on EEG records during discrimination performance in cats. Evaluation by computer analysis. Electroenceph. Clin. Neurophysiol., 18:25–35.
Aghajanian, G. K., and Bing, O. H. L. (1964). Persistence of lysergic acid diethylamide in the plasma of human subjects. Clinical Pharmacological Therapeutics, 5:611–614.
Barron, F., Jarvik, M. E., and Bunnell, S., Jr. (1964). Hallucinogenic drugs. Scientific American, 210:29–37.
Becker, D. I., Appel, J. B., and Freedman, D. X. (1967). Some effects of LSD on visual discrimination in pigeons. Psychopharmacologia (Berlin), 11:354–364.
Benabud, A. (1957). Psycho-pathological aspects of the cannabis situation in Morocco: Statistical data for 1956. Bulletin on Narcotics, 9(no.4):1–16.
Blos, P. (1962). On adolescence: A psychoanalytic interpretation. Glencoe: The Free Press.
Bowers, M., Chipman, A., Schwartz, A., and Dann, O. T. (1967). Dynamics of psychedelic drug abuse—A clinical study. Archives of General Psychiatry, 16:560–566.
Bowers, M. B., and Freedman, D. X. (1966). Psychedelic experiences in acute psychoses. Archives of General Psychiatry, 15:240–248.
Bowers, M. B., Goodman, E., and Sim, V. (1964). Some behavioral effects in man following anticholinesterase administration. Journal of Nervous and Mental Disease, 138:383–389.

Bradley, P. B., and Elkes, J. (1957). The effect of some drugs on the electrical activity of the brain. Brain, 80:77–117.

Bradley, P. B., and Key, B. J. (1958). The effect of drugs and arousal responses produced by electrical stimulation of the reticular formation of the brain. Electroenceph. Clin. Neurophysiol., 10:97–110.

Chandler, A. L., and Hartman, M. A. (1960). Lysergic acid diethylamide (LSD-25) as a facilitating agent in psychotherapy. Archives of General Psychiatry, 2:286–299.

Chopra, R. N., and Chopra, I. C. (1957). Treatment of drug addiction: Experience in India. Bulletin on Narcotics, 9(no.4):21–33.

Chwelos, N., Blewett, D. B., Smith, C. M., and Hoffer, A. (1959). Use of d-lysergic acid diethylamide in the treatment of alcoholism. Quarterly Journal of Studies on Alcohol, 20:577–590.

Clark, W. H. (1958). The psychology of religion. New York: Macmillan.

Cole, J. O., and Katz, M. M. (1964). The psychotomimetic drugs: An overview. Journal of the American Medical Association, 187:758–761.

Cohen, S. (1964). The beyond within. New York: Atheneum.

———. (1966). A classification of LSD complications. Psychosomatics, 7:182–186.

———, and Ditman, K. S. (1963). Prolonged adverse reactions to lysergic acid diethylamide. Archives of General Psychiatry, 8:475–480.

Editorial (1898). Paradise or inferno? British Medical Journal, Pt. 1, p. 390.

Eggert, D. C., and Shagass, C. (1966). Clinical prediction of insightful response to a single large dose of LSD. Psychopharmacologia (Berlin), 9:340–346.

Elkes, J. (1966). Psychoactive drugs: Some problems and approaches. In P. Solomon, ed., Psychiatric Drugs. New York: Grune & Stratton.

Ellis, H. (1898). Mescal: A new artificial paradise. Contemporary Review, 73:130–141.

Fink, M., Simeon, J., Haque, W., and Itil, T. (1966). Prolonged adverse reactions to LSD in psychotic subjects. Archives General Psychiatry, 15:450–454.

Frank, J. D. (1961). Persuasion and healing. Baltimore: Johns Hopkins Press.

Freedman, D. X. (1966). Aspects of the biochemical pharmacology of psychotropic drugs. In P. Solomon, ed., Psychiatric Drugs. New York: Grune & Stratton. Pp. 32–57.

———, and Aghajanian, G. K. (1966). Approaches to the pharmacology of LSD-25. Lloydia, 29(no.4):309–314.

———, Aghajanian, G. K., and Coquet, C. A. (1964). Effect of reserpine on plasma binding and brain uptake of LSD-25. Fed. Proc., 23:147.

———, Appel, J. B., Hartman, F. R., and Molliver, M. D. (1964). Tolerance to the behavioral effects of LSD-25 in rat. J. Pharmacol. Exptl. Therap., 143:309–313.

Freud, S. (1949). An outline of psychoanalysis. New York: Norton.

Frosch, W. A., Robbins, E. S., and Stern, M. (1965). Untoward reactions of lysergic acid diethylamide (LSD) resulting in hospitalization. New England Journal of Medicine, 273:1235–1239.

Giarman, N. J., and Freedman, D. X. (1965). Biochemical aspects of the actions of psychotomimetic drugs. Pharmacological Review, 17:1–25.

Gordon, N. (1963). The hallucinogenic drug cult. The Reporter. August 15.

Grinker, R. R. (1964). Bootlegged ecstasy. Journal of the American Medical Association, 187:768.

James, W. (1916). Varieties of religious experience. New York: Longmans, Green.

Keeler, M. H. (1965). The effects of psilocybin on a test of afterimage perception. Psychopharmacologia (Berlin), 8:131–139.

Key, B. J., and Bradley, P. B. (1958). Effect of drugs on conditioning and habituation to arousal stimuli in animals. Nature, 182:1517–1519.

Klee, G. D., and Weintraub, W. (1959). Paranoid reactions following lysergic acid diethylamide (LSD-25). In P. B. Bradley, ed., Neuro-Psychopharmacology, Princeton: Elsevier. Pp. 457–460.

Kluver, H. (1966). Mescal and mechanisms of hallucinations. Chicago: University of Chicago Press.

Koella, W. P., Beaulieu, R. F., and Bergen, J. R. (1964). Stereotyped behavior cyclic changes in response produced by LSD in goats. International Journal of Neuro-pharmacology, 3:397-403.

Kohut, H. (1966). Forms and transformations of narcissism. Journal of the American Psychoanalytic Association, 14(no.2):243-272.

Krus, D., and Wapner, S. (1959). Effect of lysergic acid diethylamide (LSD-25) on perception of part-whole relationships. Journal of the American Psychological Assn., 48:87-95.

Laing, R. D. (1965). Transcendental experience in relation to religion and psychosis. Psychedelic Review, 6:7-15.

Leary, T., and Alpert, R. (1963). The politics of consciousness expansion. The Harvard Review, 1(no.4):33-37.

Lebovits, B., Visotsky, H. M., and Ostfeld, A. M. (1962). LSD and JB318: A comparison of two hallucinogens: Part III. Archives of General Psychiatry, 7:39-45.

Lennard, H. (1956). Lysergic acid diethylamide (LSD-25): XII. A preliminary statement of its effects upon interpersonal communication. Journal of the American Psychological Assn., 41:186-198.

Leuner, H. (1967). Present state of psycholytic therapy and its possibilities. In H. A. Abramson, ed., The Use of LSD in Psychotherapy and Alcoholism. Indianapolis: Bobbs-Merrill. Pp. 101-116.

Lidz, T., Fleck, S., and Cornelison, A. R. (1965). Schizophrenia and the family. New York: International Universities Press.

Ling, T. M., and Buckman, J. (1963). Lysergic acid and ritalin in the treatment of neurosis. London: Lambarde Press.

Loewald, H. (1955). Hypnoid states—repression, abreaction, and recollection. Journal of the American Psychoanalytic Association, 3:201-210.

Ludwig, A. M., and Levine, J. (1965). Patterns of hallucinogenic drug abuse. Journal of the American Medical Association, 191:104-108.

———. (1967). Hypnodelic theory. In J. H. Masserman, ed., Current Psychiatric Therapies. Vol. 7. New York: Grune & Stratton. Pp. 130-141.

McGlothlin, W. H. (1965). Hallucinogenic drugs: A perspective with special references to peyote and cannabis. Psychedelic Review, no.6, pp. 16-57.

———, Cohen, S., and McGlothlin, M. S. (1964). Short-term effects of LSD on anxiety, attitudes and performance. Journal of Nervous and Mental Disease, 13:266-273.

MacLean, J. R., MacDonald, D. C., Byrne, U. P., and Hubbard, A. M. (1961). The use of LSD-25 in the treatment of alcoholism and other psychiatric problems. Quarterly Journal of Studies of Alcohol, 22:34-45.

Maslow, A. H. (1962). Toward a psychology of being. New York: Van Nostrand.

Pauk, Z., and Shagass, C. (1961). Some test findings associated with susceptibility to psychosis induced by lysergic acid diethylamide. Comprehensive Psychiatry, 2:188-195.

Pious, W. (1961). A hypothesis about the nature of schizophrenic behavior. In A. Burton, ed., Psychotherapy of the Psychoses, New York: Basic Books.

Prince, R., and Savage, C. (1966). Mystical states and the concept of regression. Psychedelic Review, no. 8, pp. 59-65.

Redlich, F. C., and Freedman, D. X. (1966). The theory and practice of psychiatry. New York: Basic Books.

Rosenbaum, G., Cohen, B., Luby, E., Gottlieb, J., and Yelen, D. (1959). Comparison of sernyl with other drugs. Archives of General Psychiatry, 1:651-656.

Rosenthal, S. H. (1964). Persistent hallucinosis following repeated administration of hallucinogenic drugs. American Journal of Psychiatry, 121:238-244.

Salvatore, S., and Hyde, R. W. (1956). Progression of effects of LSD. Archives of Neurological Psychiatry, 76:50-59.

Sandison, R. A., Spencer, A. M. and Whitelaw, J. D. A. (1954). The therapeutic value of lysergic acid diethylamide in mental illness. Journal of Mental Science, 100:491-507.

Savage, C., Terrill, J., and Jackson, D. D. (1962). LSD, transcendence and the new beginning. Journal of Nervous and Mental Disease, 135:425-439.

Scher, J. (1966). Patterns and profiles of addiction and drug abuse. Archives of General Psychiatry, 15:539–551.

Shorvon, H. M. (1963). Abreaction and brain. In R. Crocket et al., eds., Hallucinogenic Drugs and Their Psychotherapeutic Use: Proceedings of the Royal Medico-Psychological Association, 1961. London: Lewis. Pp. 74–78.

Silverman, J. (1967). Variations in cognitive control and psychophysiological defense in the schizophrenias. Psychosomatic Medicine, 29:225–251.

Smith, C. M. (1958). A new adjunct to the treatment of alcoholism: The hallucinogenic drugs. Quarterly Journal of Studies on Alcohol, 19:406–417.

Snyder, S. H., and Merrill, C. G. (1965). A relationship between the hallucinogenic activity of drugs and their electronic configuration. Proceedings of the National Academy of Science, U.S., 54:258–66.

Spindler, G. (1952). Personality of peyotism in Menomini Indian acculturation. Psychiatry, 15:151–159.

Stumpf, W. E., and Roth, L. J. (1965). Dry-mounting high-resolution autoradiography. In L. J. Roth, ed., Isotopes in Experimental Pharmacology. Chicago: University of Chicago Press. Pp. 133–143.

Tenenbaum, B. (1961). Group therapy with LSD-25. Diseases of the Nervous System, 22:459–462.

Ungerleider, J. T., Fisher, D. D., and Fuller, M. (1966). The dangers of LSD. Journal of the American Medical Association, 197:389–392.

Wiener, H. (1967). External chemical messengers: III. Mind and body in schizophrenia. New York Journal of Medicine, 67:1287.

Wilson, R. E., and Shagass, C. (1964). Comparison of two drugs with psychotomimetic effects (LSD and ditran). Journal of Nervous and Mental Disease, 138:277–286.

7] CHEMICALS AND THEIR EFFECTS ON THE ADOLESCENT EGO

LEONARD NEFF

The social concern about the increasing illicit use of chemicals by adolescents has contributed to the relative neglect of a related phenomenon, the disorganization of the adolescent's ego induced by the side effects of medically prescribed drugs. Chemicals, whether self or medically prescribed, can profoundly alter ego functioning, because they induce altered physical states and altered states of consciousness. The regressive effects of drugs on the adolescent ego may be transient or prolonged, and may contribute to preexisting fixations. Under certain circumstances there may be good as well as bad consequences of such an experience and some correlations may exist between these clinical phenomena and particular developmental stages.

Adolescents are uniquely susceptible to changes in body state and defensive organization as a result of their particularly fluid developmental stage. They seek diverse forms of perceptual experiences to enhance their awareness of themselves. At other times, because of the pressure of internal processes, estrangement and depersonalization can occur. Both are part of normal adolescent development and, given a degree of resiliency of their egos, may contribute to growth (Blos, 1962). Where their egos have limited resiliency, these experiences may lead to further fixations. Artificially induced altered body states provide a direct blow to the body ego. Soporific and somnolent effects, in particular, interfere with certain highly cathected defenses, for example, intellectualization and motoric discharge activity. This results in the threat to the ego of being flooded by instinctual material. In turn regression follows with the mobilization of more primitive defenses, for example, denial and projection, and altered states of consciousness, such as, depersonalization and estrangement. These reactions are frequently transient, lasting only as long as the chemical is being used, but where a predisposition for regression and utilization of more primitive defenses exists, these responses, once triggered by the drug, may continue indefinitely.

Observations of the effects of marijuana and LSD on ego functioning have been reported (McGlothlin and West, 1968; Waskow, Olsson, Salzmann, and Katz, 1970). However, no attempt has been made to correlate these effects with the developmental stages of the patient, nor to consider the possible consequences of these effects on this stage or later development.

The consequences of such alterations in ego functioning for adolescent ego development might be studied using Blos's phases of adolescent development (Blos, 1962). He divides this period into preadolescence, early adolescence, adolescence proper, late adolescence, and post adolescence. Each phase has its particular libidinal and aggressive drive organization to develop, conflicts to resolve, and tasks to perform. Two examples of adolescents will be presented where severe ego disorganization was induced or prolonged by the side effects of drugs.

History and Review of the Literature

There have been reports of toxic and functional psychosis, anxiety attacks, and depressive reactions to therapeutic doses of various medications prescribed for children and adolescents (Done, 1960; Good et al., 1957; Jelliffe, 1951), particularly tranquilizers (Epps and Scott, 1961; Kovan, 1958; Shaw, 1960). The mechanism for the depressive reaction caused by cortisone, that is, altered body image, was suggested by Good et al. (1957). A report was published of an adolescent who developed an acute paranoid schizophrenia with depressive features while receiving therapeutic doses of cholorquin for a facial rash. The somnolence, a common side effect, interfered with his usual defenses of intellectualization and denial, allowing primary process material to break through into consciousness. In addition, the postural hypotension, another side effect, provided another assault on the already damaged body ego, resulting in further, unmanageable anxiety. Depersonalization, with an abortive, restitutive delusional formation, followed and was only partially relieved long after the drug had been discontinued (Neff, 1964).

A teenager in psychoanalysis suddenly complained of being drowsy, feeling unreal, and not being able to control his thoughts. The next day he felt that some outside force was controlling him. There was no previous evidence in the prior eighteen months of his treatment of any tendency to a thought disorder. Inquiry then revealed that he had begun taking tripelennamine, on prescription, the day before the onset of the above symptoms. The drug was discontinued and within twenty-four hours the thought disorder completely and permanently disappeared (Becker, 1964). Another adolescent on a course of piperazine for pinworms developed drowsiness, depersonalization, and somatic symptoms, all known side effects of the drug, within forty-eight hours. A mild, transient paranoid episode resulted (Neff, 1966).

The somatic changes in adolescence, the surge of sexuality and aggression, and the increased self-aggrandizement, all occurring at the same time, require vigorous defensive adaptational efforts. There is a heightened awareness of somatic changes and processes, a fear of the strength of instinctual impulses, and the possibility of ego disorganization requiring increased vigilance and intellectual control. In adolescence, intellectualization is part of the ego's customary endeavor to master instincts (A. Freud, 1946). Jacobson (1964) states: "The rapid growth and change in adolescence necessitate continuous readjustments in his self-representations. Testing of momentary and psychic bodily realities and potentialities are thus made extremely difficult." Transient feelings of depersonalization often accompany maturational changes in the genitalia and the appearance of secondary sex characteristics, because of the revolutionary increase in bodily awareness and the radical revision of the body image (Blos, 1962, p. 195). Not only can the integration of the altered body image and heightened impulses in adolescence be affected by chemicals, but the adaptational function of object relations can be interfered with as well.

Clinical Data

Two cases will be presented, the first demonstrating the transient effect of chemicals on the adolescent ego, the second the prolonged effect.

CASE 1

John, an eighteen-year-old high school senior, requested psychotherapy because of school problems.[1] For many years he was convinced that he was dumb, but recently he discovered that he could study, learn, and utilize the subject matter when he wanted to, so now he wished to go to college in order to become a gymnastics teacher. He considered himself to be a fairly good football player and a fast runner, and spent most of his after-school and weekend time playing in neighborhood games. When not playing ball, he would spend two to three hours a day practicing the drums. His other interest was comic books, which he read regularly and in large quantities. Though he had dated occasionally and had sexual intercourse twice, he was not particularly interested in girls. He expressed annoyance with his mother because she did not understand him and also was a nag, but stated that his father was "a good guy."

John was pleasant, cooperative, and related well to me at all times. He fidgeted a great deal and drummed his fingers on the arm of his chair. There was some mispronunciation of words, his vocabulary was limited, and his thinking was concrete, but there was no evidence of any thought disorder. He seemed blandly unconcerned about anything but his difficulty with mathematics and his drumming. Though he gave the over-all impression of being of low-average intelligence, occasionally he would express ideas that suggested that he was much brighter. In describing his difficulties with mathematics he could only generalize, for example, "can't understand," "carelessness," and so on. He was vague about everything, including his problems with his mother, which he felt were relatively minor.

At the age of eight he was hospitalized for four weeks, following an episode of hematuria and was diagnosed as having bilateral polycystic kidneys.[2] At eight and one-half he was taken to a child guidance clinic because of his learning difficulties and his bullying of other children. Both he and his mother were seen weekly for about eighteen months, and though his bullying stopped, his school work did not improve, so she discontinued their sessions. At fourteen he developed a left inguinal hernia that was immediately repaired, but recurred within six months. He was readmitted, but because his systolic blood pressure was over 200 mm. Hg. and his BUN was elevated (65 mgm. percent), the operation was postponed for another six months.[3]

With a history of hyperactivity, delayed speech, and learning disorder, a neurological examination and EEG were done to determine if brain damage was present. Except for mild difficulties in finger-to-finger movement and some choreoform movements in the proximal muscles of the upper extremity, the neurological examination was normal. There

111

was a suggestion "of old minimal brain damage, of academic interest only." The EEG was within normal limits.

Psychological testing [4] indicated that he was functioning in the average to bright normal range of intelligence, with constriction and blunting limiting a higher potential. Obsessive bodily concerns and extreme anxiety were related to previous medical and surgical experience and adolescent sexuality. Developmental lags of a nonorganic nature in the perceptual motor area were present. Major affective themes were of depression and anger. There was no motor restlessness, nor evidence of brain damage or thought disorders.

A complete medical workup, particularly kidney function, was requested but John's mother adamantly refused and became mildly paranoid at this recommendation.

In summarizing the results of his evaluation with him, John ventilated a great deal about his bodily concerns and obtained some relief, but reminded me that his major concern was not this, but his math problem. In summarizing my findings and impressions, I felt that the mother's need to remain ignorant of his renal status and to maintain a close tie to him and his problems, physical as well as emotional, would be the major limiting factor in any psychotherapeutic endeavor. His own need to deny and isolate affects and fantasies could not be easily differentiated from hers. I decided to see him initially twice a week on a supportive basis, encouraging ventilation, with little attempt at exploration or interpretation. At the same time I saw his mother every other week in an attempt to relieve her guilt and anxiety about his physical state, to allow her to eventually permit a renal workup [5] and, more importantly, separation.

John and his mother were seen on this basis for seventeen months. After an initial period of about two months of expressing his ambivalence to therapy, his academic work began to improve. At this point he witnessed a hit-and-run accident in his neighborhood, which gave rise to fantasies of bodily damage, repair, and restitution. These then became the central theme of his therapy, and remained so until termination. Oedipal rivalry and especially the omnipotent, intrusive preoedipal mother were seen as the causes of the damage. It was in this context that the drug reaction occurred.

Shortly after the summer vacation, when John had been in therapy for about eight months, his sister was discovered to have pinworms and the family was given a course of piperazine, a vermifuge. He had been taking the drug for four days before he had a session. A few hours after taking the first dose he felt drowsy, and experienced nausea and anorexia. The next day he complained of parasthesias in his upper extremities, followed in several hours by muscular twitchings. Lightheadedness and dyspnea began that day, and he was beginning to feel some anxiety about what was happening.[6] During his session on the fourth day of the course he began to experience mild depersonalization and blocking of thoughts. I suspected he was having a drug reaction and called the internist to verify it, but the patient decided to continue the medication. When he came in on the sixth day his neurological problems were increased, with marked akinesia, dyskinesia, and motor restlessness. Feelings of impending doom, thought disorders, estrangement, and depersonalization were pronounced. Depression alternated with euphoria, and with the latter his associations loosened. In this state he could compose music and drumming arrangements that were "great," so that "I can see why musicians take drugs. Though after this I'll never go near them." [7] However, he could not remember, even a few minutes later, what he had done, just the mood he had been in. He reported a dream the previous night in which he could not make his hands work to write a test in school or play his drums and he could not run or catch a football. He felt very depressed, hopeless, and helpless. This was, he felt, a replication of his history and current waking state. When I told him that I talked to his family doctor he was panic stricken and asked if his doctor said that he was going to die in two weeks. He had his last dose of medication that day and felt much better the next. Most of the depersonalization, thought disorders, anxiety, and depression had disappeared. By the third day after the drugs were stopped he had completely recovered.

He insisted on having the second course of medication. Within forty-eight hours all symptoms had returned, though the anxiety, depression, and depersonalization were not so intense, and some observing ego was present. Despite this, on the fifth day he first had ideas of reference and somatic delusions, "Something was choking me. . . . electricity like going through me. . . . Something seems to be controlling me . . . Winding me up like a clock and making me do things automatically." On the fourth night of taking the piperazine he was afraid to go to sleep. "It's like I was dead," and he had had pavor nocturnis. The piperazine was immediately discontinued, and within four days he had completely recovered.

After this experience John no longer had to avoid exposing the depths of his concern about his renal and academic problems. He soon was willing to go through a complete renal evaluation, and demonstrated the extent of his math problem, for example, he still had to count on his fingers. Despite great shame during these sessions, he experienced considerable relief, and his school work was soon consistently better than average, and he began engaging in appropriate heterosexual interests and activities. Therapy was discontinued at this point, about ten months after his drug experience.

Discussion

When he entered therapy, John was still in the early adolescent stage of development (Blos, 1962). His ego interests and activities were typical of this period, and his object relations were characterized by intense efforts to disengage from his preoedipal objects. This effort was made more difficult by his mother's depression in regard to his "polycystic kidneys" during latency, her near-fatal illness and surgery over the two and one-half years of his mid teens, and his own surgery near his genitals. A strong regressive pull from both his mother and his psyche required equally strong efforts to resist and left little energy for progress. At the same time, the loss of the mental representation of his latency mother, by virtue of her having withdrawn much of her emotional investment in him during and after his nephritis,[8] and the representation of the mother of adolescence, led to a state of chronic depression, while the actual threat of her loss resulted in a state of mourning. Until the time of his drug reaction, it seems that my supporting the ego's efforts to master the effects of previous bodily traumata enabled the progressive forces to assert themselves, so that development could slowly resume.

The piperazine, by assaulting his (already shaky) body ego in the form of the neurological symptoms, particularly the effects on the arms and hands, increased castration anxiety. It also interfered with one of his major defenses, motor activity. The enforced drowsiness interfered with normal thought processes, particularly intellectualizations, and forced a loosening of repression and inhibition. Memories, fantasies, affects, and impulses broke through and threatened to overwhelm the ego, leading to an intensification of its defensive efforts. The loss of ego controls of thought and action were severe blows to his self-esteem. Though only primitive defenses were available, for example, estrangement and depersonalization, the presence of an auxiliary ego providing support, information, and orientation to reality (both inner and outer) helped him to achieve some further mastery of the experience. The triple threat, castration, loss of ego integrity, and survival were involved in that order.

114

Despite, or perhaps because of, the gravity of this experience, occurring while in treatment, his ego began to develop rapidly. He had mastered a major trauma and could "know" it, talk about it, and learn from it, while it was happening and afterwards. He could learn from this experience, and subsequently risk other dangerous experiences, that is, disengagement, sexuality, and a renal evaluation.

For John, a traumatic experience with drugs did not lead to irreversible fixation. His ego showed some resiliency, and the availability of a strong therapeutic alliance, positive transference, and an auxiliary ego not only helped him weather the storm, but also may have facilitated the development of more adequate defenses.

CASE 2

Jim, an eighteen-year-old boy, a college freshman from out of state, was referred for consultation because his family and family doctor were concerned about the (psychotropic) medication he had been receiving in the previous three months.

As he slowly walked into the office, this good-looking but blank-faced boy handed me a large plastic bag full of assorted drugs. He was taking a total of 12 mgm. of trifluoperazine, 100 mgm. of thioridazine, and 2 mgm. of benztropinemesylate every day, as he had been doing for two months. He tried to answer questions, but his speech was so slurred and he was so drowsy and disoriented that nothing very coherent could be obtained other than that he was terribly worried and depressed. The drugs were gradually reduced and finally discontinued.

Until five months before he had been a model boy—a good student, polite, well-mannered, no problem to himself or anyone else. He had always been happy, self-confident, sure of his direction of college, then into business with his father, and finally, marriage and family. He went for a ride with a group of friends, and they all smoked marijuana—he for the second time. As he was smoking, he suddenly feared that the new boy in the group was an FBI agent who was going to arrest him for illegal possession. This guilty fear did not abate—as it had the first time he smoked—but rapidly increased in intensity. Now his guilt and shame would become public and he would be ruined.

His obsessive preoccupations became so severe that he dropped out of school two weeks before final examinations. He went home and announced that he was nervous and thought he should see a psychiatrist. An appointment was arranged for the same day, and he was admitted to the psychiatric ward of the local receiving hospital that evening. He told the doctor that he was so frightened and depressed that he wished he were dead. A week later, because of his increasing panic, estrangement, and despondency, his parents took him out of the hospital to see a psychiatrist in a nearby city who prescribed medication for him and arranged to see him once a week.

Within one month he was taking the dosage combination that he reported when he came to see me. Drowsiness and an inability to think (blocking) appeared about two days after beginning the medication. The muscular relaxation left him feeling "paralyzed." Though reticent before this all began, he now could rarely speak even when he wanted to, for the blocking and the effort required to articulate were more than he could cope with. His anxiety increased to terror as soon as this began, he no longer felt like himself, and his surroundings seemed unreal. Hopelessness was more pronounced.

His past history was provided by his mother, who was overwhelmed by guilt about her son's present plight. She said she always has had a "foggy memory" of the details of her children's early years. Jim was the youngest of three boys and was planned for. Her pregnancy and his birth and early development were "normal," that is, not significantly different from those of her other boys. She could not recall the time or methods of weaning or toilet training, nor his responses to them. There was no transitional object. Aside from being a "fussy eater," he was an "easy" baby and toddler. She had had a partial hysterectomy when he was three or four, but "He knew nothing about it," as he knew nothing about several other family crises. At some point before he began school he became a "hyperactive child," characterized by restlessness, destructiveness, disobedience, and insomnia. When he was six or seven the family doctor prescribed an antihistamine for this condition, and the symptoms disappeared. From about age eight he began showing great concern for his mother. If she coughed, he would anxiously ask if she was all right. If she stayed in bathroom for more than five minutes he would knock on the door and ask if there were anything wrong.[9] As he progressed in school, he was a better than average student, well liked by his peers, but never developed any close friendships. He was always in good health and had had no operations or injuries. Both parents described him as always having been quiet, introverted, well behaved, and lacking in initiative. They were never aware of any problems of his, and noticed no adolescent upheavals.

After the drugs were stopped and his sensorium began to clear, it was possible to assess his mental status. He was oriented in all spheres and seemed to be of about average intelligence. His speech was reticent and concrete; he gave terse answers to questions, offering no spontaneous comments or associations. Other than an overwhelming concern with his state, even after it had begun to improve, he expressed little doubt, nor did he question any aspect of his experiences. At our last meeting he did begin to wonder, for the first time in his life, if something were the matter with him sexually. He had only had two dates so far, and was afraid to hold his date's hand. Otherwise, prior to this drug experience, he had never had any doubts about himself or his future.

His overwhelming guilt and fear were the entire range of his affective repertoire. One evening he could not go out with his parents, nor stop pacing the floor, until he confessed that he had lied to me in our session that morning. The lie was that he had told me he was feeling better, when he really was not. His sole interest throughout our contacts was to be returned to his previous state—one of guiltless, affectless bliss.

Psychological examinations [10] indicated preexisting impairments in ego functioning, including a regressive susceptibility, poor object relations, and a tendency to concrete thinking. There was a suggestion of defensive inhibition of aggression, over and above the drug effect. A pathological degree of denial was also present, with elements of stubbornness and negativism as well. An extremely harsh, primitive superego was also evidenced. There were evidences of organicity, most probably related to the effects of the drugs that he had been taking.

The diagnostic impression was that he had suffered an acute paranoid schizophrenic episode, probably induced by marijuana, with an affective component (depression) superimposed and maintained by the psychoactive drugs that he had been taking. It was recommended that he have intensive psychotherapy, initially directed to supporting and developing the ego functions related to judgment, thought processes, and object relations; that medication be used only as an adjunct; and that the entire treatment program be carried on away from home.

Mother and son vehemently objected to the separation, and it has been subsequently learned that he did stay home. All medications were stopped for a period of time, and he was then placed on a mild tranquilizer. He is attending a local college, but has recently moved into the dormitory and is doing better than average work. It has not been possible for him to obtain any regular psychotherapy.

Discussion

Reconstructing the vicissitudes of adolescent development in this boy helps to provide a baseline for developing some understanding of his reactions to the various drugs. The regressive attachment to his mother,

117

coupled with his harsh, primitive superego apparently had interfered with conflict formation in preadolescence (Blos, 1962). His preexisting regressive tendency and the regressive pull of mounting instinctual tension facilitated further regression. Repression and denial added sufficient force to prevent instinctual tension from mounting, which is what provides the forward thrust to disengagement, weakening of the superego, and seeking of new objects (Blos, 1962). Going away to school seems to have provided a new developmental impetus, as evidenced by his finding new friends and engaging in delinquent acts.

The delinquent acts, combined with the dope-induced regression and loosening of repressions, led to his ego being flooded with instinctual tension, as in preadolescence. However, his defensive adaptive mechanisms were inadequate to cope with this, as indicated by the regressive adaptation and the pathological, paranoid restitutive mechanisms.[11] Confinement in the hospital and the presence of disturbed patients led to further flooding of the ego with instinctual material causing increased panic disorientation, and a severe loss of self-esteem—now he *was* "crazy."

The direct and side effects of the drugs used had a subsequently disorganizing effect on the ego, and provided further blows to his self-esteem. Blocking of thought and action produced further weakening of the defensive structure, resulting in depersonalization and derealization. The drugs, while adding their own complications, covered over what might otherwise have been available and resolvable with psychotherapy.

Summary

Chemicals, whether "dope" or drugs, can have a profound effect on the ego functioning of the adolescent. Their ability to induce altered states of consciousness and physical states may impair the favored defense mechanisms in this age group. Ego disorganization, regression, and depersonalization result. These effects, in turn, may alter the course of development, depending on the patient's initial developmental phase and resiliency of his ego.

Two cases were presented illustrating different aspects of such reactions. The first, an adolescent with a previously impaired body image and object relations, had an episode of regression and depersonalization as a result of taking a vermifuge prophylactically. The side effects of somnolence and impaired motor functioning disrupted his defensive organization and his adaptive activities, leading to a transient ego disruption. The resiliency of his ego and the presence of his ego and the presence of a strong therapeutic alliance, positive transference and an auxiliary ego, enabled him to work through this experience as it was occurring, and to similar experiences in the past. He was able then to achieve a higher level of adaptation and develop a more flexible defensive organization.

The second case, an eighteen-year-old boy who decompensated while smoking marijuana, had his ego functioning further impaired by the use of massive doses of psychoactive drugs. This significantly interfered with any possible progressive development of the defensive structure or adaptational mechanisms in a boy already prone to regressive methods of conflict resolution. He remained in this regressed state for several months after the drugs were discontinued.

These reactions were correlated with the patient's phases of adolescent development prior to taking the drugs, and some inferences were made as to the consequences of these reactions for their subsequent development.

NOTES

1. This is an expanded version of a case previously reported (Neff, 1966).

2. Shortly after this diagnosis was given to her, the mother went to a medical library and read up on renal disorders. She saw in one book that children with polycystic kidneys rarely live beyond twenty years. She became severely depressed and was still grieving for him at the time of referral. She also stopped recognizing his birthday and never celebrated it after she read the prognosis.

3. Immediately after his last herniorrhapy John's mother began complaining of abdominal pains and fatigue. During the next eighteen months the pains got worse, she lost thirty-five pounds and became severely anemic, without external bleeding. Following a pelvic examination she experienced excruciating left lower quadrant pain, and ten days later an emergency colostomy was performed. She had had a bleeding diverticulum that ruptured. During the next year (patient was sixteen) she had three more operations before the colostomy was successfully closed. During this time she described herself as having experienced severe depersonalization and animated many inanimate objects. She had still not recuperated from these experiences when John requested psychotherapy.

4. Done by Mirian Siegel, Ph.D.

5. This was finally begun twelve months later. No cysts nor gross renal damage was found on pyelography. Mild glomerulonephritis was diagnosed and the prognosis was fair.

6. His mother was having similar neurological symptoms, but her reaction did not appear to affect her ego.

7. Perhaps this was an example of "mind expansion."

8. It may be that his failure to internalize counting was related to an identification with his mother's refusal to count his birthdays after she had read about renal disease (see note 2).

9. Jim felt very guilty for the damage he had inflicted on her. She had been hospitalized for three weeks because of a moderately severe depression. This occurred in the midst of his reaction, and everyone attributed her illness to Jim's.

10. Done by Leonard Small, Ph.D.

11. Though Jim did not recall any depersonalization or estrangement occurring while he was smoking, it is assumed to have occurred in order to account for the development of the delusion.

REFERENCES

Becker, T. E. (1964). Personal communication.

Blos, P. (1962). On adolescence: A psychoanalytic interpretation. Glencoe: The Free Press.

Done, A. K. (1960). Drug intoxication. Pediatric Clinics of North America, 7:235–255.

Epps, R. P., and Scott, R. B. (1961). "Tranquilizers as a source of intoxication in children." Med. Ann. D.C., 30:317–321.

Freud, A. (1946). The ego and the mechanisms of defence. New York: International Universities Press.

Freud, S. (1937). Constructions in analysis. Standard Edition, London: Hogarth Press, Vol. 18.

Good, R. A., et al. (1957). Serious untoward reactions to therapy with cortisone and adrenocorticotropin in pediatric practice. Pediatrics, 19:95–118, 272–284.

Jacobson, E. (1964). The self and the object world. New York: International Universities Press.

Jelliffe, D. B. (1951). Amebic hepatitis treated with chloroquin. Journal of Tropical Medicine, 54:114.

Kovan, R. A. (1958). Acute anxiety in adolescents from abuses of tranquilizing drugs. Journal of the American Osteopathic Association, 57:370–378.

McGlothlin, W. H., and West, L. J. (1968). The marihuana problem: An overview. Journal of the American Psychiatric Association, 125:370–378.

Neff, L. (1964). Drug reactions in adolescence. General Practice, 29:112–113.

———. (1966). Another severe psychological reaction to side effects of medication in an adolescent. Journal of the American Medical Association, 197:218–219.

Shaw, E. B. (1960). Side reactions from tranquilizing drugs. Pediatric Clinics of North America, 7:257–267.

Smart, B. C., and Bateman, K. (1967). Unfavorable reactions to LSD. Journal of the Canadian Medical Association, 97.

Waskow, I. E., Olsson, J. E., Salzmann, C., and Katz, M. H. (1970). Psychological effects of tetrahydrocannabinol. Archives of General Psychiatry 22:97–107.

PART II

DEVELOPMENTAL STAGES IN THE ADOLESCENT PROCESS

INTRODUCTION

Adolescence has only recently begun to be seen as a specific phase of life with special technical problems. Freud saw adolescence as "in many ways obscure" and felt that the intermediate steps between the starting point and the final aim of the process were "an unsolved riddle." When Erikson focused on man's developmental stages, the concept of the adolescent struggling to achieve identity formation as a reaction against role diffusion was a contribution to the solution of the riddle. Gitelson saw the goal of adolescence as synthesis and called on the therapist to provide a dependable ego ideal and controls through the intelligent use of authority. Blos has recently identified and elucidated the intermediate steps in his formulation of the five phases of adolescence (preadolescence, early adolescence, adolescence, late adolescence, and postadolescence) and conceptualizes the process as a "second separation-individuation." The adult personality represents the end result of this developmental progression and from one perspective is based on a balance of intrapsychic forces, a homeostatic equilibrium maintained by a variety of adaptive mechanisms.

The chapters in this part reflect various aspects of these developmental tasks. Irene Josselyn examines three adolescent behavior syndromes from the developmental point of view. These groups manifest a marked level of self-centeredness, a longing for closeness and a wish to escape, and she challenges the child-rearing techniques in current use as the source of their development.

Baittle and Offer reexamine adolescent rebellion and find that it exists as a normal developmental phase and is significant for the teenager independently of whether parental values are accepted or rejected. They show how the normal adolescent engages in rebellious behavior as an initial step in the process of emancipation while still embracing his parents' values. Kenneth Keniston sees another aspect of the developmental stages, the emergence of a new phase of life, youth, as a consequence of the social recognition of the period between adolescence and adulthood. This recognition in a socially advanced society of a growth stage provides encouragement for its development so that it eventually becomes a meaningful and necessary stage of development.

Roy R. Grinker, Sr., presents an important study on "mentally healthy young males." To find an individual one can call healthy is an accomplishment, but to describe an entire group from a particular school in that way is most provocative. Grinker calls these subjects "homoclites," normal, healthy just plain guys.

Frederick W. Coons sees "crises" as the rule rather than the exception for college students. If there is a typical freshman problem it is the student struggling to resolve the child-parent relationship. He discusses the vicissitudes of the college student developing personal values and intimate relationships, choosing a career line, and discovering the need to leave college for an "academic moratorium" as part of the developmental tasks of adolescence.

M. Robert Wilson, Jr., further clarifies adolescence with a proposed diagnostic classification and presents a theory of affects that helps extend the descriptive capacities of the professional. This schema grew out of a committee on classification of the American Society for Adolescent Psychiatry and is currently in use in several centers.

William A. Schonfeld presents a pertinent review of the biological development of adolescence and correlates these with the developmental tasks. He gives pertinent data on the growth patterns of the various areas of the body and synthesizes his extensive studies on body-image formation. He discusses how the adolescent must realize the components of his personality in such a way that he can achieve self-acceptance.

8] ETIOLOGY OF THREE

CURRENT ADOLESCENT SYNDROMES:

A HYPOTHESIS

IRENE M. JOSSELYN

Certain adolescents have, as we know, always been a disturbing part of a culture, unless the culture has imposed such rigid rules of conduct and/or provided structured outlets for the young individual so that the adolescent phase is masked. I will not bore you with the many quotations from history that confirm this, but adolescents have always, in most cultures, been a problem to their parents and a threat to those members of a stable society who fear change. With the exception of a few individuals in the past, it has only been during this century that adults have realized that adolescents are not only a problem to others but that they may also be a problem to themselves and that, with cause, their parents and the social structure are equally problems to them.

Students of human psychological maturation—Erikson (1968), Deutsch (1967), and Blos (1962) to mention a few—have given us insight into the significance of the maturational [1] phase of adolescence. Paralleling the gradual clarification of this phase has been a rapidly enriched knowledge of the psychological steps from birth on. It is possible that our knowledge of the steps of childhood have advanced more rapidly than our guidelines for fostering optimum development of the personality.

Observation of child behavior and a study of adult psychopathology give clues as to what has influenced the gradual maturation of the indi-

This chapter was presented as the 1970 Distinguished Service Award address, annual meeting of the American Society for Adolescent Psychiatry, May 10, 1970, San Francisco, Cal.

vidual. I would suggest, however, that the most productive phase to study is adolescence. The adolescent's format is fluid, blending the various psychological streams of childhood. Its resolution is the attainment of adulthood, at which time the final psychological structure has become relatively crystallized. It is during adolescence that we can most clearly understand the impact of childhood experiences and can observe the gradual formation of the adult defenses against and adaptation to those early experiences and the reality of living. For this reason I have chosen to present a question: "Do we see in some of the adolescents of today a behavioral Gestalt that, on the basis of our knowledge of adolescents, should be offered as a challenge to present theories of child-rearing?"

There are at least three different groups of adolescents whose behavior, though not necessarily reflecting their childhood experiences, may do so. If it does in a sufficient number of cases it would raise serious questions concerning the current concepts of child care, as well as offer an important therapeutic challenge to those of us working with the adolescent. I have chosen these three groups because certain members of them present a constellation of behavioral and attitudinal characteristics that I did not see, except in seriously disturbed young people, prior to about fifteen years ago.

There is a group of adolescents who show a marked level of self-centeredness. It is axiomatic that the adolescent is primarily interested in himself and that much of his interest in others is because of projection of his own needs and/or wishes. However, I have at times felt that the degree of self-centeredness I now observe I did not see fifteen years ago unless the individual's psychological state was seriously pathological. An example will perhaps clarify what I have in mind.

Tom, a seventeen-year-old boy, was very strongly antiwar and had made elaborate plans for avoiding the draft. The argument he gave was an ideological one: He did not believe in killing people; war, therefore, was never justified. If his country were attacked he would not defend it because that, he stated, would be a violation of his ideals. When I asked what if the attack on his country might possibly involve his own destruction his answer was, "At that time I will no longer be in this country so they won't have a chance to kill me." This discussion went on at a time when it looked as if the administration would use as a justification for continuance of the war in Vietnam the fear of a widespread massacre of South Vietnamese should the United States suddenly withdraw all troops. I suggested to him that we consider a hypothetical condition. Suppose it were true that the South Vietnamese would be massacred in toto were we suddenly to withdraw. If he would consider this hypothesis, though he might think it an absurd fantasy, would he feel that under such conditions the United States should withdraw? His answer was, "Yes, I don't want to be killed to save the life of a South Vietnamese." I cited an example of people having stood by watching a woman murdered in an attempted rape, the observers making no move to save the victim. I asked him what he would have done had he been in the crowd. He said, "I would have done as the rest of the crowd. Why should I run a risk of being hurt, or maybe killed, in order to save somebody else's life?"

Time does not permit me to give all the details about this boy. I had known him for many years; in my judgment, in any situation except where his own life, or some other severe disadvantage to him, were concerned, he gave the impression of being a generous, idealistic, thoughtful boy; his statements would seem superficially to be incompatible with his personality. They were not give'. for the sake of arguing; the same self-preservation theme came out in a variety of contexts.

In the past an adolescent boy with the same instinctual self-preservation impulse would more typically have kept the mask of his idealism intact. His ideal for himself would have been a fantasy of noble martyrdom, his dying for his belief that one does not kill even to save one's country or oneself, and expressing the conviction that a saint-like approach to the rapist would have stopped him. Tom's idealism, at times unrealistic perhaps, but admirable, was his philosophy of life, except when it, even in fantasy, inconvenienced him.

The second group that has interested me comprises those adolescents who long for closeness and readily verbalize that they have never really felt close to anyone. Adolescents characteristically seek closeness with others, particularly with special peer group members and with nonparental adults who, they feel, understand them. They have always, in phases, denied closeness to their parents. But typically a tone of nostalgia crept in, a recall that at one time parents and child were close. They also, in spite of their attempt to emancipate themselves, had turned to parents for emotional support when they felt too overwhelmed. (Now they turn to them for financial support.) As members of this group verbalize their wish for closeness there is a chronic, frantic quality or a chronic, deep, depressive tone. Again I was aware of these reactions in the past, primarily in those who were extremely deprived in their childhood and/or had alienated themselves from peers and adults because of their atypical behavior.

During the love-in festivals and devotion of flower children the young people put adults to shame; the young people impressively expound the value of "love" as a basis for interpersonal relationships. They extoll Judeo-Christian philosophy as if it had suddenly come into style. I asked one boy, who had an excellent sense of humor, that if one should love everyone, why not his parents whom he violently disliked; he did many acts primarily to make them miserable. His answer, with a smile, was immediate. "They," he said, "are subhuman. I don't go for this stuff of loving spiders and worms."

The group whose members extoll love accept, excluding the Establishment, the behavior of everyone as long as the behavior is the Thing of the other person and does not hurt anyone else (except the Establishment). Such seeming tolerance may be in reality interpersonal indifference; it is scarcely a pathway to closeness; closeness implies a mutuality of either identical or complementary nature. Is it really love of another person that prompts them to say that if their friend wants to blow his mind with Speed it is his mind, his Thing, and therefore his right? What seems clear from my experience with certain participants in the group's love philosophy is that, as many other students of this age currently have said, these particular members of the group love everyone, but no one individual.

A patient of mine spent a summer away from her family. Her time during that vacation was chiefly devoted to a group of young people who lived, took care of, and protected one another with a verbal conviction that their mutual intimacy and closeness made others unnecessary to them. After her return to the parental nest her description of her experience was enviable. Love had encompassed the group like a benign, billowing cloud. When she paused for breath I asked her if she planned to return to that area the following summer. She said that she did not know where they would be then. One boy had been particularly meaningful to her. She and he had found real closeness. When I asked if she planned to keep in touch with him by correspondence during the winter she indicated she could not because they had never exchanged last names or addresses. Is this true closeness?

In contrast to the members of this group who seek but never find real closeness are those who do find closeness in sexual behavior that involves a meaningful relationship with the person with whom they share the experience. Though in some ways this would seem to indicate sexual maturity, what is absent is the realness of true heterosexuality. The girls in this group find it unimportant whether they have an orgasm. This, of course, is not so true with the boys because of the fear of manifesting a masculine inadequacy either to others or to themselves. However, both the boy and the girl stress not the sexual gratification per se, but rather the feeling of deep closeness, experienced through the sexual act, and the happiness this brings.

A very interesting example of the use of sex as a way to experience closeness was manifested by a young couple, the boy a patient of mine. He repeatedly stressed the value of their mutual sexuality, emphasizing the sense of closeness it provided for both of them. They finally decided to marry. With this decision they also decided they would have no further sexual experiences until marriage. Their primary gratification from that time on was in mutually planning for the present, their marriage, and the future. The boy reported a discussion that he and his fiancee had the night prior to a therapy hour. They had both agreed that they had never felt as close as they had since the day they decided to marry. Neither of them had had any impulse to have intercourse; there were too many other things with which they were mutually occupied. What this attitude foreshadowed for their sexual adjustment after marriage was, of course, problematical. I did receive one letter from him after they had settled down to married life in a new community. He indicated he hoped it was just a passing phase, but in spite of their happiness together they were not often sexually interested in each other. The aspect that I wish to stress is that the primary goal for both these young people prior to marriage was to be close to someone; they had never experienced that before. Yet from the family history it would appear that both these young people had had a relatively normal childhood, with both of them reared by parents who did care about their children.

The members of the third group are those adolescents who wish to escape. Instead of feeling challenged by the possibility of utilizing their adolescent understanding to modify the world, they have no confidence that they can do so. It is possible to identify with them and say, "Well, who thinks it can be changed?" But why are adolescents oriented this way? The adolescent in the past typically felt that he knew the answers and in the future would make those answers effective. Then the relatively healthy adolescent faced with dissatisfactions in the current situation, particularly if the dissatisfaction was in the broad abstractions of the social world, believed that adults had been stupid and that he and his friends alone had the solutions that, once they had an opportunity, they would put into effect.

Currently, certain members of this third group do not accept that

129

challenge, or else do not believe in their ability to meet such a challenge. Instead they escape from the real world into a world that does not challenge them but rather offers gratification without effort. Many of them have superior intelligence, are creative, sensitive, and within the limitations of their experience capable of formulating new solutions to old problems. They abandon educational goals because the institution does not teach them the way they want to be taught; to learn beyond what is taught they consider requires too much effort. There is a tragic validity to their castigation of the educational system, but if the system will not modify, their retribution is not to be educated. They drop out of the social world, a world that certainly has real disadvantages but also positive values. They see no hope, or experience no wish to remove the disadvantages or enrich the positive aspects. Instead they live on the desert or in a cave either within a big city or in the mountains, often with their materialistically oriented and therefore subhuman parents providing the funds that prevent starvation. They may or may not use drugs.

Others of the group, even though they remain physically a part of their home and school, use drugs. They become dependent on drugs not through addiction or even habituation, but rather with a specific goal in mind—that of escaping into a fantasy world rather than living within the limitations of the real world. They avoid what is faced by other adolescents who, while protesting, endure reality because of the anticipation that eventually the world will change, an event that will occur when adolescent dreams of today become the reality of life tomorrow. Certain users of drugs accept the philosophy that parents or the Establishment are to blame. Because parents are biological necessities, and the Establishment controls today, there is nothing to do but drop out of the current world and live in the artificially induced state drugs provide.

Parenthetically it is interesting to speculate whether the Establishment has not become the symbol of the omnipotent father who, according to Freud, in the past became God as the child recognized the clay feet of his real father. It is difficult to carry on the child-father battle with a God; he is feared but loved. The Establishment furnishes a father figure who is unlovable and hostile or crippling. It is easier to fight an omnipotent, omnipresent father symbol whose clay feet are always visible and toward whom one can avoid the ambivalence that cannot be avoided toward the real father, or God. The longing to be loved by the father is not consciously experienced in the relationship with the Establishment.

Is it possible that certain members of these three groups of adolescents are manifesting an understandable response to their childhood past? Their rearing was dictated by a misconception of the implications of the insight that has been gained into psychological disturbances, be they the psychosis, the neurosis, personality or character disorders, or the autism and symbiotic psychosis of childhood. In broad terms, it has been assumed that such conditions are primarily the fault of neurotic parents utilizing the child as a tool of their neurosis, with an additional factor increasingly being introduced related to the inherent ego potential of the child. There has been a response to the knowledge of the etiological factors of such conditions, which would have a parallel if, when the cause of the symptoms of diabetes was recognized and insulin given to alleviate those symptoms, it had been advised that *all* children be given insulin. Not all children have diabetes, nor are all parents neurotic!

For some time our culture has been proud that our children are reared in a child-centered world. The behavior of many parents, in large part because of advice they have been given, has implied that the only reason for adults existing is to make sure that children have a truly child-centered world. Though there is a sound basis for flexibility in the feeding schedule for the small infant the implication of demand feeding, a current popular concept, is that what the infant wants must be immediately gratified, an attitude that remains one of the major pillars of child-rearing long after physiological idiosyncrasies are no longer dominant. There is minimal recognition that the child grows through wise frustration as well as the avoidance of arbitrary frustration.

There are apparently sound reasons for providing a child-centered milieu for a child who as a result of inability to handle certain deprivations manifests signs of psychological disturbance, sound reasons until the symptoms disappear. Is it valid however to assume that, because the damaged child requires such a corrective experience, all individuals through their entire childhood should find that they need not explore to find happiness, but rather that it will be served to them on a silver platter by a slavish waiter-parent who anxiously seeks assurance that his services are satisfactory to the child? Are we now, perhaps, in some situations, facing the consequences of the failure to understand the real needs of a child, which if met will help him mature to a true adulthood?

Initially I became aware of these questions not through work with adolescents, but rather with adults who were either contemplating divorce, were already divorced, or had been divorced and were planning a new marriage. By no means do I wish to imply that I have found the universal cause for divorces. But there is an aspect to divorce at the present time that, though it was present in some instances in the past, has become much more frequent. The explanation for the divorce, succinctly stated, is "My marital partner does not make me happy." This does not mean that the marital partner is an alcoholic, is unfaithful, is promiscuous, fails (if a man) to fulfill his basic responsibilities of supporting the family or (if a woman) to maintain the home and take care of the children. It is much less limited than that. The one definitive statement that people involved make is that they are (or were) not happy. They want (or wanted) to get out of the marriage, with no implication that either one wants (or wanted) to work at the marriage to see whether they could find mutual enjoyment in it.

One woman's chief complaint about her husband was that he did not pick up his clothes and put them in the dirty clothes chute. When I asked her if that was really so catastrophic, would it really be too much work to pick them up herself, her answer was, "Why should I live the rest of my life with a man who won't pick up his own clothes?" I will grant that this women was an unusually rabid battle-ax; I felt that if her husband could not even revolt against her by not picking up his clothes he was well out of the marriage. But this example is a caricature of the type of complaints that I hear repeatedly from those seeking divorce, or from those who are already divorced, with little or no evidence that they have tried, before seeking the divorce route, to share the responsibility of preserving the marriage. In some instances they have sought marriage counseling, but soon abandoned that approach because it did not result in the other partner changing. They act like the small child living in a child-centered world in which the entire implication is that it is the responsibility of others to make him happy.

In a child-centered world the assumption by adults is that the child will be damaged psychologically if he is not provided a world in which he is happy. The child's needs are paramount and must be met by others, not by his own initiative, let alone his own creative imagination. If he is bored, activities must be provided to alleviate his boredom. If he does not like the food offered at the family meal and must be coaxed to eat it, other food that he does like should be provided. It is the child's right to be happy, and the parents obligation to provide a ready means for that happiness.

The historically typical self-centeredness of the adolescent is now flavored by the expectation that his child-centered world of yesterday should continue as his right. If he does not like the peas and carrots served as part of his current psychological dinner he wants to pull the tablecloth off and destroy the entire dinner, rather than enjoy what he does like about the meal, while loudly protesting and expounding that when he can plan his own meals he will not serve peas and carrots, but lima beans. The implication in much of the anger of this group is that they have been promised they can always have what they want and now they are refused.

Fred's was a typical response. He had reached driving age. He refused the second-hand car that his parents offered to him, demanding a new sports car. His father had suffered financial reverses and realistically could not afford to purchase the car his son wanted. When I discussed the reality with Fred his comment was, "Dad's financial difficulties are his problem. He promised me a sports car when I was sixteen. He *owes* the car to me." Fred has been reared in a child-centered world.

The child-centered world has resulted possibly in another fallacy. One of the most essential components of a happy childhood is the child's confidence that he is loved. The biological need for care during the neonatal period is the anlage of the psychological need to feel loved. It has been assumed that from this need to be loved develops later a capacity to love others. Is this necessarily the pathway toward a mature capacity to fuse the desire to be loved and to love in return? In a previous work (Josselyn, 1968) I have suggested that not only is there the biological anlage of a psychological need to be loved, but there is also a biological response of turning outward for need gratification which is the anlage of a later response of a need to love. Is it possible that in our present theory of child-rearing the child's longing to love is not given sufficient nutriment to develop into a need to find a real area of gratification?

To document this would obviously require an intensive study of very subtle manifestations, but there is a suggestion in an example which may seem too superficial. The present-day parent freely gives toys. The affluence of the society is blamed for this; the parent believes that giving a toy to the child is indicative of his love for the child. It often is; but it is not always a compensatory means of handling the guilt over not loving the child sufficiently. If the toy is broken, the toy is replaced. The child is not encouraged to love the toy, let alone the giver of the toy. The toy, to the child, is his right; its ready replacement encourages the child not to love the toy. Parents say to the child crying over a broken toy, "Don't cry. We'll get you another one." The child is deprived of the experience of mourning for something lovable.

Not only is the child not encouraged to love, but the parents, possibly by their eagerness to show love for the child without anticipating any reciprocal response, do not foster any inherent potential of the child to love. They, to cite a familiar example, often say to the misbehaving child, "I love you; I just don't like the act." Actually this is usually an insincere statement; the parent does not love the part of the child that misbehaved. If parents repeatedly separate the act and the child in their response, is it surprising that the more sophisticated adolescent says that his associate is doing his Thing and has a right to do so, even if the Thing is using heroin, without recognizing that to be loved one must be lovable, and love for another is expressed in part by concern for the latter's welfare?

There is another aspect of the concept of the value of mutual love that is possibly important; it involves a peculiar contradiction in the current theory of optimum child development. Whatever the source of a capacity to love may be, the critical time for its development is probably during the developmental phase when the child is becoming aware of his own individuality and the symbiotic tie, as formulated by Mahler (1965) and others, is beginning to disintegrate. It would seem justified to postulate that during this period the child gradually experiences being loved as an individual and also being aware of love for someone separate from himself. How quickly this interrelatedness becomes established is speculative.

In the current culture there is an urgency to physically separate the mother and the child. Day care centers for the lower economic group and nursery schools for the more affluent society are encouraged. Two contradictory messages are promulgated by the same school of thought. The primary relationship, the beginning of all meaningful relationships, is hypothesized as having roots in the child-mother relationship, with expansion to others of the family group. On the other hand, it is strongly urged that as soon as the child is toilet trained the child should be separated from the mother and find substitutes. Is it not possible that this fosters the establishment of secondary, transient relationships before the primary and in-depth relationships are well crystallized? At present the primary relationship is treated as a dangerous form of medication; it is necessary during the acute infection of infancy, but once the disease shows signs of lessening its effect, it is essential that the drug be stopped.

The wish for closeness in the adolescent implies something quite different from what is offered in a pure and simple child-centered world. I suspect that many adolescents of today have never really experienced

closeness to their parents. Closeness is the result of a mutual interchange in which the gratification from loving is equal to the gratification
of being loved. The longing for closeness in some may indicate that a
frustration of a basic need to love has led to a hunger, the relief of
which is sought by trying nonnutritional sawdust, or trying substitutes
that are inadequately nutritional, chosen because of lack of knowledge
based on early experiences. They use drugs to artificially create closeness
because they do not know how to find it in reality; they use sexuality as
a means of regressing to the infantile experience of closeness through
bodily contact.

The third group of adolescents, those wanting to escape, are possibly
also responding to a childhood experienced in a child-centered world.
The current attitude is that the child's needs must be met by avoiding a
challenging situation for him. If he does not like his teacher he is
changed to another classroom. If he is afraid at night someone sleeps
with him. If he has difficulty learning to read a tutor is provided whose
responsibility is to teach him to read. I would put in the same category
the pattern of our educational system at present. When the child begins
to study history, for example, he is not challenged to understand history, he is drilled in remembering the details of history. A person who
is an enthusiast for, and supposedly a specialist in, sex education told
me with a great deal of pride that the program he has organized starts
now in kindergarten, and he hopes to get it into the nursery schools. He
wishes the child to be given sexual information that is just a step beyond where one would expect the child's curiosity to be. In other words,
one should not wait for a child to ask a question; one should know at
what age it is anticipated he will ask the question and be sure that prior
to that age he is already being given the answer.

Examples I have given in the last paragraph are obviously not valid
as generalizations. There are some children who should have their class-
rooms changed; there are those who, because of night terrors, should
have someone sleep with them. Certainly the child with a reading disability needs the help of a tutor who knows special techniques for over-
coming reading handicaps. Certainly children who fear their sexual
curiosity should be given knowledge they have not sought. Too often,
when any of these steps is taken it is taken with the philosophical approach that the child should not be asked to take part in the necessary
adaptation; the immediate situation must be remedied so that he will
not have to face any challenge in it. This same attitude is observable in
some of our adolescents who are using drugs. They either insist they

135

should not be expected to make an effort, or else their self-concept includes the conviction that they are incapable of succeeding if they did make an effort to find in reality what they are seeking in their use of drugs.

A semihumorous, if not so tragic, example is the very artistically talented girl who was describing to me the glorious pictures she saw during a psychedelic trip, pictures that were primarily a vivid blending of colors. We were standing where we could see a rather unusually brilliant sunset and I commented that it seemed to me she was describing what we could see then in the west. Her answer was,

> I get your point, but you know usually I'd have to make some effort to find things that are beautiful. I might have to drive out to the desert, for instance, to see a sunset. Why bother when LSD will give it to me whenever I want it without waiting until the sun sets and without having to go to look for it? After all, I've never had a bad trip with LSD, but imagine going out to the desert and seeing nothing but a big yellow ball going down over the horizon.

I commented that the desert is surrounded by colorful mountains; even if the sun is just a round yellow ball, the shadows on the mountains offer a kaleidoscopic panorama. Her answer was, "Yes, but you can't lie down and have that panorama before you; you have to look around. You don't have to move with LSD."

Another adolescent, very talented in music, justified his former use of LSD on the basis that he had never appreciated Bach until he took LSD; now Bach was one of his favorite composers. When I questioned whether he had ever had a teacher who helped him to see the beauty of Bach's music, his answer was, "No, my teacher always praised me for how well I played. He never shared with me his enjoyment of music."

The patient who did not want to make the effort to see a sunset felt all life's pleasures should be provided to her on a silver platter that someone else would hold. The one who learned to love Bach under LSD had had an unstimulating childhood, also served on a silver platter.

Not all individual adolescents who are found in one of these groups, or a combination of the three groups, had a childhood that was provided by well-intentioned parents striving to make their child's life easy by creating a child-centered world. Many of the members of these groups did. Also, many from such a milieu have handled the crisis of adolescence without manifest difficulty, not because their childhood was so ideal, but possibly because they have been able to overcome the handicap created by those years. Many adolescents of today appear to

136

be ill equipped emotionally to relate to a world other than that of which they are the center; they are hungry for closeness and yet have difficulty in finding it; they are frightened about the world they are in because they do not believe they can meet, without chaos, the challenges it presents.

I am confident that a large majority of today's adolescents will weather the turmoil and contribute to the evolution of a better world than the one they entered. I have not discussed, but I realize that today's real world is confusing and disturbing to adults; little wonder it is to adolescents. Is it possible, however, that the tasks the adolescents face are more difficult for them than would be inevitable, more difficult because they were reared in a child-centered world rather than in a world dedicated to the proposition that the validity of childhood is as preparation for a rich adulthood?

Those of us who strive to understand the adolescent, where he has been and where he is going, have a contribution to make to the understanding of the effect of child-rearing practices on the modes of seeking and on the final configuration of adulthood. As therapists it is important that we not only recognize the reality, both internal and external, in which the adolescent is struggling to find himself and striving to change so it will comply more with his idealism; it is equally important to recognize that he is also, in some instances, seeking to find fulfillment of basic needs and inherent potentials that were not fulfilled in childhood.

We adults should listen to the adolescent's current ideas and strivings. By so listening we can learn about the individual adolescent's struggles to find an answer to the multiple problems pressing on him. As he reveals these problems and the tentative solutions he envisions, we will be protected from becoming static in our thinking!

We, with our expertise, should be acutely attuned to the individual adolescent's past milieu, not just share with him our negativism toward the adult world. Our ultimate goals and his may appear identical; our empathic response should not indiscriminately encompass his current or projected method of attaining those goals. The method he advocates may not be determined so much by his drive to attain the goal because it is a response to earlier emotional deprivation. If we, as we empathize with the adolescent, lose sight of our responsibility as therapists and instead accept uncritically his strategy for reaching his goal, we may strengthen destructive impulses and encourage him to strive for a goal that, masked by idealistic formulations, is in actuality that of correcting egocentrically the defects of his childhood maturational steps. The further evolution of our society will not come through adults who as adolescents failed to gain a perspective beyond that offered by their own idiosyncratic needs; as therapists and as interpreters of adolescence we can encourage either maturation beyond or fixation at the egocentric level.

Our country as never before in its history is caught in a vicious circle. The responses of the adolescent group have created extreme anxiety among many adults, resulting in hysterical deafness and emotionally charged attempts to stifle the younger group. The latter response has created a degree of frustration in the young, which has stimulated emotional striking out against a basic philosophy as it is imperfectly expressed in the social structure. The consequences will be that the vicious circle either will be chained down to a static state or will explode into anarchistic lack of any structure. We therapists, of all people, should as students of the adolescent age be able to find the means and urge approaches by which to reconvert the vicious circle back to its former spiral path of which the apex is progressive growth from its base.

NOTE

1. The term "maturation" in this context connotes the attainment of a "ripe" stage, the origin of the word according to *Webster's* (1969). Development manifests the maturational process but is affected by external circumstances that may result in deformity or optimum fulfillment of the inherent maturational potential. Child-rearing practices, social structures, and events beyond control affect the way in which the inherent maturational process develops to be "ripened" into adulthood.

REFERENCES

Blos, P. (1962). On adolescence: A psychoanalytic interpretation. New York: The Free Press.
Erikson, E. H. (1968). Identity: Youth and crisis. New York: Norton.
Deutsch, H. (1967). Selected problems of adolescence. New York: International Universities Press.
Josselyn, I. M. (1968). How many basic drives? Smith College Studies in Social Work, 39:1–19.
Mahler, M. (1965). On the significance of the normal separation-individuation phase: With reference to research in symbiotic child psychosis. In M. Schur, ed., Drives, Affects, Behavior. New York: International Universities Press. 2:161–169.
Webster's Third New International Dictionary. (1969). Springfield, Mass.: Merriam.

9] ON THE NATURE
OF MALE ADOLESCENT
REBELLION

BRAHM BAITTLE AND DANIEL OFFER

The aim of this chapter is to clarify and elucidate the concept of adolescent rebellion in boys. At first glance, it might be thought that this is a well-worn topic in the literature of the psychology of adolescence. Though this is true for current social psychology, we were unable to find much discussion in the psychiatric literature and even less in the psychoanalytic. Sigmund Freud hardly mentions the term, and Peter Blos' (1962) recent book does not have the words in the index, though he does discuss it several times in his text. This is owing, no doubt, to the fact that rebellion usually denotes overt behavior and does not describe an intrapsychic state. Yet rebellious feelings to internalized parental images must accompany rebellious acts toward the real parents. Furthermore, it is more than likely that this specific form of aggression in adolescents is not without conflict. It is further assumed that there is not one but a variety of intrapsychic processes that accompany overt rebellious acts and that these processes arise at different stages of psychic development. It is the task of this chapter to explore some of the inner meanings of adolescent rebellion and to clarify them as much as possible from a dynamic point of view. Attention will be paid to whether normal adolescent rebellion exists, and if so, what functions it serves.

According to *Webster's* (1956), rebellion is defined as "open resistance to, or defiance of, any authority." The most important authorities to the adolescent are, of course, his parents, though other authority figures are included in his battles.

Much of the recent social science literature suggests that adolescent rebellion implies overthrow of parental values. We maintain that adolescent rebellion exists and is significant for the teenager independently of whether parental values are accepted or rejected. In particular, we shall submit evidence that the normal adolescent can engage in meaningful rebellious behavior and still embrace his parents' values.

In a similar fashion, the concept of rebellion has to be distinguished from the concept of emancipation from the parents. In tracing the relationship between the two we shall suggest that the main function of rebellion, in the more or less normal adolescent, is to achieve an initial step in the process of emancipation from the parents. However, not all adolescent rebellion is in the service of emancipation. The concept of emancipation is not inherent in rebellion, though it is often associated with it. We think clarification will be served if the definition of rebellion is kept strictly to the phenomenon of open resistance and defiance of any authority. With the establishment of this definition of rebellion, some clarity may be brought to the literature. Such questions as the relative frequency of rebellion in different generations of adolescents and the healthiness or pathology of rebellion may be more easily and accurately answered when the definition is not complicated with the questions of values and emancipation. This, of course, has been known for a long time, but confusion in some of the recent literature abounds (Coleman, 1961; Davis, 1940; Westley, 1958).

For the purposes of this chapter we will present data from three sources: (1) the normal adolescent project conducted at Michael Reese Hospital by Daniel Offer, (2) the adolescent delinquency project conducted at the Institute for Juvenile Research by Brahm Baittle,[1] and (3) intensive psychotherapy of disturbed adolescents conducted by both authors.

For the normal adolescent project the aim was to select as typical a group as possible. We were, therefore, not interested in asking for volunteers; we made the selection. We developed a self-image questionnaire based on our clinical knowledge of adolescents and the findings of major investigators in the field (Offer and Sabshin, 1963). Utilizing this questionnaire as a screening device we selected, during the fall of 1962, typical middle-class adolescent students from a total sample of the entering freshmen boys in two local suburban high schools. Seventy-three students were studied for seven years. Each subject had ten psychiatric interviews, Rorschach and Thematic Apperception Tests, and all parents were interviewed at least once. We also have follow-up questionnaires on the parents and the students who moved out of the area. In addition, the school records (including teachers' ratings) were available to us.[2]

The adolescent delinquency project consisted of an interdisciplinary study of a moderately delinquent gang in a midwestern urban ethnic working-class community. This study covered a four-year span of the adolescent period of boys ranging from thirteen years to eighteen years of age (Baittle, 1961; Baittle and Kobrin, 1964; Kobrin, 1961). The psychiatric workup consisted of one to five standard psychiatric interviews with each boy, one or more interviews with each of his parents, and information obtained from the street worker during the course of weekly conferences over a three-year period. Several members of the group were seen in short-term psychotherapy. In addition, Rorschach tests and Thematic Apperception Tests were administered to all but one of the boys. Of the sixteen boys studied, nine were considered neurotic or borderline. The remaining seven functioned within the normal range.[3] Both of us also drew material from our intensive treatment of private patients who were disturbed adolescents.

Rebellion in Borderline and Neurotic Adolescents

The main emphasis in this chapter concerns rebellion in the normal adolescent. However, because some of our concepts are derived from the study of psychopathology, accounts of rebelliousness in borderline and neurotic adolescents will precede the description and dynamics of the normal.

BORDERLINE AND PSYCHOTIC ADOLESCENTS

In Case 1, Leonard, an adolescent in his late teens, was seen for severe emotional problems. Two years after intensive therapy began, the patient gradually became aware that he did not feel like an individual. He had always acted as if he were an extension of both parents and was engaged in a constant struggle to prove that he had a mind of his own. A stubborn negativism manifested itself, always to his disadvantage. His parents, highly intellectual but chronically dissatisfied with their own achievements, poured all their frustrated longings on him and exerted much pressure for high intellectual achievement. The patient responded to this by dropping out of high school for a short time a few months before he began therapy. He did go back, finally graduated, but did not enter college as his parents wished him to do. Two years later, he gradually began to realize he felt in danger of being engulfed by his parents, particularly by his father, and at this time was able to enter college. He constantly complained, with some justification, that his father was trying to run his college life for him. As an example, his father talked with his advisers before the patient did, telling them of the patient's wishes and problems, so that when the patient saw the adviser himself, everything he had to say was already known. Leonard began to realize that he contributed to this himself in many ways; for example, he told his father every move he was going to make, thus provoking him to take some action. Next, he decided not to take courses he thought his father had an investment in, even though he was interested in them himself. A short time later he considered eventually studying for a business career, after some realistic appraisal of the matter. However, the chief reason for this move was that his father, a minister, had no interest whatsoever in business. All the same, Leonard said he would not tell his father about his business ambitions lest his father back him up, in which case he would be unable to go through with it. It was suggested to him that he was afraid that if his father went along with his decision he would not know whether it was really his decision or his father's. To maintain his own integrity he could only do the opposite of what his father wished, at the expense of his own desires. Leonard laughed in agreement. During the next session, he told me in a truculent manner that he had an insight about something he did the day before, but did not want to tell me about it. He was afraid that would be "just what you would say," and this would rob him of the feeling that he had come on this insight independently. He could only see it as my interpretation.

A similar situation existed in a thirty-three year old man, a borderline character. During the initial interview he told the therapist he had wanted to obtain psychotherapy ten years earlier because of problems in college. Why he had procrastinated for a decade was not clear. After three years of therapy, he confided that his mother also wanted him to have treatment and pushed him in her usual intrusive way. The patient would not go, in defiance of his mother. He could only see treatment as his mother's wish. This so-called rebellious act gave him a feeling of independence. He finally realized that this feeling of independence was spurious. He could not act on his own wish, and in avoiding therapy, he maintained his symbiotic attachment to his mother. In these cases, rebellious behavior, which on the surface appears to be in the service of adolescent rebellion, really functions as a desperate attempt to protect some semblance of individuation in a patient struggling with a symbiotic relationship.

Adolescent rebellion may be a presenting symptom in many different types of borderline conditions, or it may be a manifestation of incipient psychosis. Experiences in a psychiatric residency program in a community setting with the aim of juvenile delinquency prevention (Baittle, 1968) as well as in other community programs, has shown that this can occur with significant frequency. For example, in community psychiatry consultations, teachers, recreation workers, and clergy will describe what they term rebellious behavior in adolescent boys, some of whom, on further examination, prove to be grossly disturbed. Very often it is difficult to convince workers who ask for psychiatric consultation that the boy they refer is psychotic or borderline, and not just engaged in the usual adolescent rebellion. This is especially true in cases of paranoid characters who rationalize well. Such a teenager may be able to convince a sympathetic adult worker that he is engaged in a just cause against the forces of evil in society, especially when the worker shares the same values and ideology. However, in these cases, aggression is extremely intense and precariously controlled, or it may become out of control. In more severe cases, bizarre types of rebellion may augur an acute paranoid psychotic break. Needless to say, the diagnostic category does not imply an evaluation of the social values or ideology that may be espoused.

NEUROTIC ADOLESCENTS

Rebelliousness also occurs in adolescents with neurotic character disorders. It is characterized by chronic nagging and fighting with and defiance of both parents. Often all three are involved in a triangular situation. This behavior begins—not in adolescence—but before the age of five. It soon spreads beyond the family to the school and other authority figures. The child is described by his parents as being always disobedient, though there may be some change during the early grade school years. However, in spite of this behavior, signs of passivity and dependency are readily discernible. These youngsters are often inextricably involved with their parents in their struggles with them, and show very little ability to become even moderately detached from them. They tend to tag along, or even cling to adult teachers or youth workers that they like. Boys may take very quick offense at any threat to their masculinity. Rebelliousness, or the underlying pathology behind it, continues to be a major problem beyond adolescence. In some, rebellious behavior remains as a character trait throughout adulthood. This type of chronic adolescent behavior is not infrequent. However, more often, as in the following case, neurotic rebellious behavior may fade out in middle or late adolescence, and the underlying conflicts about passivity and femininity may be exposed. Other forms of masculine protest may take its place, or the underlying passivity may become the predominant manifest personality characteristic.

Case 2: Danny was the leader of a moderately delinquent gang (Baittle, 1961; Baittle and Kobrin, 1964) from the age of thirteen to fifteen. Besides now leading his group in exciting delinquent activities, since the age of three or four, he was openly defiant of, and rebellious to, both his parents and to authority figures outside his family. He would flagrantly disobey his parents, refuse to do the family chores, come home late at night, and be rude and openly contemptuous of his father, whom he grossly devalued as a weak, ineffectual man. He was in constant battle with his teachers, refused to study to the extent that he was in constant danger of failing in high school, though he had above average intelligence. When his gang rebelled against his manipulative and sadistic behavior, they voted him out of office in a sudden and unexpected coup. Within a few months a change was noted in his manifest personality. He lost his aggressive, arrogant stance and became phobic. He could only go out in the streets with considerable fear and discomfort. In particular, he could not face his former male friends, and even avoided them by walking on the other side of the street when they approached. He feared that he was not a "man" and was worried that his friends would consider him a homosexual. Still he was uneasy about going steady with his girlfriend because he would become "hooked" to her. At the same time, he complained that his mother did not really understand or love him enough. All this was said with amazement and humiliation which was in such contrast to his previous concept of himself as a fearless, strong, confident, tough, masculine leader of his gang.

Rebellion in Normal Adolescents

Rebellious behavior was found in practically all teenagers, including normals, who participated in our research projects. In all our subjects, particularly in the normal boys, rebellion manifested itself most clearly and intensely during early adolescence, at twelve and thirteen years of age, and continued with decreasing intensity throughout adolescence. The subjects described themselves as "getting into fights with our parents" for seemingly small and insignificant issues. The teenagers would break the rules of the house constantly. For example, they would refuse to clean up their rooms and balk when it was their turn to do chores. They would go out with the wrong crowd and would come home late. Arguments over the car, clothes, and hair styles were common. In the normal research group, teenaged boys did not go to church as often as their parents did. Rebellious behavior carried over to schoolteachers, agency workers, and other significant adults. At times it led to overt delinquent behavior aimed at the society at large. The rebelliousness was often characterized by high spirits, humor, verve, versatility, and charm. The above observations were confirmed by interviews with parents and teachers and by the observations of the street worker in the delinquency research.

Follow-up information confirms what is known through the treatment of adults concerning the fate of adolescent rebellion in normal adolescents. Rebelliousness declines in intensity and frequency throughout adolescence and for all practical purposes mostly disappears in young adult life as true independence emerges.

Some qualities of adolescent rebellion require emphasis. For example, when an adolescent rebelled, he often expressed his intentions in a manner resembling negation. He defined what he did in terms of what his parents did not want him to do. If his parents wanted him to turn off the radio and study, this would be the precise time to keep the radio on and claim he could not study. If they wanted him to buy new clothes, the old ones were good enough. Another quality of normal adolescent rebellion concerns the nature and content of the controversies involved. As has been seen, the rebellion in normals is characterized by in-fighting with parents and schoolteachers, more or less intense at different times and occasions, over issues that seemed small or nondramatic. There were usually no great pitched battles over crucial or world-shaking issues. However, they seemed significant both to the teenagers and his parents. In the normal adolescent study, the overwhelming majority of the parents said this was the most difficult time they had in raising their children. However, there was much evidence that the teenagers maintained the same middle-class values as their parents. They had the same class biases, claimed allegiance to the same religious de-

145

nominations as their parents, and intended to follow in the footsteps of their father's occupations, either the same or class-related ones.

Case 3, taken from the normal adolescent study, illustrates some of the issues we have been discussing: Lester was thirteen years old when his parents moved to the suburbs from the city. He was a short, stocky boy, eager to please the interviewer and proud of his athletic achievements. One major reason for the move was to allow Lester to benefit from the better school system in the suburbs. Lester did not see the move in a similar perspective. He was now far away from his friends and was not yet part of the group in his new environment. He missed his old friends and went back to the old neighborhood (almost an hour away by public transportation) whenever he could. His performance in school was poorer than before, and though he was passing all his subjects his parents were concerned with his academic standing. When his parents found out about his trips to the old neighborhood they strictly forbade it. Nonetheless, Lester, who was now fourteen years old, continued to go. A few months later he got into a serious physical fight with another member of the old clique who made fun of his small size. The fight led to serious injury to the other boy, and the fight had to be broken up by the police. The police told Lester that they would not inform the parents of the incident if there would be no recurrence and he would "stay out of trouble." Up to the present, the parents are not aware of this particular incident. Lester learned from his experience and was motivated after the above incident to drop his old friends and develop more appropriate friendships in his new environment. The rebellion was over.

The gang's behavior followed much the same pattern as that of the normal adolescent group. For example, they, too, maintained the same values as their parents. However, the relationship between the adherence to parental values and rebellion against the parents became clearer in our work with them. During the course of data-gathering for other purposes, three questions were asked in an interview to determine at what age a boy felt he could make decisions independent of his parents in respect to (1) leaving school and going to work, (2) time at which he might return home in the evening, and (3) choice of friends when his parents disapproved of them. The gang members were asked to indicate any age between twelve and eighteen. In regard to the first two questions, all adolescents believed that no boy under sixteen is grown up enough to overrule a parent's decision on these matters if they disagreed with their wishes. Most felt that by the time he reached eighteen a boy would have the right to insist on his wishes on these issues, but some even thought eighteen was too young. One boy, for example, who already quit school some months before he was given the questionnaire at age seventeen, gave the opinion that an eighteen-year-old should not quit school if his parents did not want him to. However, most felt more independent of their parent's wishes and values as to choice of friends, and if there were a conflict, slightly more than half said a boy should go against his parents wishes over this issue by the age of fourteen. One boy, when asked what a boy should do at twelve, replied, "Well, he probably would pal around with them, but I don't think he should. He should listen to his parents when he's that young." The remainder cited sixteen and eighteen as appropriate ages to assert one's choice of friends. However, in the same interview most of these boys admitted to fighting from time to time with their parents over these same issues. The group worker's informal contacts and psychiatric interviews indicated that conflict occurred regularly and routinely, and direct observations by the worker and interviews with the parents made it clear that they disobeyed their parents, particularly during the earlier years.

In both studies, no subject was found who did not have some pattern of adolescent rebellious behavior (see Spiegel, 1958).

Adolescent Rebellion and the Family

The adolescents belonging to the delinquent gang rebelled against both parents. In the normal adolescent study, rebellious behavior was directed mostly toward the mother. This may be because the fathers tended to be more remote, not so often at home, and when at home, passive in respect to the mother. The administering of discipline emphatically was the mother's task. There was evidence that rebellious behavior toward the mother was libidinized. This was confirmed by psychological tests. It is also possible that rebellion against the father was not reported so easily as that against the mother.

In the delinquency project, the parents of the normal adolescent boys, especially the father, dealt with rebellion in their children with considerable firmness. Mothers tended to be somewhat more permissive, but they did not encourage delinquent behavior either consciously or unconsciously as far as we could tell. Not so the mothers of the adolescents who manifested a neurotic type of rebellion. They were usually more

147

aggressive than the father and, in addition, depreciated him. The rebellion and delinquency of the sons were often sources of unconscious gratification to these powerful, but masochistic, mothers. For instance, it was not unusual for mothers in this small subgroup to rant and rave over the behavior of their sons, then feel guilty and proceed to let the boys get away with murder. They would then complain that their sons made life miserable for them and were uncontrollable. They blamed the father for not exercising discipline, which was usually true, because these fathers were passive and saw themselves as weak, helpless, depreciated persons. Yet when they occasionally took some disciplinary action, the mothers opposed the fathers, took the boys' side, and won. In one case, by contrast, a father subtly provoked his son's rebelliousness and delinquency by denying that it was serious. He boasted about his own rebelliousness as a teenager, claiming that his son could never achieve the same reputation that he had in his youth.

Social Phenomena

Observations in the delinquency gang study revealed that patterns of conformity were more important than rebelliousness in peer relationships. This statement needs some modification. As is usual, there were subgroups of three to five people, that is, cliques, within the gang of sixteen members. It was not unusual for cliques of lower status to rebel against higher status cliques. The gang members as a rule were good followers. However, if a leader became overbearing and too arrogant and manipulative, the gang was able to rebel successfully and oust him, as they did with Danny in Case 2.

Social institutions, such as the schools, were willing to permit adolescent rebellion within certain limits. An example of this was found in the normal adolescent project. During high school, rebellion tended to take on a more systematized and institutionalized form. In the two high schools 50 percent of the students were active smokers at any one time. They wanted to smoke during the lunch hour, but in contrast to the teachers, the students had no lounge where this was permitted. Therefore, they developed the following arrangement in which they did not really defy the rules openly, and yet did not accept them either. In one of the high schools the students crossed the street, stood within half a block of the school and smoked during their lunch hour. In the second high school many students smoked in the bathroom while one of their peers watched for the teacher on patrol that particular day. When the teacher came near the bathroom the student would whistle a particular tune and all the cigarettes would be flushed down the toilet. The teacher would go into the washroom, which was, of course, full of smoke, but he could not catch any of the students smoking. He then simply asked all of them to leave the bathroom. This was, of course, repeated many times each day. Such accommodations seem to be passed down to the next generation of adolescents and a tradition developed.

Some Concepts Concerning Adolescent Rebellion

In this theoretical section of the chapter, we shall discuss the following topics: (1) a conceptual framework for the classification of adolescent rebellion, (2) the frequency and quality of adolescent rebellion and its relationship to societal values, (3) psychodynamics and developmental stages leading to adolescent rebellion, (4) the role of the family, and (5) some aspects of the role of the social order in adolescent rebellion.

A CONCEPTUAL FRAMEWORK FOR THE CLASSIFICATION OF ADOLESCENT REBELLION

In the introduction to this chapter, it was implied that there are many motives behind adolescent rebellion. It is expected that this type of behavior is overdetermined and that the inner meanings of the same act differ or assume different emphases in each individual. Our data have clearly shown that rebellious acts were performed by adolescents who were more or less normal and by boys with all types of psychopathology, thus lending support to the concept that this behavior has multiple meanings and functions. Thus, it is germane to attempt to classify the meanings of rebellious acts and to relate them to other aspects of the adolescents' psychic functioning, such as developmental factors, psychic structure, object relations and psychodynamics, including the presence or absence of psychopathology.

The phenotype, adolescent rebellion, is the behavioral manifestation of many conscious and unconscious wishes, anxiety, and defenses against the anxiety. However, it is suggested that rebellion conceptualized in terms of object relations lends itself most easily to classification and ordering. Rebellion is directed to authoritative external objects.

149

These reflect desires, wishes, and reactions to these wishes directed to internalized objects. Because psychoanalytic theory has made attempts to delineate categories of object relations based on developmental levels (see A. Freud, 1963), it should be feasible to classify rebellion if we can correlate it to different stages in the development of object relations. A similar type of conceptualization has been applied by Baittle (1970) to the field of juvenile delinquency.

Object relations in the normal adolescent are characterized by a loosening and discarding of ties to infantile incestuous objects and by finding and cathecting new external objects outside the family. Thus, rebellion in the normal adolescent is adaptive, rather than defensive, and is mainly in the service of emancipation from the incestuous parental objects. In the neurotic adolescent, object relations are characteristic of oedipal and preoedipal stages of development, and we would predict rebellion in these adolescents to take on phallic, anal, or oral drive qualities or defenses against them. Object relationships in the borderline or psychotic adolescent are characterized by failure to achieve object constancy, by the predominance of need-gratifying types of object relations or of symbiotic object relationships. We would expect these qualities to color the rebellious behavior in these categories of adolescents. Thus classes of adolescent rebellion can be correlated with the (1) level of object relationship achieved and (2) gross psychopathology and normality. It follows that the more mature the stage of object relations in the teenager, the more rebellion will be in the service of emancipation. In similar fashion, we would expect as the maturity of the level of object relations increases, aggression would be more neutralized and better controlled and mastered by the ego.

Rebellion can also be correlated with the mechanisms of defense. If rebellion occurs in the normal adolescent, its defensive function would be minimal. In the normal adolescent, rebellion is a transient phenomenon and is not imbricated into the permanent character structure. To use Glover's (1950) terminology this rebellious behavior is "functional." In early adolescence, changes in the drive organization may give rise to transient conflicts and anxiety, which can be handled by temporary defenses. For example, passive feminine wishes, which are ego alien, may be stirred up at this period, and the resultant anxiety may be defended against by rebellious behavior.

In contrast, we may examine a similar conflict that results in rebellious behavior in the neurotic adolescent. Quantitatively the components of the conflict are more intense and are chronic, arising within the oedipal period. The conflict never gets adequately resolved but, for example, may be repressed and accompanied by reaction formations in latency and reappear in the regression of preadolescence. After adolescence, the conflict remains significant, even though other defenses may be now employed. Thus, the conflict is imbricated into the character structure, and rebellious behavior or substitute symptoms or character traits become a way of life. Again, to borrow from Glover (1950), we may call this characterological rebellion in contrast to "functional" rebellious behavior in the normal early adolescent.

Rebellious behavior in the adolescent who has not yet achieved object constancy may be intimately tied up with the ego disorganization and restitution seen in the psychotic and the borderline patient.

FREQUENCY AND QUALITY OF ADOLESCENT REBELLION AND ITS RELATIONSHIP TO SOCIETAL VALUES

At present, the battle against entrenched values of society and the Establishment is overt. However, this is a relatively recent phenomenon. Because very few of our subjects have been involved in this struggle, we cannot make generalizations from our groups. Yet, in spite of the current unrest, demonstrations and student riots, it is our opinion that the majority of adolescents do not actively participate in these protests. In fact, in the lower and lower middle class, nearly all adolescents accept and actively support societal and parental values.

The image of the adolescent during the late 1950's and early 1960's was quite different from the present one. The social-psychological literature described the adolescent of that decade as nonrebellious. For example, Nixon (1962) implied that because adolescents of that generation were essentially conformists in their peer groups, they were therefore not rebellious. We have also observed adolescent conformity to a marked degree in our studies. However, adolescent conformity in peer groups does not make them any less rebellious to their parents. By definition, the object of rebellious behavior is authority figures, and conforming ritualistic behavior does not rule out defiance to parents and parental substitutes. Rather, they go hand in hand. In addition, there is evidence that on occasion, adolescents also rebel against their leaders.

Another group (Keniston, 1957; Adelson, 1964; Douvan and Adelson, 1966) claims that because most adolescents of the 1950's and early 1960's generation did not rebel against entrenched and significant parental values, their rebellion was insignificant. Moreover, these writers believe that this behavior connotes complacency and a loss of autonomy or identity, terms more or less vaguely defined. We also have found that most adolescents in our investigations did not attempt to overthrow established parental values. It is true that the rebellion we have observed concerns microscopic issues that may appear trivial and unimportant to the adult. However, we emphasize that this miniature guerilla warfare has vital and significant meaning to the adolescent at this stage of his development. Though he conforms to his parents' values, his moderate rebellion over manifestly trivial issues helps him achieve emancipation and aids in the establishment of identity. Incidentally, not only do these boys share their parents' values, but they strive to acquire adult prerogatives earlier than their parents feel they should and even earlier than they feel they should. Peter Blos (1962) has described this as one type of adolescent rebellion. He also formulates another type of adolescent rebellion, that is, the adolescent who actually rejects parental values. However, these teenagers in a few years will find their own niche in society and will enter into an environment into which they can adapt. They tend to be creative people, innovators, and reformers. On the other hand, some of them become delinquents or fanatics (Blos, 1962).

PSYCHODYNAMICS AND DEVELOPMENTAL STAGES
LEADING TO ADOLESCENT REBELLION

If normal adolescent rebellion is essentially independent of acceptance or rejection of parental values, what then is its main function? As stated in the introduction, and as many others have theorized (Pearson, 1958; Blos, 1962), the main function of rebellion in the normal adolescent is to initiate and/or reinforce a process that leads to emancipation from the parents.

There are probably many ways in which rebellion functions as a means of giving up an incestuous internalized object. Blos (1962) mentions two that we can confirm in our work. During early adolescence, rebellion functions as an active opposition to passive feminine tendencies in boys. These drive derivatives are an essential part of the negative oedipus complex, which along with other oedipal phenomena, emerge once again in early adolescence. Rebellion serves as a temporary defense against these transient drives and at the same time, lends force and direction to the adolescent's attempt to loosen his ties to the oedipal father representation. Here rebellion is concomitant with a cathectic shift that normally occurs during this phase of development.

In decathecting the parental internalized objects the libido is deflected to the self-representation. A transient narcissistic stage develops which is closely interwoven with giving up the incestuous object on the one hand, and finding new nonincestuous objects on the other. This narcissism is manifest in many ways characteristic for adolescents. For the purposes of our discussion, the dynamics of only one outcome will be formulated. The libidinal investment in the self interferes with the boy's previous idealization of the parents; now they are no longer held in awe and may even be devalued. The adolescent becomes arrogant and rebellious, defies rules and regulations to some degree, and flouts parental authority, though, as we have seen, he respects his parent's opinion at the same time. The adolescent's rebelliousness is in the service of disengagement from the parental authority, and usually disappears, or at least diminishes in intensity when a heterosexual object is found.

The oscillation between the adolescent's idealized parent and his narcissistic rebelliousness is illustrated in the questionnaire given to the delinquent gang. It will be remembered that there is a discrepancy between what these boys say and what they actually do, a discrepancy that reflects their ambivalence and conflict. Their actions indicate rebellion, while their verbal answers to questions regarding independence of action reflect a passive dependent orientation to idealized parents (in addition, probably, to "good judgment"). In action, the adolescent says, "I know best." In talking to a sympathetic interviewer, he says "They know best." We assume he means both.

The conflict between dependency and emancipation is further demonstrated in our data, which have shown that, to some extent, the adolescent's defiant decisions are contrary to the parent's wishes, rather than based on their own positive desires. They express their intentions in a manner resembling negation (Freud, 1959). What they do, and the judgments they make, are in fact dependent on their parent's opinions and suggestions, but in a negative way. This may be termed "negative dependence." Thus, though oppositional behavior and protest against their parents are indeed manifestations of rebellion and in the service of emancipation from the parents, at the same time they reveal that passive dependent longings are still in force. The adolescent is in conflict over his desires to be emancipated, and his rebellious behavior is a compromise formation that supports his efforts to give up the parental object and, at the same time, gratifies his dependent longings.

The just described dynamics of normal adolescent rebellion also pertain to some extent to neurotic adolescents and even borderline psychotics. In neurotics, these behavioral patterns are in the service of defense and become permanent aspects of character structure, in contrast to their transient nature in normal adolescents. In borderline psychotics and in psychotics, they appear in the context of problems of individuation and/or restitution phenomena. A. Freud (1958) notes that the difference between normal development and psychopathology depends in part on whether cathectic shifts in adolescence are gradual or sudden and precipitous. When gradual, detachment from the parents takes place; the defenses are transitory, less intense, and do not have an all-or-none quality. When sudden, the sequence of events assumes more of a defensive and pathological quality, rather than that of normal growth. Grinker (1962) has made similar observations on his homoclite group. We believe that the criteria of gradual versus sudden detachment from parental objects in determining normality deserves more emphasis than it has received in literature. This may lead to reevaluations and modifications of theories, such as Erikson's "adolescent crises."

In discussing the developmental stages leading to adolescent rebellion, it is instructive to turn to Case 1. In this borderline adolescent, the rebellious behavior masked a symbiotic attachment to a parent. However, on pursuing the matter, we wondered whether his defiance or rebellion against the parent's wish was motivated by a need for further differentiation and individuation. Possibly the negative behavior bore resemblance to Spitz's (1957) description of the infant's first achievement of saying "no" either by word or gesture. Spitz points out that the achievement of the head-shaking "no" is a result of the infant's attempts at identification with the prohibiting parent. The child achieves active mastery over situations previously experienced as passive. This occurs from fifteen to eighteen months of age, the time the child becomes able to separate from the anaclitic object. "The consequences of being able to turn the 'No' against the libidinal object, against what had only recently been the need-gratifying motor executive of the child's ego, are: (1) a becoming aware of the separateness of the self from the object; (2) a far-reaching enrichment of the child's object relations" (Spitz, 1957, p. 57). Concurrently, in the ego there is a beginning capacity for abstraction.

Returning to the two borderline patients, it is suggested that an analogous situation to these developmental circumstances exists. Their defiance against the symbiotic parent preserves at least a modicum of primitive autonomy and individuation. However, they seem to be arrested at this symbiotic stage. Nevertheless, by negating their parent's wishes, a potential path is available for them to continue to differentiate self from object, and thus to attain more autonomy.

We speculate that rebellion in the normal adolescent serves an analogous function to the "no" gesture and word in the fifteen- to eighteen-month-old child. Such rebellion in early adolescence promotes emancipation from internalized incestuous objects and leads to the search for an external love object. The "no" in the beginning of the second year of life facilitates loosening of dependent ties to the anaclitic object and, by turning the "no" against the emerging libidinal object, aids in the increasing awareness of the separateness of the self from the object.

Falstein (1967) in a discussion of this essay, correctly pointed out that rebellion in the service of autonomy also takes place during the anal-ambivalent stage of development. In fact, this process repeats itself in all stages of development, but achieves critical importance, aside from the first manifestation of the "no," in adolescence.

ROLE OF THE FAMILY

The adolescent rebels against both parents. According to Blos (1962), boys rebel against their mothers first. The adolescent rebels against his dependency on the incestuous love object. To this may be added Anna Freud's (1958) observations that the adolescent also defends himself against the actual parental objects by turning to members of peer groups. Rebellion against the father follows when the negative oedipus complex becomes predominant.

W. Lederer (1964) has emphasized the adolescent boys' need for a strong father who not only loves and provides but also inspires fear and respect for authority and his values. This gives him not only a worthy adversary, one who can set limits to his rebellion, but also provokes admiration and an opportunity to identify with his strengths and prohibitions. The strict father enables the boy to take responsibility for his own rebellion. It has been observed that good detached street workers never condone a boy's delinquency and let him know they do not approve of it. Erik Erikson made similar implications when he participated in a children's bureau seminar on delinquency. Discussing mass media, he stated:

I do not like to fool around with such questions as to whether certain movies, T.V. shows, or comic books are good or bad for children. As a citizen and as a father I would insist that they are ugly and worthless, and I for one, would tell my children so and would try to restrict their opportunities to see them. If they want to see them anyway, that is up to them. It is better for them to rebel than to have parents with totally compromised values. (Erikson, 1956, p. 15).

155

The following are descriptions of several types of fathers encountered in our clinical experience. No attempt at a systematization is made. For example, fathers who are overbearing and rigid provoke their sons to rebel to more extreme lengths. This may have happened with Lester (Case 3). On the other hand this type of father may totally suppress any vestige of rebellion. Some weak passive fathers make it difficult for the son to rebel against anything and at the same time provide no image of a strong father for identification. The superego of such a boy is apt to prove tyrannical under such circumstances and the aggression is turned back to the self. Another father may seduce his son to act out his own unconscious rebelliousness, deriving vicarious gratification for himself. Such a teenager does not take responsibility for his rebelliousness, remains dependent on his father, and may use rebellion to gratify his father. Such a father may be extremely devalued, and eventually, the adolescent identifies with his devalued father. This was especially noticeable where the rebelliousness was part of a neurotic character structure, for example, Danny in Case 2. In the neurotic delinquent group (Baittle and Kobrin, 1964) it was found that the mothers provoked their sons' rebelliousness to a remarkable degree and received vicarious gratification from their acts. This is similar to the "superego lacunae" that Johnson (1949) found in the families she studied, but it is not quite the same. The mothers of three of the neurotic adolescents in the delinquency group masochistically provoked their sons to sadistic action that took the form of rebelliousness. The mothers got hidden masochistic and sadistic gratification from this: masochistic gratification when their sons tortured them, and sadistic gratification when their sons got into trouble, which was not infrequent.

SOME ASPECTS OF THE ROLE OF THE SOCIAL ORDER

It is not feasible to systematically discuss the role of the social structure and social forces in adolescent rebellion in this chapter. However, the data suggest some theoretical remarks in two areas: (1) the role of the peer group in adolescent rebellion and (2) the role of some institutions in maintaining a "psychosocial moratorium" (Erikson, 1959, 1963), which attempts to cope with rebellious behavior.

Group behavior in adolescents often tends to support, and at times, to exacerbate rebellious behavior. Citing Freud's "Group Psychology and the Analysis of the Ego" (1955) as a point of departure, Redl (1942), Redl and Wineman (1957), and Janis (1963) have outlined some of the psychodynamics of childhood and adolescent group delinquent behavior. These writers emphasize that their findings and formulations are relevant to normal group behavior. Our findings of marked conformity in adolescent peer groups does not rule out rebellion of the group against its leaders (see the case of Danny above) and the rebellion of cliques of inferior social status against subgroups of superior status. Though much of the latter type of rebellion is a displacement of behavior originally directed toward the parents, it also seems to have an autonomous quality. As Anna Freud (1958) has observed, we have also seen adolescents fleeing from incestuous objects to peer groups; under favorable circumstances the peer group and especially its leader support the vulnerable adolescent's rebellion toward parental authority. We are not implying, however, that the group solely or mainly encourages adolescent aggression.

Adolescent group codes also set limits to aggressive activity. An increase in the intensity of libidinal feelings, problem-solving activities, and the gratification of ego interests are some of the many other functions of the group. Thus all group adolescent rebellion cannot be accounted for by psychopathology any more than individual rebellion.

The attitude of the schools to adolescent rebellious behavior (described above) supports the concept of psychosocial moratorium described by Erikson. According to Erikson, a psychosocial moratorium is provided by each society to allow a period of time for the adolescent to experiment, play around with, and test before he commits himself to a certain role, or segment of behavior. It seems as if rebellious behavior is an example where the adolescent is free "to try his wings," and the family and school are willing to give him time by permitting it within certain limits, and, as it were, not letting it count. He is not expected to be rebellious all his life, and his behavior is considered, to some degree, experimental. Thus the adolescent is not unduly penalized. The school's method of coping with its pupils' behavior seems to be an example of both the social institution's and adolescent's provision for a psychosocial moratorium. That the behavior of both parties becomes ritualized and institutionalized for succeeding generations of adolescents bespeaks for some permanence and structuralization of this specific example of a moratorium.

Summary and Conclusions

Rebellion is defined as open resistance to, or defiance of, any authority. Thus, it is distinguished from emancipation and the repudiation of parental values, but the relationship between these phenomena is explored. A differential diagnosis of rebellious behavior is offered and correlated with aspects of psychic functioning. The dynamics of each of the categories are formulated, with special attention being paid to the normal adolescent. Some aspects of the role of the family and society are explored.

It is speculated that the anlage of normal adolescent rebellion resides in the infant's capacity to gesture or say "no" in the beginning of the second year of life. In our experience, most adolescents rebel, whether normal or disturbed, except those who have not achieved the developmental stage of adolescence. Our conclusions are:

1. Clinically, attention must be paid to the nuances, intensity, duration, and age of rebellious behavior among adolescents before one can accurately assess the significance of the behavior.

2. Theoretically, moderate rebellion in the young normal adolescent is a step toward emancipation from the parent and striving toward the adult role. Rebellion in its more extreme forms, as well as continuous rebellious behavior throughout adolescence, is a sign of psychopathology.

3. We need to develop more specific criteria for the study of adolescent behavior in different social and cultural settings in order to make more exact statements about particular forms of adolescent rebellion.

NOTES

1. I wish to gratefully acknowledge the services and help of Mr. Joseph E. Puntil, my colleague in the juvenile delinquency project at the Institute for Juvenile Research who provided me with an entrée into the community and was responsible for some of the data presented in this essay—B. B.
2. For detailed results see Offer (1969).
3. For further details, see Baittle (1961).

REFERENCES

Adelson, J. (1964). The mystique of adolescence. Psychiatry, 27:1–5.
Baittle, B. (1961). Psychiatric aspects of the development of a streetcorner group. An exploratory study. American Journal of Orthopsychiatry, 31:703–712.
———. (1968). A psychiatric residency training program in juvenile delinquency in a community setting. Paper presented to a joint meeting of the Illinois Psychiatric Society and the Illinois Academy of Criminology on Youth Crime and the Psychiatrist, March 20, 1968, Chicago.

———. (1970). A conceptual framework for the psychoanalytic study of juvenile delinquency. Unpublished manuscript. Chicago, 1970.

———, and Kobrin, S. (1964). On the relationship of a characterological type of delinquent to the milieu. Psychiatry, 27:6–16.

Blos, P. (1962) On adolescence: A psychoanalytic interpretation. Glencoe: The Free Press.

Coleman, J. S. (1961). The adolescent society. Glencoe: The Free Press.

Davis, K. (1940). The sociology of parent-youth conflict. American Sociological Review, 5:523–535.

Douvan, E., and Adelson, J. (1966). The adolescent experience. New York: Wiley.

Erikson, E. H. (1956). Ego identity and the psychosocial moratorium. In Helen L. Witmer and Ruth Kotinsky, eds., New Perspectives for Research on Juvenile Delinquency. Children's Bureau Publication, no. 356, Department of Health, Education and Welfare. Pp. 1–23 et passim.

———. (1959a). Growth and crises of the healthy personality. Psychological Issues, 1:50–100.

———. 1956. The problem of ego identity. Psychological Issues, 1:101–164.

———. (1963). Childhood and society, 2d ed. New York: Norton.

Falstein, E. I. (1967). Discussion of: "On the nature of adolescent rebellion," at the Psychosomatic and Psychiatric Institute of Michael Reese Hospital, Chicago, November 1967.

Freud, A. (1958). Adolescence. Psychoanalytic Study of the Child, 13:255–278.

———. (1963). The concept of developmental lines. Psychoanalytic Study of the Child, 18:245–265.

Freud, S. (1955). Group psychology and the analysis of the ego (1921). Standard Edition, London: Hogarth Press. Vol. 18, pp. 67–143.

———. (1959). Negation (1925). Standard Edition, 19, London: The Hogarth Press, pp. 235–242.

Glover, E. (1950). On the desirability of isolating a "functional" (psychosomatic) group of delinquent disorders. British Journal of Delinquency, 1:104.

Grinker, R. R., Sr. (1962). A study of mentally healthy young males (homoclites). Archives of General Psychiatry, 6:405–453. [Chapter 11, this book.]

Janis, I. L. (1963). Group identification under conditions of external danger. British Journal of Medical Psychology, 36:227–238.

Johnson, A. M. (1949). Sanctions for superego lacunae of adolescents. In K. R. Eissler, ed., Searchlights in Delinquency. New York: International Universities Press. Pp. 225–245.

Keniston, K. (1957). Social change and youth in America. Daedalus, 91:53–74.

Kobrin, S. (1961). Sociological aspects of the development of a streetcorner group: An exploratory study. American Journal of Orthopsychiatry, 31:685–702.

Lederer, W. (1964). Dragons, delinquents and destiny: An essay on positive superego functions. Psychological Issues, 4 (no. 3): monogr. 15.

Nixon, R. E. (1962). The art of growing. A guide to psychological maturity. New York: Random House.

Offer, D. (1969). The psychological world of the teenager: A study of normal adolescent boys. New York: Basic Books.

———, and Sabshin, M. (1963). The psychiatrist and the normal adolescent. Archives of General Psychiatry, 9:427–432.

Pearson, G. H. J. (1958). Adolescence and the conflict of generations. An introduction to some of the psychoanalytic contributions to the understanding of adolescence. New York: Norton.

Redl, F. (1942). Group emotion and leadership. Psychiatry, 5:573–596.

———, and Wineman, D. (1957). Children who hate: The disorganization and breakdown of behavior controls (1951). In F. Redl and D. Wineman, The Aggressive Child. Glencoe: The Free Press. Pp. 11–250.

Spiegel, L. A. (1958). Comments on the psychoanalytic psychology of adolescence. Psychoanalytic Study of the Child, 13:296–308.

Spitz, R. A. (1957). No and yes. On the genesis of human communication. New York: International Universities Press.

Webster's New Twentieth Century Dictionary, 2d ed. (1956). New York: World.

Westley, W. A. (1958). Emotionally healthy adolescents and their family backgrounds. In I. Galdston, ed., The Family in Contemporary Society. New York: International Universities Press. Pp. 131–147.

10] YOUTH AS A STAGE
OF LIFE

KENNETH KENISTON

Those of us who concern ourselves with young men and women who have passed puberty but not entered adulthood need to recall that our modern concept of adolescence is itself a very recent invention. Sigmund Freud (1905), in his *Three Essays on Sexuality,* wrote of the "transformations of puberty," and did not mention adolescence. If we search through the psychiatric literature preceding World War I, we find little reference to any modern concept of adolescence. Puberty as a biological stage was recognized and there was a vague concept of "youth," unspecified as to age or precise psychological contours, but the adolescent, as we think of him today, was virtually unknown.

The recent elaboration of the concept of adolescence points to a readily overlooked fact. Our present definition of the stages of the life cycle, despite its claim to universal historical validity, grows out of an unprecedented set of historical and social circumstances in advanced societies. It may indeed be true that all children at birth have the capacity to go through the variety of stages of life we now recognize; but historically, it seems the social conditions have often conspired to prevent them from actually doing so. Social and historical conditions affect not only the content and coloration of the human life cycle, but also the extent to which the average individual in any society is likely to pass through any given stage of the life cycle. Measured against our modern standards of psychological development, it seems clear that the development of the vast majority of men and women in the world, even today, is foreclosed, retarded, fixated, or aborted by the absence of requisite environmental facilitations for psychological development.

Originally presented as the Second Annual Lecture of the Society for Adolescent Psychiatry, New York City, October 29, 1968.

My remarks will basically be an elaboration of this central thesis. I propose to examine briefly the emergence of previously unrecognized stages of life over the past few centuries in Western societies. I will emphasize that at least two such stages, the stages of late childhood (the latency period) and of adolescence, have been recognized in Western Europe and America only since the end of the Middle Ages. There is a close connection between the social recognition of these life stages and the new opportunities for psychological development created first by mercantile capitalism and then by industrial society. Finally, I want to suggest that we are witnessing, in our own day, the emergence of still another stage of life that intervenes between the end of adolescence proper and the beginning of adulthood. I will term this the "stage of youth." I will speculate provisionally about some of the characteristics of psychological development during youth, and about some of the reasons why a stage of youth becomes, for a growing minority of young men and women in advanced societies, a psychohistorically meaningful, if not necessary, stage of development.

To make clear the level at which I am speaking, I want to distinguish between three types of change that routinely occur during the course of human life. The first I will term "maturation," by which I mean the biological, physiological, and anatomical changes in the human body and the brain, changes that underlie, make possible, and in many instances require changes in psychological functioning, social role, and so on. Second, we need a concept such as socialization to point to the fact that in all societies, individuals pass through age-graded social roles whose requirements they must learn. For example, in every society a distinction is made between what is expected of the prepubescent child and the postpuberty young man or woman. Behavior and attitude both change in response to these age-graded patterns of social expectation. Finally, there is a third process of change, which most concerns us as helpers of the young: the process of psychological development or growth. Though psychological development is premised on maturation and is often stimulated by socialization, it is not identical with either. One can mature physically and learn the social ropes without automatically growing in a psychological sense. By psychological development (or growth) I will mean a process of increasing psychic complexity, differentiation, and individuation, accomplished by the resynthesis of accrued experience, often manifest psychologically by qualitative shifts in levels of functioning, and manifest behaviorally by increased flexibility and adaptability to the environment, along with increased autonomy and capacity for self-direction.

In discussing stages of life, I will not be talking about maturation or socialization, but only about psychological development, I take it for granted that maturation occurs almost without regard to social and historical setting, and similarly, that in all societies, a great majority of individuals are socialized—that is, they pass through the age-graded social roles that their societies provide for them. Whether real psychological development occurs at each socially defined stage of life is more problematical. Clinical practice and research have shown that many individuals become fixated, retarded, or "stuck" at one stage of life, and fail to make the next step forward in human growth. We are familiar with environments that are harshly depriving or fail to provide necessary stimulation to growth and that, as a result, retard (or at times arrest entirely) psychological development. I will be discussing recent psychohistorical conditions that have, in fact, made it possible for larger and larger numbers of individuals to undergo a longer and more complex process of psychological development.

Philippe Aries (1962), in his provocative *Centuries of Childhood,* has reexamined the concept of the life cycle from the Middle Ages to the present. Aries concludes that during the Middle Ages the concept of childhood as we define it today was virtually unknown. A stage of infancy, lasting until approximately the age of seven, was clearly recognized. Thereafter what we would consider children were simply assimilated into the adult world. The art and social documents of the Middle Ages show children and adults mingled together in one unified community, wearing the same clothes, performing the same functions, undifferentiated with regard to status or psychological development. The vast majority of children were totally unschooled. Even those who obtained some minimal schooling so as to become priests or clerks were taught in ungraded schools where children, adolescents, and adults unself-consciously intermingled.

Only during the seventeenth and eighteenth centuries did a concept of childhood as a separate stage of life slowly emerge. A new sentimental view of childhood was defined, and new theories of education concerned with promoting the moral and intellectual development of the child, with protecting him from the evils and corruptions of adult society, and with preserving childhood virtues, began to be enunciated. At the same time, schools became increasingly age-graded, and the average length of schooling, like the numbers of children who received formal schooling, began to increase.

Aries is concerned with documenting the emergence of the concept of childhood, not with explaining it. But it seems clear that childhood began to be defined as a separate stage of life only as larger numbers of men and women entered the bourgeoisie, as the amount of available leisure increased, and as the rate of infant mortality decreased. Childhood as a separate stage of life, then, began in the aristocracy and the middle classes and was made possible by the increased prosperity and new social and economic arrangements of mercantile capitalism. As bourgeois prosperity grew, there was less need for the children of the affluent to enter the labor force in order to ensure their families' economic survival. The new mercantile capitalism required a larger portion of the citizenry to be literate to a degree that was difficult to teach at home; education, therefore, became an intermediary experience before adulthood.

Aries's analysis of the emergence of a concept of childhood has far-reaching implications for understanding the relationship between historical change and psychological development. For though Aries is speaking implicitly of concepts of childhood, his argument indicates that the experience of childhood—the behavior of children and the way they were reared—changed as well. During the Middle Ages most children died before the age of six, and those who survived were apprenticed out or put to work at an early age. They were often treated with what we would now consider shockingly little tenderness, protectiveness, attention, or care. Parents as a rule invested far less emotional energy in their children than they do at present: Children were rarely spoken of as precious possessions to be cherished and protected.

As a concept of childhood as a separate stage of life began to emerge, the experience of those in this stage of life was also altered. A larger proportion of those between the age of six and fourteen were deliberately segregated into schools, which in turn were increasingly organized around age-graded classes. Children were increasingly sheltered from the demands of adult work, and were provided new freedom to play and experiment, systematic opportunities to develop new interpersonal and technical skills—in short, were given a period of age-graded segregation from the adult world, during which psychological development was far more possible than during the Middle Ages. In advanced Western societies, this process of segregation of childhood is now virtually complete, having extended from the aristocracy and bourgeoisie to the working and lower classes only during the twentieth century. The full institutionalization of childhood is marked by universal primary education. During the span of four centuries, we have moved from an era in which childhood was not recognized to an era in which we take it

164

completely for granted and protect it with a great array of legal, social, and educational institutions.

If the concept of childhood originated in Western societies only during the seventeenth and eighteenth centuries, the concept of adolescence is of even more recent origin. Only after childhood had been demarcated from adulthood could adolescence be interposed between them. Adolescence as we think of it today was "discovered" only during the nineteenth and twentieth centuries, and the extension of adolescence as a stage of psychological growth is far from complete even today. Puberty, that is, biological maturation, has of course occurred in all societies, though in the past it occurred later than at present. But in earlier eras, puberty seems to have gone largely unnoticed by Western societies. Children are considered neither innocent nor importantly different from adults; the fact of puberty constitutes neither a fall from innocence nor a change in status and therefore has little special meaning.

The modern definition of adolescence is of even more recent origin. When a postpubertal stage of life was first noted during the eighteenth and nineteenth centuries, concepts of adolescence centered on two images: the cherubino, the androgynous youth, and the recruit, the young soldier in training. Only in our century (specifically, after World War I) did the modern concept of adolescence appear, and even today, images of adolescence are fluid and changing. As Joseph Adelson (Douvan and Adelson, 1966) has noted, we still alternate between older images of the adolescent as awkward, gawky, and anguished, and newer images that view the adolescent either as deviant, wild, and uncontrolled or as idealistic, an accurate critic of society and repository of the future's hope.

In noting the recent emergence of the concept of adolescence, I am not proposing that one never ever had an adolescence before the concept emerged. Clearly, the potential for this experience is part of our endowment as human beings, and many men and women have passed through what we would now recognize as an adolescent experience. However, three things have changed during the last century. First, adolescence as a stage of life has been socially recognized and acknowledged. Second, society has begun to sanction and support adolescence, increasingly buttressing it with educational, familial, institutional, and economic resources. Third, these new resources, coupled with other changes in society, have opened up to an ever-larger proportion of the thirteen- to eighteen-year-old age group the possibility of continuing psychological growth during the adolescent years. A further protection from adult responsibilities has been granted, educational institutions

165

have been created to fill this moratorium, and a positive image of a postchildhood, preadult stage of life, adolescence, is now almost universally held.

As with the recognition of childhood, the discovery of adolescence is closely related to other social, economic, and historical changes. Increasing industrialization has allowed those past the age of puberty to be freed from the requirements of farm and factory labor. Indeed, these rising standards of economic productivity today make the adolescent, especially the uneducated adolescent, a drag on the labor market. Freedom from the iron law of economic survival has in turn created new attitudes toward adolescence, expressed in laws that make full-time employment before the age of sixteen or eighteen illegal. Growing affluence provides individual families and society as a whole with the wealth needed to support economically unproductive adolescents in school. All of this has happened, on a mass scale, almost within living memory. Even the antichild labor laws were passed in America as recently as the twentieth century.

Industrialization has also increased the schedule of societal demands on the adult personality, and a phase of adolescent psychological development appears to help the individual meet these demands. To begin, highly developed technical skills are necessary for a person to find a respected job within an industrial economy. Furthermore, the young must often be trained in skills with which their parents are unfamiliar. All of this requires an increasingly protracted period of extrafamilial education, extending long past the age of puberty.

Equally important, industrial society demands special psychological characteristics of its citizens. The individual in a complex, changing, highly organized industrial or industrializing society must have a highly developed sense of independence, adaptability, and self-direction. He must be able to leave his parental family, to set up a new family of his own. In a rapidly changing society he must learn to deal virtually alone with continual novelty and change. He must be able to postpone immediate gratification, operate at a high level of symbolic thought, be gratified by relatively intangible operation and rewards. What we know of adolescent development tells us that, by the large, this experience helps promote precisely the qualities of independence, adaptability, and self-direction that are required in our modern society.

In emphasizing the increasing extension of adolescence, I do not mean to suggest that this process is in any way complete. Those who have attempted to study representative groups of American teenagers

166

have usually concluded that most show marked signs of foreclosure, stasis, and resistance to the process of internal development and change which we consider desirable in adolescence. Douvan and Adelson (1966), working from intensive interviews with a large series of American teenagers, conclude that growth toward real emotional autonomy, detachment from the family, and reanalysis and synthesis of the ego-superego constellation occur only in a "bold, sometimes stubborn, often unhappy minority."

Even if the process of extension of adolescence is not complete, the direction of change is clear. In his brilliant *The Vanishing Adolescent,* Edgar Freidenberg (1959) argued that the opportunity for a real adolescence is increasingly being foreclosed by modern conformity, the abuse of counseling services, and the pressure for blind acceptance of the status quo. My argument here suggests that, historically, Freidenberg is wrong. Despite short-range ups and downs, the long-range trend is clearly toward the prolongation of adolescence, with a slow extension of facilities and opportunities for real psychological development during this stage of life. Historically, what is remarkable is that so many young Americans in fact have something approximating an adolescence.

To summarize my thesis so far, I have emphasized that the opportunity for psychological development is closely related to social and historical trends. During earlier periods in Western societies, opportunities for development during and after childhood were largely absent for the vast majority of individuals. By modern standards, the vast majority were prevented from developing anything like the inner complexity, flexibility, and differentiation that we now consider virtually the birthright of young Americans. Children matured physically and were socialized into the adult roles of their society, but the conditions of child-rearing prevalent during the Middle Ages were such as to retard, if not arrest altogether, many important processes of psychological growth.

Insofar as we define the life cycle as an ordered sequence of psychological development in each stage of life, the life cycle is not an escalator up which all men move regardless of social setting and historical circumstance but rather a ladder from which many (and possibly most) individuals may fall in certain social and historical settings. Obviously, some exceptional individuals will grow psychologically almost regardless of their environment. However, most of us need, for our continuing psychological development, social confirmation, support, protection, and challenge. These constitute the stimulus to psychological growth. When such facilitations are missing, psychological development is slowed, retarded, or at times stopped altogether. Certain societies or subcultures may systematically produce retardations of development during childhood and adolescence, with the result that members of these societies or subcultures may be, on the whole, less advanced psychologically than members of other cultures and groups. We may have to look at societies not only in terms of their national characters and child-rearing patterns, but in terms of what might be called their model developmental level, asking how far up the developmental ladder that society or subculture allows the average individual to climb.

If the life cycle, psychologically speaking, is a creaky ladder and not an automatic escalator, then it is conceivable on theoretical grounds that new or previously unrecognized stages of psychological development may emerge with still new historical conditions. I now want to postulate that the contours of still another stage of life, one that intervenes between adolescence and adulthood, is now becoming visible in certain youth groups, largely in the more advanced nations. I will term this stage of life the "stage of youth," attempting to give to this ancient but vague term a more specific psychological meaning. My remarks about youth as a stage of life are preliminary and speculative, and I present them only in the hope that they will stimulate others to correct and amend what I say.

The need for postulating still another stage of psychological development may be questioned. After all, such writers as Sigmund Freud (1905), Anna Freud (1958), Harry Stack Sullivan (1953), Peter Blos (1962), Erik H. Erikson (1950), and Helene Deutsch (1967) have provided enormously important insights into the nature of adolescent development. Yet most of what they say applies more to the fourteen-year-old than to the twenty-four-year-old. My point is that we have tried to stretch the concepts of adolescence to include too much and that it will be more profitable to examine the development of what we have heretofore called the late, late adolescent in its own right, without insisting on some fundamental developmental similarity between the twenty-four-year-old graduate student and the fourteen-year-old eighth-grader.

For a number of years, I have worked intensively with students of college and graduate student age, most of them nonpatients, many exceptional in talent and psychological strength. Recently, for example, I had the opportunity to study in some depth an élite group of young radical activists, most of whom were in their middle twenties. In a sociological sense, none of these young men and women were adults, that is none was involved in the institutions of marriage and career which we normally use to differentiate the adult from the adolescent. Psychologically, many of these young men and women seemed already to have accomplished what we have learned to consider the traditional tasks of adolescence: emancipation from parental family; relative tranquility concerning sexuality; formation of a stable and relatively integrated identity sense; capacity for commitment, intimacy, and play; a considerable synthesis of ego and superego; a history of having passed through and beyond earlier adolescent rebellion; and so on. Yet despite these developmental accomplishments, the particular young men and women I studied continued to place enormous emphasis on psychological change, on remaining open, fluid, and "in motion," on not foreclosing their development in any way, and on not becoming integrated into the established society. In this respect, they were not yet adult. These young men and women seem to be in an uncharted stage of life that intervenes between the end of adolescence proper and the beginning of adulthood.

Not everyone between the ages of twenty and thirty can be placed in this stage of life. On the contrary, those who can constitute a small minority of their age group. Yet among young radicals, among college and graduate students, among Peace Corps and Vista volunteers, among college and graduate students dropouts, and in the hippie world, I believe there are at least some who have similar characteristics. Though they have mastered most of the tasks we consider central to adolescence, they are reluctant, unprepared, or unready to enter adulthood. Such young men and women are characteristically preoccuped with their relationship to the System or Establishment, asking themselves and others how, when, where, or whether they can enter it. They are clearly a minority of their age group; still they exercise an influence out of proportion to their number.

Existing theories of adolescence are useful in characterizing the earlier lives of such young men and women. Peter Blos, Sr.'s (1962) concept of protracted adolescence clearly applies to some in this age group. There are others whose unwillingness to accept adulthood seems less a function of fear and overweening narcissism than of an accurate analysis of the faults, inconsistencies, and problems of their society. Erik Erikson's concept of a "psychosocial moratorium" is highly relevant to many of these young men and women, but with the major qualification that many show few signs of the acute identity diffusion that is thought to inspire such a moratorium. Anna Freud's (1958) discussions of adolescence are relevant to understanding these young men and

169

women in their midteens, but have less applicability to them at present. Concepts of postadolescence developed by Helene Deutsch (1967) and Harry Stack Sullivan (1953), though useful, generally assume that the postadolescent is in the process of making precisely the marital and vocational commitment that those I term youth are profoundly unwilling to make.

Let me therefore suggest, as a provisional hypothesis, some of what seems to me the characteristics of youth as a stage of life. First, the central conscious focus of concern that unifies those I term youth is the ambivalent testing of the connection of self and society. What most distinguishes the youth from the adult is that the nature of this bond with society remains unsettled. The adult is committed to an enduring style of relationship with established institutions, a style that may be deviant, revolutionary, or criminal, or that may be conformist, accommodating, and accepting. But the youth is still exploring his fundamental position toward society. Thus, youth's psychohistorical position is that of disengagement from society. Whatever his formal relationship to society, whether student, dropout, revolutionary, or service volunteer, his inner position is one of noncommitment to existing institutions. Disengagement of course is not inevitably rejection. Among some youth one finds a questioning attitude, a feeling of a personal readiness or unfittedness, rather than a radical rejection of society.

Another characteristic of youth is the adoption of youth-specific identities that are not expected to outlast their youthful usefulness. Youthful identities differ from the more enduring identities of the adult in that the identities of youth are thought of as temporary, self-limiting, and transient. Youth radicals, for example, do not expect to remain young radicals all their lives, but are prepared neither to become professional radicals (that is, old radicals) nor to enter into some nonradical relationship to the Establishment. But though the identities of youth are limited temporally, they differ from the shallower, more fluctuating enthusiasms of adolescence in that they last many years, inspire deep loyalty, and generally provide a vantage point outside of the System from which youth can explore both society and self, testing the two against each other and attempting to find some lasting pattern of relationship. Once a more definitive engagement with society occurs— whether this engagement takes the form of a more enduring commitment to revolution and social change, a more enduring acceptance of the existing society, or some intermediate position—youth is over.

I have said that the most prominent issue in youth is the ambivalent

170

relationship between the self and society. The psychological work of youth consists of two tasks: first, renegotiation of the relationship between the individual and the past and the existing society; second, reformulation of that part of the self, of the personality, that represents and reflects social reality and cultural inheritance.

Let us consider first the renegotiation of the relationship between the individual and society. The way this work is done varies enormously. One youthful solution involves a determined attempt to change the society or some part of it so as to bring society in line with the individual's principles and needs. This, of course, is the solution of radicals, activists, and reformist youth, whether of the Right or the Left. Another contrasting solution is a systematic attempt to change one's self, rather than society, so as to fit with less anxiety or discomfort into the existing system. A third approach during youth is the effort to locate or carve out some special niche within the society where the essential qualities of the self can be preserved, enhanced, or acted upon.

The polar extremes during youth, then, are defined by societal activism and personal self-reform—by the revolutionary and the patient. The pure revolutionary seems to accept his own core values and seeks to transform the world in their image. The pure patient, the self-reformer, nominally accepts the demands of society, and attempts to transform himself so as to meet them. Clinical experience has shown that these apparently opposite positions are often secretly related. For one, both self and society are infinitely complex, changing, and ambiguous. There is no such thing as perfect congruence or total conflict between them. Equally important, the ambivalence inherent in human development means that no one ever blames himself or society totally. As we know, the psychoanalytic patient, though nominally committed to a rigorous program of self-transformation, often harbors an obdurate attribution of blame to society. Even the most radical revolutionary must suppress his deep and conscious doubts about whether his critique of society is simply an expression of some personal inadequacy. Indeed, without this profound ambivalence about both self and society, youth does not occur. The young man or woman who is sure that he is right and society is wrong is by his certainty committed to the adult role of revolutionary, exile, or internal emigré. Ambivalence, then, is an essential characteristic of youth; alternations between fantasies of self-change and social transformation are the rule.

The intrapsychic work of youth involves the analysis, synthesis, consolidation, and reformulation of the social and cultural aspects of the personality. At one level, this involves the further elaboration of the superego, but there is a greater advantage in examining those portions of the personality that reflect society and cultural inheritance. In addition to the powerful dictates of parental precept and practice, we have other societal reflections. In particular, we have an internalized symbol system, including a value system built on the superego, which by the end of adolescence should transcend it in a variety of ways. Second, we all possess an image, or an internalized representation, of society, consisting of our accrued and elaborated experience with social institutions, their representatives, their potentialities and defects. We all carry within us some notion of the social order, of how it works, of how it affects us, and of what we can expect from it. In most men and women, this image is largely implicit and rarely articulated, and in all of us, importantly related to other internalized images.

Part of the intrapsychic work of youth, then, involves a reexamination, a redefinition and rearticulation of the internalized culture. Youth focuses on questions of social ethics, personal integrity, problems of compromise and accommodation, the relationship of value and practice, the effect on the self of involvement in social institutions, and the relative priority of self-reform and social change. The youth is likely to be concerned with the price of success, the real meaning of achievement, the possibilities of reward for effort, ethic, and work, and the price in integrity of social effectiveness. The youth is also likely to be engaged in earnest efforts to root out personal characteristics that seem, in retrospect, to have developed merely from an effort to gain popularity or social approval. The most intellectual youth often develops an idealized image of the social order toward which he strives in personal and political actions. Finally, one witnesses among more sophisticated youth a self-conscious examination of the entire cultural inheritance, of the traditional, political, social, and moral symbols he has inherited from his parents and his society, and a selective rejection and reassimilation of the parts of this culture that continue to serve him and his history well. In brief the adolescent reexamines his superego, but the youth reexamines his cultural inheritance as a whole.

Relatedly, youth involves efforts to transform, differentiate, elaborate, and modify the internalized representation of society. The behavior of youth typically entails an active exploration of the social order, by a deliberate self-exposure to new groups, new people, new places, and new social strata. Youth is a period of geographic and social-class mobility, during which the person may identify far more profoundly with those of other classes, regions, and historical eras than with his own. This exploration sometimes requires deliberate self-immersion in poverty, in the underlife, even depravity. It frequently involves exaggerated geographic mobility, continual and even compulsive movement "on the road," an intense fluidity, an outlook in which motion, personal change, and identification with the most diverse and opposite groups and individuals are apparent.

The characteristic behavior of youth is related to a large extent to their psychological disengagement from society and the active testing of both self and society. On the one hand, youth is a period of at times euphoric omnipotence, a sense that all things are possible, a feeling of utter freedom, limitless horizons and opportunities, a conviction (not without some basis in reality) that the self is malleable and can be shaped and bent in virtually any direction. The obverse of this euphoric omnipotent, the dysphoria of youth, is a feeling of complete absurdity, uprootedness, a disconnectedness that is a consequence of both inner ambivalence and the psychohistorical position of youth. Undefined by social role and institutional obligation, youth is a stage of life during which feelings of exile, meaninglessness, unrelatedness, of having no home, of being useless, and of aimless drifting are common and intense.

The central psychological achievement of youth is the acknowledgment of both self and society—both personality and sociohistorical process—without denying either. Just as men and women sometimes achieve mutuality in which the separate uniqueness of each is a precondition for loving the other, so in youth, acknowledging independent reality and valid claims for both self and society is a precondition for achieving a social engagement in which self and society exist as distinct yet interlocked entities.

Youth ends (relatively) when the person moves into a more enduring relationship with society. The amateur becomes the professional, and the individual accepts (or is forced by the passage of time) into a social role that is likely thereafter to define his relationship to society. This social role may of course be a deviant one—revolutionary, criminal, mental patient, artist, innovator, or crank. However, the individual's relationship to society is relatively settled, and he need no longer proclaim he will not abandon his youthful commitments; this fact or its falsity is obvious in what he does.

The ending of youth may provoke a new period of turmoil and crisis. Abandoning the openness, fluidity, disengagement, and omnipotence of youth in favor of a defined position vis-à-vis society commonly entails the fear of selling out, of becoming frozen to a social role, bogging down in marriage and career, and inhibiting further development. In the future, growing numbers of the most talented, ethical, and/or most disturbed young men and women will seek to prolong the qualities of youth indefinitely, maintaining throughout life a youthful commitment to openness, fluidity, and flux.

From a psychodynamic viewpoint, there may be two contrasting pathways to the stage of youth. One might be considered the pathway from psychological strength, a pathway that leads some young men and women, whose development has been unusually successful, to be dissatisfied with their society to seek to continue processes of inner development, and to postpone for years or decades their entry into the established society. On the other hand, there are clearly many who enter youth for neurotic reasons, who are unable to accept society or the self whose origins lie in unexplored and unintegrated childhood experiences. In my experience, most youths fall somewhere between these two poles, showing a mixture of neurotic reluctance and principled unwillingness to accept standard adulthood.

Social and historical factors are also critically important in understanding the prolongation of youth. Let me mention two factors. The first is the rapid and progressive increase in the expected amount of education in the advanced nations. Historically, it is completely without precedent for virtually all the citizens of a society to continue their education through high school, for approximately half of them to enter institutions of higher education, for half of these freshmen to graduate eventually from some institution, and for approximately half of all college graduates to go on for graduate and professional education. The extraordinary prolongation of education in American and other advanced societies provides a major facilitation for the entry of young men and women into a postadolescent but preadult stage of life. Second, it is often noted that we live in an era when social change is more rapid, more unrelenting, and more thoroughgoing than in any previous historical era. Under these conditions, past technologies become obsolete at an ever-increasing rate. Equally important, the ideologies, values, and systems of symbolic interpretation that were taken for granted by our parents and grandparents often seem to us, and even more to our children, largely irrelevant and useless. The most articulate of today's youth thus express a vivid, even anguished, feeling that their cultural inheritance is inadequate to their contemporary and future world.

Many other social and historical facts might be discussed as contributing to the slow emergence of youth as a separate stage of life. For example, we might consider the youth's emphasis on hypocrisy. Or we might examine the charge of depersonalization leveled at American society by activist youth, relating this to the growing contrast between the warmth, intimacy, and personalism of American families and the bureaucratic, impersonal, and emotionally neutral structures of adult society. Similarly, we might examine in detail the peculiar ambivalence of American adults toward youth—the mixture of envy, admiration, and hopefulness toward youth with reflectiveness, fear, and repugnance that we have seen so clearly voiced in this recent national election. Yet to detail these themes would merely be to underline the thesis that I have tried to present here: namely, the intimate but often ignored or misunderstood connection between historical process and individual psychological development.

REFERENCES

Aries, P. (1962). Centuries of childhood. New York: Knopf.
Blos, P. (1962). On adolescence: A psychoanalytic interpretation. Glencoe: The Free Press.
Deutsch, H. (1967). Selected Problems of Adolescence. New York: International Universities Press.
Douvan, E., and Adelson, J. (1966). The adolescent experience. New York: Wiley.
Erikson, E. (1950). Childhood and society. New York: Norton.
Freidenburg, E. (1959). The vanishing adolescent. Boston: Beacon Press.
Freud, A. (1958). Adolescence. In the Psychoanalytic Study of the Child, no. 13. New York: International Universities Press. Vol. 12, pp. 255–278.
Freud, S. (1905). Three essays on the theory of sexuality. Standard Edition, 7:125–145, London: Hogarth Press, 1953.
Sullivan, H. S. (1953). The interpersonal theory of psychiatry. In Chap. 18. Late adolescence. New York: Norton.

11] "MENTALLY HEALTHY"

YOUNG MALES:

HOMOCLITES [1]

ROY R. GRINKER, SR., *with the collaboration of*
ROY R. GRINKER, JR., AND JOHN TIMBERLAKE

This report is primarily an attempt to describe and explain the mental state of a special group of young adult males who seem to be healthy. They were "discovered" fortuitously in a quest for subjects to participate in a larger program of psychosomatic research. We had turned from studies on anxious and depressed patients to subjects free from psychiatric disturbance, that is, normal, in order to investigate their psychosomatic processes during an idling phase and to observe their stress responses under conditions of psychological and physical strain. We finally found a nearby small college whose students and administration [2] willingly cooperated in our research.

During 1958 more than half of the entire student body of George Williams College was presented with psychological tests including: Taylor's Manifest Anxiety Scale, Mandler's Perception of Feeling, Barron's Ego Strength Scale, and Nowlis' Adjective Check List. The purpose of these preliminary tests was to select subjects within a healthy range located around high and low poles of a stability-liability axis. A discussion of some of these test results on 140 subjects is presented by Korchin and Heath (1961): Thirty-one subjects screened by the above methods were then interviewed to determine their suitability for our

Reprinted from the *Archives of General Psychiatry,* 6: (June 1962), 405–453. Copyright, 1962, by the American Medical Association.

psychosomatic research, the results of which are reported by Oken, Grinker, Heath, Herz, and Schwartz (1962).

The impact of these interviews on me was startling. Here was a type of young man I had not met before in my role as a psychiatrist and rarely in my personal life. On the surface they were free from psychotic, neurotic, or disabling personality traits. It seemed that I had encountered some mentally healthy men who presented a unique opportunity for study.

Perhaps this experience could serve as a tentative definition of "mental health"—its startling impact on a psychiatrist who has devoted most of his professional life to working with people who complain unhappily, suffer from disabling symptoms, and behave self-destructively. Three years after my preliminary shock and after this peculiar population was systematically studied, I came across the following reassuring sentence written by Henry Murray (1951): "Were an analyst to be confronted by that much-heralded but still missing specimen—the normal man—he would be struck dumb, for once, through lack of appropriate ideas."

This report is essentially an account of an investigation into the personalities and the familial, social, and cultural matrix of a group of mentally healthy young male adults. The research is not definitive but is designed for the purpose of developing hypotheses. The following procedures were utilized:

1. An overview of the psychiatric, psychological, psychoanalytic literature on personality and family background, and values involved in the concept of "mental health."
2. A description of the setting in which the subjects function.
3. Unstructured and structured interviews of thirty-one preselected subjects in 1958 and of thirty-four subjects self-selected from among eighty male students entering George Williams College in 1959.
4. Findings from a 700-item questionnaire delineating the "average subject."
5. A comparison between the questionnaired, interviewed, and non-interviewed subjects.
6. Statistical analyses of the questionnaire data.
7. Rating scales.
8. An assessment of adjustment.
9. Differential perception of parents.
10. A review of a few comparison groups.

An Overview of the Literature on Mental Health

A thorough review of what has been written on the subject of normality, or mental health, is almost impossible. Certainly no one person could understand or assimilate the concepts, observations, and experiments contributed by many scientific disciplines from genetics to anthropology, encompassing as well the philosophical aspects of values. Furthermore, the concern with health is not recent; it has extended far back into history.

Without making any pretense for completeness I shall review small samples of the literature in order to indicate the main points of view and frames of reference established by the disciplines of psychiatry, psychology, psychoanalysis, and sociology as it considers the contemporary family. Only contributions from the behavioral sciences will be considered, because other writings from the biological sciences, cogent and numerous though they may be, are not directly applicable to the psychological and psychiatric data reported here.

PSYCHIATRIC LITERATURE

Aubrey Lewis (1958) writes:

A rather silly but often repeated truism says that the aim of psychiatric treatment is to promote mental health. It is hard to tell what the latter phrase means. Mental health is an invincibly obscure concept. Those who have attempted to define it in positive terms have twisted ropes of sand, telling us, for example, that a man's mental health consists in

(a) active adjustment or attempts at mastery of his environment as distinct both from his inability to adjust and from his indiscriminate adjustment through passive acceptance of environmental conditions; (b) unity of his personality, the maintenance of a stable, internal integration which remains intact notwithstanding the flexibility of behavior which derives from active adjustment; and (c) ability to perceive correctly the world and himself.

This clutter of words is groping towards an ideal, a sociobiological ideal; but much of it can have no operational referents and it abounds in terms which are undefined and at present undefinable. Most of those who state criteria of mental health follow the lead of disease or infirmity as the characteristic feature; they do not say a man is well when he is free from manifest illness but speak instead of "optimal growth and happiness of the individual," "full maturity," "adjustment to the world and to each other with a

178

maximum of effectiveness and happiness," using quantitative words like "full" and "maximum" to qualify immeasurable states like happiness.

Shepherd (1958) states: "Very few could usefully apply the World Health Organization's global view of mental health as: 'a condition, subject to fluctuation due to biological and social factors, which enables the individual to achieve a satisfactory synthesis of his potential conflicting instinctive drives; to form and maintain harmonious relations with others; and to participate in constructive changes in his social and physical environment.' "

The sociologist Eaton has argued cogently that mental health is in fact a conceptual abstraction that may take five different forms: a clinical judgment; a self-judgment; a group-judgment; a typological idea; and a statistical norm. A variety of ideas and activities have followed the banner of mental health in the United States where the concept has gained its broadest appeal; indeed, official attention has had to be called the "flavour of morals and ethics, religious fervour, personal investment, unvalidated psychological concepts, value judgments, psychiatric theory, political science, welfare movements and cultism," which are associated with the term.

Szasz (1960) goes still further in condemning the concept of mental illness:

Our adversaries are not demons, witches, fate, or mental illness. We have no enemy whom we can fight, exorcise, or dispel by "cure." What we do have are *problems in living*—whether these be biologic, economic, political, or sociopsychological. . . . My argument is limited to the proposition that mental illness is a myth, whose function it is to disguise and thus render more palatable the bitter pill or moral conflicts in human relations.

Redlich (1957) states: "We do not possess any general definition of normality and mental health from either a statistical or a clinical viewpoint. In any case, meaningful proposition on normality can be best made within a specific cultural context." Lois Murphy (1959) in discussing her coping project concludes:

In all that we have said about the role of the professions in contributing to mentally healthy patterns of infant and preschool child care, we have in mind the possibility of culture-wide shifts in attitudes and goals, and the importance of the following for mental health:

1. Feeling good to be oneself (from infancy on) depending on *good physiological functioning, libidinal gratification, freedom.*
2. Being able to work actively toward constructive exchanges with, rela-

179

tions with, feelings about the environment, from infancy on—promoting interest, *flexibility, autonomy, warmth toward people, relevant uses of help,* a clear grasp of *reality* and *sense of mastery.*

3. Learning to handle one's own impulses, drives, energies and conflicts in an integrative way.

Murphy adds that normal people are not uncomfortable, and she quotes the mothers whose children she studies as saying that "life is not easy but you make the best of it." This intuitively is a paraphrase of Freud's statement that life is not very much, but it is all we have.

Finally Hoffman (1960) comes to grips with the problem of values:

> Our attempt to define "health" in psychiatry has not really produced satisfactory results, *and* we always have to define "health" within a specific cultural context of *values.* It would seem that our difficulty in defining "mental health" is due *precisely* to the fact that it is not properly a scientific term. In fact it can only be meaningful when ultimate values have already been postulated by some extrascientific (e.g., religious, cultural) means. It may be doubted whether any two theorists in the field will ever agree on the same order of ultimate values. Consequently we shall never have a "true" definition of "health" within legitimate scientific discourse, any more than we can have a scientific definition of "justice."

It is a purpose of philosophic analysis to clarify the meaning of concepts used in scientific discourse. An attempt to do so has been made here, with special reference to the value terms used in psychiatry. Such terms as "mental health," "mental illness," "normal," "abnormal," "neurosis," "psychosis," "perversion," "psychopathic," or "sociopathic" personality have been subject to scrutiny. It has been shown that such terms cannot be defined scientifically. Therefore, it is suggested either that they not be used or that a precise statement of the basis of their use in any given case be made. Such attention to our use of language will bring rewards both in the clarity of our discourse and in the elimination of issues hitherto considered unsolved problems of science.

The above selected quotations from the psychiatric literature, few though they may be, give in substance all that has essentially been said recently. The authors in their own authoritative words describe well the elusiveness of the concepts of health and disease. But the discourse becomes monotonous and holds no promise for the task of the psychiatrist who, by profession, is called on to treat mental illness without a definitive outline of what it is. The psychiatrist himself establishes no boundaries around illness but says he alone can treat it. Furthermore he cannot define that health to which he hopes to return his patients. Fi-

180

nally the more philosophical contend that the whole discussion is unscientific, in that health and illness are ultimate values and could only be the subject of philosophical analysis.

PSYCHOLOGICAL LITERATURE

There is a tremendous literature written by psychologists on facets of normality and health, for after all psychology has been concerned with ego psychology and the conflict-free sphere of the ego long before psychoanalysts rediscovered this process. In the *Annual Review of Psychology* hundreds of contributions are abstracted each year dealing with little pieces of normal or healthy development, functioning, relationships, and so on. Only a few relevant recent papers will be mentioned.

Charlotte Buhler (1959) considers that there are four basic tendencies of life: need satisfaction, upholding of the internal order, adaptation, and productivity. Health is achieved through balance and integration of these functions. She attempts to unify the concepts of others under her four categories. Maslow (1959) selected persons who were considered to be self-actualizing for study and characterized them as follows: They see reality clearly, accept self and others, are spontaneous, are problem-centered, philosophical, and creative, discriminate between means and ends, feel at one with mankind, and so forth.

A number of other psychologists differentiate personality soundness, which as a long-term process may be called a structure, from well-being, which refers to the immediate state. The latter is then an equilibrium concept which refers to stability, elasticity, or resistance against disintegration. Klein (1960) proposes several kinds of stability: namely, general, specific, inherited, and acquired.

Bettelheim (1960) deals essentially with the concept of autonomy and the consciousness of freedom:

One's sense of identity, the conviction of being a unique individual, with lasting and deeply meaningful relations to a few others; with a particular life history that one has shaped and been shaped by; a respect for one's work and a pleasure in one's competence at it; with memories peculiar to one's personal experience, preferred tasks, tastes and pleasures—all these are the heart of man's autonomous existence. Instead of merely allowing him to conform to the reasonable demands of society without losing his identity, they make it a rewarding experience, quite often a creative one.

These remarks are topical, for our age, which offers so many chances for escaping personal identity, requires at least equal strengthening of the sense of identity. As Bettelheim states: "A time that offers so much

181

seduction to letting machines provide what seem like the essentials of living, needs, more than other societies, to understand clearly what are the essentials, and what are the accidentals of human living."

In 1958 Jahoda, working for the Joint Commission on Mental Health and Illness, published a monograph with the startling title of *Current Concepts of Positive Mental Health*. The unusual word was "positive," which implies that mental health is not only the absence of illness, and sidesteps the notion of a continuum of health and illness to which Barton (1958) strongly objects.

No matter how objective and scientific one views the problems of mental health, the specter of value systems enters and plagues the investigator. But these too can be subjected to investigation. For example, Jahoda (1958) states that "One value in American culture compatible with most approaches to a definition of positive mental health appears to be this: An individual should be able to stand on his own two feet without making undue demands or impositions on others." This corresponds to Kluckhohn's delineation of the American value system of "doing and becoming" and is open to scientific scrutiny.

Jahoda points out that absence of illness, absence of mental conflicts, the adherence to the statistical concept of normality, the satisfactions with self in social function, are not adequate definitions of health. However, her inspection of the literature results in uncovering six major categories of health concepts: attitudes toward self; degree of growth, development, and self-actualization; integration; autonomy; perception of reality; and mastery of the environment. Jahoda concludes that there is probably a diversity of types of mental health and that these may be viewed from the standpoint of multiple criteria. Using these multiple criteria, research tactics may be planned for tapping empirical data in varying conditions and over various blocks of time through such methods as self-description, interviews, observations, and tests.

M. B. Smith (1961) most recently asks whether the term "positive mental health" is only a slogan. He clearly points out how value systems enter into every facet of the problem of health and illness and that everybody wants to live a good life, but what is that? What ought to be is not science. He proposes that, in addition to the use of frontal descriptive attacks on specific populations (Maslow) and the use of multiple criteria (Jahoda), systems theory be employed.

Without committing themselves to a definition of "mental health," Gurin, Veroff, and Feld (1960) explore it through a number of measures of adjustment. The measures, however, all derive from the self-appraised, experiential realm of the respondent. In the area of general life adjustment, such measures are obtained from the information about the extent of worrying, evaluation of personal happiness, whether the respondent ever felt close to a nervous breakdown, and if he ever experienced a problem relevant for professional help. In the more specific area of functioning, namely, marriage, parenthood, and work, adjustment is studied via consideration of such variables as satisfaction with the particular role, feelings of adequacy in performing it, degree of involvement, expectations about future, and the type of problems and their prevalence encountered in each role. It is worth pointing out that, in taking a multiple-criterion approach to mental health, the investigators are implicitly in agreement with the current view of Jahoda and Smith, that the search for a conceptual formulation of mental health that could meet with a general consensus is futile because of the unavoidable valuative assumptions in all such formulations.

Probably Lois Murphy (1959) and her coworkers have done more work on the problems of coping in our time than anyone else. Their coping project is producing results of great interest, especially in the context of mental health. Murphy introduces the subject of coping as follows:

All across the United States and outside as well, studies of large samples of children had shown that what we call problems actually occur with almost predictable frequency in any group of normal children. It became increasingly clear that there is no such thing as a child who goes through the complete developmental span from infancy to adulthood without problems. The difference between children who become seriously disturbed and those who are considered to remain within the normal group could not be thought of in terms of the presence of problems in one group and absence of problems in the other group, but rather in the way in which problems are handled.

Our studies of mechanisms of dealing with conflicts had been derived from studies of neurotic individuals so that the mechanisms used were often considered to be pathogenic in themselves, even though many writers pointed to the necessary structuring of personality by defenses through which even normal people deal with their conflicts and problems. We wanted to find out, then, whether there were additional mechanisms used by children who managed to stay more or less normal or whether the differences between becoming disturbed and remaining normal were rather a matter of the ways in which these mechanisms themselves were utilized.

We also wanted to find out anything we could about factors in individual children which tended to make certain children rely more on certain kinds of problem-solving methods and defense mechanisms while other children used different ones; in other words, to find out what were the factors contributed to different styles of coping as well as to extend the inventory of coping devices and methods.

Grinker (1955, 1956) and later White (1959) discuss the potentials of growth in the process of achieving health. Grinker differentiates between "goal-seeking homeostatic regulation and goal-changing growth processes." White emphasizes search for tension, excitement, and the novel—exploration, play, and investigation all giving the feeling of efficacy and competence. Scott (1958) discusses the multiple factors in mental health which include social adjustment, psychiatric diagnosis, subjective feeling, objective psychological tests, conformity to social values, and adaptation.

Friedes (1960) states:

> Psychology should stop asking the question "What is normal?" Personality theory requires another orientation. It seems to me that, for purposes of scientific theory construction and also for practical clinical purposes, a rather different and potentially more fruitful approach can be taken. This would entail the viewpoint that human beings have a variety of potentialities, and that the achievement of certain potentialities may entail certain limitations and that achievement and limitation vary with conditions.

Bee (1959) states:

> One must distinguish between three concepts: the *norm*, the *normal*, and the *ideal*. The *norm* is an average characterizing the "typical" in a given class or group. It is statistically derived and describes what *is* without reference to whether it is good, bad or indifferent. The *normal* is an expression of a practical ideal which assumes the absence of the pathological. The *ideal* is a theoretical standard of "perfection" which in many instances is a goal to be pursued without expecting to attain it.

PSYCHOANALYTIC CONCEPTS OF NORMALITY

The psychoanalytic literature on normality or health is not very extensive and suffers from the restricted range of interest of psychoanalysts in psychopathology. Furthermore, their focus on internal dynamics limits their interest to the so-called psychic agencies. For example, Freud (1959) stated that "it is impossible to define health except in terms of metapsychology, i.e., of the dynamic relations between those agencies of the psychical apparatus. . . ." Gitelson (1954) writes that normality is often a defense by way of rigid identifications (with the aggressor) leading to so-called adjustments. Normality then is referred to internal dynamics rather than to behavior: "An open system of communication between various institutions of the mind, a fluid process of checks and balances." He further adds the curious statement that adaptation to a culture has no place in psychoanalysis which needs to be free of the gravitational pull of a specific culture (Gitelson, 1952).

In another context Freud stated: "Every normal person is only approximately normal—his ego resembles that of the psychotic in one point or another, in a greater or lesser degree . . ." Hartmann (1931) in a similar vein states that mental health and its causes require consideration of nonconflictual functions as well as central conflicts. Defenses and instincts are not normal or pathological; it is their balance that counts.

Jones (1948) was one of the first psychoanalysts to write about the normal mind. He uses the criteria of happiness (capacity for enjoyment and self-content); efficiency in mental functioning, including relationship with fellow men; a positive social feeling; and a capacity for adaptation to reality.

Erikson (1950) has developed in some detail the concepts of stages in the psychological development of man. Based on the species and genic given sets of potentialities, culture, represented by significant early objects of care, nutriment, and training, imposes conflict, values, and internalized images which influence the way in which eight stages of development occur. The resulting hypothetical functions of trust, autonomy, initiative, identity, intimacy, generativity, and ego intensity are in contrast to failure in part or whole characterized by mistrust, shame, doubt, guilt, self-diffusion, and so forth. Health then represents to what degree the potentialities of the individual are successfully developed into the positive qualities of each stage.

A host of other psychoanalytic writers could be quoted, but the end result would only be confusion; their combined product is a combination of words dealing with internal processes from a metapsychological point of view only and with little reference to human beings in action. For example, Eissler (1953) states that the ego's potentials can achieve full realization and "physiological normality becomes abnormal when it leads to ego modifications," and Reider (1950) that normality is an intellectual defense against anxiety. Waelder's (1936) classification includes the following: Behavior is normal if it gratifies and does not frustrate instinctual (id) needs, leads to ego success rather than failure, and produces social praise rather than superego punishment. Hartmann (1939) states: "Recognition of reality is not the equivalent of adaptation to reality. The most rational attitude does not necessarily constitute an optimum for the purposes of adaptation." He furthermore writes that neither defense nor instinct is normal or pathological—their contextual balance or imbalance is the criterion.

Glover's (1956) psychoanalytic writings seem most sensible of all, for he starts out with the recognition that there is no psychoanalytic agreement about ego strength or weakness, normality or abnormality. Yet, if we discuss disorder or abnormality, we cannot escape from considering order and normality. In all of medicine there is no standard of normality. Glover's definition of mental health includes freedom from symptoms, behavior unhampered by mental conflict, satisfactory working capacity, and the ability to love someone else. With tongue in cheek he ventures the speculation that, if no adult normality is possible without an adolescent psychosis, then likewise it is impossible without an infantile psychosis. Normality, thus, is a state in which the subject's psychotic estimate of the object world coincides with an objective estimate in two respects: the amount of love that can be satisfied and the amount of danger to the ego that is present. Glover advises that we do not worship or idealize an absolute concept of normality. In the final analysis the degree of normality is an adaptive concept: conforming to social standards of adequate adaptation plus the quality of elasticity and the capacity for anxiety tolerance.

Actually, despite the emphasis by psychoanalysts on evidences of internal balance among psychological forces as indices of health, in practice their criteria are behavioral. Some so-called orthodox, or classical, analysts treat patients interminably, hoping to reconstruct personality and to achieve that illusory idea of mental health. Most sound therapists, however, are willing to settle for adaptive and self-satisfying behavior.

Kubie (1954) has reconsidered the concepts of creativity, normality, and neurosis from the frame of reference of the interplay among unconscious, preconscious, and conscious forces. The preconscious system is the essential implement of creative (and normal) processes that are absent until these processes can flow freely:

> Whenever the conscious-preconscious alliance is dominant among operative forces, the resultant pattern of behavior, no matter how varied, will have one basic characteristic in common—i.e., any repetitiveness which it exhibits with respect to impulse, thought, action, or feeling, or any combination thereof, will be flexible, modifiable, satiable, and under voluntary control. A dominantly unconscious alliance will be the opposite: i.e., repetitive, obligatory, insatiable, and stereo-typed. This is neurosis.

Rapaport's (1951) delineation of ego autonomy coincides in general with Kubie's concept of balance. Primary autonomy of the ego protects it from being driven from the id on the one hand and being bound to external stimuli on the other. The apparatuses of primary autonomy are memory, motor skills, perceptual sensitivity, and threshold processes. Other secondary autonomies that arise from experience are ideals, identities, superego forces, values, and so on. Compulsive defenses maximize ego autonomy from the id. Fantasies and temporary regressions assist in freeing the subject from the slavery of external stimuli.

Warner and Saul (1961) state:

> There is no one research design or bit of evidence which can conclusively prove that child-rearing practices and parental attitudes are etiological antecedents to personality development and behavior, as well as adult character traits. A survey of all the different available studies, research and reports, however, is *strongly suggestive* that overall parental attitudes and, to a less extent, techniques used in rearing children are largely responsible for later personality and behavior development.

Relatively recently even the most determined of the advocates of experimental etiology and those who see nothing but psychogenesis are beginning to recognize genic and constitutional factors. The *Ergänzungsreihe* of the Germans is being revived. Lois Murphy (1959) for example, considers that there is a continuum of vulnerability in children dependent not only on mother-child relationships but also on degree of brain damage, patterns of autonomic reactivity, kind of biochemical or genic-derived enzymatic function, body type, structural and developmental imbalances, and so on. Escalona and Heider (1959) recognize that the motoric, perceptive, drive, and energy equipment at birth influence subsequent development of the child and influencing prediction. In fact, psychoanalysts now speak of the "givens" of structure and function as important, admitting but sidestepping the significance of heredity and constitution as if these were grudgingly admitted.

LITERATURE ON THE FAMILY AND MENTAL HEALTH

Stein et al. (n.d.) in their study of creativity remark on frames of reference that can be applied to normality. Psychiatrists observe disorders of personality, and they and psychologists look at forces within the individual; sociologists emphasize the milieu. Stein and his coworkers conclude:

> All behavior, however, is a function of the transactional relationships between the individual and his environment. Individuals affect and are affected by their environments. During any one period of time or during any one transaction, factors within the individual or within the environment

187

may be prepotent but the dominance of either does not imply complete absence of the other.

Ackerman (1958, 1959) states:

The inter-relations of the individual and family group determine dispositions to illness and health at every stage of growth, infancy, childhood, adolescence, adulthood, and old age.

In the dimensions of time, longitudinal development produces patterns for weakness and vulnerability, but current interaction of individual and family group may precipitate illness, mold the course, shape the recovery or bring the risks of relapse. The role of the family in the maintenance of positive mental health for the adult is crucial. The final outcome, in life performance in individuals or families, is the result of the balance of forces as between those that move toward sickness and others that move toward health.

The family is changing rapidly according to Ackerman. Industrialization, urbanization, advances in technology, clashes in values all result in many changes in nursing, religion, motility, and the like. There is a loss of family consciousness and a downgrading of parental authority. Not only in the infantile period but at every stage of growth the relationship between the individual and his family is an essential factor in determining the disposition to illness and health. Ackerman believes the focus on the sick aspects of the family should be supplemented with a knowledge of its normative functions.

John Spiegel (1958) points out that:

Most of the things that we now tell families to do turn out to have very little relationship to mental health, but are based on the values of the middle-class family; the problem of the degree of strain in "well" vs. "sick" families. In "well families" the strain and the degree of change in culture value orientation is much less. Also, when the strain is evident, it is more openly dealt with.

Westley (1958) describes the emotionally healthy adolescent in the usual terms so often repeated before. However, from his study of a special group he concludes that the family backgrounds conducive to stability are characterized by (1) the father being upwardly mobile, (2) a democratic atmosphere with freedom of expression for the children, (3) warm positive relationships, (4) no adolescent rebellion, and (5) the mother having a high masculine image of her husband (even if unrealistic).

Weisberg and Springer (1961) in discussing the environment of gifted children found that characteristically the family favored expressiveness without dominance, accepted regressions, and the parents were not de-

188

pendent on each other or on the child—they were two well-defined adult personalities. They knew who and what they were even if this was painful, and they could openly express hostility to each other. The result was a strong identification with the parent of the same sex by the child, lesser binding to reality, anxiety that was handled not by repression but by restructuring. The child was able to regress and could endure the illogical quality of fantasy without feeling guilty. The curious combination of anxiety, open conflicts, security, and a strong self-image seemed to be conducive to healthy creativity.

SUMMARY

Only a small sample of the literature on mental health and normality has been extracted from the behavioral sciences. The articles and books on the subject are numerous but highly repetitive, repeating the same "clutter of words." Most of the discussions are theoretical and conceptual and, as Lewis (1958) states, without operational referents. Nevertheless, there are authors who contribute observations and descriptions of special populations in what M. B. Smith (1961a, 1961b) terms a "frontal attack" in empirical research, and others, such as Ruesch and Bateson (1951), who analyze the value problems involved in our communications about health and illness.

The College Setting and How the Students Get There

George Williams College in Chicago, unlike its Canadian counterpart, Sir George Williams College, is not a YMCA school; it has an independent administration and board of trustees. The following pertinent information about its setting is taken verbatim from the literature published by the College:

GEORGE WILLIAMS COLLEGE
. . . Has a Unique Purpose.
  The College was founded and has been maintained through the years by professional and lay leaders of the Young Men's Christian Associations, primarily for educating young men and women who seek to prepare for a life of Christian service with the world-wide movement of YMCA. Its closest relationships have been with, and its major support has come from the Young Men's Christian Associations. In order to re-emphasize and clarify the central purpose of the College, the Board of Trustees in 1952 adopted the following statement: The basic goal of the College is to provide professional

education for Christian leadership, primarily for Young Men's Christian Associations.

Since the training provided in the two major professional areas of specialization, namely, (1) Group Work and Recreation and (2) Health and Physical Education, meets the required educational preparation for leadership in other youth and recreational agencies, churches, schools, and colleges, George Williams College welcomes men and women of all faiths and races who seek to prepare themselves in a Christian atmosphere in one of these fields of specialization.

. . . Is Avowedly Christian.

It welcomes to its fellowship persons of all faiths and creeds and makes no attempt to proselytize; but it is avowedly Christian in purpose, motive and program. Chapel and other worship services are conducted on a voluntary basis. The College upholds Christian ideals and standards of conduct in humble recognition that these are imperfectly observed, even by their most earnest supporters.

. . . Is a College for the Professional Education of

1. Secretaries of the Young Men's Christian Associations. Specific programs of study are offered to prepare Boys' Work and General Program Secretaries, Physical Directors and Women's and Girls' Secretaries. The courses required for Certification are included in all of these programs.

2. Teachers in the area of health and physical education for the schools, and leaders for Boys' Clubs, settlements, and community recreation centers.

. . . Offers Education on Two Levels, Undergraduate and Graduate.

Graduates of approved high schools who meet the other admission requirements may enter George Williams College and take a four-year course leading to a Bachelor of Science degree. This course offers a broad educational background plus a major in either Group Work Education, Community Recreation, or Health and Physical Education.

PROGRAMS OF STUDY

The college awards the Bachelor and Master of Science degrees with majors in health and physical education, group work, and community recreation. Though the first two years of the Bachelor's program are devoted primarily to courses in the general or liberal education subject matter fields, emphasis is also placed on preprofessional courses that assist in orienting the student to his stated field of interest and that also help to test his basic skills and leadership abilities. During the last two years more stress is placed on assisting the student with the acquisition of knowledge, understandings, insights, methods, techniques, and skills in his major field of study.

ACADEMIC REQUIREMENTS FOR ADMISSION

1. Three years of English (one major).
2. Three years of either mathematics, science, social studies, or foreign language (second major).
3. Two years of either mathematics, science, social studies, or foreign language (one minor).
4. Rank in the upper half of the graduating class, or
5. Possess a grade average of 85, in academic subjects where 75 is the passing mark, and
6. Recommendation of high school counsellor or principal.

WHAT STUDENTS LEARN AT GEORGE WILLIAMS COLLEGE

1. A broad background of general education integrated into the total program of professional education.
2. Essential technical skills.
3. An understanding of people and ability to work with them effectively.
4. Understanding and skill in program leadership and supervision.
5. An understanding of community forces and how to relate effectively to them.
6. Some understanding of administrative problems and processes.
7. A philosophy of profession.

Students usually attend George Williams College because of its goals and plans of study. Some have matriculated because the scholastic demands of the college for entrance and continuance are lower in practice than of most of the larger colleges and universities; others enroll because they live close by. The early history of many students begins with enrollment during childhood in the local YMCA for gymnasium or swimming-pool privileges and instruction. The secretaries intuitively pick out the most promising youngsters for locker room and other odd jobs. As time goes on and they continue to meet approval, they are given better jobs after high school, weekends, or in the YMCA summer camps. Finally the boy is advised to attend George Williams College, at which a scholarship, paying partial tuition, can be arranged. During this process the boy develops a strong identification with the secretary and the ideals and goals of the organization he represents. Thus many of

191

them enter college with strong convictions and motivations for the YMCA work or that of settlement houses, community playgrounds, and the like. They have little difficulty getting good jobs, after certification, with adequate salaries for this type of work, because graduates of this college are preferred and sought after throughout the country.

Thus there is a sense of stability achieved by entering and graduating from George Williams College, and uncertainty about the future is minimal. The YMCA has likewise achieved assurance that its goals, policies, and status will be preserved. The YMCA is indeed a stable and relatively unchanging organization; both inside and outside there is no trouble in identifying a YMCA. Apparently the personnel tend to reproduce themselves by selecting, as candidates for college, personalities who resemble themselves. For the purposes of stability and maintenance of goals, the average student and the organization are in near-perfect equilibrium.

Before describing and qualifying the George Williams College students as a sample of mentally healthy subjects attracted to this college by the magnetism of its fit with their motivations, personalities, and abilities, it should be understood that there are also many individual differences, and subgroups showing significant variations can be isolated. Yet as a total sample they have such specific characteristics that individual members can be identified easily. When special students attend classes at a nearby university to study subjects not available at their own college, they stand out and have created an image in the minds of the professors as the upright young men.

The Interviews

Subjects who fell within the healthy range according to the preliminary 1958 psychological tests were invited to participate voluntarily in our research on the basis of (1) a monetary return, (2) an interest in participating in and learning about scientific experiments, and (3) a desire to make a contribution to psychosomatic research. Appointments were arranged at the thirty-one subjects' convenience for interviews.[3] A year later thirty-four additional male students who entered the college during 1959 were also interviewed. These subjects received no financial remuneration. The results reported in this section are thus based on a study of sixty-five subjects.

Each subject was interviewed and observed by me for approximately an hour during which he was first encouraged to speak freely about himself, his worries, anticipations, goals, and anything that he wished to discuss. Then he was asked to talk about special topics such as his background, home life, school, emotions, and image of himself. In general this unstructured and structured interview was conducted in the manner of psychiatrists' usual approach to a diagnostic evaluation. As much information as possible was elicited to enable fifteen questions to be answered.

WHAT WAS LOOKED FOR

1. General socioeconomic, family, developmental, and so forth background
2. Physical health
3. Motivation for participation in experiment
4. Capacity for verbal behavior
5. Kinds of usual interpersonal relations
6. Range of feelings (variations)
7. Ease of emotional arousal and shifts of feelings
8. Degree of affective response to stressful situations and recovery or defenses (coping devices)
9. Familiarity and comfort with own feelings (self-communication)
10. Cognizance of physiological concomitance of feelings
11. Consciousness and ability to report feelings and self-image in the interview
12. Freedom of play, fantasies, and dreams
13. Anecdotes of past emotional disturbances to reveal the intensity and nature of precipitating factors and the recovery process
14. Presence and type of impulsive behavior
15. Character and personality structure; structured defenses

DESCRIPTION OF SUBJECTS

Socioeconomic Background

The occupations of the subjects' fathers fell in the laborer, semi-skilled workmen, or white-collar classes. They included janitors, truck-drivers, street repairers, watchmen, farmers, schoolteachers, and so on.

Geographical Origin

The interviewed students came to Chicago from all over the country and Canada, though the Midwest was most highly represented. Ten came from rural small communities or farms, others from villages or small towns, and a few from large cities.

Estimate of Intelligence

This was not based on formal testing but on a general impression obtained by the interviewer. All subjects fell in the average range. Only one subject gave the impression of having superior intelligence. However, when the reports of testing at the school by the Otis Self-Administering Test of Educational Progress were available, it was discovered that the I.Q. averaged 110 (range 88–133). At a follow-up one year later, most of the students had remained in school or had been graduated. Two had resigned for financial reasons, two were dropped for poor scholastic achievement—their I.Q.'s were 88 and 102, the lowest of any subjects interviewed. The grade-point average for the first year was 1.33, slightly better than C, as contrasted with the total school average of 1.58 or a C +.

Impulsivity

Among the initial thirty-one subjects very few showed evidence of impulsivity, or a high degree of rebellious behavior. However, in the second interviewed group four out of thirty-four, or 12 percent, told of having a period of rebellious and asocial behavior. One stole a car, another stole from a store, and two were on legal probation after having come in conflict with the law for general disorderly conduct. All four of these subjects stated spontaneously that they suffered from persistent childhood enuresis, a remarkable confirmation of Michaels' (1955) theory that persistent enuresis is a psychosomatic reflection of the lack of internal inhibition just as delinquency reflects a later sociopsychological defect of inhibition.

Communication with Self

This trait was rated quite low for all groups of subjects because they were not given to introspection and rarely asked themselves, "How do I feel?" or why. In fact their characteristic response to affects cued off by external events or appearing spontaneously was to "kick it off." They diverted their attention to other matters, engaged in physical activity, especially sports. They essentially *did* something. Concomitant with this defensive procedure, their lack of introspection was associated with a poor ability for abstraction. Furthermore they could not use fantasy in the service of creativity. In only two or three cases was the subject able to use heroic compensatory fantasies as a surcease from the pain of external disappointments. They simply had to go into action. At the same time for them there were no bothersome internal anxious problems. Reality was there, and one did his best to adapt.

Self-Image

During the interviews each subject was asked what he thought about himself: "What kind of a guy are you?" The answers corresponded with other data and indicated that their self-evaluation seemed accurate and honest. Most of them talked about their families without exaggeration or condemnation and hoped they could do better. As for their assets, they too were correct. Studies of interviews reveal few evidences that this image was forged by an *identity crisis*. With few exceptions passage through puberty and adolescence was smooth and devoid of turbulence (Spiegel, 1951). Some talked about experiences of "coming to terms with myself." Only two turned bitter and paranoid, and a like number became "angry young men" (at the world), and one turned into a shy, quiet person full of damped-down rage.

Early Work

As children many subjects worked after school, delivering papers or groceries, mowing lawns, caddying in summer, from early years of grade school through high school. Many were putting themselves through college with earnings from part-time jobs. The reasons given for this early work were to supplement the family income, to buy extra things for himself, to save for the future, and often parentally directed "to teach the boy the value of money."

Early Parental Discipline

Two-thirds of all subjects indicated that discipline in the home was firm. Boundaries were established and well known to the subjects. They felt discipline was fair and deserved. Usually the father administered the punishment, occasionally the mother, but in both cases the parents agreed on its necessity and form. Punishment varied from whippings to deprivation of privileges. There seems to be no resentment harbored toward the parents at the time of interviewing; in fact, there was general agreement that the punishment was beneficial.

Athletic Interests

George Williams College offers preparation for the semiprofessional careers of group leaders and activity directors. These occupations spec-

195

ify considerable knowledge and skill in games requiring motor profi-
ciency and in playground and camp sports. It is no surprise that many
of the students in grade and high school and during summer vacation
became proficient in athletic activities, and many were members of high
school teams. The use made of these skills will be discussed later.

Religious Training

The college is of Protestant denomination, but among the students
were Catholics, Jews, Mormons, and various special fundamentalistic
sects in small proportions. No matter what the religious faith, it was
rare to find a subject who had not had a strict and rigorous religious
training. This consisted of Sunday school, church social activities, and
later church attendance on Sundays with the family. Most of the boys
also spent a great deal of time at the local YMCA. Only eight did not
have a strict religious background. Though, as stated before, the boys
engaged in little introspection and fantasied very seldom, they did engage in discussions sparked by religious concerns. In that sense they
were interested in the hereafter, the meaning of life, and, conceived
broadly, in existentialism.

Anxiety

Only three of the first thirty-one interviewed subjects denied experiencing free anxiety. The anxiety in all but one case was set off by external meaningful cues; none was spontaneous. The affect occurred while
waiting for a competitive game to begin, prior to examinations or while
waiting for their grades, anticipating bad news from home, and so on.
No chronic reportable anxiety existed in any subject. Following are the
subjective visceral accomplishments and their frequency as described by
the first thirty-one subjects: "butterflies" in the abdomen, 16; sweaty
palms, 14; excessive eating, 14; rapid heart beat, palpitation, 13; restlessness, 3; globus, 2; diarrhea, 1; headaches, 1; tremor, 1; syncope, 1;
hot flushes, 1; nail biting, 1; rapid breathing, 1. These subjective sensations occurred singly or in various combinations. They quickly disappeared when the stress stimulus ended or when defenses and coping
mechanisms were applied. None continued for long after the conditions
that elicited them were corrected. No physical disease was present in
any of our subjects.

Depression

Sadness and low degrees of depression were reported in most of the
subjects and were related to difficulties with their studies or poor

grades. Two had spontaneous mood swings and two felt unhappy most of the time. In most subjects, effective coping devices quickly alleviated the sad mood.

Anger

As stated previously, this emotion differentiated the designated high lability group from the low. Only two subjects seemed to maintain chronic resentments. The others dissipated the feeling by muscular activity.

Coping Methods

The subjects of this study had many problems, as do all humans, with which they had to cope. School work, the necessity to graduate, and the future were all serious matters on which the students were sharply focused. They had many difficulties in view of their limited talents, and experienced anxiety and depressions in relation to reciting in class, taking examinations, and facing their grades. They, like all students, were also seriously involved in how they were handled by the faculty in school and by the monitor of their dormitories. In general, their emotional stress was less stirred by interpersonal problems than by their performances in school and athletics. It was before contests and examinations that their anxieties were aroused. It was after failures in games, examinations, and work that their depressions occurred.

From the subjects' statements we may classify the most common coping devices as follows: (1) muscular action: sports and games, driving, walking, and the like; (2) denial: "It doesn't matter"; (3) isolation: withdrawal, sleep, fantasy, concentration on music.

Most rarely did the subjects focus on the problem, intensify their problem-solving devices, introspect, and think through the difficulty. They utilized the typical "buck up" technique characteristic of people who rarely consult psychiatrists and drop out from psychotherapy if they should start.

Morality, Sex, and Marriage

Christian ethics and morality pervade the school as befitting this particular college, but the general morality and honesty of the students were characteristics achieved long before entering college. It was a product of their early religious training and the ideals of goodness, helping others, and morality held and taught by their parents.

Among the first group of subjects interviewed eight members were married and an additional four had sexual experiences without anxiety.

197

All those who were married or who had sex experiences were potent. None was overtly homosexual. The student body did relatively little dating. They lacked money, and they worked late after school either for financial support and/or as part of their field training. There was relatively little drinking, though occasionally there was a dormitory hell-raising beer-drinking spree that got out of hand.

Psychopathological Trends

Interviews of sixty-five subjects disclosed a relatively homogeneous group free from gross psychopathology. Yet the technique used could by no means disclose the deeper problems not available for conscious reporting nor evidenced in behavior. However, the following indications of psychopathology were evidenced in a few subjects. Two were chronically unhappy and two had fairly wide mood swings, two indicated excessive degrees of suspiciousness, three stuttered, and one had recurrent nightmares. Capacity for close and deep human relationship was evident in most subjects—to members of their families, peers, teachers, and to the interviewer. After a brief period of anxiety most subjects were able to relate well and intimately with the interviewer and establish a positive empathic system of communication. Only a few somewhat suspicious characters, two of whom were definitely paranoid, could not do so.

SUMMARY OF INTERVIEW DATA

The sixty-five subjects interviewed constitute a homogeneous sample of a population scattered over the country. They stem from all parts of the United States and Canada and from farms, rural communities, and cities. It can be assumed that they represent a large population diffusely located everywhere, not within isolated groups or geographical pockets. Despite this fact their homogeneity is striking. They can be characterized as follows:

1. Reared in upper-lower or lower-middle class environments
2. Average intelligence
3. Early work experiences
4. Early strict religious training (mostly Protestant)
5. Parental discipline firm, fair, and agreed to by both parents; subject well informed of behavioral boundaries
6. Self-image fair and realistic and achieved without identity crisis

7. Mild affective emotional responses of anxiety, depression, and anger usually evoked by real external events

8. Rapidly stimulated and effective coping devices within categories of muscular action, denial, and withdrawal

9. Interest in physical activities, sports, and participants in athletics

10. Little introspection or capacity for internal communication with self and low degrees of creativity and fantasy

11. Fairly strong impulse control

12. High degree of ethics, morality, and honesty

13. Little heterosexual experimentation

14. Minimal and infrequent psychopathology

15. Good capacity for adequate human relationships

Questionnaire Studies

The interviews afforded only a glimpse of the subjects' personalities and their social and cultural backgrounds. It was hoped that more could be ascertained concerning the subjects as they were at present and much more about how they got that way. For this purpose a questionnaire consisting of 700 items within eighteen subdivisions was devised on the basis of traits described in the literature, previous questionnaire studies (helpful also for form), and our current American values.

Before introducing the questionnaire it should be emphasized that answers to its queries represent the subject's image, memory, and distortions of his current and past experiences, attitudes, and feelings. As Azrin, Holz, and Goldiamond (1961) have reported, the response bias in questionnaire reports requires that they be validated by objective measurement. Insofar as possible, our interviews, observations, tests, and reports from the college served this purpose. Interviews with parents, teachers, counselors, peers, and so forth were impossible owing to the wide geographical distribution of their place of origin. Consideration was given to submitting questionnaires to the parents and significant others through the mails, but this was abandoned because answers obtained in this manner would only compound the distortions. However, we believe that the answers given by the subjects are reasonably accurate because of the number of repetitive items that could be scrutinized for consistency and the coherence and logical fit obtained from the integrated responses and from the interviews. Nevertheless, it must be remembered that our descriptions of the subjects' present and past are derived from their images.

The questionnaire was introduced with the following instructions:

CONFIDENTIAL

Introduction

This questionnaire is presented to you, with the approval of the administration of George Williams College, by a group of behavioral scientists. Earlier studies demonstrated that students of this college are unusually mentally healthy. The purpose of this survey is to learn more about you as a group in order to advance our understanding of mental health. Your cooperation in this scientific study is greatly appreciated.

Although the questionnaire seems bulky, it should not require an excessive amount of time for completion if you follow directions. It is not necessary to ponder over each question; answer as spontaneously as possible. Quickly answer each question and go on to the next, but *be sure to check the answer for every single query.*

We assure you that all information received is strictly confidential. We expect frank and honest answers to each question, and remember, even though we consider that you are healthy, like everyone else, there have been and are problems in your life and conflicts in your personality. These are just as important to us as the positive aspects.

It closed with the statement below, which prepared the subjects for an interview:

Thank you very much for your cooperation. Your answers will undoubtedly be of great help to us. In pursuing our work, however, it may be that we will find it necessary to have a personal interview with you to discuss in more detail some further questions that may arise during the course of the research. In that case we will contact you and make an appointment for a personal meeting at your convenience, during which we also may be able to answer some questions that may occur to you.

The questionnaire was given in September 1959, during orientation week, to all the eighty male students entering George Williams College for the first time whether they were undergraduates or graduates, freshmen, or transfer students. The students sat at comfortable desks and were asked to read the introductory page carefully and then proceed. There was no time limit. Three of us who knew the instrument well circulated around the room as monitors to help the students when problems of interpretation of various questions arose.

It would serve no purpose to reproduce the questionnaire itself; it contained over 700 questions, almost all of which were to be answered by a check. It is only necessary to outline the headings of the large sections or categories:

1. Vital statistics
2. Home and family
3. Childhood and its vicissitudes
4. Adolescence
5. Schooling
6. Discipline
7. Religious training and attitudes
8. Physical health
9. Hobbies and recreation, social life
10. Sex
11. Stresses, disappointments, troubles
12. Prejudices
13. Relationship to authority
14. Expectations, ambitions, and values
15. Neurotic traits
16. Evaluation of self
17. Emotionality
18. Marriage and children

FINDINGS FROM THE QUESTIONNAIRE

Median figures were used to derive the description of the average George Williams College student, though no subject has actually answered the questionnaire in such a manner. The median, or average subject, comes from a small to medium-sized city in the Midwest. Both his parents are living, and he has one to two siblings. His father is typically a semiskilled or white-collar worker earning slightly more than $5,000 a year. As yet he has not married, but this is not surprising in that the average age is eighteen years and he still has his college education to complete. His religious preference is Protestant.

Home Life and Parent-Child Relationships

His home life is happy and peaceful and there seems to be very little discord between his parents. Neither of the parents is particularly dominant, but both tend to share responsibilities and interests. Birth of next younger sibling is only vaguely remembered, and there seems to have been no overt antagonism toward the child.

The parents were usually concerned about neatness and orderliness, though we have no data on the severity of the toilet training. The typical student confided with mother for the most part and also feels that it is she who loves him most. On the other hand, he feels that he is more like his father, so that closeness to mother has not made him a mamma's boy. Both parents are seen as loving and giving individuals. When asked to describe their worst traits, father is described as rigid or having a violent temper or drinking. Mother's worst traits are nervousness, rigidity, or aggressiveness. When asked for the worst thing about the home life, either "arguments" or "father as a problem" is mentioned. When queried about the subject of most family quarrels, "money" heads the list.

A picture begins to develop of parents who are concerned about neatness, orderliness, and money. With their low income and children to raise, one could interpret this attitude toward money as thrifty rather than penurious. The positive aspects outweigh the negative, however, in the total picture of the parents. All that can be said is that there does appear to be a certain amount of parental inflexibility and overemphasis on control which might have limiting effects on the subjects' development. But correspondingly the subject usually knew what to expect from his parents as far as moral judgments, emotional reactions, and disciplinary measures were concerned. He was somewhat less sure about the same responses in other adults.

Mother was seen as somewhat more encouraging than father, also warmer and somewhat closer. In the company of mother, the subject as a child felt above everything else secure. The over-all picture, then, of parent-child relationships is very positive. The child knew what to expect, and in general he was loved and made to feel secure. Though the subject received slightly more love from mother both in childhood and adolescence, he does not feel that he got less than he wanted from father. Father was the stricter disciplinarian in childhood, though by no means harsh. Discipline was consistent and appeared fair to the subject, consisting mainly of scolding, physical punishment, and deprivation. The withholding of love was seldom threatened, perhaps one of the reasons why our subject felt so secure in the presence of mother.

Family ideals are contentment and to a somewhat lesser extent responsibility. Money and fame, the other two alternatives presented to the subject, are seen as relatively unimportant.

Childhood and Adolescence

The subject had a relatively active childhood. He enjoyed school and did fairly well. Outside of school he was busy with hobbies and interests and frequently worked after school and during summer vacations. He had few serious illnesses but mentioned that nail biting was a problem. Poor eyesight and reading difficulties were also present. Six students of the total population had been stutterers in childhood but with no current remnant.

Adolescence was a period of increased conflict with the parents. The subject also became more rebellious and at times somewhat moody. There was also some concern over the future. All this appears within the expected range; the subject did not check the more extreme items, such as "developed bad habits" or "disturbed over changes in my body." The item most strongly endorsed was "became more responsible." The rebelliousness then seemed to have been a step toward gaining independence from the family and the development of self-initiative and responsibility.

Team competition in high school was enjoyed by most subjects, and they fantasied that best of all they would like to be athletes when they grew up. Solitary activities were enjoyed least of all by the subjects, and they would rather be with others than alone. On the other hand, only sometimes did one claim to be the leader of a social, work, or sport group.

School

The decision to go to college was made by the subject himself with full approval from his parents. In the specific choice of George Williams he was influenced by the YMCA itself and friends.

In high school his grades were fair, ranging between B and C. His best subject was one of the social sciences, and he had difficulty with mathematics and English, indicating that like most students in this country his high school preparation for college was inadequate. Though the average subject is no scholar, he enjoys school, particularly George Williams. He does have some trouble studying, however, and experiences anxiety in preparing for and, especially, just before taking examinations. Some of this tension may result from fairly strong family pressure to do well in school. There is also some awareness of competing with other students for grades. It would appear that the student is a somewhat anxious achiever; that is, he seems to be motivated more by the fear of failure than the positive rewards of success. However, his major focus of interest, his anxieties, and depressions concern little else than his school work.

Religion

The subject comes from a Protestant background. Both he and his parents are active in their religion, and he finds his religion both helpful

203

and important. His reason for going to church is mainly because of a belief in God and not for social purposes.

Health

The subject is presently in good physical health, as are both his parents. He describes his appetite and physical fitness as excellent but his sleep as only satisfactory. He complains of occasional headaches, stomach pains, constipation, and diarrhea but nothing more serious than these. In general, then, his physical health is quite good, though anxiety may at times be interfering with his sleep.

Leisure and Cultural Activities

In his high school years the subject belonged to a boys club. He is extremely active both as a spectator and a participant in sports events. Though he does not play an instrument himself, he is particularly fond of music, especially semiclassical selections. He reads but not avidly. Most of his reading material consists of best sellers, and his knowledge of current affairs is derived from newspaper headlines. When attending the movies he prefers a musical comedy, and his television watching is mainly of sports or plays. His interests then are not extremely diversified or intensive. Neither before nor during their college careers were the subjects' interests broad or in depth. The subjects were school-, course-, and test-oriented and rarely left the campus for excursions into the city for concerts, museums, or lectures. True, they were poor or barely subsisting on scholarships, but their interests in the cultural or abstract aspects of life were missing. For their leisure moments they expect entertainment rather than intellectual stimulation.

Heterosexual Activity

The subject was fourteen when he had his first date. On it he felt anxious but not guilty, ashamed, or disgusted. There also appeared to be no conflict with the family about his dating. His current sexual practices are confined to necking and occasional petting. Masturbation if indulged at all is practiced only occasionally. His sex experiences are pleasurable and are in conflict neither with himself nor his family. He finds dating pleasurable and gets along well with girls but does not plan to marry soon. Eventually he does plan to marry and at that time would definitely want children.

Goals

The subject's present chief aims are to finish college and go into group work. These are certainly realistic goals well within his grasp. In his chosen work he expects to earn between $5,000 and $6,000 a year, approximately his father's present earning. Whether he makes more or less money than his father or is famous is of little concern to the subject. The things he wants most out of life are happiness, a family, and service to others.

Both parents approve of his objectives, and the subject states that these have not changed to any extent in the last year or so. He feels that his future earning capacity will be adequate, and he expects to afford a house, have an active social life, and live comfortably. There is some doubt in his mind as to whether he will be able to afford a new car. On the whole his specific life goals are not like the father's, but the general pattern is similar. He is slightly apprehensive lest he not reach these goals, but this is not a grave fear. On the whole he is confident that he will succeed.

Self-Image

The subject feels quite positive about himself. He sees himself as "sensitive to others' feelings about him," as "realistic about himself and others," as "upright and honest," and "as a leader of others." He does not picture himself as "nervous" or "solitary." He "accepts himself as he is," "cares what other people think of him," and fundamentally "respects himself." He realistically does not "consider himself superior to his classmates" and "accepts advice easily." He is "tolerant of new ideas" and has a "secure" social adaptation, "many friends," and is "average" in his class participation in which he often "contributes ideas." He feels that he has "moderate potentiality for growth" and pictures himself both as a "thinker and a doer." Thus it appears that he has managed to preserve his feeling of self-worth.

Impulsivity

The usual family origin, the developmental milieu, and the personality of the subjects were not those characteristic of juvenile delinquents, and correspondingly such behavior did not occur frequently. They had suitable male models, help in occupational choice, freedom, opportunities for socially acceptable group participation, family tradition, and so forth. In addition most of the students characterologically had substan-

205

tial and effective internalized controls. The average subject has had practically no trouble with those in authority but is perhaps somewhat less than flexible when he maintains that he would abide by rules that he considered to be unfair. This view is not surprising, however, in the light of his somewhat dependent nature. This coupled with a tendency toward compulsivity gives the picture of an individual who would be submissive to authority, but not slavishly.

Neurotic Qualities

There is some tendency for the subject to do things repetitively and also to think repetitive thoughts in order to be sure they are correct. There seems to be a mild compulsive flavoring to the subject's personality—not crippling but still enough to decrease his spontaneity. Earlier it was stated that both parents evidenced similar characteristics in their behavior.

Though he claims to "like responsibility," he feels that he "needs advice on important matters." These two statements are not, of course, mutually exclusive, but it is interesting to note that along with an expression of independence there is also an expressed need for aid from others. There may be "some difficulty in getting started doing things," yet "carrying out assigned tasks" is very easy for the subject. Mild dependency needs seem to be expressed in these statements, and thus the lack of leadership qualities hinted at in the section on adolescence seems more understandable. Operating within an established framework, however, the subject might make a very good leader. He can be aggressive, and he can lead others if he feels it is for the good of a cause or in order to please a superior.

Emotionality

The subject claims that he is not easily made sad, angry, or anxious. Depression, anger, and excitement, when they do occur, are overcome mainly through physical activities, for example, walking, swimming, working it out. The method of coping with anxiety, on the other hand, is through relaxation. Envy, shame, guilt, and embarrassment are handled mainly by denial, for example, "forget it," "talk myself out of it," "think of something else." The subject reacts to depression by a feeling of boredom and tenseness which makes work and study difficult. When angry there is a tendency either to speak out, argue verbally, or plunge into activities.

Certainly, the subject's emotional life is not a stormy one. When depressed, his efficiency is somewhat reduced, but he has a tendency to work out his emotional low periods by hard work and physical exercise.

He does not seek refuge in fantasy nor do his moods persist for any appreciable time. The greatest trouble, crisis, or disappointment experienced by the subject was school failure, losing a girl friend, or death in the family. His reaction to the crisis was relatively short-lived and was overcome mainly by burying himself in work or some other form of striving. Again we see evidence of the subject's resiliency in response to stress. The subject maintains that the best thing that ever happened to him was either a woman ("meeting my wife," "going with a girl") or scholastic success. There has been no mental illness in any subject's family. If he were emotionally troubled, he feels that he would probably see a psychiatrist. He does not feel that mental illness is a stigma.

SUMMARY FROM QUESTIONNAIRE DATA

As an instrument the questionnaire was intended as a check on the findings elicited by interviews and as a means of complementing the data concerning the family, social, and cultural background of the subjects. In brief, it was devised as a personality and cultural inventory to confirm, complement, or differ from the interview data.

The typical student came from a stable home environment. He received much love from both parents and was treated in a consistent manner. He knew what to expect and because of this was secure in his relationship to them. Family ideals were conservative, the stress being on responsibility and orderliness. His childhood was an active one, and he preferred the company of others to solitary play.

In high school he was not an outstanding student but was active socially and an ardent enthusiast for sports. There was and is continuing pressure from his parents to do well in school. This may be a source of some tension to the subject in that he is not primarily disposed toward intellectual pursuits. He finds studying somewhat difficult and is tense before examinations. He does not sleep as well as he would like, and he occasionally becomes depressed. It is at these times when school work becomes particularly difficult for him.

His interests are not particularly broad, and he lacks intellectual aspirations. He is motivated mainly by the wish to help others in a life of service. Though not particularly aggressive, he is capable of leading others. He does this mainly by virtue of strength which he receives from identifying with a cause greater than himself. He is religious and obtains considerable satisfaction from his beliefs, but he is not an ascetic.

The questionnaire findings revealed the following differences from the interview data: (1) indications of greater subject compulsivity and inflexibility; (2) greater emphasis by parents on neatness, orderliness, and control; (3) moderate adolescent rebellion; (4) several subjects (four in all) with past asocial or delinquent behavior; (5) more evidence of fear of failure in school; (6) greater evidence that money was the focus of parental dissension.

Differences between the Questionnaired Interviewed and Noninterviewed Subjects

The sixty-five interviewed students were derived from two groups. One consisted of thirty-one subjects seen in 1958 after they had been screened and diagnosed as healthy by psychological tests. They were paid volunteers for stress experiments, and the initial interview was part of the plan of procedure. The other group was composed of thirty-four self-selected students from eighty new male students who filled out our questionnaire during indoctrination week at the college in September 1959. They received no remuneration for answering the questionnaire or for the interview. Not one of them even asked for carfare, even though most of them worked after school and were financially hard pressed.

All of the subjects who had completed the questionnaire were contacted by mail and telephone in the hope that they would be available for an interview in which further information could be obtained. They were told that one of the purposes of the interview was to discuss the findings of the questionnaire as we had promised at the time it was filled out. The thirty-four who came to be interviewed obviously had immediate problems that they wished to discuss during the session. It was speculated that those who did not make an appointment to be interviewed might be less troubled or have fewer problems to discuss. On the surface, then, it appeared that those students who came for interviews were less healthy, more troubled, and more in need of help and guidance than the noninterview students. Did the questionnaire results substantiate these notions?

Because the results of the questionnaire could be tabulated separately for the two groups, it was only necessary to scan the data sheets and isolate those items for which relatively large differences appeared. Contingency tables were constructed and x^2 tests were calculated in order to determine the statistical significance. Differences which are significant at the 0.05 level or better will be reported (Table 11–1).

TABLE 11–1

Differences between Interview and Noninterview Subjects

ITEM	INTERVIEWED % (n = 33)	NONINTERVIEWED % (n = 47)	p VALUE
Subject was father's favorite	10	36	<0.05
Concern in family about			
Eating habits	36	74	<0.01
Staying out late	30	62	<0.02
Physical illness	24	63	<0.01
Clothes	39	66	<0.05
Orderliness	52	79	<0.02
Cleanliness	30	68	<0.01
Friends	30	66	<0.01
Discipline	33	66	<0.01
Respect for elders	30	64	<0.01
Social life	36	62	<0.05
Work	27	68	<0.001
Physical sports	30	57	<0.05
Dating	25	51	<0.05
Drinking	39	72	<0.01
Manners	36	72	<0.01
Routines	15	57	<0.001
Completion of tasks	33	72	<0.01
Responsibilities	36	68	<0.02
Mother's worst trait is "rigidity"	27	5	<0.05
Father is warm and understanding	58	83	<0.05
As a child, parents agreed with respect to my social life	59	32	<0.05
Father "slightly" or "not at all" successful as a father	29	6	<0.05
Received "none" or "some" love from father as a child	31	11	<0.05
Leader of a social group	65	37	<0.05
Leader of a sport group	60	88	<0.02
Suggestions accepted when member of social group	67	40	<0.05
Gets tense and anxious preparing for exams	39	70	<0.02
Hates to recite in class	6	36	<0.01
Doesn't like living in the dorm	37	9	<0.02
"Never knew what to expect" in way of discipline from mother	3	21	<0.05
Interested in participant sports	79	98	<0.02
Prefers classical music	58	28	<0.02
Relationship with woman "best that ever happened"	39	15	<0.05
Consider myself "changeable"	62	87	<0.05

First, it should be noted that none of the demographic variables differentiate the groups. There is a slight tendency for the interviewed group to come from larger cities, particularly Chicago, though this is not statistically significant. On the whole, the two groups come from the same socioeconomic background, are of the same religion, and do not differ significantly in age, marital status, intelligence, or class standing.

Half of the items that differentiate the two groups deal with concern in the family regarding various standards of behavior. On all of these variables there was more concern expressed by the families of the non-interviewed group. It is difficult to know whether more concern indicates a compulsive attitude or greater affectionate interest, and whether less concern indicates indifference or greater permissiveness for independence. Actually, the use of the term "concern" was the most ambiguous and ill-advised aspect of the questionnaire, a fact discovered by the monitors while the instrument was being used.

The relationship between father and subject appears to be quite different for the two groups. More of the noninterviewed subjects felt that their fathers were "not at all" or only "slightly" successful as fathers, and, as children, they more often felt that they received "none" or only "some" love from father. The severity of disciplinary measures meted out by father is not different for the two groups. The fathers of the interviewed group, then, though not harsh tyrants, seem to have shown less love and understanding of their sons in childhood than was true of the noninterviewed group.

The more positive relationship with father experienced by the noninterviewed group may have resulted in a stronger masculine identification in later years. The data seem to bear this out. Though the interviewed group subjects were more often leaders of social groups in adolescence, the noninterviewed people were more often leaders of a sport group. As children the interviewed group claimed that their parents always agreed with respect to their social life. The interviewed subjects are less interested in participant sports and more often prefer classical to other varieties of music. There are more objections to living in the dormitory by the interviewed subjects, presumably because of interference with their social life. The interviewed people seem to be more socially oriented than the noninterviewed group. They are more the indoor type, less interested in sports, and somewhat more aesthetic in their interests. Their relations with women are more important to them than is the case with the noninterviewed subjects. They more often named a relationship with a woman as the "best thing that ever happened to them."

School work is more anxiety-provoking for the noninterviewed group. They become tense and anxious preparing for examinations and more often hate to recite in class than do the interview people. The fact that the interviewed group more often had suggestions accepted when members of a social group indicates that they were more persuasive—perhaps more facile verbally.

SUMMARY

Though we have concentrated on the differences between the interviewed and noninterviewed group, it should be emphasized that, in the main, their responses to the questionnaire were very similar. The picture of the George Williams student applies equally well to both groups. The differences that exist are not on the health-sickness continuum but rather reflect different sets or basic orientations toward their life goals.

The interviewed group is more socially oriented, perhaps more verbal and more aesthetic in their interests. They are less the rugged outdoor type which characterizes the noninterviewed group. They seem to have less difficulty in school and work under less tension.

One might speculate that the interviewed group would make better group workers than the noninterviewed people, who might fit in better as athletic directors or in jobs that involved them directly in activities with youth. They are less prone to talk about things and feel most at home in doing them. Perhaps it is for this reason they avoided the interview situation, seeing nothing of value in talking, whereas those that came sensed a chance to learn more about themselves so that they, in turn, could be more effective in dealing with others.

Statistical Studies of Questionnaire Data

Though the George Williams group presents a general picture of healthy mental functioning and adequate adjustment to its environment, elements of pathology show through. We saw evidences of moderately rigid character structures, passivity, paucity of interest, and indications of anxiety related to possible failure. If several indicators of pathology cluster together in the same individuals and not in others, statements could be made about their relative mental health. To gain further information on this point, it was first decided to divide the questionnaire into various functional categories (according to our value judgments) and obtain scores for each. In this way a given individual could be represented by a relatively small number of scores, and correlations between areas could be obtained across subjects. Such a procedure would be difficult if we used all the questionnaire data consisting of 700 items. The significant categories seemed to be home life, parental relations to each other, mother image, father image, childhood interests, adolescent problems, religious intensity, ambitions, self-image, and neurotic symptoms. Originally it was our intention to give each subject a score for each of these categories that would reflect either the intensity or the positive aspects of the behavior, feelings, or activities involved. We could then examine the subjects' profiles to determine the presence of patterns or clusters. This attempt was discarded, however, as many of the categories seemed to defy any rational sort of codification. For example, the questions making up the category home life tapped so many different areas that to weight and sum these items for a meaningful over-all score would be arbitrary at best. Therefore, a different approach was adopted in which sixteen selected items from several different sections of the questionnaire were subjected to analysis. The items and the percentage of subjects answering either true or false are listed in Table 11–2.

TABLE 11–2

Questionnaire Items Used in Intercorrelation Study

	ITEM	PERCENTAGE YES	NO
1	Amount of love received from father in childhood*		
2	Amount of love received from mother in childhood*		
3	Increased conflict with parents in adolescence	53	47
4	Gets tense and anxious preparing for exams	57	43
5	Strictness of father's discipline during childhood and adolescence*		
6	Discipline from parents upsetting	48	52
7	Punishment received from parents inconsistent	45	55
8	Belong or belonged to a boys' club	67	33
9	Play a musical instrument	38	62
10	Do not enjoy sex experiences	26	74
11	Expect to earn more than father	56	44
12	Worried about reaching goal in life	38	62
13	Tend to do things repetitively	53	47
14	Need advice on important matters	68	32
15	Suspicious that other people don't like me	22	78
16	Consider myself to be nervous	37	63

* These items are not yes-no and so were dichotomized at the median.

ITEM INTERCORRELATIONS

Items were selected on the basis of (1) their being representative of some fairly global areas (for example, discipline, amount of love received from parents) and (2) the degree to which they are differentiated by the group. An item that is endorsed by all subjects would obviously have to be rejected; because the item has zero variance, it is impossible to determine its covariation with other items. Consequently items that approximated a 50-50 dichotomization (that is, endorsed by half of the group) were included, whereas those endorsed by only a small percentage of the group were rejected. Sixteen items met these criteria of representativeness and discriminability.

Tetrachoric correlations were computed, resulting in a 16×16 correlation matrix. The correlations are low, though thirty are significant at better than the 0.01 level.

The highest correlation is between amount of love received in childhood from mother (item 2) and amount received from father (item 1). Amount of love received from father correlates positively with boys' club membership (item 8). One might infer that love received from father is instrumental in fostering male identity in the subjects which would predispose them to joining a boys' club.

Increased conflict (item 3) with the parents during adolescence correlates positively with both the inconsistency of discipline (item 7) received from parents and the degree to which this discipline was upsetting to the subject (item 6). Increased conflict (item 3) also relates to suspicion (item 15) on the subject's part that others do not like him. Finally there is a negative correlation between getting tense and anxious while preparing for examinations (item 4) and increased conflict with parents at adolescence (item 3). It is interesting to note that conflict is related to disciplinary measures and not to amount of love received during childhood.

Being tense and anxious (item 4) while preparing for examinations correlated positively with the upsetting nature of punishment (item 6), worrying over life's goals (item 12), and describing oneself as nervous (item 16). This seems to be a general anxiety or apprehension syndrome connected with fear of possible failure. The degree to which punishment is upsetting is also correlated with wanting to earn more than father (item 11) and feeling that others do not like one (item 15).

Playing a musical instrument (item 9) correlates positively with the tendency to do things repetitively (item 13). Individuals who state that

213

TABLE 11–3

Behavior Rating Scale A

	1	2	3	4	5
1. Does he appear to be characteristically placid and relaxed, or tense and "nervous"? (Consider such signs as fidgeting, tremors, muscle twitching, body rigidity, and sweating)	Placid and relaxed	As relaxed as average	Distinctly tense	Conspicuously tense	
2. Compared with others are his reactions (walking, talking, gestures) slower and more deliberate or do they appear faster or hurried?	Markedly slower or delayed	A little slower	As fast as average	A little faster	Conspicuously faster or hurried
3. Compared to the average person, how taciturn or talkative is he? (Judge only the amount of speech; do not consider its relevance or whether it was spontaneous or elicited by questioning)	Mute throughout interview	Distinctly less	As talkative as average	Distinctly more	Conspicuously overtalkative
4. Compared to others how hostile is he? Does he bear little hostility or a high degree of ill will, resentment, bitterness, or hate?	No hostility	Relatively low	As much as average	Relatively high	Extreme hostility
5. Is he, or does he easily become, concerned, uneasy, or apprehensive to a degree not called for by external circumstances?	Unconcerned	A little anxious	Distinctly anxious	Paralyzing or disrupting anxiety	
6. Compared to others, how loud or intense is his speech? Is it barely audible or is it loud and (or) intense?	Almost inaudible	Distinctly less audible or less intense	As loud as average	Distinctly louder or more intense	Shouts or yells
7. To what degree is he concerned or preoccupied with his health and the functioning of his bodily organs?	No concern	A little concerned	Moderately concerned	Extremely concerned and preoccupied	

TABLE 11–3 (continued)

	1	2	3	4	5
8. Consider how favorably he appears to regard himself. Does he tend to be self-depreciatory (feel inferior, inadequate) or conceited (feel self-assured, important, superior)?	Conspicuously self-depreciatory	Inclined to be self-depreciatory	Neither self-depreciatory nor conceited	Inclined to be self-important	Conspicuously conceited
9. Compared to others, is he controlled, restrained, inhibited and unable to show feelings, or is he more inclined to be unrestrained, uncontrolled, or free in showing feeling?	Conspicuously restrained or frozen	Distinctly restrained	As restrained as the average	Distinctly unrestrained	Conspicuously unrestrained
10. Consider his typical emotional tone or mood. Is he depressed or elated? If a subject is so lacking in emotional responsiveness as to provide no basis for a judgment, mark unratable.	Deeply depressed	Moderately depressed	Neither depressed nor elated	Moderately elated	Highly elated
11. How emotionally responsive does he appear to be? Does he tend to show an under-reaction or an over-reaction to situations?	Little or no sign of feeling	Inadequate feeling	Adequate feeling	A distinct overresponse	A marked overresponse
12. To what extent does he display neurotic symptoms?	Marked absence of symptomology	Slight evidence of symptoms	Symptoms present but not well defined	Clearly defined symptomological pattern	
13. How well adapted is he to present life demands?	Poorly adapted	Marginal adaptation	Fairly well adapted but with heavy cost	Normal adaptation, few costs	Effortless adaptation, no costs

sex is not enjoyable (item 10) also tend to do things repetitively (item 13). Whether masturbation guilt is involved in this pairing of compulsivity and denial of sex is an open question. Finally it was found that being worried about reaching life's goals (item 12) is correlated with feeling that people do not like one (item 15).

FACTOR ANALYSIS

In an attempt to isolate clusters of variables, a factor analysis of the correlation matrix was undertaken employing Thurstone's centroid method with subsequent orthogonal rotation. Two factors were only doublets; others were generally weak and unsatisfactory and indicated only tenuous relationships between the present and the past. Two factors representing polarities suggesting the extremes among this sample population are factor A: received much love from father during childhood, received much love from mother during childhood, belong or belonged to a boys' club, play a musical instrument; factor B: discipline received from parents upsetting, increased conflict with parents in adolescence, punishment received from parents inconsistent, get tense and anxious preparing for examinations, suspicious that other people don't like me, received little love from father during childhood.

Factor analyses did not give us much more insight into the item interrelationships than did the raw correlations. The absence of any factor with high loadings (rarely above 0.35) on a number of the items is in part a result of the relatively low order of correlations. The items, then, though sharing some common variance, are relatively independent of one another.

Rating Scales

A rating scale was drawn up which included 11 items from Lorr's Psychiatric Rating Scale plus 2 additional items. The items were selected on the basis of their applicability to normal subjects. The scale, hereafter referred to as Behavior Rating Scale A (BRSA), is reproduced in Table 11–3. Items 12 and 13 are particularly germane to this study, in that they are both global measures of adjustment.

The thirty-four interviewed subjects of the eighty who filled out questionnaires in 1959 were rated on BRSA approximately a year after the psychiatric interviews by the interviewer utilizing notes made at the time of interviewing. Most of the scales show little spread, there having been a tendency by the single rater to use only one or two points on the scale indicating the homogeneity of the group. The distributions for item 4 (hostility) and item 12 (neuroticism) and item 13 (adaptation), however, cover all scale points, with items 4 and 13 approximating normal distribution. Because items 12 and 13 are both global measures of adjustment, a product moment correlation was computed. The resulting coefficient was −0.537, which indicates a moderate degree of relationship. The relationship is negative, because high adjustment scores are rated at opposite ends for the two scales.

Because a factor analytic procedure failed to yield factors highly loaded on a number of variables, a more rational approach to scale construction was attempted. A scale measuring neuroticism (Table 11–4) was constructed from the trait universe of the questionnaire. Only one subject has a score higher than 14. Because the possible range on this specific scale is from a zero score (absence of neurotic symptoms) to thirty-five, our subjects are on the low end of the continuum. We have no index of consistency for this scale nor have we tested it on other populations, either normal or neurotic.

TABLE 11–4
Neuroticism Scale

1	I have trouble studying	19	People find it difficult to know me
2	I get tense and anxious preparing for exams	20	Have many conflicts in my mind
3	I get tense and anxious before exams	21	Tend to do things impulsively
4	I feel inferior to my classmates	22	Mind can be changed easily
5	Am alarmed when I get sick	23	Have missed lots of important things in life
6	Do not enjoy sex experiences	24	Have feelings of inferiority
7	Sex causes conflicts in me	25	Cannot plan and carry out assigned tasks
8	Dating is not enjoyable	26	Difficult to get started doing things
9	Do not get along well with girls	27	Repeat things to be sure they are correct
10	Worried about reaching my goal in life	28	Difficult to confide in people
11	Am not confident that I can achieve my goals	29	Not well liked by classmates
12	Tend to do things repetitively	30	Can be upset easily
13	Tend to think thoughts repetitively	31	Upset at others' disapproval
14	Trouble making decisions	32	Have trouble solving problems
15	Delay decisions	33	Cannot take a firm stand on important issues
16	Do not like responsibility	34	Do not feel emotionally free
17	Upset by obstacles requiring time and effort	35	Am a compulsive person
18	Find it hard to make friends		

Questionnaire neuroticism scores were correlated with items 12 and 13 of the psychiatric ratings on the BRSA. Questionnaire neuroticism correlated 0.279 ($p =$ NS) with item 12 (neurotic symptomatology) but -0.616 ($p <0.001$) with item 13 (adaptiveness). Because the items that make up the neuroticism scale are statements reflecting the degree of adjustment or the kind of adaptation to the subject's environment, it is not surprising that they fail to correlate highly with amount of overt symptomatology. What is encouraging, however, is that psychiatric ratings of adaptation to life demands correlate so highly with the individual's own statements concerning this capacity.

Assessment of Adjustment

Because the questionnaire neuroticism scores correlated so highly with the psychiatric ratings, it was decided to use them as measures of adjustment for the entire George Williams sample. Of the eighty subjects originally included in the sample, three were dropped because they had failed to answer five or more items on the neuroticism scale. This score range was 0–24 with a mean score of 9.38 and a standard deviation of 5.06. The group was divided arbitrarily into three fairly equal groups. One included twenty-four subjects whose scores ranged from 0–6; one included thirty subjects whose scores ranged from 7–11; and the third included the remaining twenty-three subjects with scores higher than 11. Hereafter these groups will be referred to as very well adjusted (VWA), fairly well adjusted (FWA), and marginally adjusted (MA), respectively. In a comparative study of these three groups on the basis of their questionnaire responses, particular attention will be focused on the differences between the two extreme adjustment groups.

The result will be discussed with reference to the following areas: home life, parental relationships, mother, father, siblings, childhood interests, adolescent activities, adolescent problems, school, health, sexual adjustment, goals and ambitions, self-image, and emotionality (Table 11–5).

The composition of the three groups does not differ significantly with respect to the major demographic variables of age, religion, marital status, place of birth, graduate or undergraduate status, number of siblings, father's salary, or father's occupation. Though there is no difference in birth order, there are fewer individuals in the VWA group with sisters

218

TABLE 11-5

The Marginally Adjusted Group compared with the Very Well-Adjusted Group

HOME LIFE	p VALUE
Few complaints about home life	<0.02
Few arguments in home	<0.20
Parental	
Less permissiveness for independent strivings	<0.20
Less concern in family about:	
Not telling them everything	<0.20
Dating	<0.20
Smoking	<0.20
Drinking	<0.20
Confided in both parents rather than only one	<0.20
"Take after" one or the other parent rather than neither	<0.10
Parental loving attitudes to each other were open	<0.20
Parents agreed with respect to child's discipline	<0.20
Father less often made disciplinary decision alone	<0.10
Parents agreed with respect to child's social life	<0.10
Father less often made decision alone on child's social life	<0.20
Father less often made decision alone regarding parental social life	<0.20
Discipline meted out by parents less upsetting	<0.20
MOTHER	
As a child, saw mother as warmer, closer, and more relaxed	<0.05
As a child, more grateful in the presence of mother	<0.05
More consistency in mother's discipline during childhood	<0.05
Earliest memory less often included mother	<0.05
More mothers in good health	<0.02
Less often stated that they were raised mostly by mother	<0.10
Did not describe mother as aggressive	<0.20
More often considered as stable by mother	<0.20
As a child, saw mother as more encouraging and attractive	<0.20
As a child, felt that mother was a more successful housewife	<0.20
FATHER	
Received as much love as wanted in childhood and adolescence	<0.05
More often considered as stable by father	<0.05
As a child, saw father as closer and more sympathetic	<0.10
As a child, saw father as warmer, more permissive and more active	<0.20
More fathers in good health	<0.10
SIBLINGS	
Next oldest or next youngest sibling less often a girl	<0.05
Greater age difference between subject and next younger	<0.02
Helped take care of next younger sibling	<0.05
Less often want to do better than siblings	<0.20
CHILDHOOD INTERESTS	
Did better in school	<0.05
Enjoyed school more	<0.10
As a child, wanted to be professional person when grown up	<0.20
Earliest memory more often painful experience	<0.20
ADOLESCENT ACTIVITIES	
More often played with older children	<0.05
More often played with children of own age	<0.10

More often enjoyed group activities	<0.20
Was more often leader of a work or study group	<0.20
As a member of a social group, more often suggested games, etc.	<0.20

ADOLESCENT PROBLEMS

Less conflict with parents	<0.02
Less misunderstood by parents	<0.05
Less worried over the future	<0.05
Less often developed jitters	<0.20
Became more responsible	<0.20

PRESENT FUNCTIONING

School

More often contribute ideas in class	<0.05
English more often best high school or college subject	<0.10
Less often hate to recite in class	<0.20

HEALTH

More often have headaches	<0.10
More physically fit	<0.20

SOCIAL ACTIVITIES

More often watch television musicals	<0.20
More often prefer "sweet" music	<0.20

SEXUAL ADJUSTMENT

More often date girls who are like mother	<0.20

GOALS AND AMBITIONS

More often state that they will do YMCA work after college	<0.02
Less often state that they will enter the service after college	<0.10
More value placed on family and parents	<0.10
More often state that present ambition is to finish college	<0.20
More often expect to have an active social life	<0.10

SELF-IMAGE

More often leaders of others	<0.01
More often strong as a personality	<0.02
More often determined	<0.05
More active social participation	<0.05
Not suspicious that others don't like them	<0.01
Less often need advice on important matters	<0.05
More often see self as affectionate	<0.02
Fewer troubles, crises, or disappointments in life	<0.10
Reaction to disappointments or crises of short duration	<0.01
Less often like to be left alone	<0.10
Less often have daydreams	<0.20
Fewer daydreams about fame and winning	<0.20
Less sensitive to other people's feelings about them	<0.10
Less often consider self as solitary	<0.10
Less often consider self as gregarious	<0.20
Consider self to have many friends	<0.10
More often discriminating in accepting new ideas	<0.10
More often secure in social adaptation	<0.10
Greater potentiality for growth	<0.20
More often describe self as thinker	<0.10

EMOTIONALITY

Better emotional adjustment	<0.05
Less often nervous or anxious	<0.01
Less easily made anxious	<0.05
Less sweating when anxious	<0.10
Less difficulty in thinking when anxious	<0.10
Less easily depressed	<0.05
Less often depressed	<0.10
Less often feel hopeless when depressed	<0.01
Less often bored when depressed	<0.20

TABLE 11–5 (*continued*)

Less often angered at disapproval	<0.05	Less often shameful	<0.20
		Less often guilty	<0.05
Less often become silent when angry	<0.20	Less often embarrassed	<0.20

in comparison with both the FWA and MA groups. The difference is largely accounted for by the relatively small number in the VWA group who have older sisters. On the other hand, both the VWA and FWA groups include a greater percentage of individuals who have brothers than is true of the MA group. Thus, the very well-adjusted (VWA) group differs from the marginally adjusted group in having relatively more individuals with at least one brother and relatively fewer individuals having at least one sister. The well-adjusted group might be thought of as brother-oriented, whereas the marginally adjusted group is sister-oriented.

When we look at the next oldest and next youngest siblings, we find that only three of the VWA group displaced or were displaced by a girl. In the MA group this occurred for slightly more than half the subjects. The mean age difference between individuals in the VWA group and their next youngest sibling is four years, eight months, for the FWA group, three years eleven months, and for the MA group, two years nine months; the VWA-MA and FWA-MA differences are significant.

HOME LIFE

The VWA group had fewer complaints about their home life than did the two less well-adjusted groups. There were also somewhat fewer family arguments in the VWA group. Of the remaining five items concerning home life, the VWA group indicates more positive feelings than the MA group on four. The over-all attitude toward the home is more positive for the very well-adjusted group than the marginally adjusted with the fairly well-adjusted group falling somewhere in between, albeit somewhat closer to the VWA group.

PARENTAL RELATIONSHIPS

The parents of the MA group were somewhat more permissive in encouraging independent strivings in their sons, though there was more concern over dating, smoking, and drinking. We might infer from this that the MA parents were more conservative or moralistic in the han-

221

dling of their children. We do not know whether their relatively greater permissiveness was a reflection of lack of concern or a genuine interest in sponsoring their children's sense of independence. The greater concern over their children "not telling them everything" may reflect an unrealistic, overly demanding attitude on the part of the MA parents. What is pointed up, however, is the inconsistency of these parents who, on the one hand, seem to be more permissive, yet, on the other hand, demand more from their children.

There was more open expression of affection between the parents of the VWA group. In fact, there appears to have been much more compatibility and agreement in a number of areas for the parents of the VWA group. They more often agreed with respect both to the child's social life and disciplinary measures to be administered. Perhaps, because of this, the VWA group were less upset by the discipline actually received.

Identification patterns seem to be more strongly fixed in the VWA group, in that they, more often than the MA group, state that they take after at least one of their parents. There is some indication that the MA group may have played one parent against the other, in that they less often confided in both parents. Unfortunately our data do not reveal in which parent confidence was placed.

Subjects checked twenty-six areas of concern ranked in order of importance placed on each area by their own family. These items were ranked by order of importance within each adjustment group, and group correlations were computed. All relationships are highly significant, showing that the relative significance of the items does not differ from group to group; for example, concern over masturbation was minimal in all three groups, whereas concern over order is maximal. This demonstrates the cultural uniformity in the home background of the subjects and the homogeneity of their value orientations. Group differences, then, are more clearly the end result of the interpersonal relations the subjects experienced during their formative years.

The over-all picture, then, of parental relationships is much more positive for the VWA group. Their parents were more often in agreement about their children's upbringing, were more often in agreement with one another, and more openly expressed their affection for one another. There also seemed to be a less rigid concern over dating, smoking, and drinking. The FWA parents, though somewhat more rigid and less in agreement than the VWA parents, are not so cold and restrained in their relationships as the MA parents.

MOTHER

The relationship with mother is quite different for the two extreme groups. We shall report the most significant ($p < 0.05$) differences first. The VWA group state that, as children, they saw their mother as warmer, closer, and more relaxed than did the MA group. In the presence of mother they also felt more grateful. One gets the picture, then, of a much closer and more rewarding mother-child relationship for the VWA group. In addition to the closeness there is also a greater degree of consistency. The VWA group mention more consistency in mother's discipline during childhood.

There is some indication that, though the mother-child relationships for the MA group were less rewarding, they were nevertheless important. When asked for their earliest memories, significantly more of the MA group include mother. They also state more frequently that they were raised mostly by mother. One certainly does not get the picture of openly rejecting mothers. An interesting relationship is that between degree of adjustment of the subjects and the present physical health of their mothers. Practically none of the VWA group as contrasted with slightly more than one third of the MA group state that mother is not in good health. This concept of poor physical health of the mother is not likely to be real but perhaps a way in which the mothers of the MA group held their children close to them and more dependent.

Other, less significant (statistically) findings parallel those already discussed. The VWA group as children perceived mother as more encouraging and attractive. Furthermore, they felt mother was more successful in her role as a housewife. Mothers' present views of them are more positive: They more frequently consider their sons as stable. In describing mother's worst trait, more of the MA group mention some form of aggressiveness. The fairly well adjusted (FWA) group more closely resembles the MA group in its relationships to mother. As a matter of fact, as children they saw mother as even less encouraging than did the MA group.

FATHER

As was the case with mother, the VWA group perceives father in more positive terms than does the MA group. A significantly greater percentage of VWA individuals stated that they received as much love as they wanted or needed from father, both during childhood and ado-

223

lescence. Furthermore, the VWA group is more often considered as stable by their fathers.

Though statistically less significant, the VWA group viewed father in a more positive light even during childhood. They saw him as warmer, closer, and more sympathetic, also as more permissive and active. The over-all picture than is one of a closer, more intense relationship with father by the VWA group.

Interestingly enough, we obtained a significant relationship between degree of adjustment of the subjects and the present physical health of father. To say that physically healthy parents tend also to be mentally healthy parents who are more likely to raise mentally healthy children appears to be a grossly oversimplified explanation, though the relationship seems to exist.

That the fathers of the MA group are less permissive is also indicated by their rather strict control of family decision-making. Among the MA group it was the father's word that prevailed with respect to the child's discipline and his social life. Also it was father who most often made the decision regarding parental social life. As was indicated in a previous section, there was less parental agreement in a number of areas for the parents of the MA group. Apparently father's word was law or at least more so in the MA group than in the families of the VWA group where mutual decision-making was the rule.

The FWA group is much closer to the very well-adjusted group both in their perception of father and in the amount of love received from him. As a matter of fact, they perceived father as slightly warmer and closer than did the VWA group, though the difference is not statistically significant.

SIBLINGS

More of the VWA subjects state that they helped take care of their next younger sibling. In a previous section it was shown that the age difference between the subject and his next younger sibling was greatest for the VWA group. It is reasonable to conclude, therefore, that more of the VWA individuals would have been old enough at the time of the birth of the next younger sibling to help in caring of the infant, whereas the MA subjects, who were only two plus years of age, would still be dependent on their mothers. The MA subjects might have been more resentful of the new child and perceived him more as a competitor for mother's love. There is some indication of sibling rivalry in the MA group, in that they more often state that they want to do better than

224

their brothers and sisters. Open hostility to their siblings is not evident, however, since 90 percent of the individuals in each adjustment group maintain that they get along well with their brothers and sisters. With respect to sibling relationships the FWA group closely parallels the VWA group.

CHILDHOOD INTERESTS

As children, the VWA did significantly better in school than the MA group, whereas the FWA group was intermediate. More of the VWA and FWA individuals enjoyed school, indicating stronger motivation for study. That the difference in performance levels for the three groups is not owing to intelligence factors was substantiated by a comparison of the test scores which do not differ significantly.

When asked what they, as children, fantasied or imagined they would want to be when they grew up, more of the VWA group mentioned some type of professional person. More frequent for the MA group were choices of fireman, policeman, soldier, and the like. It would appear then that the VWA group, even as children, set higher goals for themselves, though we shall see in a later section that none of the groups are particularly motivated for personal achievement.

Subjects were asked to describe the earliest event that they could recall. More of the VWA group mentioned incidents which involved painful experiences, for example, falling or being hit by a rock. Did these subjects actually experience more trauma during their early years, or is it merely that they have had to repress less than the MA group? If they actually were exposed to more trauma and in small enough doses, it may have made them more immune to disturbances later in life.

ADOLESCENT ACTIVITIES

Members of the VWA group were socially more active during adolescence than individuals in the MA group. Not only did the VWA adolescents more often enjoy group activities, but they were also more often leaders of work or study groups. Furthermore, as members of social groups, the VWA individuals more often suggested games, topics of conversation, and the like. The MA group, on the other hand, showed a tendency to enjoy solitary activities more, though the difference fails to be significant. Members of the MA group played relatively more with younger children or contemporaries, whereas the VWA group individuals played with all age groups and significantly more often than the MA people with older children. Adolescence, then, was a period of greater

225

social involvement for the very well-adjusted group. During this period they developed their leadership abilities and were probably exposed to more stimulating and challenging contacts by virtue of their associations with older children. The pattern for the FWA group is intermediate to the two extreme groups in this area.

ADOLESCENT PROBLEMS

Adolescence appears to have been a much more stressful period for the MA group. They reported increasing conflict with their parents, felt that their parents did not understand them, and worried more over the future than the VWA group. Practically none of the VWA group state that they developed "jitters" during adolescence, whereas almost one out of four in the MA group voices this complaint. The very well-adjusted group more often claims to have become more responsible during adolescence.

SCHOOL FUNCTIONING

In a previous section it was indicated that the MA group not only did less well in school as children but also enjoyed it less than those in the VWA group. Does this pattern exist at present as far as their work at college is concerned? Both groups indicate that they enjoyed George Williams College. Two of the VWA group flunked out whereas four of the MA group failed, not a significant difference.

Members of the VWA group, however, do appear to be more involved in their school work. They more often contribute ideas in class and less often state that they "hate to recite in class." The relative nonparticipation of the marginally adjusted group may be a way of expressing their resentment of and subsequent hostility to authority. Their resentment of mother as children and their adolescent rebelliousness point to this possibility.

When asked to name their favorite high school or college subject the VWA group more often mentioned English. This may possibly reflect a greater verbal fluency on the part of the very well-adjusted group. It would coincide with their greater participation in class discussions and more frequent volunteering of suggestions in social groups.

HEALTH

The present physical health status of all subjects is good. Fewer of the MA group, however, describe their present physical fitness as excellent. Whether emotional factors are operating here or not is an open question. More of the VWA individuals are bothered by headaches.

SEXUAL ADJUSTMENT

Present sexual experiences are quite similar for the three adjustment groups. Because four of the items concerning present sexual adjustment were included in the neuroticism scale, which in turn was used to assess the subject's present level of adjustment, any consideration of sexual adequacy to adjustment would involve circular reasoning. One item, however, that does seem to be independent of the adjustment criterion is the degree to which individuals date girls who are like mother. More individuals in the very well-adjusted group claim this to be so.

GOALS

Individuals in the VWA group are more specific in stating the nature of the work they intend to do after completing college. The majority of them want to go into YMCA work of one kind or another. The MA group appears to be less focused in their goals; they more often mention that they will either go into the service or merely "work," the nature of which is unspecified. Although the VWA group appears to be thinking in terms of the future, they set up realistic short-term goals for themselves. When asked about their present chief ambition, more of the VWA people mention "finishing college." With respect to expectations for the future, more of the VWA people feel that they will have an active social life. This would appear to be a reasonable extrapolation from their childhood and adolescent experiences when they displayed more social participation than the MA group.

SELF-IMAGE

The VWA group currently displays a more active participation in their dealings with others. They state that they have many friends and more often than the MA group describe themselves as leaders of others. The MA group, on the other hand, more often like to be left alone and more often describe themselves as solitary.

The VWA individuals describe themselves as being "strong as a personality" and "determined." This general aspect of strength and stolidity is also reflected in their greater resiliency to stress. Though the VWA group has experienced fewer troubles, crises, and disappointments in life than the MA group, the adverse reactions to the crises that they did encounter were of shorter duration. Their strength and determination may also be viewed as a reflection of their relatively greater autonomy. The VWA group less often claimed that they needed advice on important matters. The MA people, on the other hand, though being more dependent on others, are more suspicious that others do not like them. They are also more sensitive to other people's feelings about them. These facts, coupled with their resentment noted earlier, suggest an individual characterized by needs both to approach and to avoid others.

There is some indication that the marginally adjusted group attempts more fantasy solutions to their problems. They more often engage in daydreaming and have relatively more dreams concerning fame and winning than do the VWA people. This ties in with rivalrous feelings toward siblings noted in an earlier section.

The VWA group is more often "discriminating in accepting new ideas," feel that they have a "greater potentiality for growth," and more often describe themselves as "thinkers." Findings for the FWA group parallel those for the VWA group.

EMOTIONALLY

The marginally adjusted individuals are less sure of their emotional adjustment. They more often admit to experiencing anxiety, depression, shame, guilt, and embarrassment. Individuals in the MA group are more easily made anxious than those of the VWA group. Moreover, when anxious they more often experience sweating and difficulty in thinking. None of the other anxiety symptoms differentiate the groups. Anxiety, then, does appear to be disruptive for the marginally adjusted group. It could well have been a contributing factor in their relatively poorer showing in school during childhood.

The MA people are more easily depressed than the VWA group. When depressed they more often feel hopeless and bored. Emotional states appear to inhibit their functioning, and there is a tendency to give up. Fantasy solutions provide some outlet but are apparently not wholly satisfactory.

How do the marginally adjusted people handle their anger, and what makes them angry? About one third of the MA group is angered at disapproval. Their chief way of handling their anger, however, is by becoming silent. They harbor resentments and fail to act on their feelings. The VWA and FWA groups, on the other hand, handle their anger more constructively by speaking out. This mode of response is most characteristic of the FWA group. In general, the FWA group more closely resembles the VWA than the MA group with respect to their over-all emotional adjustment.

Differential Perception of the Parents

In the questionnaire were included two questions concerning subject's memory of his childhood feelings about his parents' attitudes.[4] These are condensed in Table 11–6. The scales consist of ten descriptive bi-

TABLE 11–6

Differential Perception of Parents

AS A CHILD I FELT MY FATHER (MOTHER) WAS

	NOT AT ALL	SLIGHTLY	FAIRLY	VERY	NOT AT ALL	SLIGHTLY	FAIRLY	VERY
a	__	__	__	__	__	__	__	__
	encouraging				discouraging			
b	__	__	__	__	__	__	__	__
	permissive				authoritarian			
c	__	__	__	__	__	__	__	__
	rewarding				punishing			
d	__	__	__	__	__	__	__	__
	sympathetic				antagonizing			
e	__	__	__	__	__	__	__	__
	warm				cold			
f	__	__	__	__	__	__	__	__
	close				distant			
g	__	__	__	__	__	__	__	__
	active				passive			
h	__	__	__	__	__	__	__	__
	relaxed				tense			
j	__	__	__	__	__	__	__	__
	consistent				inconsistent			
k	__	__	__	__	__	__	__	__
	attractive				unattractive			

polar adjectives (warm-cold, relaxed-tense, and so on), which the subject rates separately for each parent. The range of scores possible for any single item is from 1 to 7. If, for example, a subject described father as very warm and not at all cold, he would receive a score of 1. At the other extreme, the description of father as being not at all warm and very cold would receive a score of 7. Thus, low scores reflect positive feelings, whereas high scores reflect negative or mixed feelings. The range of possible scores for the ten is 1 to 70. The actual ranges for our subject group are for father, 10 to 54, and for mother, 10 to 52. The scores are displaced toward the positive end of the scales. None of the subjects perceived the parents in a completely negative light.

What sort of questions will the data answer? First, we can determine the degree to which the three adjustment groups maintain positive feelings toward each of the parents. Second, we can determine whether or not positive feelings for one parent are associated with positive feelings for the other parent. Third, we can look at the patterning of responses for the three adjustment groups to see whether there are differences among them.

In Figure 11–1 the rating profiles for father are presented separately for each of the three adjustment groups. The mean over-all score for the VWA group is 26.2 and for the FWA group it is 26.8. The difference between the VWA group and the MA group (33.9), however, is highly significant ($p < 0.01$), as is the difference between the FWA and MA groups ($p > 0.01$). The two better adjusted groups then do not differ significantly in their over-all perception of father, but both regard father more positively than does the marginally adjusted group.

The patterning of responses presents a somewhat different picture. The VWA group correlates most highly with the MA group. The middle adjustment group (FWA) is deviant in several respects. It places relatively greater emphasis on father's consistency.

The rating profiles for mother are presented in Figure 11–2. The mean over-all score for the VWA group is 19.2, and for the FWA group it is 22.8. This difference is significant at the $p < 0.05$ level. The difference between the FWA and MA group (24.9), however, falls short of significance. The difference between the two extreme adjustment groups is highly significant ($p < 0.02$). For mother, then, the perceptions of the two less well-adjusted groups do not differ, though they both see mother in a more negative light than does the very well-adjusted group. The patterning of responses for the three groups is very similar as indicated by the profiles. Though there are differences in intensity of feeling for mother in the three groups, they all view mother in the same way. For instance, all three groups see mother as predominantly warm, close, encouraging and relatively less relaxed, rewarding, and permissive.

These results indicate that the very well-adjusted group sees both parents in a more positive light than the marginally adjusted group. The fairly well-adjusted group resembles the VWA group in the positive perception of father but resembles the MA group in the negative perception of mother. This raises an important question for further study. Does a positive father-son relationship make the difference between a

As a child I felt my father was:

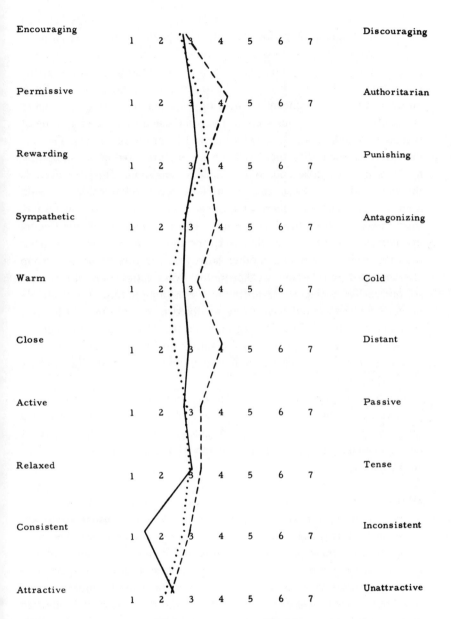

FIGURE 11–1. *Rating profiles for fathers. VWA* (———)*; FWA* (. . .)*; MA* (– – –)*.

fairly good adjustment and a more marginal adjustment, particularly in those cases where the mother-son relationship is weak?

Figures 11–3, 11–4, and 11–5 illustrate the relationships between the mother-father profiles for each of the adjustment groups separately. First, it should be pointed out that mother is seen as significantly more positive for all three groups. What is more interesting, however, is the patterning of the responses for the three groups. Only in the FWA group is there a significant correlation between the ratings for father and mother. In a previous section it was indicated that the patterning of responses to father for this group differed from the other two. The difference was such that the FWA group pictured father as somewhat more warm and close and somewhat less consistent. This, however, is the way mother is viewed, thus the high degree of relationship. It would appear then that the fathers of the FWA group are more "maternal" than fathers in the other two groups. The implications of this finding are not clear at this point; however, one might venture the hypothesis that father is acting as a mother surrogate for this group—a group characterized by relatively weaker mother-son relationships. If this were so, our earlier conjecture regarding the redeeming nature of a positively perceived father would have to be modified to include the notion of a "surrogate mother." The FWA group and the MA group differ both in the intensity of feelings toward the father and in the degree to which father is viewed structurally similar to mother; that is, the two factors are confounded.

Finally, one last consideration. Do individuals who view mother in a positive light view father positively also and vice versa? The answer is a qualified yes. The VWA and FWA groups show a marked degree of correspondence in their ratings, but the MA group shows no relationship whatsoever.

SUMMARY

In each of the areas investigated, the very well-adjusted group appears in a more positive light than the marginally adjusted. The relationships with their parents were quite satisfactory, and family life in general was more harmonious. Their parents agreed with respect both to their own activities and in matters concerning their children's rearing. More warmth was expressed in the homes of the very well-adjusted group, while the marginally adjusted group was more often characterized by somewhat rigidly demanding parents who were more inconsistent in their handling of the child.

232

As a child I felt my mother was:

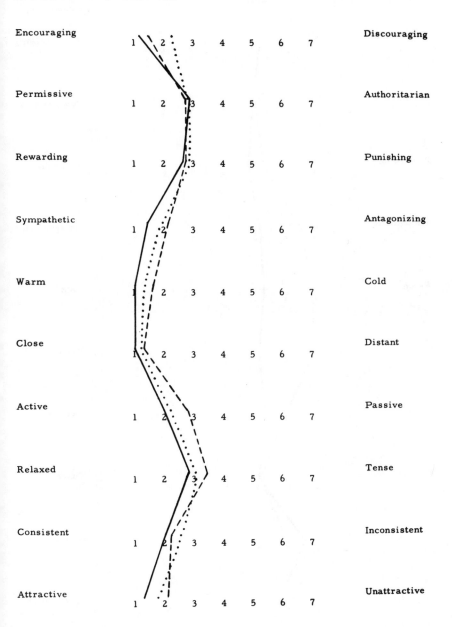

FIGURE 11–2. *Rating profiles for mothers. VWA* (——); *FWA* (. . .);
MA (– – –).

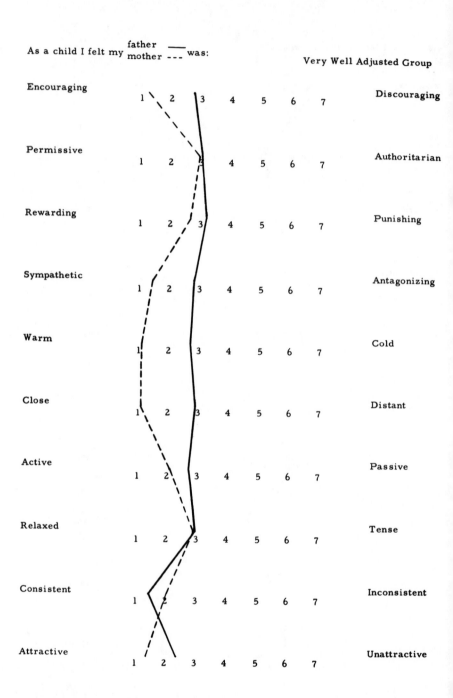

As a child I felt my father ——— mother - - - was:

Very Well Adjusted Group

Encouraging							Discouraging
Permissive							Authoritarian
Rewarding							Punishing
Sympathetic							Antagonizing
Warm							Cold
Close							Distant
Active							Passive
Relaxed							Tense
Consistent							Inconsistent
Attractive							Unattractive

FIGURE 11–3. *Relationship between mother and father profiles in VWA.*

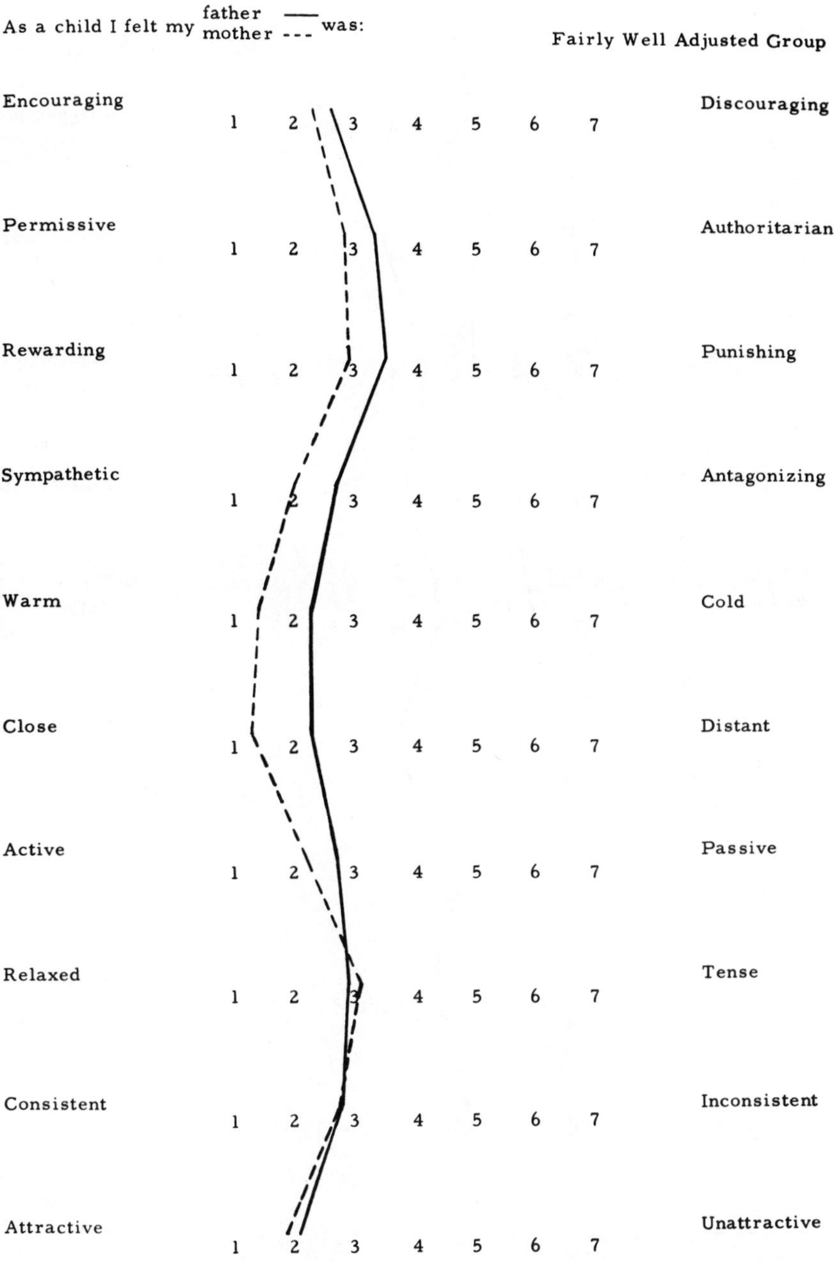

As a child I felt my father ——— was:
mother --- was:

Fairly Well Adjusted Group

Encouraging		1	2	3	4	5	6	7	Discouraging
Permissive		1	2	3	4	5	6	7	Authoritarian
Rewarding		1	2	3	4	5	6	7	Punishing
Sympathetic		1	2	3	4	5	6	7	Antagonizing
Warm		1	2	3	4	5	6	7	Cold
Close		1	2	3	4	5	6	7	Distant
Active		1	2	3	4	5	6	7	Passive
Relaxed		1	2	3	4	5	6	7	Tense
Consistent		1	2	3	4	5	6	7	Inconsistent
Attractive		1	2	3	4	5	6	7	Unattractive

FIGURE 11–4. *Relationship between mother and father profiles in FWA.*

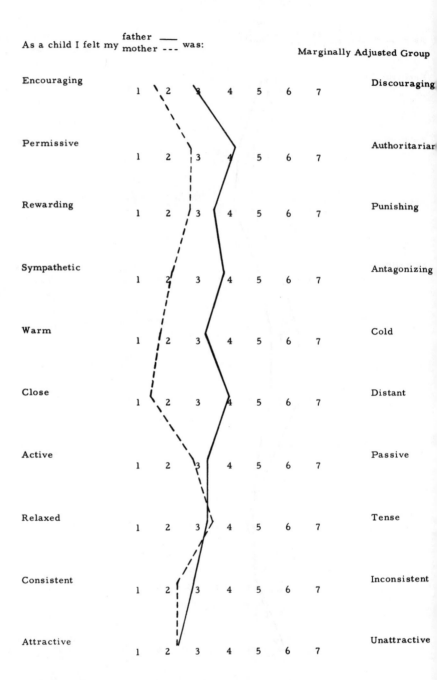

As a child I felt my father ——— mother - - - was:

Marginally Adjusted Group

Encouraging							Discouraging
Permissive							Authoritarian
Rewarding							Punishing
Sympathetic							Antagonizing
Warm							Cold
Close							Distant
Active							Passive
Relaxed							Tense
Consistent							Inconsistent
Attractive							Unattractive

FIGURE 11–5. *Relationship between mother and father profiles in MA.*

Though the marginally adjusted subjects feel that it is important to outdo their siblings, and desire fame and achievement, the record shows that they have fared less well than the very well-adjusted group. The MA group not only did less well in school as children but encountered more problems in adolescence than did the VWA group.

The very well-adjusted individuals are much more involved with others. They participate more openly both in their work and in their social relationships. They consider themselves as leaders of others more often than do the MA people and less often harbor resentments and antagonisms toward others.

The VWA group is more resilient to stress and less often experiences painful emotions. The MA group, on the other hand, suffers from anxiety and fits of depression in which things look hopeless and bleak. Though resentful of others and angered by disapproval, they seldom talk out or deal constructively with their anger.

The pattern, then, that seems to run through all the material is one of involvement and a decreased capacity for adequate functioning on the part of the marginally adjusted individuals. They want more than the very well-adjusted group but achieve less. It is this basic incongruity between desire and action wish and fulfillment that characterizes their less adaptive functioning.

Comparison Groups

A great amount of thought was expended in considering the problem of "controls" in order to neutralize biases implicit in the value judgments regarding "normality" and "mental illness." What should we control for —healthy versus sick, culture versus culture, or normal versus normal in different cultures? As the group for the Advancement of Psychiatry (1959) report, matched groups in this type of investigation are not comparable.

Our lack of a control group consisting of an entirely different population was compensated for by the use of our own fairly large sample of eighty students. These were expected to and actually indicate a good distribution into three groups that, within a generally "healthy" population, were very well-adjusted, fairly well-adjusted, and marginally adjusted. Comparisons among these groups resulted in significant differences which could be correlated with variations in behavior, performance, and feelings.

Though we had the possibility of internal comparisons for purposes of control, we still felt the need for comparison groups outside our population sample. It was decided to make comparisons with known and already studied groups and in the future, comparisons with other populations as their characteristics become known by research now in progress or planned. Aside from the comparisons already made in the text as individual variables were discussed, the populations described by Glueck, Golden, and Mandel (n.d.), Friedenberg and Roth (1954), Murphy (1959), and Lu (1961) are similar. Those described by Stein et al. (n.d.) as creative, and Silber, Humburg, Coelko, Murphey, Rosenberg, and Pearlin (1961) as competent, are contrasting groups. Certainly a more detailed literature search should disclose other similar and dissimilar groups.

Glueck et al. (n.d.) have recently reported their studies of a group from Minnesota similar to the George Williams subjects. During the ninth grade, at age fourteen, the subjects had been given the MMPI. Twelve years later at age twenty-five to twenty-six members of the group were restudied by means of interviews and further tests. About half had gone to college, and the others were white-collar or professional workers. Their goals and aspirations were unimaginative. Personalities were limited, and breadth of interest and strivings were shallow. The family and cultural backgrounds were strikingly similar to those reported for our subjects. However, these subjects also showed very little evidence of psychopathology.

Friedenberg and Roth (1954) studied the differences between students who achieved success or failure in graduate social science school at the University of Chicago. Their research design and their stereotyped profile of successful students are not essential to this context. However, among the nonachievers certain groups or classes were delineated, one of which (class C) resembles the George Williams students. These are termed the "muscular Christians" because they have a need for activity and a missionary zeal. They reveal the following traits:

1. Are practical-minded with a zeal to accomplish.
2. Sixty percent, though failing in school, feel that the university is giving them the interest and support they need.
3. Confidence produces conviction that their tasks are virtuous and satisfy their needs and values—though this has not helped them.
4. Interested in solidarity in campus life and leadership.
5. Need for activity.

6. Dislike of competition—belief in friendliness.
7. As a group, subjects are more satisfied than other groups.

Lois Murphy (1959) describes her subjects and their families as follows:

It is an unusually stable group in terms of job and residence. One might consider many of them "core American" families, stable, nonmobile, nonsuburban, nonambitious even. They do not look for more interesting or challenging work or higher salaries; nor do they move because they'd like to live in a different or more pleasant climate or find out what California looks like. They are Kansans. The families are not part of a crowd, nor do they want to be.

There is very little that is lush, vivid, aesthetic, emotionally rich, highly imaginative or creative about their homes, the way the families dress, or what they do. They are not colorful, not rebellious, not very aggressive. In some ways they remind us of Margaret Mead's New Guinea Manus group: realistic, autonomous, competent, sincere, in their approach to life in general. They are by and large free from pretenses; they live in neighborhoods and communities where the leadership comes from the middle-class group itself. There is no tradition of aristocratic family snobbery of the sort defined by cliché, the Cabots only talk to the Lowells and the Lowells only talk to God. These families talk to their neighbors and they and their neighbors alike talk to God. For some of them God is a major support in time of trouble and a constant object of faith.

The preceding quotation indicates how similar Murphy's population is to my own subjects, who came to Chicago from all over the country. Their preselection into a focal group was determined by the nodal point of the college as Murphy's group was concentrated by preselection in the prediction project of Escalona and Leitch.

Murphy found that her subjects' preschool I.Q. averaged 111. The mothers were not emotionally demanding or seductive, nor did they complain about poor or only moderately providing husbands. They were not rejecting or overprotective. Furthermore the father was important in the children's lives, for he gave to them a notion that things could be fixed (solution in action). In fact, one of the criteria of vulnerability Murphy states is "high perceptual sensitivity with low motor resources" which are certainly not present in my subjects.

Further support of the significance of the muscular activity as a form of coping is given by Escalona and Leitch in their studies on prediction and outcome. They found that a high amount and vigor of motor activity in infancy was predictive of a better later performance and intelligence. In fact, one of the factors in these same children—"motor

239

coordination, skills and impulse control"—correlates negatively according to Murphy.

Lu (1961) in a discussion considering the problem of schizophrenic family backgrounds describes a healthy control group who (1) were not raised in isolation; (2); had many significant others; (3) were permitted self-selection of relationships and tasks and schools; (4) had parents in harmony and the family affairs settled by a process of democratic decision; and (5) had expectations not high for intellectual achievement but high in morality and faith.

Finally, a personality description that has some relevance to the George Williams population was written in the form of a novel by Thornton Wilder (1935)—*Heaven's My Destination.* The hero, who is a missionary, religious, unrealistic, and not very intelligent, goes around the country doing good, converting people, and accepting no return. He says: "George Brush is my name/America's my nation/Ludington's my dwelling place/and Heaven's my destination." This old doggerel exaggerates but describes an orientation to the world not unlike the "muscular Christians."

Fortunately there is already available a series of well-documented studies made after many years' study on a dissimilar group of creative scientists (chemists) by Morris I. Stein et al. (n.d.). His report lends itself well for comparisons between his subjects and mine. Because not all traits are significantly characteristic, I have selected, in Table 11–7, those that emphasize the differences.

A dissimilar group was reported by Silber et al. (1961). They studied postadolescent high school students who were effectively preparing for college. Their subjects were selected on the basis of competence in (1) academic work in school, (2) interpersonal closeness with a peer, and (3) participation in social groups. These subjects came from a suburb of Washington, D.C., a middle-class residential area, populated by professional, managerial, and supervisory people with high incomes. The students all had high intellectual endowments and stood high academically in their classes.

Under general personality attributes are included (1) reaching out for new experiences; (2) tendency toward responsible activity; (3) pleasure in mastery—enjoyment of problem-solving. The ego operations developing and maintaining a self-image as an adequate person in a new situation are (1) referring to analogous past experiences; (2) referring to continuity with the present self-image; (3) learning about the new situation in advance; (4) role rehearsal; (5) group identifica-

TABLE 11–7

CREATIVE CHEMISTS (STEIN)	SUBJECT STUDENTS
50 percent of fathers graduated from college	Almost all fathers high school graduates only
Mothers often even higher level of education	Maximum: High school
Father or mother often held high-level positions	None
Middle class	Lower class
Parents upwardly mobile from grandparents	Rare
Relatively early loss of father (12 percent between ages thirteen to twenty-five)	Rare
Religious interest not serious	Religion a serious matter
Father interested in science	None
Goals: scholarship and science	Goals: do good, and be liked
Discipline medium in childhood and adolescence	Discipline firm
Parents happy together	Usually
Much love experienced from both parents	Usually
Self-ratings high (self-esteem)	Self-ratings low but realistic
Less confident in stability of outer world	Less confident in inner world
Expectation of higher success than parents	Satisfied with same
Father more important than mother	Mother more important than father

tion; (6) lowering level of aspiration; (7) selectively perceiving encouraging elements in the new situation.

Attributes of maintaining distress within manageable limits are (1) supportive function of shared experience; (2) usefulness of worry; (3) present activity in anticipating future concerns; (4) rehearsal in fantasy of future behavior.

Comment

Though the voluminous literature on mental health has been reviewed all too briefly, its relationship to the current investigation warrants comment. Too often there is a feeling of frustration by writers, indicating that most considerations of health are characterized by empty words and clichés. Others abandon the area as a matter of values that cannot be analyzed scientifically. The psychoanalysts state that health and illness are related only to what goes on inside the psyche without reference to culture, though it is questionable whether in practice they are actually so unrealistic. Because they deal with regressive phases of transference neuroses they are more exposed to their patient's liabilities than to their assets. The psychologists consider behaviors as more important criteria but more rationally include clusters of traits and experiences as significant explanatory concepts.

Anselm Strauss, the sociologist, states that psychiatrists have been locked into their restricted samples of patients and into their own middle-class educated perspective. However, the same may be said about behavioral scientists from all disciplines. Such investigators as Murphy (1959) in Kansas, Glueck et al. (n.d.) in Minnesota, Lu (1961) and Westley in Illinois have studied real people away from the mazes of the rat race. My own sample, strikingly similar to theirs, stems from all parts of the United States and Canada, clearly indicating a widely distributed population not limited to the Middle West or to rural areas.

The subjects on whom this investigation was made happened to be collected at a single geographical locus at a particular time. Discussions with teachers and administrative officers of the college indicate that the delineated average characteristics have been vaguely recognized over a long period of time and are not specific for the two classes of 1958 and 1959. The students originate in every area of the United States and Canada—the latter country furnishing 8 percent of the student body. As representatives of their home environments they constitute a sample of indefinite numbers in North America.

This population as a whole has certain general characteristics, and it is relatively homogeneous. In fact, its members are psychologically more alike than different. Yet by certain criteria they can be divided into subgroups which can be compared.

The sample of subjects first interviewed made a dramatic impact on me when I recognized that their psychological qualities were healthy. Now that the study is completed how can they be described more accurately? In general it cannot be stated that there is an absence of psychopathology for, like anyone living, they have had conflicts, established defenses, and have had to sacrifice potential assets in the process of adjustment. Some are suspicious, unhappy, withdrawn, depressed, compulsive, phobic, and so on, and are crystallized into a variety of personality types easily recognized. But the average subject shows little evidence of crippling, disabling, or severely handicapping illness. So much for the negative—the absence of mental illness.

On the positive side, the average subject can work well on his job, and with the usual American students' procrastination and rapid cramming, passes his school examination and graduates with a C average. He plays well and with satisfactions. He copes adequately with stimuli that arouse emotional reactions. There is adequate adjustment to reality. The subject has a firm sense of identity; he feels good and has hope for the future. Also, he has had warm human relationships with parents, teachers, friends, and girls.

Within the general population of the United States this group is relatively silent. Its members are goal-directed, anxious only in striving to do their jobs well in which they will have moved up from their fathers' positions, but with little ambition for upward social or economic mobility. By the nature of their aspirations to do well, to do good, and to be liked they plan to carry on their lives quietly in simple comfort, marry and raise their families, and retire on small pensions plus social security. The psychiatrist does not often see this population of homoclites and, should he chance to come in contact with them, he will be as surprised as I was.

Scientists, too, are beset by values in what interests them, what hypotheses they test, what techniques they use, and what variables they study. Certainly the psychiatric value system is evident in the questions raised in my interviews and the items specified in the questionnaire and in the various scales used. From the values utilized, the contrast between these healthy subjects and psychiatric patients became clear and exciting.

In the literal sense the subjects had little ambition. Certainly they were goal-directed, and most of them tried to "do the best I can." They took school and work seriously, especially their jobs at settlement and field houses. Capacities for leadership required hard cultivation. But ambition to rise higher socially, earn more, and live better than their parents was universally lacking. They expressed little dissatisfaction with their home environments: "We lived in a nice house; our clothes were good; we always had enough to eat. True we had an old car, but it ran." Why did they need to earn more? "A job you like is better than one you don't even if it pays more." Several men who had worked in industry and earned good wages came back to become trained for work they preferred but that would pay far lower salaries.

I often described my subject population to various social and professional groups characterized by driving social upward mobile or prestige-seeking people, who, though outwardly serene, were consumed with never-satisfied ambitions. The invariable comment was "those boys are sick, they have no ambition." In the broadest sense to "do the best I can" seems to be a true ambition.

Intense commitment to change in itself may be one of the elements in neurosis-building. Change is accelerating at a rapid pace, as the students of the modern American family have so well documented. The healthy population demonstrates little participation in this rapid pace, nor have their parents. They move ahead slowly at a pace that does not overly strain them.

From the standpoint of function within the total population, people like the George Williams students form a solid steady core of stability. They are the middle-of-the-roaders in every way, neither liberal nor conservative, neither hoarders nor speculators, neither grimly tight-lipped nor high-steppers. Without them the ambitious, fast-moving climbers would slip into the mire of political, social, and economic chaos. They are not only Kansas, as Lois Murphy (1959) states, they are America.

We have described the family and personal backgrounds of members of the George Williams population and indicated factors that may be significant for their stability and mental health. Any one, or all, may be important for the development of the type of personality that has been described. Attention must be called to the factor of intelligence which is not high, not that low intelligence is conducive to mental health. But average intelligence with a capacity for honest and accurate self-appraisal is an antidote to useless goal-seeking disappointing activity. Instead, goal-maintaining is the kind of ambition our subjects demonstrate most clearly.

These young men cannot be understood apart from the culture in which they were reared. Parental emphasis on early work, sound religious training, and the ideals associated with doing good associated with the parents' rigidity and concern constitute aspects of protestant virtues and ethics acceptable without rebellion because of the sincere manifestations of love and consistency toward the child. Identifications thereby were favored. The character structure included slight compulsivity, hard work, neatness, orderliness, and concern about school and avoidance of failure rather than attaining great success, and "doing the best one can" became a virtue as a way of life.

Early in life most of the members of George Williams' student body gravitate as muscular Christians to the YMCA for exercise, sport, camp, often at the same time earning money. Over the years they gradually go through filtering devices under the watchful eyes of the YMCA secretaries. The successful ones are advised to attend George Williams College, and the best are given scholarships. This is a well-established process of indoctrination acceptable to boys who can make an identification with the YMCA secretaries for which their relationships to their fathers have prepared them.

For most of them the college and the future career for which they are preparing is the right place for them. There the goals are limited and predictable either as a career of group-work education or health and physical education. Some who have made mistakes in these choices leave. Others who, though successful in business or industry, feel uncomfortable and sense they are in the wrong place, give up their jobs and come to George Williams. This may be contrasted with the plight of the students at many modern universities at which an infinite number of goals are possible. Here, many students move from one college to another, from one degree to another, in and out of school and in again, unable to decide on what to do as life speeds by. The George Williams model has no such dilemma. In the military services ineptness and failure or neurotic symptoms are not necessarily indications for discharge or psychiatric treatment. Rather the soldier is studied and reclassified for a job for which he is more suited. The civilian in a democracy cannot be reclassified; it is only good fortune when he finds his niche in life and stays there contented.

Psychoanalysts have difficulty in accepting the parameters of adequate behavior, adaptation, adjustment, and so on as indicating health, because they are more concerned with internal forces and balances. They ask the strange question: "What are the costs of mental health?" In contrast, general psychiatrists are constantly publicizing the "cost of mental illness."

In all seriousness there is a cost as a result of adaptation, but this is difficult to differentiate from the factors related to the cause. For example, are the somewhat compulsive character and rigidity, the sharply focused and limited interests; the use of activity to maintain comfort; the absence of creativity, fantasies, and introspection; and so on the costs of the subject's stability and mental health? Or are these some of the conditions, among others, of clusters or characteristics that lead to mental health, given the proper environmental conditions? Is the mediocre intelligence (I.Q.) a predisposition to stability but associated with lack of creativity and ambition, or is the lack of early intellectual stimulation in a lower-class family responsible for the subsequent performance on the intelligence tests?

At the present time we cannot answer such questions which assume

245

linearity of cause and effect until we unravel the time-space sequences by longitudinal studies of many more populations. Viewed, however, from a distance at the time of college-student days we would have to say that internal comfort, adequate adjustment to the environment, goal-directed behavior, and subject-environment fit are associated with stability and a special type of happiness, but also with narrowness and limitations of interests, mobility, creativity, and excitement characteristic of the American postadolescent model—all this from a point of view based on the American cultural model of individual change. From the standpoint of the culture as a whole there is, however, more gain than cost. To have a population of relative stability is necessary for the activity of those who possess creativity. The maintenance of social structure is necessary as a background for the process of progressive change. Every American boy could become President of the United States, but those that do need the common citizen to elect him and for him to govern. Every country needs its proletariat, using the work in Toynbee's (1946) sense. It constitutes the majority, which is led by the creative individual who withdraws from his society, returning to lead it in the light of his discoveries. Yet in the process of a disintegration of a civilization it is the internal proletariat that resists the barbarians and re-creates the civilization. Toynbee's concepts were amply demonstrated by the less devastating plight of the Dutch Jews during the Nazi occupation because the majority were members of the proletariat.

Though there are many individual exceptions, the average George Williams student would probably do badly in a social setting characterized by the hustle, bustle, and restless activities of very ambitious or creative persons. Also it is likely that a creative person would suffer and become emotionally disturbed within a George Williams social structure. An exceptional, very intelligent and creative student, to follow Toynbee's hypothesis, would leave the environment of George Williams to become creative in another culture and return to be president of the college.[5]

Among the sixty-five subjects interviewed, only four indicated that they had acted out rebelliously in an asocial manner and had come in conflict with the law. Questionnaire data indicated that there had been a period of increased conflict with the parents, yet there was little indication that adolescence was a period of crisis overtly expressed, as contrasted with Westley's normal adolescents. No information is available concerning such crises, if they could be experienced unconsciously, and hence be nonreportable. Yet a psychological crisis should either be subjectively experienced or observable in behavior.

246

Erikson (1950) has developed an outline of eight stages of man from orality to maturity, each with its corresponding polarity, such as trust versus basic mistrust to ego integrity versus despair. Erikson states that each stage has a critical psychological conflict always carried within the subject and "each stage is a crisis."

Anna Freud (1960) has quoted Bernfeld to the effect that protracted adolescence is conspicuous by tendencies toward productivity, idealistic aims, and spiritual values. This leads her to conclude that when the adolescent crisis is not present and the children are good they are developing crippling defenses that act as barriers against maturation. She believes that a steady equilibrium during adolescence is in itself abnormal. Josselyn (1954) also believes that adult normality is not possible in the absence of an identity crisis.

On the other hand, the cultural and family background of our subjects was conductive to growth and change without difficulties that precipitate crises or overt conflict. During easy stages of progression from home, church, YMCA, high school, and college, the value systems of their environment remained constant. Biological and psychological growth or maturation is not naturally associated with crises. Rather it is the rapid shifts within environments or sudden movements of the individual among two or more external social and culturally dissimilar environments that precipitate crises. Whatever changes took place in the worlds of our subjects were gradual and could be absorbed without too much strain.

In tracing the careers of the students into George Williams College the directness of the pathway, the gradual steps, and the familial and social approval and support probably created firm identities, self-esteem, and confidence. Rarely were these attributes subjected to severe stress. On the other hand, before arrival at the college, they were not subjected to intellectual stimulation that might lead to wider intellectual horizons or creativity. We know individuals with the same characteristics of the average George Williams student who have sunk to a Skid Row or risen to scientific fame. The final outcome for our subjects has not been determined, but experience indicates that the majority will move slowly along the same pathway to the simple satisfactions they have stated as their goals.

In discussing the lack of creativity, the Protestant-oriented ethics leading to a "good life" not tarnished by pursuit of pleasure, prestige, and money have been emphasized. Can the associated narrowness of interest and cultural poverty and the limitation of abstract thinking and imagination be owing to the absence of stimulation rather than an early process of identification? Interviews indicated little evidence of creativity in the literal sense. True, most of these were interested in attaining a helping role and doing good for children or adolescents. Many showed evidences of ingenuity in sports. In general they have a well-established reputation for handling people well in social and group settings.

Kubie (1954, 1958) in discussing the neurotic distortion of the creative process points up the price man has paid for the superimposition of conscious symbolic functions over primary-process thinking, to which creative persons are partially exempt. Our subjects seemingly are more attached to reality, which in their culture is considered to be objective, definitive, and precise. In other words, reality, fairly strict conscious control, and more or less direct imitation are patterned as a result of environmental influences. There seems to be little freedom for "regression in the service of the ego."

It is clear that the average subject experienced adequate love from his parents, stability in his relationships, and has learned the boundaries of behavior and the discipline resulting from transgressions. He acquired a sharp image of his parents and knew and knows their expectations. Parental concern and rigidity and the subjects' compulsivity seem on the surface to be restrictive against growth, ambition, and upward mobility.

Yet it is too early to state that ambition and creativity are entirely absent. The subjects, except for a few, have not yet settled the problems of masculinity by sex experiences or marriage. They are still in school and not in independent jobs. They are goal directed and earnestly strive toward achievement of success and avoidance of failure. Upward mobility is obvious in that they are in college as contrasted with their poorly educated parents; yet their image of future social and economic position and kind of life remains fixed to the level they experienced at home in childhood.

How much is the compulsive quality discernible in their personalities, responsible for this partial mobility, goal-seeking rather than goal-changing, and value systems of doing good and being happy? Asked in reverse: How much spontaneity, impulsivity, and deviance from the past are associated with need achievements? Perhaps the range, if it can ever be at least roughly demarcated, is the range of psychic homeostasis. However, like all homeostatic processes the spread between the boundaries shifts, with greater or lesser speed of adjustment, in relationship to alterations in the environment—physical, social, or cultural.

The question, then, that should be raised about any population or sample thereof is not only "How are they doing?" but also "How would they do if the environment shifted or if they moved into a new setting?" As I shall discuss later this depends on certain aspects of identification, associated with early transactions, which provide a repertoire of roles for the future. The permutations of past experiences, later learning, and environmental states and processes lead to an astronomical number of patterns of behavior that should be subjected to at least rough classification into categories or types.

A CLUSTER OF CONDITIONS ASSOCIATED WITH A MENTALLY HEALTHY POPULATION

We have observed, studied, and described a population of relatively healthy young male adults. Among the contributing factors to this end result we have emphasized certain conditions:

1. Constitutionally sound health from birth on.
2. Average intelligence.
3. Relatively low socioeconomic family of origin.
4. Satisfactory positive affectionate relationship with both parents.
5. Parental agreement and cooperation in child-raising.
6. Definite and known limitations on boundaries placed on behavior.
7. Punishment reasonable and consistent.
8. Sound early religious training.
9. Early work history.
10. The world is conceived as being external and calling for action —not introspection of an internal world. One *does* something about problems.
11. Ideals involve contentment, sociability, doing good, and making friends; money is not a goal but only a means.
12. Goal-seeking rather than goal-changing behavior leading to concern for success at what one chooses to do rather than ambition for upward (prestige, social, or economic) mobility.
13. Strong identification with father and father figures.

The last item is clearly revealed in the various analyses presented from the questionnaire. Love, respect, and emulation of the father, however, came out even clearer in the sixty-five personal interviews and made a strong impression on me. I consider identification with the father to be an extremely significant factor in the process of becoming and remaining healthy.

Identification is not simply imitation or becoming in part or totally the same as the model thinks, feels, and acts. Psychoanalytic theory includes among the processes of identification (1) introjection of the gratifying object to become an endopsychic representation in the ego; the ego becomes a precipitate of lost object cathexes, a record of past object choices (Fenichel, 1953); (2) identification as a defense as, for example, identification with the aggressor or putting oneself in the other's place (A. Freud, 1946); (3) identification with stable object representations fused with self-representations of pleasurable, constantly changing, inner experiences (Jacobson, 1954).

If child-rearing with adequate amounts of infant care, love consistently experienced through the years, and experience in frustration, consistency in attitude and control of deviant behavior, are the bases on which character and personality are built, then our subjects had a good preparation for being healthy. On the basis of adequate need gratifications as children and minimal conflict with their parents, our subjects experienced little adolescent rebellion and hostile identifications or counteridentifications. Evidences of positive identifications are apparent in those allocated mental functions that we call ego, ego ideal, and superego, which enable the subjects to feel comfortable and function well in specific environments. How does this come about?

According to Parsons and Bales (1955), what is internalized is always a reciprocal interaction pattern of matched or complementary expectations. Those who play a part in socialization and internalization must participate with a subject on his own terms and for his own needs but must also play an authentic role in a wider system. This constitutes the leverage and definition for the internalization of the next role for the developing child. The theoretical formula is permissiveness, support in spite of failure, increasing denial of reciprocity, and reward for achievement on a supraordinate level. The balance between denial of reciprocity and positive reward leads to the establishment of a stable system of expectations in the child. This constitutes internalization of the parent-mother in her role as the source of care, and identification of that aspect of her with the self that has stood in a meaningful relationship.

Internalization creates appropriate attitudes toward family role figures, capable of generalizations and substitutions. Later identifications, after the primary one with the mother, which sets the pattern, are more complicated because of the multiple role relationships among various members of the family. To each, a new set of values is attached. Identi-

250

fication becomes a process of internalization of any transaction and its values.

In another context (Grinker, 1957) I have described identification as an end result of transactions between a subject, who may be any human individual, and any other human individual. In general, we use the terms "subject" and "object," referring to the components of transactions. It should be clear that the object, whose transactional processes with the subject are internalized, furnishes to the subject not only personalized qualities and attributes, but also signs and symbols of a particular culture, the knowledge of the institutionalized and instrumental roles of the particular society and expressive roles characterized by a specific sex.

The self and objects are never isolated but always in relationship. Others are seen in the light of our own needs, and we view ourselves according to the opinion of others. Neither the "I" nor the "you," the "we," or the "others" can be torn apart. Identification is a transactional memory residue, always composed of subject and object.

Now we may ask, how do the primary introjects help the person to fit into various social roles? The end result of the primary introjects determines the capacities of the individuals to perform social roles. In this sense, the intervening variables between personality and society are implicit identifications, which are integrated and synthesized, later to be activated on appropriate occasions. However, the degree of integration and synthesis determines the strength of silent ungratified implicit roles which impede the success of socialization. Social equilibrium, then, which is an idealized state of role complementarity, is related to a dominant identification, but there are many internalized roles that are not satisfied at the moment and produce or initiate cyclic responses that require a rapid shifting or changing of explicit roles. If such disequilibrium occurs, it may lead to an internal disturbance, producing or threatening anxiety or depression, and a new equilibrium will have to be found, either immediately in the acting-out individual or later in the repetition compulsion of the more silently neurotic person.

In the previous discussion we have gone over the processes of identification without reference to what psychological functions are influenced. Our subjects show that ego processes, ego ideals, and superego all bear the stamp of early identifications. Satisfactions, goal-maintaining, social ideals, pressure for achievement in performance, and fear of failure all bear the explicit stamp of early experiences. These seem almost puerile in their clearness and faithfulness to the past, coloring be-

251

havior, choice of occupation, and all subsequent identifications (YMCA secretaries, teachers, and so on). They also are held fairly rigidly to type with little deviation and with a degree of compulsivity. Finally the subjects' identifications, though strong, are limited corresponding to the restricted number of roles they can play effectively.

Furthermore, the nonhuman environments to which these persons gravitate and in which they feel most comfortable are patterned but not identical with the environment of childhood. This is owing not only to the fact that the personality establishment of these people fits this category of environment well, but also because the processes of identification of early transactions with the parents include the setting or field in which those transactions occurred. The concrete or duplicopy quality of these processes again becomes apparent, because in all identifications involving people, things, or situations there is little abstraction. Thus thinking, feeling, and behavior are action oriented, not introspective or creative.

In *sum,* I have presented a "multifaceted frontal attack" using the methods of observation, description, and statistical analyses of images of the subjects' self, parents, situations, and so forth. The techniques used included interviews, questionnaires, and a behavior rating scale. Comparisons between groups indicate the range of variables and permitted us to describe the more and less healthy within our population. Despite these differences, from the population as a whole certain inferences were drawn concerning one type of mental health. Imbedded in the data presented in the previous sections and in this overview of the research are many interpretations, inferences, and formulations that are available for the development of hypotheses for future research. However, future research among many kinds of populations will be necessary to delineate other kinds of health or normality. Combining the results of many such studies may enable us to develop suitable abstractions and theories which contain more than words and generalities.

Until such time is at hand, we should approach the problems of health and illness not as states but as processes occurring within a large field. Limited theory, whether organic, psychological, psychoanalytic, or sociological, does not encompass all the significant variables or their many possible transactions, or designate the operational procedures to be used in such research. Ultimately, of course, a scientific study of values involved in concepts of health and illness is necessary. However, even without concern for values, many scientific methods may be applied to the study of populations, and ultimately the results of these methods may be synthesized into a comprehensive description. It is only then that the many significant factors responsible for the causes, costs, and effects of a variety of mental healths may be more accurately defined.

NOTES

1. Because such words as "normal" and "healthy" are so heavily loaded with value judgments, a neutral word was sought but not found in the English language. Even the Greeks did not have a word for the condition I am describing. Dr. Percival Bailey made the suggestion that, in as much as "heteroclite" means a person deviating from the common rule, the opposite, or "homoclite," would designate a person following the common rule. The reader will soon discover that the population to be described is composed of "normal," "healthy," "ordinary," "just plain guys," in fact homoclites!

2. I am deeply indebted to Mr. John W. Dubocq, Dean of Students at George Williams College for unfailing cooperation during the several years of this study.

3. For this portion of the research, the interview (unstructured and structured) was the only instrument used. Utilized by me this instrument has been tested previously in a number of other researches, and through the years it has been constantly checked and recalibrated. Its use in this research on the first group of thirty-one subjects achieved validity as attested by: (1) Psychiatric ratings of affect-levels correlated significantly with the previously administered psychological tests (Taylor, Mandler, Barron, and Nowlis). (2) The ratings of the specific affect of anger in the later experiments discriminated between high and low groups as determined by the interviews with statistical significance ($p < 0.02$). (3) In the psychosomatic stress experiments in which the subjects participated, the high effective lability group showed greater levels of physiological activity than the lows and greater responses to stress in their change scores but not statistically significant. Thus despite differences built in by the objective of discriminating a high and low group among healthy subjects, the group as a whole was relatively homogeneous. (4) The data obtained by the interview technique were strongly confirmed by the results from questionnaires. (5) The Catell Neuroticism Scale (IPAT) administered by Robert Yufit, Ph.D., and Barbara White to all the students of the 1959 group showed that, on the basis of the norms given by the authors on the test, none of the students closely approximated the neurotic profiles.

4. These two questions are borrowed from an instrument developed by Morris I. Stein, Department of Psychology, New York University.

5. This actually happened in 1961.

REFERENCES

Ackerman, N. W. (1958). The psychodynamics of family life. New York: Basic Books.
———. (1959). Emotional forces in the family. E. S. Liebman, ed., Philadelphia: Lippincott.
Azrin, H. J., Holz, W., and Goldiamond, I. (1961). Response bias in questionnaire reports. Journal of Consulting Psychology, 25:324.
Barton, Walter E. (1958). Viewpoint of a Clinician. In M. Jahoda, ed. Current Concepts of Positive Mental Health. New York: Basic Books.
Bee, L. (1959). Marriage and family relations. New York: Harper.
Bettelheim, B. (1960). The informed heart. New York: The Free Press.
Buhler, C. (1959). Theoretical observations about life's basic tendencies. American Journal of Psychotherapy, 13:561.
Eissler, K. (1953). The effect of structure of the ego on psychoanalytic technique. Journal of the American Psychoanalytic Association, 1:104.
Erikson, E. H. (1950). Growth and crises. In Milton L. Senn, ed., Symposium on the Healthy Personality. New York: Josiah Macy, Jr., Foundation.

Escalona, S., and Heider, G. M. (1959). Prediction and outcome. New York: Basic Books.

Fenichel, O. (1953). Collected papers. New York: Norton.

Freud, A. (1946). The ego and the mechanisms of defence. New York: International Universities Press.

———. (1960). Adolescence. In Joseph Weinreb, ed., Recent Developments in Psycho-Analytic Child Therapy. New York: International Universities Press.

Freud, S. Analysis terminal and interminal (1959). In Collected Papers. New York: Basic Books. Vol. 5.

Friedenberg, E. Z., and Roth, J. A. (1954). Self-perception in the university. Chicago: University of Chicago Press.

Friedes, D. (1960). Toward the elimination of the concept of normality. Journal of Consulting Psychology, 24:128.

Gitelson, M. (1948). Problems of psychoanalyst training. Psychoanalytic Quarterly, 17:206.

———. (1952). The emotional position of the analyst in the psychoanalytic situation. International Journal of Psychoanalysis, 33:pt. 1.

———. (1954). The analysis of the "normal" candidate. International Journal of Psychoanalysis, 35:175.

Glover, E. (1956). Medico-psychological aspects of normality. In On the Early Development of Mind. New York: International Universities Press.

Glueck, B. C., Jr., Golden, J., and Mandel, N. (n.d.). A summary description of fifty "normal" white males.

Grinker, R. R. (1955). Growth, inertia and shame. International Journal of Psychoanalysis, 36:242 (pt. 4).

———. (1956). Toward a unified theory of human behavior. New York: Basic Books.

———. (1957). On identification. International Journal of Psychoanalysis, 38:379 (pt. 6).

Group for the Advancement of Psychiatry. (1959). Some observations on controls in psychiatric research. Report No. 42. New York.

Gurin, G., Veroff, J., and Feld, S. (1960). Americans view their mental health. New York: Basic Books.

Hartmann, H. (1931). Technical implications of ego psychology. Psychoanalytic Quarterly, 20:31.

———. (1939). Psychoanalysis and the concept of health. International Journal of Psychoanalysis, 20:308.

Hoffman, M. (1960). Psychiatry, nature and science. American Journal of Psychiatry, 117:205.

Jacobson, E. (1954). Contributions to the metapsychology of psychotic identifications. Journal of the American Psychoanalytic Association, 2:239.

Jahoda, M. (1958). Current concepts of positive mental health. New York: Basic Books.

Jones, E. (1948). The concept of a normal mind. In P. Halmos and A. Iliffe, eds., Readings in General Psychology. New York: Philosophical Library.

Josselyn, I. (1954). The ego in adolescence. American Journal of Orthopsychiatry, 24:223.

Klein, D. C. (1960). Some concepts concerning the mental health of the individual. Journal of Consulting Psychology, 24:288.

Korchin, J. J., and Heath, H. A. (1961). Somatic experiences in the anxiety state: Some sex and personality correlates of "autonomic feedback." Journal of Consulting Psychology, 25:398.

———. (n.d.) Congruency between clinical judgments and self ratings of affective "traits" and "states."

Kubie, L. (1954). The fundamental nature of the distinction between normality and neurosis. Psychoanalytic Quarterly, 23:167.

———. (1958). Neurotic distortion of the creative process. Lawrence, Kan.: University of Kansas Press.

Leighton, A., Clausen, E., and Wilson, R. N., eds. (1957). Explorations in social psychiatry. New York: Basic Books.

Lewis, A. (1958). Between guesswork and certainty in psychiatry. Lancet, 1:170, 227.

Lu, Yi-chaung. (1961). Mother-child role relations in schizophrenia. Psychiatry, 24:133.

Maslow, A. H. (1959). Motivation and personality. New York: Harper.

Michaels, J. (1955). Disorders of character: Persistent enuresis, juvenile delinquency and psychopathic personality. Springfield, Ill.: Charles C Thomas.

Murphy, L. (1959). Unpublished lectures. Veterans' Association Hospital Forum. Topeka, Kansas, March 25, 1959.

Murray, H. A. (1951). In nomine diaboli. New England Quarterly, 24:435.

Oken, D., Grinker, R. R., Sr., Heath, H. A., Herz, M., and Schwartz, N. B. (1962). The relation of physiological response to affect expression. Archives of General Psychiatry, 6:336.

Parsons, T., and Bales, R. F. (1955). Family specialization and interaction process. New York: The Free Press.

Rapaport, D. (1951). The autonomy of the ego. Bulletin of the Menninger Clinic, 15:133.

Redlich, F. C. (1957). The concept of health in psychiatry. In A. H. Leighton, J. A. Clausen and R. N. Wilson, eds., Explorations of Social Psychiatry. New York: Basic Books.

Reider, N. (1950). The concept of normality. Psychoanalytic Quarterly, 19:43.

Ruesch, J., and Bateson, G. (1951). Communication: The social matrix of psychiatry. New York: Norton.

Scott, W. A. (1958). Research and definition of mental health and mental illness. Psychological Bulletin, 55:29.

Shepherd, M. (1958). Public health and psychiatry in Great Britain. Medical Officer, 100:141.

Silber, E., Hamburg, D. A., Coelko, G. W., Murphey, E. B., Rosenberg, M., and Pearlin, I. (1961). Adaptive behavior in competent adolescents: Coping with the anticipation of college. Archives of General Psychiatry, 5:517.

Smith, M. B. (1961a). Research strategies toward a conception of positive mental health. American Psychologists, 16:299.

———. (1961b). "Mental health" reconsidered. American Psychologist, 16:673.

Spiegel, J. P. (1958). In I. Galdston, ed., The Family in Contemporary Society. New York: International Universities Press.

Spiegel, L. A. (1951). A review of contributions to a psychoanalytic theory of adolescence: Individual aspects. Psychoanalytic Study of the Child, 6:375.

Stein, M. I., et al. (n.d.). Explorations in creativity: Social and psychological factors affecting the creativity of industrial research chemists.

Strauss, A. Personal communication, Chicago, 1960.

Szasz, T. S. (1960). The myth of mental illness. American Psychologist, 15:113.

Toynbee, A. J. (1946). A study of history. Abridgement by D. C. Somervell. London: Oxford University Press.

Waelder, R. (1936). The principle of multiple function. Psychoanalytic Quarterly, 5:554.

Warner, S. L., and Saul, L. J. (1961). Evidence for the effects of child rearing on personality development. Paper presented to the Third International Congress for Psychiatry, Montreal.

Weisberg, P. S., and Springer, K. J. (1961). Environmental factors influencing creative function in gifted children. Archives of General Psychiatry, 5:554.

Westley, W. A. (1958). In I. Galdston, ed., The Family in Contemporary Society. New York: International Universities Press.

White, R. W. (1959). Motivation reconsidered: The concept of competence. Psychological Review, 16:297.

Wilder, T. (1935). Heaven's my destination. New York: Harper.

12] THE DEVELOPMENTAL TASKS

OF THE COLLEGE STUDENT

FREDERICK W. COONS

One of the characteristics of man that makes him unique among mammals is his tremendous and prolonged capacity to learn. Within the limitations of heredity and genetics, we are whom we are because of what we have been taught. An intimate acquaintance with the student's historical background is essential for the understanding of the problems and life style he presents in his relationship with teacher, counselor, or therapist. Tyler (1964) points out that the physiological dependence of the infant on an adult human for his individual, as well as species, survival, is the crucial factor in the development of those behaviors we term "social" and "psychological," that is, the humanizing process. He goes on to say, "There is no reason to believe that the newborn infant seeks anything other than physiological survival from his adult. Almost immediately, however, the adult unintentionally begins to condition him to seek psychosocial survival as well." As the primary family unit has become smaller, probably owing to our increased affluence, decreased interdependence, and increased geographical mobility, the developing child's exposure to meaningful adults is now limited to his parents, especially for the first five or six years of life. If the parents are unrepresentative adults in the culture, the child has little chance to discover this through an intimate acquaintance with an extended family unit and must wait until he turns away from the family and toward school and the larger world. Erikson (1963), in his eight stages of man, seems to support the thesis that such crucial characteristics as trust, autonomy, and initiative are discovered primarily in the nature of the relationship between the child, his parents, and his siblings.

It seems that perhaps the college situation, with the geographical sep-

256

aration of the student from his parents in an environment focused on the reexamination of all those things previously taken for granted, offers a unique opportunity to correct some of the distortions learned in an unrepresentative family unit. Erikson (1968) uses the word "crisis" to designate a necessary turning point, a crucial moment, when development must move one way or another, marshalling resources of growth, recovery, and further differentiation. It is therefore to be expected that crises are the rule rather than the exception for college students. At the same time, the student's unique milieu, intelligence, and flexibility offer the mental health worker an ideal opportunity for rapid but highly effective therapeutic intervention.

Havighurst (1952) has defined a developmental task as one that arises during a certain period in the life of an individual. These tasks may arise from the processes of physical maturation, the pressure of cultural processes on the individual, and the desires, aspirations, and values of the emerging personality. Usually, the tasks arise from combinations of interactions of these factors. Successful completion of a developmental task leads to happiness and success in later tasks, whereas failure leads to unhappiness in the individual, disapproval by society, and difficulty with later tasks.

Many people have written about the developmental tasks, especially in adolescence, but perhaps none so poetically as H. S. Sullivan (1953) who says:

> Making very much sense of the complexities and difficulties which are experienced in adolescence and subsequent phases of life depends, in considerable measure, on the clarity with which one distinguishes three needs, which are often very intricately combined and at the same time contradictory. These are the need for personal security—that is, for freedom from anxiety; the need for intimacy—that is, for collaboration with at least one other person; and the need for lustful satisfaction, which is connected with genital activity and the pursuit of the orgasm.

In speaking more specifically of the college student, Sanford (1962) says:

> The proposal here is that there is a stage of late adolescence that intervenes between adolescence proper and early adulthood . . . the freshman seems more likely to be in this stage than do the other categories of younger or older people. In the college freshman, the maximum crisis of adolescence is over, and controlling mechanisms are again in the ascendancy, but the controls developed for the purpose of inhibiting impulses are still unseasoned and uncertain; they are likely to operate in a rigid manner, that is to be overdone, as if the danger of their giving way altogether were still very

257

real. This picture of the freshman's psychological situation is essentially a picture of an authoritarian personality structure.

Blos (1962) reinforces the idea that late adolescence is a decisive turning point and consequently a time of crisis, which so often overtaxes the integrative capacity of the individual and results in adaptive failures, ego deformations, defensive maneuvers, and severe psychopathology.

The Resolution of the Child-Parent Relationship

In the ideal situation, the parents of a newborn infant are psychologically prepared to acknowledge the fact that this small, utterly helpless being will one day become an autonomous individual capable of reproducing the species and establishing a family unit of his own. They are able to accept the gradually changing nature of the parent-child relationship, so that the mutual trust and respect characteristic of an adult-adult relationship may become predominant. This expectation is communicated continuously to the child so that as his capacity for autonomy develops, he will be able to exercise it to the fullest extent permissible within the culture. The testing of autonomy characteristic of the three- to five-year-old again comes to the forefront with the onset of puberty and adolescence. By the time the individual leaves home to begin his college career, the change in the relationship with the parents is well on its way, and in the normal situation is nearing completion by the second or third year of college. It is not uncommon to hear sophomores and juniors in college reassuring the freshmen that parents are not really so bad as they seem, and in fact may become rather interesting people.

Berne (1964) offers a very enlightening transactional analysis of social intercourse with its complementary stimulus and response. He postulates three levels of interaction—parent, adult, and child—for each individual. To be complementary, the stimulus and response of a transaction must be parallel. If the stimulus is from the child part of one individual to the parent part of another, the response must flow from the parent back to the child. "Crossed transactions" occur when the stimulus flows from the adult of one individual to the adult of another, whereas the response comes from the child of the second individual to the parent of the first. Such crossed transactions are the source of much confusion in both the student and his teachers. Blos (1962) comments:

The typically rebellious adolescent of adolescence proper not only turns against his early love objects in his attempt to detach himself from them; he simultaneously turns against the view of reality and morality which was imparted to him by them. The infantile sexual tie has to be irrevocably severed before a reasonable rapprochement between the self and the parental ego interests and attitudes can be affected.

Difficulties in the resolution of the child-parent relationship are seen most characteristically in only and youngest children, because of the tendency for parents to hold on too long, and because of the strong ambivalence about growing up that can be generated in the student. We live in a society that worships youth and fears growing old. One way that a parent may deny his own aging is to deny the maturing of his children. So long as the parent can pretend that his offspring is still a child, he can better confront himself in the mirror and deny the wrinkles, the graying hair, and the sagging abdomen. The tendency to fulfill one's own frustrated ambitions by directing and manipulating the life style of one's offspring can be very strong and inherently disastrous.

If there is a typical freshman problem, it is probably the student who has become bogged down in his attempts to resolve the child-parent relationship. He will frequently complain bitterly of his overly protective, excessively involved parents who insist that he call home twice weekly and inform them of his every move. One may initially sympathize with the student, but he will soon say something like, "And not only that, but I called home last week for an extra $25 to attend the dance this weekend, and they're going to send only $15." At this point, the counselor can assume an air of perplexity and perhaps suggest to the student the possibility of a contradiction. On the one hand, he seems to be saying he wishes to be autonomous and relate more maturely with his parents, but on the other hand he requests additional support. He seems to want to be autonomous when it is convenient, and dependent when autonomy requires some effort on his part. Students are frequently surprised and enlightened by this confrontation, and can often accept the suggestion that they might want to find a part-time job to help finance their extracurricular activities. A more serious example of this conflict occurs in the freshman girl who never really wanted to come to college in the first place, but did so at the insistence of her parents. She finds herself emotionally and perhaps intellectually ill equipped to deal with a college environment, and as her anxiety mounts, she makes a suicide gesture. On being brought to the infirmary, her first words are, "You're not going to tell my parents, are you?" Her fear that it will "just kill my

259

parents if they find out" is unfounded, and their response is usually, "We knew she was having trouble, but we didn't know how serious it was, and what can we do to help?" After this exchange between the student and her parents, the relationship may begin a rather rapid maturation. In our experience (Friedman and Coons, 1967), girls have a much more difficult time leaving home and establishing autonomy than do freshman boys. This impression is supported by the consistently disproportionate number of freshman girls seen during the first six weeks of the academic year.

One of the more difficult things for the teacher and counselor to avoid is falling into the trap of continuing to play the child-parent game with their students. Our colleges and universities are finding that many of today's students feel that they are ready to go beyond this stage in their development and to try experiencing adult-adult relationships. Sanford (1962) points out that ego growth is hampered both by authoritarian or overprotective and by permissive-chaotic regimes. The former do not give functions of the ego a chance for exercise; the latter, through too much stimulation of impulse with subsequent anxiety, may put too heavy a strain on the developing ego. This means that those dealing with students must walk a tightrope between authoritarianism and permissiveness. It seems that most of the complaints one hears about students can be represented by the statement, "Why don't they act like adults?" They do not act like adults because they are not; they are late adolescents who are flexing their psychological muscles in the difficult task of becoming adults. The Group for the Advancement of Psychiatry (1968) report on adolescence comments that

> The conflict between generations can be an enriching experience in a society, and often is the nodal point for cultural change. Change may occur on either side of the interspace between the generations; adolescents, especially late adolescents, introduce much that is new; and adults can respond with new attitudes and solutions. Commonly, however, there is a derogation of adolescence—an understandably defensive reaction on the part of the adults, who feel that they are being displaced.

The Solidifying of a Sexual Identity

In the constricted family unit, the developing infant and child knows primarily two adults, mother and father. During his first five years he observes their life styles and their modes of interacting and says to himself, "Mother is a woman, therefore all women are like mother; father is a man, therefore all men are like father." If the child is correct in his basic assumption, that is, that his mother is more representative of women in the culture than not, and his father is more representative of men in the culture than not, and that the relationship is more representative of marriage than not, he will be relatively well prepared to deal with other adults and to fulfill the psychosocial role dictated by his biological sex. Grinker (see chapter 11) considers identification with the father to be an extremely significant factor in the process of the male child's becoming and remaining healthy. Blos (1962) says that "in order to reach maturity, the young man has to make peace with his father image and the young woman with her mother image." In those families where the parents as individuals and their marriage as a union are not representative of societal norms, the groundwork is laid for potentially serious adjustment problems for the child when he reaches adolescence. We are all familiar with families in which the mother is really the father and the father is really the mother. The mother is the more dominant, competent, intellectually and perhaps financially superior partner, and the father is a very mild-mannered, physically or psychologically absent male who more or less does the mother's bidding. In such families, the young boy may say to himself, "It seems to me that mother is the more competent of the two, and the person to be most emulated. She really seems to have the best end of the deal." He looks at his father and says, "If that's a man, I don't care to become one." He also recognizes that though mother is to be admired and perhaps emulated, she is a very dangerous person with whom to become intimately involved, inasmuch as the boy blames her for his father's emasculation. In this situation a male may identify with his rather masculine mother, but rules out women as a source of intimacy, openness, and mutual trust. It seems to him that men are much safer, and when the needs for intimacy and sexuality arise in adolescence, he tends to turn toward the safer of the two objects. If, somewhere along the line, he is able to establish a meaningful relationship with another adult, such as a teacher, den mother, or cub scout master, he may be able to correct his basic misinterpretation and find that all women are not like mother and all men are not like father. If this does not happen, one has the classic predisposition to a homosexual adaptation.

Sanford (1962) points out that fears of homosexuality are likely to be very much in the picture with the college student. These homosexual concerns (in young men not predisposed to homosexuality as described here) are sometimes intensified in the close contact with members of his own sex which occurs in the settings of residential college living. In such situations, genuine friendships among men, which require revelation of inner feelings, are difficult to form. The sensitive young man will most probably express his more human side in a friendship with a young woman. This is an important determining factor in the early marriages so common on campus today. Such marriages solve, for the time being, many of the young man's problems; but they do not promote genuine friendships with his fellows—which may be missed by him later on—nor a mature choice of spouse, which may also be regretted later. The individual who is late in developing techniques for meeting his need for intimacy may establish a preadolescent relationship with an actually adolescent person. This does entail some very serious risks to the personality and can have a great deal to do with the establishment of a homosexual way of life, or at least a bisexual way (Sullivan, 1953).

A perhaps more typical situation is that of the young man who has grown up in a family where mother is not all that frightening and father is not all that inadequate, but because of their own concerns they have not pushed his heterosexual development in high school and have been satisfied with his gaining recognition in athletics, academics, or music. This young man has usually been associated with three or four other women haters in high school, and has not felt particularly isolated or singled out because of his differentness.

This adaptation has worked well for him in his small town, but on coming to the university, he finds himself in a fraternity house or dormitory unit with fifty other fellows, at least half of whom are older than he, walking about in various states of undress, talking about nothing but sex from morning to night. Our student fails to recognize that they have not really done much of what they talk about, and for the first time is traumatically confronted with his differentness. Our society plays a very dirty trick on its males by telling them that they must either be heterosexual or homosexual and that they must make this choice at about age sixteen or seventeen. The other assumption is that if one is not heterosexual, one must be homosexual, whether there is any conscious awareness of sexual attraction toward the same sex. The homosexual panic of the college freshman or sophomore usually arises in such a predicament. He gradually becomes aware of his differentness and will usually present to his dormitory counselor or psychiatric service the statement, "My God, I'm a homosexual." On listening to the student, one hears nothing about overt homosexual behavior, or indeed, the predominance of homosexual fantasies. One may ask him how many men he has been to bed with, and he replies, "None." Asked if he is aware of a sexual attraction toward other fellows in the shower room, he replies, "No." He may confess some mutual sexual exploration with friends during early adolescence, but no behavior identifying an homosexual adaptation. One is then in a position to point out his apparent heterosexual retardation and ponder with him whether he has not confused heterosexual retardation with homosexuality. At this point, the student usually breathes a sigh of relief and one can now begin working on the real problem. Such students are extremely gratifying to the counselor because of the very rapid progress they make in catching up with their peers in the realm of heterosexual relationships.

Sullivan (1953) defines three classifications of intimacy, four classifications of general interpersonal objectives in the integration of lust, and six classifications of genital relationship. This results in seventy-two theoretical patterns of sexual behavior in situations involving two real partners. Only forty-five patterns of behavior are reasonably probable, but the classification scheme does point out how fatuous it is to toss around the adjectives "heterosexual," "homosexual," or "narcissistic" in an attempt to classify a person as to his sexual and friendly relationships with others.

In this section on sexuality, we have focused primarily on the male. It seems to me that psychiatrists and mental health workers in general have as much difficulty explaining the female of the species as do other men. Actually, the model of the skewed parental relationship serves almost equally well to explain sexual confusion in the female college student. One encounters situations in which father is described as a real tyrant who rules the house with an iron hand and treats people like things. Mother is described as a warm but ineffectual woman who was unable to protect her daughter from the father. In this case again, the daughter emulates many of the father's more aggressive characteristics but eliminates men as a potential source of intimacy. She much prefers the safeness of a soft, gentle relationship with another female. Again, there are many variations on this theme with milder degrees of distortion. In general, it seems that women are much less hung up with homosexuality than are men, primarily because of the degree of intimacy and overt display of affection we allow our women without labeling it as bizarre or peculiar. Two young girls who are college roommates during their freshman year but separated over the summer vacation are allowed to greet each other with hugs and tears on arriving back at school. Indeed, this is a very warm and tender scene, displaying some of the better attributes of mankind. Should the same behavior be displayed between two male roommates returning in the fall, however, they would immediately be labeled as peculiar. If one asks, while speaking to a group of girls in a dormitory, what really bugs them most about the fellows, an inevitable reply is, "They just don't seem to know how to be tender." They seem to point out the unfortunate fusion of tenderness and genital sexuality in males. We teach our males that every time they experience a warm glow in the presence of another person, especially a female, one ought to have an orgasm. This attitude, of course, requires repression of intimacy toward inappropriate objects such as male friends, and distorts the basic need for touching, holding, and caressing.

The Formation of a Personal Value System

Children in our society are raised with a set of values and beliefs imposed on them primarily by parents, but also influenced by church, school, and community. This is necessary because the child has not yet developed the capacities necessary to form a value system of his own. Sanford (1962) says, "For values to become internalized, they must be reflected on, and made the objects of the individual's best efforts and judgment in decision making; they must find their way into the personality structure through the activity of the conscious and developed ego rather than through automatic conditioning or unconscious mechanisms." The manner in which values are presented to a child may be crucial to his later development as a college student. In the ideal situation, his parents tell him, "We believe this is wrong and this is right. There are others in the world who believe differently, and we have no corner on the truth. As you grow older, you will have to examine these beliefs for yourself and compare them with the values presented to you by others, so that you may make your own choice. Until you develop this capacity, however, you will use ours." In this ideal situation, the child learns the relativity of most values and begins to get practice in developing the tools to make the judgments and decisions that will be necessary later on. If the child has been raised in an exceedingly authoritarian environment where his family or his church tells him, "This is right and this is wrong and don't ever question the two," and he complies, he will experience rather intense anxiety when he moves from his insulated family and community setting to the environment of a large state university. One way to conceptualize the college experience is as a situation in which one is confronted day in and day out by radically differing value systems, be they religious, political, economic, racial, or philosophical, and whether they be presented by one's professors, classmates, friends, or roommates. Students are going to meet at least one avid atheist who will challenge them to examine and defend their religious beliefs. There is always the free love proponent in every dormitory, who challenges one to examine the basis of one's sexual values. The sanctity of our capitalist economic system will be challenged on several fronts. A student who has had no practice in listening, weighing, and discriminating may be overwhelmed. There is also the tendency to rebel against the authoritarian parents and the possibility that the whole house of cards may come tumbling down about his ears is a very real one. The total collapse of the value system is a catastrophe of major proportions. The student may cease to function both academically and interpersonally within as short a time as forty-eight hours. The anxiety is intense, and he complains vigorously of a total loss of meaning and purpose and feeling "like an empty shell of a human being." There is no purpose to getting up in the morning, going to bed at night, attending classes, or in fact doing anything. The student in college today can only afford to cease to function for about seven to ten days and still have any hope of rebounding and catching up on his work to complete a semester.

There seem to be two major alternatives to the cessation of function and withdrawal from school. The first is for the catastrophe to be recognized by faculty, counselors, or friends, and appropriate help sought quickly. Admission to the infirmary and medication may be needed to help the student handle the anxiety. Usually after one or two sessions with a therapist, the student can identify the crux of the disaster and can be supported temporarily by the therapist's own value system so that he may resume functioning. The student must learn to live with a degree of anxiety about the existential questions of purpose and meaning of life until he is able to create a value system that fits him as a unique individual human being. This is really a lifelong process, which hopefully is never entirely completed.

A second response to the collapse of a value system may be to find another ready-made set of beliefs that one may "swallow whole and relieve the emptiness." There are many such systems on any university campus, and cover the range from right to left. We have chapters of the John Birch Society, fraternities and sororities, fundamental religions, hippies, political radicals, and most recently, the Blacks. In fact, all of the "isms" in essence present to the individual a ready-made system of do's or don't's, rights and wrongs, regulations for behavior and dress, and usually even an initiation rite. Becoming a member of one of these groups and adopting their value system may well save the individual from academic failure and may be one of the more valuable functions of such groups. My observations over the past five years have led me to the hypothesis that should we examine the members of any of these groups ten years hence we would find that a majority of the individuals are indistinguishable from the rest of their fellows, and have been able to accept that of the original group that fits them, rejects that which does not, and draw in numerous other sources to formulate a system of their own. Sanford (1962) feels that when conscience is individualized and enlightened, the individual's moral standards and values are supported by his own knowledge, thought, and judgment, they are no longer mere remnants of the training of childhood, nor mere copies of what is espoused by figures of authority or contemporary social groups. The standards and values are then the individual's own. They are based on his own experience and may serve his own motives. When conscience is enlightened, there is no longer any great gap between what the individual wants to do and what he feels he ought to do. Erikson (1968) describes an ethical sense that is the mark of the adult and that takes over from the ideological convictions of adolescence and the moralism of childhood.

It is crucial that the counselor or therapist be an individual who has created his own value system and is aware of the process and its inherent anxiety. Only when one's value system is one's own is there enough flexibility and lack of defensiveness to truly listen to another person. One must also be able to distinguish between cramming one's value system down another's throat, and exposing one's beliefs to a student who may be in desperate, but temporary need of them.

Development of the Capacity for True Intimacy

In some respects, children seem to be inherently intimate. Their freshness, lack of inhibition, and physical expressiveness appear spontaneous, and it is only after long contact with adults of the species that they become more restrained. There does, however, seem to be a continuum along which it is possible to categorize newborn infants into huggers at one end, and kickers at the other (Blaine, 1962). The same characteristic differentiation usually continues throughout childhood— one child will tend to cling to adults, jumping into their laps at every possible opportunity, whereas his brother or sister may seem to shun demonstrations of physical affection from grownups and to remain stand-offish and aloof. The example set by parents in their own display of affection and intimacy may set the stage for the development or the repression of their child's own spontaneity. One may be familiar with the typically American scene of the five- or six-year-old boy who has been used to kissing Daddy good night, until owing to the father's own increasing discomfort with male-male intimacy, he is met with the statement one night, "I think you're getting a little old for this now; we men don't do this sort of thing." One can imagine the child's confusion at being told that a feeling he assumed was normal and acceptable will have to be denied. Students who complain primarily of difficulty in establishing close, meaningful relationships frequently give a history of "refrigerator parents." They have much difficulty recalling open expressions of affection between their parents other than the ritual peck on the cheek as the father leaves for work. Some report that their parents "just seem like two people who happen to live in the same house." A particularly moving experience occurred during the therapy of one young man, when I attempted to describe how one goes about holding and kissing another person, a phenomenon the student had never experienced.

Sullivan (1953) says,

The onset of pre-adolescence is heralded by the appearance of a specific new type of interest in a particular member of the same sex who becomes a chum or close friend. This change represents the beginning of something very like full-blown, psychiatrically defined love. In other words, the other fellow takes on a perfectly novel relationship with the person concerned; he becomes of practically equal importance in all fields of value. Nothing remotely like this has ever happened before. All of you who have children are sure that your children love you; when you say that, you are expressing a pleasant illusion. But if you will look very closely at one of your children when he finally finds a chum—somewhere between 8½ and 10—you will discover something very different in that relationship—namely that your child begins to develop a real sensitivity to what matters to another person.

My clinical experience with college students seems to confirm Sullivan's (1953) statement that

I am practically convinced that capacity for ease, for maximum profit from experience, in carrying on the conventional business of life with members of one's own sex requires that one should have been fortunate in entering into and profiting from relationships with a chum in the pre-adolescent phase of personality development.

A student who is unable to give a history of a close chum or best friend with whom he has shared the anxieties and ecstasies of preadolescence and puberty has a major impediment to forming satisfactory heterosexual relationships. In therapy with such a student, it is almost essential that he reenact such a relationship, either with the therapist or with a receptive peer. The difficulty at this late date, of course, is that genital sexuality is a very predominating influence and usually arouses concern about the homosexual nature of such a relationship. In dealing with adolescents, one should remember that their involvement, whether they have physical expression or not, can be far from casual:

A boy's first love is a love apart, and never again may he hope to recapture the glory and the anguish of it. It is heavy with portent, yet withal so tender and selfless a thing as to touch the very hem of the garment of God. Only once in a life comes such loving as this . . . (Hall, 1957).

That love will often be for another boy. The shock and bitterness of a boy who is denounced for having such feelings may well make it harder for him to reach a satisfactory heterosexual sexual adjustment later (Heron, 1964). Again, Sullivan (1953) says,

I would hope that pre-adolescent relationships were intense enough for each of the two chums literally to get to know practically everything about the other one that could possibly be exposed in an intimate relationship, because that remedies a good deal of the often illusory, usually morbid, feeling of being different, which is such a striking part of rationalizations of insecurity in later life.

The establishment of an essential degree of comfort with human intimacy is a major problem, not only on our campuses, but in our society in general. Delayed autonomy and independence, which is necessitated by a college education, sexually segregated dormitory systems, and intense competition, all make the establishment of true intimacy more difficult. The university focuses the majority of its efforts on expanding the cerebrum, and expends minimal effort on developing the sensitivity and awareness of feelings so necessary to a truly human relationship. Erikson (1968) says,

It is only when identity formation is well on its way that true intimacy —which is really counterpointing as well as a fusing of identities—is possible. Sexual intimacy is only a part of what I have in mind, for it is obvious that sexual intimacies often precede the capacity to develop a true and mutual psychosocial intimacy with another person, be it in friendship, in erotic encounters, or in joint inspiration. The youth who is not sure of his identity shies away from personal intimacy or throws himself into acts of intimacy which are "promiscuous" without true fusion or real self abandon.

It is not unusual to see a young woman who complains initially that she seems to end up in bed with every boy she dates. She describes a series of brief, unsatisfying affairs that have left her with an increasing feeling of uneasiness. You ask her to tell you about the last young man, Tom. She says they met last weekend at a local pub; she found him an attractive, appealing young English major, and proceeds to give you a physical description. You push her for more personal information about Tom, and she finally admits that she does not know him, in spite of the fact that they ended up having intercourse on the first meeting. It is as though she were saying to herself, "I know I have trouble getting close to people; maybe if we go to bed together, we'll be close." It is her disillusionment with this phenomenon that has brought her to see a therapist. She is becoming aware that intercourse does not necessarily have anything to do with human closeness. You are now in a position to point out to the young lady that the quality of her human relationships seems to leave something to be desired, and she has already told you she is not getting much out of sex. You suggest that perhaps she stop this behavior until together you can explore her difficulty. She almost breathes an audible sigh of relief, because someone has presented her with a rationale to cease what she already knows is destructive behavior. In my experience, it is possible to provoke useful anxiety in a student by focusing on the quality of his human relationships, whereas invoking the old sexual taboos is fruitless.

As mentioned earlier, much of the college male's concern about homosexual feelings and behavior is a result of his confusion of intimacy and tenderness with genital sexuality. It seems that the American male is taught from birth that every time he begins to feel a warm glow and a desire for physical closeness with another person of either sex, he must have an orgasm if he is going to be a "real man." Perhaps if the male's early signs of sexual arousal were as inconspicuous as the female's vaginal sweating, our television commercials would be much less successful in confusing our pregenital needs of physical closeness, physical comfort, and satiation of hunger with genital sexuality.

One of the more pathogenic myths that we still pass on to the young girls in our society is that some day each will meet her knight in shining armor, fall in love, get married, and live happily ever after, needing no other human being. These girls have essentially been taught, usually by their fathers, that they are helpless, dependent creatures who cannot exist without the support of a strong male. This confusion of dependency and intimacy is frequently very flattering to the male, who has his own ego boosted by believing that this poor, helpless little thing can not get along without him. If a rapid commitment, such as marriage, is made, the therapist or counselor may see this couple about two or three years later when the absolutely smothering nature of the relationship has been discovered, usually by the male. His attempts to obtain some breathing room have intensified his wife's anxiety and caused her to cling even harder. Thus we see them tugging and pulling at each other down life's road. Recognition that a variety of human relationships will be necessary to fulfill one's needs for intimacy is essential for a satisfactory marriage. One will still need friends, colleagues, intellectual companions, and perhaps children. The most successful destroyer of the myth of the helpless girl awaiting her knight, in my experience, has been for the young woman to be able to work, feed, clothe, and house herself for a year or so before marriage.

Choosing a Life's Work

Choosing a life's work need not be synonomous with choosing a vocation. A given vocation may allow for a wide variety of specialized interest areas and life styles. Choosing seems to imply selecting among a number of consciously known alternatives. The freshman student who says he wants to become an astrophysicist has probably not chosen a life's work or even a vocation because he is not yet acquainted with the other alternatives available to him. The most selective he could become at that stage would be to say he preferred the sciences to the arts or the humanities. After exploring one or the other of these broad categories for a year or two, he may then be in a position to begin narrowing his vocational choice. It may be several years beyond college before an individual can begin to settle down into a life's work. For example, the student who obtains his bachelor's degree in education may eventually find that his talents lie in the area of administration, or he may choose to pursue his education further with the goal of becoming a college teacher. One of the advantages of a college education is that it may allow the individual a wider range of choices in his life's work.

Perhaps as a result of our increasing affluence, a large number of students come to college without ever having really chosen to do so. It has always been a "given" in their lives, and the closest they have come to a decision lies in what size or type of college they may attend. There seems to be enough excitement and newness in the freshman year to sustain their interest, but frequently by the end of that year they are aware that they have not achieved up to their potential, and that their motivation is rapidly waning. They say to themselves, "Well, next year will be different; I'll really begin to get a feel of what it's all about." By midterm of the first semester of the sophomore year, large numbers of these students are seeking out one variety of counseling or another, because things are not different and they have no feel for the purpose of the whole process. In my experience, this is the time for the student to begin making plans to not be a student. It is difficult to find a faculty member who can talk with one about not being a student. The typical response if a student is making good grades is that he would be foolish to leave, while if he is making bad grades the assumption may be that he is not college material. One of the very significant services a mental health or counseling division can offer is the opportunity for a student to explore the possibilities of not being a student. He needs to consider where he would live, where work is available, and generally how he wants to structure his life. One makes the assumption that the student will not return home, at least not for any very extended period of time, as there is really no place for him at home now. He needs most the opportunity to concretely demonstrate to himself that he has the capacity to feed, clothe, and house himself. This can be an exceptional maturing experience, and if the student will remain out of school for at least a year, the probability of his returning and successfully completing his academic career is greatly enhanced. Blaine (1962) states that

> Taking a year or two away from school seems to serve two chief purposes. The first is that these students come back for their own reasons. No longer are they following a path which was laid out for them the day they were born—public school, high school, and college in a time-worn sequence. After some time out of school, they have broken out of this previously prepared rut. Being out in the world has taught them that college is an important and valuable experience which will be helpful to them, not just a meaningless, prolonged period of dependence sponsored by their tradition-bound parents. The other result is therapeutic affect of finding one area, no matter how simple or mundane, in which one can be competent

. . . such work gives concrete evidence of accomplishment which studying for an examination never can.

In this nation's current predicament, the recommendation of an academic moratorium for a male student usually means his becoming eligible for the draft. In many instances this is not a distasteful alternative to the student, and the counselor may be of some help in directing him to appropriate sources of information regarding the military service. If the student's reaction to the prospect of being drafted is overt panic, this usually indicates a very shaky identity severely threatened by the fantasy of a dehumanizing military machine. Draft counseling centers are available on most of the larger campuses, and can be of a great service to these students. When one recommends an academic moratorium, it is usually quite helpful to communicate and explain the recommendation to the patient's parents with his permission. The parents frequently need a good deal of reassurance that interrupting one's college education is not always a disaster, and in fact remaining in college with no motivation is probably the more destructive of the two alternatives. In remaining in college, the student only accumulates a large quantity of mediocre grades, which essentially block his entrance into graduate or professional schools should he begin to find his motivation leading in this direction later on.

Conclusion

I have attempted to present a frame of reference in which those working with college students can think about the concerns and problems presented by a particular individual. No claim is made as to the universality of this theoretical scheme, and I am well aware of the dangers of making generalizations about modal behavior from work with disturbed adolescents seen in a clinical setting (Offer, Sabshin, and Marcus, 1965). One of the encouraging things about this presentation is that it seems to make sense to the students themselves. The recent studies of symptomatic adolescents (Masterson, 1967; Masterson and Washburne, 1966) indicate that the relatively healthy adolescent, though he may be in turmoil, does not show symptoms that simulate a psychiatric illness and differs quite distinguishably from those with psychiatric illnesses. A five-year followup study indicates that 62 percent of those with psychiatric illnesses still had moderate to severe impairment of their function. Josselyn (1968) has pointed out that outgrowing adolescence does not ensure a healthy adulthood and that while the roots of adult personality are fixed in the soil of childhood, it is during adolescence that the final solutions, successful or not, of the maturational stages of psychological development are gradually concretized. It seems that to take the position that "they will grow out of it" may cause us to miss one of the most opportune times to intervene in a maladaptive life style with a minimum expenditure of professional time and expense. The four qualities that are especially needed in the psychotherapy of adolescence are (1) engagement; (2) flexibility; (3) partiality; (4) a willingness to play or not to play a parent surrogate role as needed (Slaff, 1962). Erikson (1968) feels that "we cannot separate personal growth and communal change, nor can we separate the identity crisis in individual life and contemporary crisis in historical development, because the two help to define each other and are truly relative to each other." Thus as the emphasis on the particular developmental tasks changes as a result of the s:udent's relationship with his parents and his community, the particular developmental tasks most in evidence at a given time affect the student's relationship to the college or the university.

REFERENCES

Berne, E. (1964). Games people play. New York: Grove Press.

Blaine, G. B., Jr. (1962). Patience and fortitude. Boston: Little, Brown.

Blos, P. (1962). On adolescence: A psychoanalytic interpretation. Glencoe: The Free Press.

Erikson, E. H. (1963). Childhood and society, 2d ed. New York: Norton.

———. (1968). Identity: Youth and crisis. New York: Norton.

Friedman, W. H., and Coons, F. W. (1967). Unpublished data. Indiana University Student Health Center.

Hall, R. (1957). Adam's breed. New York: Hammond. P. 134.

Group for the Advancement of Psychiatry. (1968). Normal adolescence. New York: Scribner's.

Havighurst, R. J. (1952). Developmental tasks and education. New York: McKay.

Heron, A. (1964). Towards a Quaker view of sex: An essay by a group of Friends. Friends House, Euston Road, London, N.W. 1, England.

Josselyn, I. (1968). Adolescents: Everyone's special concern. International Journal of Psychiatry, 5:478-483.

Masterson, J. F., Jr. (1967). The symptomatic adolescent five years later: He didn't grow out of it. American Journal of Psychiatry, 123:1338-1345.

———, and Washburne, A. (1966). The symptomatic adolescent: Psychiatric illness or adolescent turmoil. American Journal of Psychiatry, 122:1240-1248.

273

Offer, D., Sabshin, M., and Marcus, D. (1965). Clinical evaluation of normal adolescents. American Journal of Psychiatry, 121:864–871.

Sanford, W. (1962). Developmental status of the entering freshman. In W. Sanford, ed., The American college. New York: Wiley.

Slaff, B. (1962). Adolescent psychiatry: Myth or reality? Read as part of a panel before the annual meeting of the American Psychiatric Association, Toronto, May 10.

Sullivan, H. S. (1953). The interpersonal theory of psychiatry. New York: Norton.

Tyler, E. A. (1964). The process of humanizing physiological man. Family Process, 3:280–301.

13] A PROPOSED DIAGNOSTIC CLASSIFICATION FOR ADOLESCENT PSYCHIATRIC CASES

M. ROBERT WILSON, JR.

Rationale

The recognition and classification of psychiatric disease among adolescents represent twin sources of frustration and dissatisfaction to the psychiatrist, to other physicians, and to mental health workers. In young persons, the most common source of distress or disease often is emotional in nature. The increasing number of psychiatrists whose work is exclusively devoted to adolescents and the recently chartered organization of a professional society, The American Society for Adolescent Psychiatry, reflect the profession's response to this growing need, as well as the appreciation by those specializing in this field that psychotherapy of the adolescent differs markedly from therapies employed either with adults or with children. In other articles in preparation I will enlarge on technique and related issues; this essay will confine itself to classification and diagnosis, emphasizing nomenclature and definition.

As a brief prelude to this section, I would submit that the first definition requiring clarification is the term "adolescent," which is central to the proposed diagnostic classification and also requisite to the identification of those persons to whom the classification is applicable. Though adolescence is viewed as a developmental period, and therefore its perimeters are roughly chronologically determined, beginning with puberty and terminating at eighteen or nineteen, the "development" from which this (generally accepted) scope of adolescence is derived reflects only biological and physiological development. A holistic view, incor-

275

porating psychological development with biological and physiological dimensions, would extend the span of adolescence at least through the college years, and thus in terms of age, would suggest that a comprehensive definition of adolescence must include those persons still in the process of fulfilling certain age-determined psychological developmental tasks, notwithstanding the termination of biological and physiological developmental processes. One must, however, exclude from this comprehensive definition of adolescence those many older persons who have, through diverse emotional impediments, become "arrested" at the adolescent stage, and in whom unfulfilled adolescent developmental tasks have been avoided or denied; the psychiatric techniques employed in therapy with such persons cannot realistically provide retrospective fulfillment, nor can the classification proposed below be construed as applicable to the "perennial adolescent." As a working rule, adolescence is defined, at the Mayo Clinic (for the purposes of referring a given patient to the appropriate section of the psychiatry department), as including all persons under eighteen, who are biologically pubescent, together with all undergraduate college students, who by inference have acknowledged a continuing need to be dependent, in contrast to the nineteen-year-old, who has chosen to marry, is employed or otherwise "emancipated," and thereby has, realistically or not, closed his psychological epiphyses. Hence, the definition of adolescence to which this proposed classification is applicable is both comprehensive and selective.

The requirements that must be met in any new diagnostic classification for adolescents include (1) a universal vocabulary for the concise transmission of information about patients among and between psychiatric colleagues and other physicians, as well as paramedical personnel, educators, parents, and patients; (2) a suitable codification of diagnostic impressions, for purposes of records, statistics, and research; (3) an applicability to the information so classified, which must reflect the specific and unique qualities inherent in these data; and (4) the rubric (which, in my opinion, should be mandatory in all diagnostic classifications), dictating that deductive principles, rather than inductive principles, constitute the syllogistic vector from which diagnosis is derived. This is particularly vital to the classification of psychiatric disease among adolescent patients; for to infer, from manifestations or symptoms, conclusions about the person and his internal struggles, which may or may not represent a psychiatric problem, is both inconsistent with the diagnostic tenets of medicine and exquisitely inconsistent with a comprehension of the adolescent patient. The practice of "labeling," though perhaps useful (and, when the label is deductively derived, is consistent with "sound medical and scientific canons") if employed for the adolescent patient, must be based on appropriate labels not connoting pejorative qualities that will likely augur for him future encumbrances in college or graduate school applications, vocational choice, and inestimable other obstacles.

The currently accepted psychiatric classifications are not applicable to the adolescent psychiatric patient because they do not meet the third and fourth requirements stipulated above. The standard nomenclature of the American Psychiatric Association as outlined in the *Diagnostic and Statistical Manual of Mental Disorders* (1968) includes the category "Behavior Disorders of Childhood and Adolescence" (308). This is the major category devoted to disorders occurring in childhood and adolescence, and is limited to those disorders "which are more stable, internalized and resistant to treatment than the transient situational disturbances, but less so than psychoses, neuroses and personality disorders." The seven categories enumerated under this general heading are (1) hyperkinetic reaction (308.0); (2) withdrawing reaction (308.1); (3) overanxious reaction (308.2); (4) runaway reaction (308.3); (5) unsocialized aggressive reaction (308.4); (6) group delinquent reaction (308.5); and (7) other reactions (308.9). I submit these are vague and ambient, in descriptive content as well as in age groups included therein. DSM-II also includes under "Transient Situational Disturbances" (307) the following categories which are relevant to childhood and adolescence: (1) adjustment reaction of infancy (307.0); (2) adjustment reaction of childhood (307.1); and (3) adjustment reaction of adolescence (307.2). These attempt to identify specific reactions occurring during childhood and adolescence, but they also suffer from the vagueness and nonspecific shortcomings of category 308.

In DSM-II there is also listed a classification, "Special Symptoms" (306), in which are included a number of symptoms predominately limited to childhood and adolescence. These are (1) specific learning disturbance (306.1); (2) feeding disturbance (306.5); (3) enuresis (306.6); and (4) encopresis (306.7). Implicit in DSM-II is the expectation that diagnoses in adolescent patients not specifically classified in one of the above categories can be established by selecting the most appropriate and applicable classification from the remaining seven categories provided. The assumption that the adolescent psychiatric patient does not warrant the application of diagnostic labels synonymous with those ap-

277

plied to adult patients is fundamental to the rationale for a separate diagnostic nomenclature and classification, because adolescent psychiatric symptoms, or peripheral manifestations of presumptive adult disease, may merely reflect normal adolescent turmoil.

The Group for the Advancement of Psychiatry (GAP) volume entitled *Psychopathological Disorders in Childhood: Theoretical Considerations and a Proposed Classification* (1966) presents a diagnostic classification for children that reflects the inadequacy and inappropriateness of the standard nomenclature in its application to the psychiatric disorders of children. The GAP proposals recognize the dynamic and kinetic properties of childhood by bestowing on the developmental tasks, which are age-specific, a primacy in the classification scheme, and relegating to a subordinate role the specific symptom list. Again, the suitability of the GAP classification in its application to adolescent psychiatric disease is doubtful. The GAP nomenclature has been employed for two years in the section of child and adolescent psychiatry at the Mayo Clinic; in our effort to apply these classifications to adolescents we have found the principal obstacle to be the omission of a comprehensive understanding and breakdown of specific adolescent issues, complicated by a symptom list which is neither adequate nor appropriate in many areas, when one applies it to the adolescent patient.

Numerous attempts (Jenkins, 1964; Laufer, 1965) have been undertaken to classify psychiatric disease in childhood; however, nearly all of these proposals have included both children and adolescents, and none has been put forth that is specific for adolescent psychiatric disorders.

Psychodynamic Issues of Adolescence: A Proposal

Erikson (1963) has stated that the adolescent is embarked on the task of developing his identity; he declares that the developmental task of adolescence is forging an identity and its antithesis is role diffusion. The establishment of a comfortable identity, independent of family, and based on new and differently meaningful attachments, with the ultimate goal of becoming self-dependent, spans the entire period of adolescence. Erikson used the simile of the trapeze artist in describing the adolescent. Inherent in this simile is the invitation issued to the adolescent to take a chance, namely, to give up what is known, secure, and predicta-

278

ble (childhood) and to work toward an ill-defined future (adulthood) which promises to be better. The acceptance of this invitation, and the implicit risk or chance thus taken, is the first requirement for matriculation as an adolescent.

Until he has reached his goal, forged a self-dependent identity, and completed adolescence, the adolescent can be seen searching for the middle ground between diathetical polarities in five specific dimensions of his existence: dependence-independence, impotence-omnipotence, passivity-aggressivity, altruism-narcissism, femininity-masculinity. His efforts to deny the totality and thus the painful attributes of either side of each of these diatheses might take the form of exaggeration and corollary elision of each issue. His final recognition that he is a mosaic of all, and that no one occupies a position apotheotic to the whole, is the consequence of healthy antecedent developmental periods. He wants neither his abject dependency nor his total independency verified; neither his inferior impotence substantiated nor his lonely vulnerable and isolated omnipotence; neither his painful, easily wounded, and sensitive passivity acknowledged nor his potentially lethal aggressivity. Each action of the adolescent (whether feeling, thought, word, or deed) seeks to produce the proper combination of effect and reaction in others. An overabundance of effect verifies his omnipotence, and the converse is true when there is only reaction and no effect: his impotence is verified.

The state of flux, biological and sociological, which characterizes adolescence, contributes to the adolescent's need to establish concrete, immutable, and absolute anchors that are relinquished with great reluctance. These anchors, notwithstanding their frequently patent irrationality, serve to dilute or palliate the discomfort of the adolescent's fluid and ambiguous condition. In the psychiatrically disabled adolescent person, identification of the nature and character of the inherent polarization of any or all of the above diatheses, as the initial phase of the diagnostic evaluation, takes cognizance of the anchoring quality to the adolescent represented by this polarization: Polarization is fundamental to the genesis of his disability, and consequently equally fundamental to the process of rehabilitation is its depolarization. The therapist's acknowledgment of his need for a safe anchor dictates the necessity to exercise caution and to construct an acceptable substitute anchor as the initial step in therapy. The design for such a substitute is easily discerned, if one recognizes that implicit in the annealing of the adolescent's polarized identity is the belief, usually unconscious or preconscious, held by the adolescent, that there exists an object characterized by those qualities that are the obverse of his identity, equally absolute and totally inflexible.

Endowing the therapist with these characteristics is a universal phenomenon in the therapy process with adolescents; for therein he is provided with an alternative anchor and its nature reflects the underlying needs, once provided by parents, but now disenfranchised by the loss of childhood and undoubtedly prior vulnerability.

The Diagnostic Classification: Adolescent Psychiatry

The classification I have proposed is constituted of three echelons: primary, secondary, and tertiary diagnosis. Under this classification all adolescent patients referred for psychiatric evaluation would be subject to a primary diagnosis. Most of these patients would also qualify for classification based on the identification of specific developmental vulnerabilities (or psychodynamic issues), together with the structural distortion incidental to the vulnerability (the secondary diagnosis). Most adolescent patients referred for psychiatric evaluation would also qualify for the inclusion of a tertiary diagnosis, which would catalog all clearly identifiable signs or symptoms of malfunctioning (see Appendix). However, for practical purposes, the diagnosis entered into official records would be limited to the primary diagnosis only, with the secondary and tertiary diagnoses reserved for confidential records, data retrieval, and appropriate communication with colleagues or other persons where the sharing of such qualifying data about a patient is in the patient's best interest.

THE PRIMARY DIAGNOSIS

The primary diagnosis, identified as *adolescent crisis* and qualified by the assignation of the appropriate class (I, II, III, IV, or V), would be inherently applicable to all adolescent patients referred for psychiatric assessment, in that the five categories range from "healthy reactions" (adolescent crisis, class I) to "failure to matriculate into adolescence" (adolescent crisis, class V).

Adolescent Crisis, Class I

Presumably the request for a psychiatric diagnosis is based on concern generated about the adolescent person in his parents, teachers, family physician, or other referring sources. Thus the evaluation must provide some conclusions, even when the consulting psychiatrist judges that no evidence exists of psychiatric disease; the classification therefore provides a category within the primary diagnosis for such patients, implicit in which is the acceptance and acknowledgment of concern about the patient, by the consulting psychiatrist, coupled with his conclusion that the anxiety or concern generated by him is not accompanied by malfunctioning, and is explained by "working through" age-appropriate issues common to all adolescents. The explanation of the normalcy—notwithstanding its disruptive or anxiety-generating potential—to those who have sought the consultation is reassuring, and represents a responsibility incumbent on any psychiatrist who has been requested to assess a given adolescent. The tempering of the primary diagnosis with a subsidiary secondary diagnosis, is limited, in the class I patient, to indicating a specific adolescent developmental vulnerability only. In no instance would a patient diagnosed as adolescent crisis, class I be a candidate for secondary diagnoses, identifying preadolescent developmental vulnerabilities or structural distortions. Nor would there be any tertiary diagnosis unless a concurrent organic malfunction, clearly limited in its genesis and its consequences to the physical or organic dimensions thereof, existed; in such cases tertiary diagnoses should be listed.

Adolescent Crisis, Class II

This category would reflect psychiatric diseases in which there was no evidence of emotional disability prior to adolescence, and in which the crisis and symptoms clearly represent a pathologic reaction to the confrontation of age-dependent issues. Therefore, adolescent persons to whom this diagnosis would be applicable should not qualify for secondary diagnoses indicating either "preadolescent developmental vulnerability" or "structural distortion," but would clearly only qualify for a secondary diagnosis identifying the specific and predominant adolescent vulnerability, together with its manifestations, and indeed, where discernible to the consulting psychiatrist, as many of the five issues (A–E) together with the apparent pathologic reactions to them should be incorporated in the secondary diagnosis.

Inherent in the rendering of this diagnosis is the inclusion of the subsidiary tertiary diagnosis including as many subcategories of malfunction as appropriate. In contrast to class I crises, malfunctioning indicated with class II crises will always include functional symptoms in addition to any organic ones.

Adolescent Crisis, Class III

The decision to employ this primary diagnosis will be based on evidence of antecedent or preadolescent vulnerabilities, together with corollary structural distortions; however, persons so diagnosed will have shown no overt evidence of emotional disorder or malfunctioning prior to adolescence. Hence, the assumption is that regardless of the ongoing vulnerability and structural distortion, the individual did not manifest any demonstrable symptoms of psychiatric disease until he was confronted with the specific stresses of adolescence.

Class III diagnoses must always include secondary diagnoses in all subcategories, together with tertiary diagnoses, including both functional symptoms and organic signs.

Adolescent Crisis, Class IV

Persons warranting this diagnosis not only have been assessed as harboring vulnerabilities and structural distortions before adolescence but have manifested symptoms of emotional disease before adolescence as well. Presumably, the confrontation with adolescent developmental issues has led to a pathologic reaction, and the presenting illness may frequently be the initial source of concern to the referring party, despite prior symptomatology. The present illness may be manifested in an amplification of previously overlooked symptoms of malfunctioning, or it may be manifested in a completely different guise.

All three subcategories of secondary diagnosis should be included, as well as a comprehensive symptom profile (tertiary diagnosis).

Adolescent Crisis, Class V

Persons diagnosed as being in class V crisis have shown preadolescent vulnerabilities, structural distortions, and symptoms of emotional malfunctioning, but differ from class IV patients in showing no evidence of pathological reaction to adolescent age-dependent issues, and generally no marked change in functioning or personality at adolescence. They have clearly balked at confronting adolescence and have remained arrested at a preadolescent stage of development, which I have designated as "failure to matriculate" into adolescence. Frequently, these youngsters are described by their parents as model teenagers and it is only through the alertness of a teacher or physician to the pathology inherent in the teen-aged boy or girl who never rebels, is always compliant, or in other ways reflects his or her clinging to childhood that these patients are ever brought for evaluation. This diagnosis must include secondary diagnoses in B-I and B-II, but not B-III (see Appendix). The appropriate tertiary diagnoses would be included.

THE SECONDARY DIAGNOSIS

As indicated in the above paragraphs describing the primary diagnostic classifications, secondary diagnosis is variably applicable, and where indicated should be so included. The secondary diagnoses are divided into three subsections: (1) preadolescent developmental vulnerability, in which should be marked, where indicated, the specific task failure, if identifiable; (2) the structural distortion (ego, ego ideal, or superego) that appears to contribute most significantly to the present illness and vulnerability to it; (3) the specific adolescent developmental issues, and the pathologic manner in which these are being confronted, which seem most appropriately to describe the current psychodynamics.

THE TERTIARY DIAGNOSIS

In all patients diagnosed class II through V there will be evidence of definite malfunctioning or symptoms, which I have arbitrarily divided into six categories of functioning: (1) affective, (2) perceptive, (3) cognitive, (4) somatic-visceral, (5) integrative, and (6) societal. An effort has been made to categorize the malfunctioning in each area as hyperfunctioning, hypofunctioning, or dysfunctioning. Whether the malfunctioning be psychogenic or organic, its existence as a manifestation of the total profile of the patient should be included wherever discerned currently by the clinician; significant historical symptoms of malfunctioning, without persistent residual manifestations, should be noted on the tertiary diagnostic list, with an indication of their historical quality included.

Affective Functions (Appendix C-I)

I have limited the term "affect" to two basic or elementary affects: love and anger. According to studies by Spitz and Cobliner (1965) the newborn is protected by a stimulus barrier that, unless the threshold to perceptual stimuli is exceeded, screens out most perceptual stimuli from his awareness. This is operative during the period of "coenesthetic" functioning, as "diacritic" functioning gradually develops, the barrier to perceptual stimuli becomes progressively lowered. The basic ingredients constituting the newborn's awareness during the earliest days of life are therefore affective in nature.

Though it is presumed that during the neonatal period the infant does not differentiate self from not-self, one can assume that the primitive determinants of communication are being formed that will constitute the ultimate patterns and shapes of communication. It is the mandate of communication to represent the vehicle through which one relates to another, and therefore, the nadir and apogee of object relationships. Because the development of the ego represents the development of a relationship to another (the object), the central role of affects therein cannot be underemphasized; neither can the singular role affects play during the neonatal period be overlooked, in that affects are the sole mental equipage with which any infant is endowed at birth and for the immediate period thereafter.

The quality of trust and its corollary, a sense of mattering, are the developmental tasks required for the development of ego, according to Erikson (1964). This quality of trust must derive from each successive dimension of mental experience, beginning with affects, and followed progressively by the stepwise activation and integration of percepts and concepts. Presumably the genesis of trust, initially, is a reaction to the candor and honesty with which the mother reveals her affective self to her child. Where her affects have not been distorted or hidden, the emulative requirement of the educational process will thus permit the infant to sense that his affects are acceptable, and therefore he will matter— because he is what he feels during those early days.

I suggest that affects represent the single domain of mental or bodily functioning which is universal in quantity for every child. By contrast, a child may be deficient or superior in any of the various perceptual or cognitive or somatic endowments. It is only the barriers to affects, or distortions thereof, that generate malfunctioning in the affective area, never deficiency.

Affects likewise have properties unique to this realm, when they are not alloyed with percepts, concepts, or actions. Among the unique properties of affects, in addition to their universal and equal presence in all human beings, are the following: (1) they are neither right nor wrong; (2) they cannot be exhausted nor consumed; (3) they cannot literally destroy; (4) they require no justification; (5) they cannot be demonstrated or expressed, except when merged with perceptual, cognitive, or behavioral modalities, but are "sensed" through extrasensory means only ("vibrations"); (6) they are the only human qualities that can be truly shared, without being lost or diminished, and without controlling or invading the person with whom they are shared; (7) they are not mu-

284

tually contradictory, but complimentary, notwithstanding the apparent antithetical nature of their elementary and basic modes (anger/love).

In all patients diagnosed as adolescent crisis, class II–V, inherently symptoms will be reflected in affective malfunctioning (Appendix C-I), inasmuch as emotional malfunctioning is one issue common to all such persons. In this section of the tertiary diagnosis or symptom list several terms require definition.

From the two elementary affects (love and anger) are derived certain affective derivatives, which are positive in their application. These positive derivatives are illustrated in Table 13–1.

TABLE 13–1
Positive Affective Derivatives

ELEMENTARY AFFECT	LOVE	ANGER
Positive affective derivatives	Closeness	Distance
	Commitment	Territoriality
	Investment	Competition
	Passivity	Aggression
	Cooperation	Rivalry
	Involvement	Avoidance
	Dependence	Independence
	Heteronomy	Autonomy

There are also negative derivatives of affects, which I have called dysphorias, and which are the results of mental mechanisms, erected early in life, reflecting the attitudes toward affects or their positive derivatives, to which the child was privy. The negative derivatives or dysphorias do not lend themselves to such a qualitative etiology regarding the appropriate elementary affect, because the mental mechanism affects both love and anger in much the same manner. Thus, dysphorias, through normal parameters of the affective realm when realistically generated, reflect the hypertrophied invocation of a specific mental mechanism rather than the elementary affect, etiologically, when their presence is sufficient to warrant the assignation of symptom to same. Though it contains an admittedly incomplete index of dysphorias, Table 13–2 illustrates the relationship of dysphorias to responsible mental mechanisms, and also suggests rough chronological correlates.

Referring to the Appendix, C-I, several terms and phrases require specific definition: In subsections A-1 and A-2, "derivatives" implies positive derivatives (see Table 13–1). In subsection A-1 (c) and A-2 (c), the phrase "deviant vectoral component" refers to the person who,

TABLE 13–2

The Negative Affective Derivatives
or Dysphorias *

MECHANISM	AGE OF GENESIS	DYSPHORIA
Introjection	birth–12 mos.	Depression
Projection	birth–12 mos.	Paranoia
Undoing	12–36 mos.	Compulsions Obsessions
Reaction-formation	12–36 mos.	Shame, doubt, other characterological traits
Displacement	36–72 mos.	Phobias
Denial	36–72 mos.	Fear, dread, "anxiety"
Repression	36–72 mos.	Guilt

* The psychiatric disability of any patient reflects either a partially blocked affective life (where only one of the two elementary affects and/or its positive derivatives are permissible) or a distorted affective life, where a negative derivative (dysphoria) predominates unrealistically and thus colors, shapes, molds, and tempers the other dimensions of mental experience and behavior, ultimately, leading to malfunctioning in these subsequently galvinized parameters of functioning as well.

unable to share or exchange the elementary affect or its positive derivatives, fixes the direction (vector) firmly on either others (allovectoral) or himself (autovectoral). The phrase "absolute ambivalence" (subsection A-3) refers to a paralysis of affect (or positive derivatives therefrom) because of the coexisting mutually exclusive feelings toward the same object, reflecting a persistence of the coenesthetic qualities, unique to affects, unalloyed with trust, through the aegis of dishonest or counterfeit models to emulate. "Absolute omnivalence" (subsection A-4) is my phrase for an affective nonpriority state wherein everything possesses the same or equal valence for one's potential investment of feelings therein, and no hierarchical system decrees some order to the feeling valence of objects. This state of omnivalence is characteristic of the chronic psychedelic intoxicant. In subsections B-1, B-2, and B-3, the "expressive affects" are synonymous with negative affective derivatives, or dysphorias; only where these dominate the affective life unrealistically, through their expression or elision, should these categories be employed.

The genesis of a sense of trust, presaging a healthy ego, thus commences during the neonatal period, based on the reaction to the affective domain of the total mental experience, which includes as well the perceptive and cognitive modalities. The liberty to eventually "go free" through the development of a sense of mattering and therefore an awareness of self versus not-self, requires an orchestration of the succeedings phases of functioning with the elementary affects and their positive derivatives; hence, attachment, the affective mode of love, and separation, the affective mode of anger, are not incompatible, but one leads logically and sequentially to the other, the additive quality of existence (in contrast to the replacement or substitutive) is confirmed, and the structural development of the ego ideal commences, roughly when the child begins to walk, talk, and do things for himself that had previously been done for him by others.

Perceptive Functions

The percepts may be divided into "contract" percepts and "distant" percepts. The former include balance, taste, and touch; the latter, vision, hearing, and smell. The continuum of trust-mattering inaugurated during the coenesthetic phase provides the basis for these same ego-syntonic qualities becoming successively derivatives of the contact percepts initially, and then the distant percepts. The gradual erosion of the stimulus barrier so that each of these perceptive modalities becomes integrated, and a part of the child's mental experience follows an orderly scheme (Spitz and Cobliner, 1965). The Appendix does not include specific sites for each sensory modality (subsection C-II); however, the dysperceptive qualities are most likely to be functional in origin, and are listed generically.

Cognitive Functions

Those qualities which reflect intelligence, logic, memory, and reason, together with "consciousness" are included in this category. The specific areas of malfunctioning require no further illumination than provided in the comprehensive tables included in the Appendix (C-III).

Somatic-Visceral Functions

The nine divisions of this category of functioning are based primarily on organ systems, and should reflect all malfunctioning, in any organ system, organic or psychogenic or both. Historically significant malfunctioning should also be included.

Integrative Functions

I have taken the liberty of selecting six functions, which are not clearly organ-system, affective, perceptive, cognitive, or motor, but

287

rather represent a combination of same, in establishing this category (subsection C-V). These include eating and drinking, sleeping, bowel and bladder control, body image, speech, and sexuality.

Societal Functions

The division of relationships with society into family authority (VI-A) and peer (VI-B) is arbitrary but, in my opinion, useful, especially as applicable to the adolescent patient. The attention of the clinician is directed especially to the deficiently rebellious adolescent.

REFERENCES

Committee on Child Psychiatry. (1966). Psychopathological disorders in childhood: Theoretical considerations and a proposed classification, report 62. Group for the Advancement of Psychiatry [Report], 6:1–343.

Committee on Nomenclature and Statistics. (1968). Diagnostic and statistical manual of mental disorders (DSM-II), 2d ed. Washington, D.C.: American Psychiatric Association.

Erikson, E. H. (1963). Childhood and society, 2d ed. New York: Norton.

Group for the Advancement of Psychiatry. (1966). Psychopathological disorders in childhood: Theoretical considerations and a proposed classification.

Jenkins, R. L. (1964). Diagnosis, dynamics, and treatment in child psychiatry. Psychiatric Research Reports of the American Psychiatric Association, 18:91–120.

Laufer, M. (1965). Assessment of adolescent disturbances: The application of Anna Freud's diagnostic profile. Psychoanalytic Study of the Child, 20:99–123. New York: International Universities Press.

Spitz, R. A., and Cobliner, W. G. (1965). The first year of life: A psychoanalytic study of normal and deviant development of object relations. New York: International Universities Press.

APPENDIX:

ADOLESCENT PSYCHIATRY DIAGNOSTIC FORM *

A. Primary Diagnosis: Adolescent Developmental Crisis (check one box only)

CLASS

☐ I. healthy reactions; crisis generated by age-syntonic psychodynamic issues; no malfunctioning in six categories of functioning demonstrable; omit tertiary diagnosis

---

* This appendix is the form employed by the Adolescent Psychiatry Unit, Mayo Clinic, devised by the author and referred to throughout the above manuscript. It represents an abbreviated, and yet extensive enough, vehicle for daily and routine use, and eventual data retrieval.

288

☐   II. malfunctioning in one or more of six areas caused by conflicts in age-syntonic psychodynamic issues; no antecedent predisposition

☐   III. malfunctioning in one or more of six areas generated principally in pre-adolescence; secondary conflict regarding age-syntonic adolescent psychodynamic issues and corollary malfunctioning during adolescence as initial manifestations thereof

☐   IV. malfunctioning both generated and manifested principally in preadolescence; deviation and/or failure of preadolescent developmental tasks; secondary conflict during adolescence related to age-syntonic issues

☐   V. malfunctioning both generated and manifested in preadolescence; no adolescent age-syntonic conflict; failure to matriculate in adolescence

B. Secondary Diagnoses: Developmental Vulnerability and Structural Distortions (check all appropriate boxes)

    I. Preadolescent Developmental Vulnerability

		Task		Failure
☐	A.	sense of trust	vs.	mistrust
☐	B.	autonomy	vs.	shame and doubt
☐	C.	initiative	vs.	guilt
☐	D.	industry	vs.	inferiority

    II. Structural Distortion

☐   A. ego
☐   B. ego ideal
☐   C. superego

    III. Adolescent Developmental Vulnerability

    A. impotence vs. omnipotence
      ☐ 1. manifest impotence—overdetermined need to deny omnipotence and to emphasize impotence
      ☐ 2. manifest omnipotence—overdetermined need to deny impotence and to emphasize omnipotence

    B. dependence vs. independence
      ☐ 1. manifest dependence—overdetermined need to deny independence and to emphasize dependence
      ☐ 2. manifest independence—overdetermined need to deny dependence and to emphasize independence

    C. altruism vs. narcissism
      ☐ 1. manifest altruism—overdetermined need to deny narcissism and to emphasize altruism
      ☐ 2. manifest narcissism—overdetermined need to deny altruism and to emphasize narcissism

    D. passivity vs. aggression
      ☐ 1. manifest passivity—overdetermined need to deny aggression and to emphasize passivity
      ☐ 2. manifest aggression—overdetermined need to deny passivity and to emphasize aggression

E. femininity vs. masculinity
 ☐ 1. manifest femininity—overdetermined need to deny masculinity and to emphasize femininity
 ☐ 2. manifest masculinity—overdetermined need to deny femininity and to emphasize masculinity

C. Tertiary Diagnoses: Symptoms of Malfunctioning (check all appropriate boxes)

 I. Affective Functions

 A. elementary affects
  1. love and its derivatives (investment, commitment, etc.)
   ☐ a. hypertrophied love or its derivatives
   ☐ b. absence of love or its derivatives
    c. deviant vectoral component
     ☐ 1. allovectoral
     ☐ 2. autovectoral

  2. anger and its derivatives (competition, rivalry, etc.)
   ☐ a. hypertrophied anger or its derivatives
   ☐ b. absence of anger or its derivatives
    c. deviant vectoral component
     ☐ 1. allovectoral
     ☐ 2. autovectoral

 ☐ 3. absolute ambivalence
 ☐ 4. absolute omnivalence

 B. expressive affects (anxiety, fear [including phobias], guilt, shame, depression, loneliness, inferiority, paranoia, distrust, suspiciousness, hostility, distance, jealousy, apathy, closeness, joy, etc.)
  ☐ 1. expression dominates affective life through primacy caused by unconscious tempering of elementary affects by adoptive mechanisms
   (specify expression: . . . .)
  ☐ 2. absence of expressive affect even with realistic stimuli
   (specify expression: . . . .)
  ☐ 3. inappropriate expressive affect
   (specify expression: . . . .)

 II. Perceptive Functions (enter modality and symptom in space to right of category selected)
  ☐ A. hyperperceptive (. . . .)
  ☐ B. hypoperceptive (. . . .)
   C. dysperceptive
    ☐ 1. hallucinations (. . . . .)
    ☐ 2. illusions (. . . .)
    ☐ 3. other (specify: . . . .)
   D. deficient perceptive organs (. . . . .)
    ☐ 1. constitutional (. . . . .)
    ☐ 2. acquired (. . . . .)

III. Cognitive Functions

    A. hypercognitive
- [ ] 1. precocity
- [ ] 2. overachievement
- [ ] 3. hyperawareness
- [ ] 4. eidetic memory
- [ ] 5. flight of ideas
- [ ] 6. other (specify: . . . .)

    B. hypocognitive
- [ ] 1. underachievement
- [ ] 2. learning inhibition
- 3. hypoawareness
  - [ ] a. decreased alertness
  - [ ] b. delirium
  - [ ] c. comatose state
  - [ ] d. fugue state
  - [ ] e. twilight state
  - [ ] f. other (specify:. . . . .)
- 4. hypomnesic
  - [ ] a. forgetfulness
  - b. amnesia
    - [ ] 1. recent memory
    - [ ] 2. past memory
    - [ ] 3. selective
- 5. hypoassociative
  - [ ] a. distractibility
  - [ ] b. retarded (slow) thinking
  - [ ] c. other (specify:. . . . .)

    C. dyscognitive
- [ ] 1. delusions
- [ ] 2. fragmented thinking
- [ ] 3. magical thinking
- [ ] 4. concrete thinking
- [ ] 5. illogical thinking
- [ ] 6. disorientation (specify:. . . . .)
- [ ] 7. dissociation (multiple personality)
- [ ] 8. poor reality testing
- [ ] 9. dyslexias (specify:. . . . .)
- [ ] 10. obsessions
- [ ] 11. other (specify:. . . . .)

    D. deficient cognition
- [ ] 1. constitutional
- 2. acquired
  - [ ] a. mental deficiency through known cause
  - [ ] b. amnesia (etc.)

    E. organically caused alterations in cognition
- [ ] 1. endogenous (specify:. . . . .)

☐   2.   exogenous
       (eg. drugs, etc.—specify:. . . . .)

IV.   Somatic-Visceral Functions

    A.   musculo-skeletal
       ☐   1.   paralysis (specify location:. . . . .)
       ☐   2.   paresis
       ☐   3.   pain (specify:. . . . .)
           4.   deficiency
             ☐   a.   constitutional
             ☐   b.   acquired (specify cause and nature, if known:. . . . . . .
                 . . . .)
       ☐   5.   hypochondriacal

    B.   integumentary
       ☐   1.   organic (specify: . . . .)
       ☐   2.   psychogenic (specify:. . . . .)
       ☐   3.   hypochondriacal

    C.   respiratory
       ☐   1.   hyperventilation
       ☐   2.   asthma
       ☐   3.   dyspnea
       ☐   4.   hypochondriacal
           5.   other conditions
             ☐   a.   constitutional (specify:. . . . .)
             ☐   b.   acquired (specify:. . . . .)

    D.   cardio-vascular
       ☐   1.   tachycardia
       ☐   2.   palpitations
       ☐   3.   hypertension
       ☐   4.   hypotension
       ☐   5.   angina
       ☐   6.   hypochondriacal
           7.   other conditions
             ☐   a.   constitutional (specify:. . . . .)
             ☐   b.   acquired (specify:. . . . .)

    E.   gastrointestinal
       ☐   1.   nausea
       ☐   2.   vomiting
       ☐   3.   diarrhea
       ☐   4.   constipation
       ☐   5.   dysphagia
       ☐   6.   hypochondriacal
           7.   other conditions
             ☐   a.   constitutional (specify:. . . . .)
             ☐   b.   acquired (specify:. . . . .)

    F.   genito-urinary
       ☐   1.   urinary retention
       ☐   2.   urinary frequency
       ☐   3.   dysuria

☐ 4. dysmenorrhea
☐ 5. dyspareunia
☐ 6. hypochondriacal
 7. other conditions
   ☐ a. constitutional (specify:..........................)
   ☐ b. acquired (specify:.............................)

G. metabolic
 1. hypermetabolic states
   ☐ a. constitutional (specify:............................)
   ☐ b. acquired (specify:................................)
 2. hypometabolic states
   ☐ a. constitutional (specify:............................)
   ☐ b. acquired (specify:................................)
☐ 3. hypochondriacal

H. nervous system
 1. hyper-states
   ☐ a. convulsive disorders
        (specify:......................................)
   ☐ b. choreiform disorders
   ☐ c. other movement disorders
        (specify:......................................)
 2. hypo-states
   ☐ a. hypotonia
   ☐ b. paralysis
   ☐ c. paresis
   ☐ d. hypesthesia
   ☐ e. other (specify:..................................)
☐ 3. hypochondriacal
 4. distorted states (organic brain syndromes)
   ☐ a. acute (specify cause)
        ☐ 1. exogenous:...............................
        ☐ 2. endogenous:.............................
   ☐ b. chronic (specify cause)
        ☐ 1. exogenous:...............................
        ☐ 2. endogenous:.............................
 5. deficiencies—degenerative states (specify cause and/or nature, if
    known)
   ☐ a. constitutional:...................................
   ☐ b. acquired:.......................................

I. hemic-lymph
 ☐ 1. hyperstates (leukemia, polycytemia, etc.)
 ☐ 2. hypostates (anemia, thrombocytopenia, etc.)

V. Integrative Functions

 A. eating-drinking
  1. hyperphagia
    ☐ a. obesity
    ☐ b. polydipsia
    ☐ c. overuse of oral medications
    ☐ d. alcoholism

293

    □   e.   finger- (thumb-) sucking
    □   f.   nail-biting
    □   g.   other (specify:...................................)

   2.   hypophagia
    □   a.   anorexia
    □   b.   food refusal
    □   c.   food fetish / fad

□   distortions—rituals / compulsions

B.   sleeping
    □   1.   narcolepsy
    □   2.   excessive sleepiness
    □   3.   insomnia
    □   4.   nightmares
    □   5.   rituals / compulsions
    □   6.   others (specify:..)

C.   bowel and bladder control
    □   1.   enuresis
    □   2.   encopresis
    □   3.   rituals / compulsions
    □   4.   others (specify:..)

D.   body image
    □   1.   phantom limb
    □   2.   others (specify:..)

E.   speech
    □   1.   stuttering / stammering
    □   2.   mutism
    □   3.   logorrhea
    □   4.   unintelligible or distorted speech
    □   5.   (associated) rituals / compulsions
    □   6.   others (specify:..)

F.   sexuality
    □   1.   hypersexuality (nymphomaniasis)
     2.   hyposexuality
        □   a.   impotence
        □   b.   frigidity
        □   c.   asexuality (rejection of all sexual thoughts)
     3.   dys-sexuality
        □   a.   homosexuality
        □   b.   excessive masturbation
        □   c.   fetishism
        □   d.   transvestitism
        □   e.   exhibitionism
        □   f.   voyeurism
        □   g.   rituals / compulsions
        □   h.   others (specify:.............................)
     4.   deficient states (specify)
        □   a.   constitutional:..................................
        □   b.   acquired:.......................................

VI. Societal Functions
   A. family authority relationships
      1. excessive rebellion and opposition
         ☐ a. delinquency
         ☐ b. stealing (kleptomania, shoplifting, etc.)
         ☐ c. drinking
         ☐ d. drug abuse
         ☐ e. physical attacks
         ☐ f. vandalism
         ☐ g. truancy; dropout
         ☐ h. arson (fire-setting)
         ☐ i. runaway
         ☐ j. others (specify):.....................................)
      2. deficient rebellion
         ☐ a. overly compliant
         ☐ b. puritanical
         ☐ c. overly cautious
         ☐ d. others (specify:....................................)
   ☐ 3. dyssocial reactions (cultural/family syntonic)
   ☐ 4. others (specify:...)

   B. peer relationships
      1. excessive
         ☐ a. overidentification with group
         ☐ b. exaggerated social life
         ☐ c. overdetermined immersion in activities
         ☐ d. overly cooperative with peer group
         ☐ e. others (specify:...................................)
      2. deficient
         ☐ a. isolated, alienated, withdrawn
         ☐ b. overly quarrelsome with peer group
         ☐ c. rejection of/by peer group
         ☐ d. others (specify:...................................)
   ☐ 3. others (specify:...)

295

14] ADOLESCENT DEVELOPMENT:

BIOLOGICAL, PSYCHOLOGICAL,

AND SOCIOLOGICAL DETERMINANTS

WILLIAM A. SCHONFELD

Adolescence is a prolonged process generally requiring more than a decade for its completion. It is neither a homogeneous nor a precipitous period but rather an evolving one in which intense and unique developmental tasks are accomplished on the biological, psychological, and sociological levels. Development at each of these levels proceeds with significant interaction and interdependence. The integration of these tasks may be appraised in the individual through an evaluation of his body image or self-image (Schonfeld, 1963, 1964).

Terminology used in the literature describing the maturational phenomena associated with adolescence is often confusing. One area of confusion centers around the definition of puberty (Stuart, 1946). It has been defined first, as the point at which an individual is capable of procreating; or second, as menarche, the first menstrual period in girls and the time of the first seminal emission in boys; or third, as a phase in which the major changes of adolescent development occur (Shuttleworth, 1949). This is further complicated when adolescence is defined as starting with puberty and ending with maturity by those who accept either of the first two definitions or wrongly assume them to be synchronous; whereas others, who accept puberty as the phase of major

I have summarized in this essay a holistic view of adolescence based on my clinical experience with adolescents over the past thirty-five years, not only in adolescent psychiatry, but also based on my earlier publications and survey of the literature in adolescent medicine, endocrinology, and genetics. The basic clinical research had been done at the New York State Psychiatric Institute, Presbyterian Hospital, and Vanderbilt Clinic of Columbia-Presbyterian Medical Center.

changes, divide adolescence into prepuberty, puberty, and postpuberty (Boutourline-Young, Zolir, and Gallagher, 1963).

To avoid confusion it would be desirable to limit the definition of puberty—as that point at which the individual is capable of procreating, which is not synchronous with menarche, or the time of the first emission; use the term "pubescence" to delineate the phase in which the major changes in development occur (Schonfeld, 1943); and adolescence [1] as the total period of sexual maturation—biological, psychological, and sociological. Adolescence may then be arbitrarily subdivided biologically into three phases: (1) early adolescence, which is initiated by the first evidence of sexual maturation and terminates with the appearance of pubic hair; (2) midadolescence, or pubescence, which begins with the onset of pubic hair and ends when the pubic hair is completely developed. It is accompanied by the peak velocity of growth in height, menarche in girls, and the first emission in boys with progressive development of the primary sexual organs; (3) late adolescence, starts when the pubic hair growth is complete and is characterized by deceleration of growth in height, completion of maturation of the primary and secondary sexual characteristics and fertility. Adolescence is preceded by childhood and followed by adulthood though the phases of each, just before and after adolescence, are often referred to as pre- and postadolescence (Schonfeld, 1969a).

Some psychiatrists have limited the use of the term "adolescence" to describe the psychological and social phenomena of this age group, and pubescence to delineate the biological phenomenon. However, our medical colleagues in adolescent medicine and lexicographers reject this distinction.

The understanding of adolescent personality development and the significance of specific behavior would be enhanced if the psychiatrists were to correlate their clinical findings not only with the chronological age but also with the level of adolescent development—namely; early, mid-, or late adolescence (Blos, 1962).

Developmental Tasks [2]

BIOLOGICAL

Anatomical and physiological maturation are the structural groundwork for adolescent development and are dependent on hereditary trends and biological capacity. In addition to specific endocrinological and chromosomal disorders, environmental factors (such as general health and nutrition) and possibly emotional factors, may delay or accelerate this process. Biologically speaking, the onset of adolescence is clinically signaled by acceleration of growth in height and the first signs of physical sexual maturation (Tanner, 1962). The end of adolescence is arrived at with the complete development of primary and secondary sexual characteristics and deceleration of growth. There is a wide range of normal development. Usually, however, it encompasses the ages of ten to eighteen years in girls and twelve to twenty years in boys with a trend today for more youth to begin their adolescence at an earlier age (Schonfeld and Beebe, 1942).

PSYCHOLOGICAL

The ego of the adolescent is presented with a multiplicity of intense problems in the struggle to make an adequate heterosexual adjustment, achieve autonomy, and attain an identity. The strength of the sexual and aggressive drives is enhanced with the advent of biological maturity so that the ego has to acquire adaptive techniques that are different or modified from previous periods of life. The ego is pressed to cope with both the heterosexual adjustments as well as the reawakening of the oedipal strivings. The oedipal wishes now shift out of childhood fantasy into the more threatening sphere of reality because of the potential for successful fulfillment. The incest barrier is therefore strongly reinforced by a withdrawing from close relationships with the parents. Withdrawal is also an expression of youth's struggle for autonomy, weakening the identification with the parents, and replacing it with a new identification with peers, rather than with adults. At times the yielding of parental relationships may be felt to be tantamount to the actual loss of the parents and a kind of grief and mourning or a depressive reaction as described by Anna Freud may place an additional burden on the already overworked ego.

Another psychological theme of adolescence is the search for a sense of personal identity as described by Erikson (1968). Only when he can envisage himself in a definite role acceptable to him and seemingly attainable does the adolescent feel identified in his own mind and as a personality reasonably related to his environment. However, to deal with this combination of inner and outer reality and maintain a homeostatic balance the adolescent must attain the ability to conceptualize at an abstract level as an evolution of what Inhelder and Piaget (1958) call the "concrete operation" of childhood through interaction with increasingly more demanding intellectual tasks provided both by formal schooling and informal social experience and appropriate environmental stimulation, which leads to the ability to think about thinking and to analyze problems at a higher level of generalization. It is this capacity for abstract thinking that accounts for his concern with the basic meanings and values of human existence.

SOCIOLOGICAL

Adolescence is also a social phenomenon. In some cultures, adolescence marks the beginning of adulthood, but in our sophisticated society it is a period of psychosocial moratorium between childhood and adulthood. For a variety of reasons, society has progressively prolonged the period of dependency (Keniston, 1965a and 1965b).

They recognize the ambivalence of their confused and uncertain parents in regard to official social and cultural values. They see the adults paying lip service to concepts they unconsciously reject and belie by their overt behavior. It is during this phase that the primary identifications of the child with the family weakens and is replaced by a new identification with the peer group and its inherent code.

Parents attempt to resolve the conflicts in their lives, as well as their neurotic and antisocial needs, by projecting the family confusions and psychopathology, often unconsciously, onto the adolescent who often ends up serving as the index case. Adelaide Johnson's "superego lacunae," Bateson's "double-bind phenomenon," Ackerman's concept of family psychopathology, Jackson's "scapegoating," and delineation of the effect of parental attitudes on the adolescent's body image are all familial mechanisms that contribute to the psychosocial problems of the youth (Schonfeld, 1966).

The direct effect is owing to the inconsistencies in cultural values. Society fails to provide the adolescent with much needed support in the form of firmly held values and beliefs against which he can safely push and test himself as he undertakes to develop his own value system. In a society characterized by rapid social change it may be that the most definite thing is change itself. And perhaps this is the special adaptation required of our youth today—to learn how to live with constant change, uncertainty, and ambiguity (Keniston, 1965a).

Physical Maturation

There is a wide range as to the age when normal adolescence begins, and the speed at which it develops but the pattern it follows is fairly uniform (Reynolds and Wines, 1948, 1951; Schonfeld and Beebe, 1942; Stuart, 1946; Tanner, 1962). Though the average age for each stage of development has no significance for the individual youth, knowing the range of normal does help to evaluate whether there is any justification for the youth's concern over his development. It is essential to have a clear picture of the wide variation that is still within normal limits and to understand that normal connotes neither average, optimum, nor ideal, but rather a range of normalcy (Gallagher, 1955).

PRIMARY AND SECONDARY SEXUAL CHARACTERISTICS

In boys the earliest manifestations of adolescence are a progressive enlargement of the testicles, with enlargement and reddening of the scrotum and increase in length and circumference of the penis. (See Table 14–1.)

TABLE 14–1
Normal Maturational Sequence in Boys

PHASE	APPEARANCE OF SEXUAL CHARACTERISTICS	AVERAGE AGES	AGE RANGE*
Childhood thru preadolescence	Testes and penis have not grown since infancy; no pubic hair; growth in height constant. No spurt.	—	—
Early adolescence	Testes begin to increase in size; scrotum grows, skin reddens and becomes coarser; penis follows with growth in length and circumference; no true pubic hair, may have down.	12–13 yrs.	10–15 yrs.
	Pubic hair—pigmented, coarse and straight at base of penis becoming progressively more curled and		

Midadolescence	profuse, forming at first an inverse triangle and subsequently extends up to umbilicus; axillary hair starts after pubic hair; penis and testes continue growing; scrotum becomes larger, pigmented and sculptured; marked spurt of growth in height with maximum increment about time pubic hair first develops and decelerates by time fully established; prostate and seminal vesicles mature, spontaneous or induced emissions follow but spermatazoa inadequate in number and motility (adolescent sterility); voice beginning to change as larynx enlarges.	13–16 yrs.	11–18 yrs.
Late adolescence	Facial and body hair appear and spread; pubic and axillary hair become denser; voice deepens; testes and penis continue to grow; emission—has adequate number of motile spermatazoa for fertility; growth in height gradually decelerates, 98 percent of mature stature by 17¾ yrs. ± 10 mos.; indentation of frontal hair line.	16–18 yrs.	14–20 yrs.
Postadolescence to adult	Mature—full development of primary and secondary sex characteristics; muscles and hirsuitism may continue increasing.	onset 18–20 yrs.	onset 16–21 yrs.

* Normal range was accepted as (80 per cent of cases) 1st to 9th decile.

Midadolescence follows within a year with the development of pubic hair, which is downy at first, becomes pigmented, but sparse and straight or slightly curled at the base of the penis. It progressively becomes more curled and profuse, forming an inverse triangle and subsequently spreading up to the umbilicus in the characteristic male distribution. This usually requires two or three years and designates the end of midadolescence. During this phase the testes continue growing with the scrotum becoming larger, sculptured, and pigmented. The penis also grows progressively in length and circumference and now becomes erect not only in response to local stimulation as in childhood but also to sexually provocative sensations and thoughts, and is accompanied by a desire for sexual release. The breast nipples also become pigmented and often a subareolar nodule may appear which disappears spontaneously during the following year or two. The deepening of the voice, associated with growth of the larynx is a gradual one, starting in midadolescence and often not complete until adolescence is practically over. Axillary hair usually first appears about two years after the appearance of pubic hair. At about the same time, hair first begins to grow on the upper lip.

Concomitant with the growth of the penis, the prostate, the seminal vesicles and the bulbourethral glands enlarge and develop, forming seminal fluid. The boy has his first ejaculation, either induced or spontaneous, during midadolescence about one year after the onset of the accelerated penis growth, the average age being just under fourteen years, with 90 percent of a large sample falling between eleven and sixteen years (Kinsey, Pomeroy, and Martin, 1948). At this point, the youth is usually sterile and only in a year to three years does spermatogenesis advance far enough for sufficient numbers of motile sperm to appear in the ejaculate so that the boy is fertile (Montagu, 1946).

In late adolescence, primary and secondary sexual characteristics continue to mature. The ultimate size of the penis and testes varies a great deal in different individuals. The relative size of the relaxed and erect penis also varies in different ethnic groups. The beard usually starts to grow in this phase and is followed by thoracic and abdominal pilosity with extension to the extremities; there is a conspicuous ethnic difference in the distribution of facial and body hair.

Most of the adolescents studied by the author (Schonfeld and Beebe, 1942; Schonfeld, 1943b, 1969a) reached full maturity by seventeen to eighteen years of age though a few achieved this level at fifteen years of age and few not before twenty years. The final secondary sexual characteristics to develop in most of the males studied had been the bitemporal indentation of the hairline, which is absent in adolescent girls.

In girls (Bouterline-Young et al, 1963; Shuttleworth, 1949; Tanner, 1962) adolescence usually begins on the average of about two years earlier in the girl than the boy. The first manifestation of adolescence in a female is enlargement of the ovary, with ripening of one of the primary graffian follicles; but because the size of the ovaries cannot be evaluated clinically we must depend on secondary changes, namely, the rounding of the hips or the more readily discernible breast development, as the first visible criteria of the onset of early adolescence (Stuart, 1946). The rounding of the hips is owing in part to broadening of the bony pelvis, but more particularly to increased deposition of the subcutaneous fat. In early adolescence the breast development is usually characterised by elevation of the areola surrounding the nipple producing a small conical protuberance, the "bud" stage. In midadolescence there is a deposition of fat under the areola with further elevation and is referred to as the "primary breast," whereas in late adolescence there is an enlargement of the breast tissue itself and further fat infiltration forming the "mature" breast, which varies greatly in size and shape. It takes several years for the breast to develop fully. (See Table 14–2.)

Pubic hair, at first downy, becomes coarse, pigmented, straight or curly along the labia, initiating midadolescence. As this phase progresses the pubic hair becomes more abundant and curly, spreading over the mons to develop the characteristic female inverse triangular pattern by the end of this stage. By late adolescence, pubic hair spreads to the medial surface of the thighs. Axillary hair usually begins to grow in midadolescence about two years after the onset of pubic hair.

In midadolescence, as a result of the hypertrophy of the uterus and cyclic changes in the endometrium, menstruation results. Menarche has been reported by various observers in the United States to occur at a mean age of 12.9 ± 1.4 years, with an age range from ten to seventeen years with 80 percent of the girls falling into the range of eleven to fifteen years. Menarche almost invariably occurs after the apex of the height spurt has passed. The variations in ages are owing to genetic factors, general health and nutrition associated with socioeconomic determinants and not to climate or race. Repeated studies indicate that the menarche has been occurring earlier by four months per decade in the past century, and there is no evidence that the trend has stopped. This again may be the result of improved nutrition and decrease in debilitating illnesses. Initially the menstrual periods are not accompanied by ovulation so that the early adolescent girl is usually sterile. Ovulatory menstruation and the ability to conceive (puberty or nubility) usually occurs three years later (Montagu, 1946). The uterus does not usually attain adult size until eighteen to twenty years of age. The histology of the uterine endometrium and the vaginal epithelium undergo cyclic changes reflecting the hormone milieu. Lactic acid-producing bacilli replaces the previously mixed and scanty bacterial flora present in the vagina, changing the vaginal secretion abruptly from an alkaline reaction in childhood to an acid reaction in adolescence.

In adolescence the vulva enlarges as a result of the marked develop-

TABLE 14–2

Normal Maturational Sequence in Girls

PHASE	APPEARANCE OF SEXUAL CHARACTERISTICS	AVERAGE AGES	AGE RANGE*
Childhood thru preadolescence	No pubic hair; breasts are flat; growth in height is constant, no spurt.	—	—
Early adolescence	Rounding of hips; breasts and nipples are elevated to form "bud" stage; no true pubic hair, may have down.	10–11 yrs.	9–14 yrs.
Midadolescence	Pubic hair—pigmented, coarse, straight primarily along labia but progressively curled and spreads over mons and becomes profuse with an inverse triangular pattern; axillary hair starts after pubic hair; marked growth spurt with maximum height increment 18 months before menarche; menarche—labia becomes enlarged, vaginal secretion becomes acid; breast—areola and nipple elevated to form "primary" breast.	11–14 yrs.	10–16 yrs.
Late adolescence	Axillary hair in moderate quantity; pubic hair fully developed; breasts fill out forming adult type configuration; menstruation well established; growth in height is decelerated, ceases at 16¼ ± 13 mos.	14–16 yrs.	13–18 yrs.
Postadolescence to adult	Further growth of axillary hair; breasts fully developed.	onset 16–18 yrs.	onset 15–19 yrs.

* Normal range was accepted as (80 per cent of cases) 1st to 9th decile.

ment of the labia majora, which in childhood is practically nonexistent. The clitoris also enlarges somewhat probably as a result of the circulating adrenal androgens, and becomes erectile.

PHYSICAL GROWTH

Growth is not synchronic, in that the different body tissues grow at separate rates. Neural tissue has a rapid postnatal growth, which slows down in childhood and stops before adolescence, whereas lymphatic tissue grows rapidly in childhood and atrophies during adolescence. The reproductive system in turn has no growth during childhood but has rapid growth in adolescence.

Stature

The characteristic adolescent cycle of growth in height starts abruptly in early adolescence with a rapid acceleration in rate of growth. This increases progressively for about a year reaching the point of maximum increment in midadolescence, about the time when pubic hair first develops. This is followed by a progressive reduction in velocity of growth during late adolescence until the rate of growth reaches the level normal for earlier childhood. Subsequently the rate of growth tapers off still further so that virtually all growth (98 percent) ceases in boys at 17 ¾ years ± 10 months and at 16¼ years ± 13 months in girls (Stolz and Stolz, 1951; Tanner, 1962).

The timing of the onset of accelerated growth is the principal factor accounting for the extreme differences in size in different youths of the same age. This spurt characteristically starts earlier in girls than in boys because of the earlier onset of adolescence. At about eight or nine years of age girls enter the period of accelerated growth, with the result that they catch up with and later pass boys, so that from eleven to thirteen years they are often taller and heavier. However, boys soon enter a phase of more rapid development, usually surpass the girls, and continue to enlarge the difference until maturity, because both the intensity and duration of the growth spurt is greater in the male than the female. The ultimate height which any individual attains depends not only on the rate at which growth occurs, but also on the age at which the growth spurt starts and the age at which epiphyseal fusion occurs and thus the duration of growth. Bayley (1946) has developed tables for predicting adult height based on sex, chronological age, present height, and skeletal age. A prediction of future height at any given age also needs to take into consideration family growth patterns.

Adolescents are taller today owing to many factors. Children grow more rapidly, there is an acceleration of the maturational process so that the growth spurt is earlier, the rate of growth is greater, and the maximum height is reached earlier. Statistics point to the fact that youth mature four months earlier each decade so that they reach their adult height two years younger now than two or three generations ago. So that though men are on the average some ten centimeters taller than they were 100 years ago indicating that the trend for adults is about a one centimeter increase per decade, the spurt is occurring earlier so that youth tend to be two and one-half centimeters taller each decade.

During this growth the skeletal proportions are modified, so that in late adolescence the measurements of the lower extremities equals that of the sitting height, whereas in the child the extremities are proportionately shorter. The ratio of the biacromial diameter to the bitrochanteric diameter changes considerably in midadolescence so that in boys the thorax becomes wider and the pelvis remains narrower as opposed to that of the female in whom the reverse is true. Characteristic changes in the shape of the pelvis differentiating the sexes occur during adolescence. Changes of proportion can likewise be seen in the face. Now the lower portion of the head begins to grow with the nose taking the lead, and the forehead appearing small by contrast. Similar disproportionate growth of the eyeballs accounts for the increased incidence of myopia evident in adolescents.

Epiphyseal Fusion

Epiphyseal fusion may be evaluated by roentogenologic evaluation of the "bone age" can be helpful in determining the general developmental status of an adolescent (Greulich, 1938; Wilkins, 1954). This is basically expressing qualitative aspects of development by quantitative units of measurement, using chronological time as a standardization device. "Bone age" thus indicates the average chronological age at which the epiphyseal development occurs. It is a more reliable criterion of "biological age" than is chronological age and thus may help in predicting a youth's ultimate height, and in evaluating the adequacy of sexual maturity (Bayley, 1946). In boys, the beginning of the spurt of growth usually occurs when the skeletal age reaches what is average at fourteen years. In girls, menarche and the growth spurt occur at an earlier bone age. Growth ceases when the epiphyses fuse.

Before the epiphyses fuse in the thirteen- to fifteen-year-old boys, it would be best to avoid strenuous sports.

Body Mass

Weight changes are considerable during adolescence. There is often a very striking increase in subcutaneous fat in preadolescence or early adolescence preceding the growth spurt. This gives rise to a configuration in some boys which has been incorrectly considered evidence of hypogonadism and diagnosed as Froehlich syndrome, while actually these well-nourished boys mature earlier (Bruch, 1941; Gallagher, Heald, and Masland, 1958; Schonfeld, 1951). However, in the male after the growth spurt, the increment in deposition of body fat tends to decrease again. In contrast the adolescent girl seems to add more subcutaneous fat (Heald, 1960). A second and greater increase in weight usually follows the growth in height.

A greater part of the weight increase in the second phase of the bimodal weight gain is due to increase in skeletal growth, musculature, and only partly because of deposition of fat (Gallagher and Gallagher, 1953). As muscles grow, the strength virtually doubles between early and midadolescence in boys, but much less so in girls. Motor skill in general increases in step with motor strength, with some elements, such as balance, not showing an adolescent spurt but increasing continually with age (Tanner, 1962). Present data do not support the concept of an "overgrown, clumsy age." According to longitudinal data, the clumsy adolescent is likely to have been the clumsy child. A youth may appear awkward, in response to sudden stimuli because of the lack of learned patterns, because his body changes may be so rapid that he is unfamiliar with his own body. However, when a pattern is established through learning a technique, whether it be athletics, dancing, or driving, the ability to coordinate becomes evident (Jones and Bayley, 1950). There is a lag of about a year between achieving full body size and the development of full musculature power, so that the youth should not be subjected to pressures beyond his capacity. However, adequately controlled exercise appears to be more effective in stimulating muscle development at this age of rapid muscle growth than at any other time.

Skin

The skin is also involved in the adolescent process, by an increase of the sebaceous secretion especially noticeable in the nasolabial folds. Acne is present to some degree in 75 to 80 percent of adolescents by the time they reach late adolescence. The primary lesion is the plugged sebaceous gland or comedo, which becomes secondarily infected and pustular formation results often as a result of a lack of cleanliness and of habitual manipulation of the skin (Gallagher et al., 1958). The sweat glands especially in the axilla, anogenital and the palmoplantar regions become hyperactive with the ensuing hyperhydrosis.

Neuroendocrine Mechanisms of Adolescence

To understand the mechanisms of morphological and physiological modifications that take place in adolescence we have to look successively at parts of the central nervous system, the anterior pituitary, the peripheral endocrine glands, and the end organs. The initial releasing factor for the mechanisms associated with adolescence is still unknown, but it appears that the changes are initiated by maturation of nuclei in the limbic system (Papez, 1937), which in turn stimulate the hypothalmus, though some neurophysiologists feel it counteracts an inhibiting factor. Rather than being "cerebral centers" they are links in an important circuit for complex behavioral and endocrinological responses. The release of adolescence parallels the earlier development of motor and speech function. The hypothalmus, in turn, either through neurohumeral secretions or nerve impulses incites anterior pituitary secretion of hormones. The pituitary had been considered to be the primary controller of all endocrine gland functions. It now appears that the hypophysis is more of a mediator between the brain and the target glands and contributes important elements of amplification, stability, and homeostasis to the mechanism. The hypophysis and the hypothalmus are also subject to regulation by circulating hormones elaborated by other endocrine glands resulting in cyclic interplay.

Wilkins (1965) feels that the initiation of adolescent processes also depends on the maturity of the end organs as evidenced by the fact that ossification must reach a prescribed level before the growth phenomena associated with adolescence can occur.

Except for the growth hormone (somatatropin), which acts directly on the somatic tissues, stimulating the rate of growth without stimulating the rate of skeletal maturation and involved in regulating fat metabolism (Sobel, 1962), the other hormones of the hypophysis are trophic hormones, stimulating their respective specific "target glands"—the thyroid (thyrotropin), the adrenal cortex (adrenal cortical tropic hormone —ACTH), and the gonads (gonadotropins—follicular stimulating and luteinizing hormones) (Friesen and Ashwood, 1965). In the male, the follicular stimulating hormone acts on the spermatogenic cells in the testes and promotes growth of the seminiferous tubules. The gonadotropins also promote secretion of androgens by the Leydig cells of the testes. In the female, follicular stimulating hormone, which promotes maturation of the graffian follicle, and the small amounts of luteinizing hormone released stimulate the secretion of estrogens. After ovulation, induced by a sudden discharge of luteinizing hormone, the newly formed corpus luteum begins to secrete progesterone. The steroid biosynthesis follows the same basic pathways in testes, ovaries, and adrenal cortex. The character of the principal final product is probably determined by quantitative differences in enzyme concentrations in the steroid producing tissues. The estrogens and androgens thus secreted affect the sexual end organs—the penis, scrotum, seminal vesicles, and prostate in the male; the uterus, vagina, and breasts in the female; and hair and skin in both. Androgens initially stimulate the rate of linear growth and muscle development, but eventually both androgens and estrogens limit the duration of growth by stimulating skeletal maturation with fusion of the epiphyses (Gardner, 1960). Prior to adolescence the gonads exert little or no influence on hormonal mechanisms.

The popularization of oral contraceptives brings to fore the need of understanding how estrogens and progesterone influence pituitary function. It is believed that in the proper level they inhibit follicular stimulating and luteinizing hormones production by their negative feedback action on the hypothalmus-pituitary axis modifying the ovulatory surge of luteinizing hormone so that ovulation fails to occur. They also have been used in some cases of menstrual disorders without apparent deleterious effects on the adolescent process.

In some animals, the afferent stimuli from genital stimulation also play a part in initiating the neural-endocrine-gonad mechanism, but this has not been proved in man. Numerous studies in the literature related to the effect of starvation on the maturity mechanism indicate that this complicated process depends not only on an inherent genetic factor but also on a variety of extrinsic factors. The effect of emotional stress on this regulatory mechanism has not been established beyond the fact that it may precipitate or delay menstrual flow and that it may vary the time of ovulation, and also the clinical observations that suggest that failure in growth may be associated with emotional deprivation (Patton, 1962). Isolated cases in the literature indicate that emotional stress may actually inhibit the development of adolescence.

Developmental Clinical Problems

There is characteristically a wide range of normal variation in adolescent development. Though pathological deviations do occur, they are not frequent. However, the adolescent, his family, and his doctor are often unreasonably concerned about normal deviations in maturation, a concern that may result in disturbances of body image. It is important to differentiate extremes of constitutional variations from the endocrinopathies (Wilkins, 1948).

EARLY MATURATION VERSUS PRECOCIOUS PUBERTY

Girls with menarche between ten and twelve and boys beginning adolescence between eleven and thirteen years have distinct social advantages in most cultures over late maturing youths, namely girls with menarche at fifteen to seventeen and boys with onset of adolescence between sixteen and eighteen years, but youths who mature "too early" may manifest personality difficulties. One variation in the pattern of sexual maturation occurring more often in girls, is early appearance of pubic hair (premature pubarche), without other manifestations. This is owing to either an increased sensitivity of the pubic hair follicles to normal preadolescent levels of androgens or to the premature increase of adrenal androgens. In the latter group the height and bone age are also accelerated (Silverman, Migeon, Rosenberg, and Wilkins, 1952). There are some girls below nine years of age with idiopathic sexual precocity beyond the appearance of pubic hair. They have breast development and even menarche with an advance in height, dental, and bone ages as well as sexual maturation age whereas the intellectual and social age as well as the level of sexual interest according to most authors (Hampson and Money, 1955) correspond to the chronological age creating marked discordance. Though they are usually of functional origin it is necessary to differentiate youths with idiopathic precocious development from those with an adrenal neoplasm, endocrinopathy, or hormone administration. There are also boys and girls who mature early, presumably because of cerebral pathology probably in the hypothalmic region resulting from neoplasms, encephalitis, or birth injuries.

DELAYED ADOLESCENCE VERSUS EUNUCHOIDISM

Though delayed adolescence is encountered in both sexes, it seems to be a greater concern in boys. By the time they reach the age of thirteen to fourteen years, most boys show at least some signs of adolescence. However, some fail to show any enlargement of their genitalia or presence of pubic hair and continue to grow at a slow preadolescent rate. They lag behind their contemporaries in height, muscular development, and personality maturation. Often, these are the boys who have been smaller than the average throughout childhood and show a delay of two to four years in their epiphyseal maturation. Though beginning late, adolescence, once begun, will progress either rapidly, with a sudden spurt of growth, or there may be a slow continuous process. Such delays in the maturation process are usually constitutional, depending on genetic mechanisms and are not owing to a specific endocrinopathy. However, extreme nutritional deficiencies as in anorexia nervosa or starvation may be responsible for a delay in maturation. The problem is to distinguish those patients with merely delayed adolescence from the very few who may remain permanently dwarfed or frail to develop sexually as a result of hypophyseal, gonadal, neurogenic, or chromosomal defects (Kallman, Schonfeld, and Barbara, 1944). Hormone assays and cytogenic studies (Ross and Tijo, 1965) help in some cases, but we must still depend on clinical acuity. In many of these cases, the earliest evidences of adolescence are present but not recognized. Most of the youths who express concern over their sexual adequacy merely have delayed adolescence or are within normal limits of development with disturbances of the body image.

SHORT NORMAL VERSUS DWARFISM

Delayed onset of adolescence with the absence of the growth spurt at the anticipated age accounts for most of the youths seen with complaints of short stature. The etiology is usually either genetic or a nutritional disturbance. In these youths the bone age more than the chronological age parallels the height and sexual development ages. There are some youths, however, who are maturing adequately but are shorter than their associates because of hereditary factors and are classified as constitutionally short normals. Short stature is more acceptable to girls than to boys. Only rarely is there a failure of both sexual maturation

311

and growth because of primary hypophyseal pathology that leads to the development of a true midget.

MENSTRUAL DISORDERS

Primary amenorrhea as evidence of delayed adolescence versus sexual infantilism has already been discussed. Dysmenorrhea is a common symptom, and only rarely is it owing to some organic condition. Usually the incapacitating cramps are an indication that the girl has difficulty in adjusting to her role as a woman or has a low threshold to pain (Gallagher, 1955). Secondary amenorrhea is also common in adolescents because menstrual irregularities are the rule during the first few years after menarche. Metrorrhagia or menorrhagia are not common but demand prompt treatment, and may indicate the presence of systemic disease, a failure of ovulation or unusual emotional tension. Girls with menstrual disorders should be reassured and gynecological examination undertaken only when truly indicated (Gray, 1960).

ADOLESCENT OBESITY

In countries where food is plentiful, obesity is a distressing problem for the body-conscious adolescent, particularly girls. A great deal has been already written in this area (Wallace, 1964). Data have been presented indicating that obese children are advanced in statural growth and maturation so that earlier than average adolescent development is the rule with obese girls and boys. This is contrary to the long held fallacious concept that obesity in adolescence is due to an endocrine disorder. So often a diagnosis of hypogonadism is made in the male adolescent merely because the penis, normal in size, appears small because it is imbedded in the supra pubic fat. The concept that obesity is caused by overeating as a result of a psychological regression or compensation is emphasized by the work of Newburgh (1944) and Bruch (1941, 1948). Werkman, however, states that it is more of a character disorder and that overeating and inactivity are part of a behavior that indicates a disturbance in a life style that was seriously distorted rather than in the development of a particular neurotic symptom.

INTERSEX

There are seven variables of sex that may go awry in problems of sexual development: the chromosomal, gonadal, and hormonal sex; the sex of the internal and external organs; the sex of assignment and rearing; and the gender role and identity (Hampson, 1964). Though incongrui-

312

ties in sexual development may be apparent before adolescence, it is often at this age that the pseudohermaphrodite, eunuchoid, or the individual with abnormal chromosome disorders, for example, Klinefelter's or Turner's syndrome are first recognized (Schutt and Hayes, 1964; Schurter and Letterman, 1967).

ABNORMALITIES OF THE MAMMARY GLAND

In the male adolescent temporary hyperplasia of the mammary gland may develop, usually palpable as a evanescent nodule in the subareolar region; however, in about one third of most groups studied the hyperplasia extends beyond the areola and is discernable as a conical protrusion in one, both, or alternating breasts, occurring during mid-adolescence and lasting six to eighteen months. In a small number of adolescent boys the breasts enlarge still further owing to a varying combination of hyperplasia of the periductal connective tissue and adipose tissue in addition to the mammary tissue resulting in a pendulous gynecomastia that does not recede; in other cases the hyperplasia is limited to adipose tissue. The pendulous adiposity of the breasts may be in proportion to or beyond the general adiposity (Schonfeld, 1961, 1962, 1970c).

Occasionally adolescent girls may develop a unilateral hypertrophy of a breast, but the usual concern of girls relates to their concern that their breasts are too large or too small based on their concepts of an ideal, which is often unrealistic.

CRYPTORCHIDISM

Bilateral cryptorchidism should be differentiated from cases in which the primary problem is a failure of development of the testicles rather than a failure of descent of normal testes. In the former androgen production is normal even though tubular degeneration may have already taken place because surgery was not performed early enough. However, normal secondary sexual characteristics will develop, unlike the cases of eunuchoidism. With unilateral undescended testes the problem may be basically the presence of a hernial sac or a short cord that arrests descent or that the testes never developed. In many cases the testicles move freely between the scrotum and abdomen and must be differentiated from the other types as these invariably descend spontaneously when the testicle enlarges with onset of adolescence or the administration of chorionic gonadotropin (Baker, 1966; Blos, 1960; Schonfeld, 1943b).

Body Image

The adolescent's body configuration and function affect every facet of his social and personality adaptation—both as to the impression he makes on others and how his body appears to himself. In addition, social, psychological, and environmental pressures further modify his self-evaluation, or body image.

The body image as a psychiatric construct can aid us in understanding the adolescent and his problems (Schonfeld, 1963, 1969a). It has been referred to in the literature (Kolb, 1959a) with minor variations as self-image, self-awareness, self-concept, the self, body ego, self-identity, ego-identity, and body schemata. Schilder (1935) defined the body image as the internal mental representation of one's own body—"the image of our body we form in our mind—the way in which our body appears to ourselves." Body being used in its broadest sense—the total self.

Kolb (1959a) by reviewing the pertinent psychiatric literature and Wylie (1961), the psychological and educational literature clarified our understanding of the several functions of self-evaluation. In the context of adolescent psychiatry, body image and self-image have been used interchangeably.

Kolb (1959b) divided body image into two components: the body percept and the body concept. The individual develops the former through the integration of multiple percepts related to his body, whereas the latter depends on the internalized psychological processes and sensations coming from within. Schilder (1935) had referred to these two components as centripetal and centrifugal psychic processes. Each of us carry around a mental picture of how we look, but the body image is more than the mirror image, and it may or may not reflect our actual appearance. It is the total picture we each have of ourselves physically, physiologically, sociologically, as well as psychologically. In adolescence this awareness of the self is particularly intensified because of the radical physical changes that occur, the increase of introspection, the increased tendency to compare oneself with culturally determined standards, and the striving for peer conformity and identification.

The rapid changes of adolescence require a revision of the body image at the very time when youth is in the midst of emotional turmoil,

314

so that even the normal adolescent often feels his body to be strange to him and is overly concerned about how he compares with his or her companions. A common area of concern is whether his development is sexually appropriate (Caplan, 1952; Schonfeld, 1963, 1964).

Repeated studies have shown that the more emotionally disturbed an adolescent is, the less tolerant he is of his physical self (Curran and Frosch, 1942; Levy, 1932). There is a fairly high correlation between difficulties in psychological and social adaptability and excessive interest in the body. So that many adolescents who are well within the normal range of development find that they cannot accept themselves for a variety of emotional reasons and will project concern to some aspect of their appearance or achievements (Stolz and Stolz, 1951).

Disturbances of body image are manifested by a variety of clinical syndromes. Direct concern and often agonizing self-consciousness over appearance and function is readily detected, whether associated with actual distortion of the body or not. In addition, we see varities of disturbed behavior; failures of adaptation, anxiety, depression, drug abuse, sexual promiscuity, learning difficulties, and disturbances in reality testing (Josselyn, 1959; Eisenberg, 1965; Schonfeld, 1968b).

Body image is part of the over-all picture the youth has of his own gender identity. Height, strength, and muscular development, length of the penis, presence of testes, and hirsuitism are important components of the male identity. Typical of the female identity are menarche, size of her breasts, and shape of her hips. Though sexually inappropriate development usually does create disturbances of body image, not all adolescents with actual defects are so affected. We cannot assume an inevitable interrelationship of structure and behavior in that other factors than appearance and function play important roles in formulating the body image (Schonfeld, 1963).

Internalized psychological factors modify the structure of the adolescent's body image. Those who in childhood experienced disturbed relationships with their parents, or having difficulties in school, and consequently encountered problems of personality adjustment, often cannot cope with the particularly stressful demands of adolescence. Lacking a proper frame of reference for self-acceptance, their adaptations are inevitably poor leading to self-rejection. The adolescent's earlier emotional experiences strongly influence his observations and interpretations, and mold a body image that in turn reflects his present and past experiences of his own body, whether the experiences are real or fantasied.

Though it is true that the personality primarily takes shape during childhood, the interrelationship of its component parts is not in full operation until late adolescence. Among the components to be evaluated are the individual's concept of his own importance, whether he has hopes for bettering himself, where he looks for status, his independence in relationships, his estimate of his own capabilities, his ability to withstand frustration, his sense of obligation, and the adaptations or defenses he uses when his security and self-esteem are threatened.

As he prepares to enter the adult world, the youth must realign the components of his personality in such a way that he will achieve self-acceptance. The physical changes in his body set in motion new attitudes toward himself. The first sign is a spurt in his striving for maturity. Life problems are tackled more aggressively. There is a speeding up of attempts to break away from the rule of parents, achieve individuation and an identity, and concentrate on peer relationships and heterosexual adjustment.

The psychology of the sexes is influenced by the biological differences. For the girl, there is the menstrual cycle, a cyclic change of hormone concentration, anticipation of her future role as mother, as well as the feminine configuration of her body. For the male there is the availability of his genitalia for visual and tactile perception in contrast to the almost hidden female genitalia. All of this makes a difference in the boy's body image as compared to the girl's. Apart from their biological differences are variations in the changing cultural reaction to gender roles (Schonfeld, 1971).

To repeat, the adolescent who had a disturbed childhood, with illness and problems of adjustment, often fails to develop a good frame of reference for his body image. When he tries to cope with even normal changes in adolescence, he bogs down under the burden of inordinately painful stresses. If such a youth's development is actually abnormal, his rejection of his body image is usually severe.

Adolescents with a variety of personality disorders reveal their disturbances through distortions in body concept. A boy's feelings of smallness or inferiority, when he compares himself to his father, are at times displayed in undue concern over the size of his own penis. Blos (1962a, 1962b) feels that such a concretization is always built on a homosexual conflict or unresolved sexual identity. Also, delay in onset of adolescence is often taken as evidence of actualization of a castration anxiety.

Today more than ever the individual is bombarded by manifold pressures from the environment. As he tries to adjust, the reactions and evaluation of others exert considerable influence on his behavior. At times the stress triggers a feedback mechanism, with tensions fed by tensions, often leading to a vicious circle.

Early in life, each child is stamped with the imprint of parental attitudes toward him. A mother shows how she feels by the way she holds the baby, feeds him, and cuddles him. Later she conveys her attitudes verbally. The child simply echoes his family's values. If he is accepted by his family he will neither overvalue nor under-value his body. If a child feels his body fails to come up to the expectations of his family, then he may develop self-deprecatory feelings. Adolescents from families that place great emphasis on the body beautiful find it much more difficult to accept any deviations in their bodies (Schonfeld, 1966).

Parents create anxiety in their adolescents by some uncalled-for remark about a son's height or genital status, or about a daughter's excess weight or delayed menarche. Many parents have been found to be rejecting of their children for any number of reasons. Often they are satisfying some unconscious psychopathological need of their own, and thus may deny their rejection and actually overcompensate. Overprotective measures by parents inhibit the development of muscular skills, often resulting in a clumsy obese adolescent with consequent stunted social activity. Furthermore, there are many parents who frankly express their disappointment with the sex of the child because they had hoped for one of the other sex. Confusion in sexual identity is often the result, this is particularly true among obese boys. When real or fancied deviations in maturation, often interpreted as inappropriate sexual development occur, they may intensify and further complicate a previously existing hostile parent-child relationship. The anxiety associated with the disturbance of development is superimposed on and interwoven with previous and current frustrations of the child's need to be loved for himself regardless of his appearance. The adolescent may feel that unrelated conflicts are caused solely by his disfigurement and his family's disappointment in him.

Adolescents in general are inordinately sensitive about their body image. They are quick to react to what they think of themselves and what they believe others think of them. With their self-image in a state of flux, they are deeply vulnerable to the judgments, the approval or disapproval of others.

The social disadvantages of inappropriate sexual development which may be abnormal or merely a delay in development (Mursen and Jones,

1957) are all too apparent. Because such a youth is unlike his age mates he will certainly not be treated like them. Adolescents with physical handicaps in the area of development are second-class citizens in their group and are often cruelly ostracized, ignored by the opposite sex, or treated with contempt. In the race for status in the group or when vying for favor with the opposite sex, teenagers are usually merciless in taking advantage of any shortcomings of rivals (Schonfeld, 1967).

Dependent on his peers for self-esteem, the adolescent is inclined to accept as real the value that is placed on him by his group. The physician, through his own attitudes, may relieve or reinforce these anxieties. It is therefore important that he be particularly careful in evaluating the development of all adolescents, but particularly individuals in the extremes of normal maturation.

Another factor that influences the adolescent's adaptation to his body is his concept of the ideal body image. This is comprised of his total experiences, perceptions, comparisons, and identifications with other persons, actual or fantasied. All through his childhood he has known what it is to be compared to others in height, weight, strength, coordination, and intelligence. Now he takes to doing it himself, constantly measuring himself up against his age mates and parent of the same sex.

General public glorification of the ideal body and overemphasis on unrealistic standards also add to the youth's distress. Then his confusion is further aggravated by an ironic development. Throughout his childhood he has accepted an ego ideal based on identification with the parent of the same sex and conceptualization of the ideal expressed by the other parent. Today, especially on our contemporary scene, the parent often falls far short as a model of what the youth now strives to become. He insists on being different.

In an attempt to find a new identification, the youth turns to his own age group, only to find there that the demands for conformity place additional pressures on him. The ego ideal is never so unstable as it is during adolescence.

These complicated constellations of physical, psychological, and social components, which determine the structure of body image, on both the conscious and unconscious levels, can be evaluated through anamnesis, a variety of inventories (Offer, 1969; Fitts, 1964; Wylie, 1961) and direct questioning (Levy, 1929; Schonfeld, 1963).

Obviously, it is up to the psychiatrist to bend every effort to mitigate the task of adaptation confronting the adolescent and to assuage his suffering by helping him cope effectively and realistically with any distur-

318

bance of body image that may exist by giving him a new outlook. Disturbances of body image are a core problem in many disturbed and disturbing adolescents. The psychiatrist can be of immeasurable help if he takes the trouble to study in his patient the ingredients that go into the making of his body image—the individual's actual appearance, the internalized psychogenic factors, the social factors, and the youth's concept of the ideal.

The adolescent in therapy must be helped to establish a realistic image of himself and his environment and to correct any distortions of body image that may exist (Schonfeld, 1970b).

Conclusions

Psychiatrists who work with adolescents should develop an holistic view of adolescence and understand the numerous changes in body structure and function that take place as a result of the adolescent process and the reasons why they occur. These changes occur normally over a wide range of chronological ages and at different rates. Developmental status as well as chronological age are significant for the understanding of specific behavior and attitudes of a youth. Thus it is helpful in any case study to delineate whether a youth is in early, mid- or late adolescence (Schonfeld, 1968 a, 1970b, 1971).

Many of the problems of adaptation in youth are owing to disturbances of body image associated with real, exaggerated, or fancied deviations in maturational status, which are often interpreted as inappropriate sexual development. Youths with actual developmental problems must be differentiated from those who are well within the range of normal. If the defect is real and can be modified, it may be desirable to do so through such means as are available—hormones, plastic surgery, medication, diet, or exercise. The adolescent psychiatrist often has the task of helping the youth overcome his resistance to treatment. However, if the defect cannot be modified we must foster in the youth an acceptance of himself. Many youths we see in therapy merely focus on a minor physical aberration as a rationalization of a profound emotional problem.

Some adolescents with disturbances of body image merely require reassurance, continuing interest, and help in developing an insight into the difference between being abnormal and not being average. The adolescent is concerned about his body and wants his physician to take his worries seriously. It is not enough to tell an adolescent that he is within the statistical limits of normal or that he will "outgrow it." Many require intensive psychotherapy (Schonfeld, 1970a).

Disturbances of body image may be manifested through a variety of unacceptable patterns of behavior, anxieties, or depression as well as through direct concern over appearance and function. Through a knowledge of the factors involved in determining the structure of the body image, namely, the individual's actual appearance, the internalized psychogenic factors, the sociological factors, and his concept of the ideal, the psychiatrist is better able to understand the adolescent's needs and concerns and thus help him develop acceptable adaptations and cope more effectively with his disturbances of body image.

NOTES

1. *Puberty:* from the Middle English *puberte,* derived from *pubertas,* noun derived from *puber,* "one who can procreate," and *pubertas,* "state or condition of being able to procreate," because they contain the root *pu,* "to beget." However, *puber* and *pubes* are also defined as "the signs of manhood, i.e. with hairness" and *puberty,* as "the time of coming of hair."—*escent—scens* (suffix): From Latin *iscentem,* beginning to assume a certain state indicates motion to the condition indicated in the root. *Pubescence:* Latin *pubescere,* "the condition of arriving at puberty" or the "state of being covered by hair in the genital area" (pubic).

Adolescence: From Latin *adolescentia,* noun derived from the verb *adolescere* (participle is *adultus*), "the process of arriving at adulthood" "to mature" also derived from *ad*-to-*olescere* "grow," literally "the state of growing," also from Latin *adolesco,* "to grow up" [Skeat, Jaeger, Oxford Universal Dictionary (1955)].

2. American Society for Adolescent Psychiatry's Workshop-by-Mail on a Definition of Adolescence, consisting of Marie C. Duncan, Peter Giovacchini, Charles W. Schlageter, Jerome Steiner and William A. Schonfeld, have corresponded over a period of two years in an attempt to delineate a definition of adolescence without reaching any uniform consensus. These are wholly my concepts, but are based on the discussion of the committee as well as on the literature.

REFERENCES

Bayley, N. (1946). Tables for predicting adult weight from skeletal age and present height. Journal of Pediatrics, 28:49.

Baker, R. (1966). Treatment of cryptorchism. Current opinion, Medical Tribune.

Blos, P. (1960). Comments on the psychological consequences of cryptorchism. Psychoanalytic Study of the Child, 15:395–429.

———. (1962a). Intensive psychotherapy in relationship to the various phases of the adolescent period. American Journal of Orthopsychiatry, 32:901–910.

———. (1962b). On adolescence: A psychoanalytic interpretation. Glencoe: The Free Press.

Bouterline-Young, H., Zoli, A., and Gallagher, J. R. (1963). Events of puberty in a group of 111 Florentine girls. American Journal of Diseases in Children, 5:451.

Bruch, J. (1941). Obesity in relation to puberty. Journal of Pediatrics, 19:365.

———. (1943). Psychiatric aspects of obesity in children. American Journal of Psychiatry, 99:752.

———. (1948). Puberty and adolescence: Psychologic consideration. Advances in Pediatrics, 31:219. New York: Interscience.

Caplan, H. (1952). Some considerations of the body-image concept in child development. Quarterly Journal of Child Behavior, 4:382.

Curran, F. J., and Frosch, J. (1942). The body image in adolescent boys. Journal of Genetic Psychology, 60:37–60.

Eisenberg, L. (1965). A developmental approach to adolescence. Children, 12:131–139.

Erikson, E. H. (1968). Identity: Youth and crisis. New York: Norton.

Fitts, W. H. (1964). Self concept scale: Counselor recordings and tests. Nashville, Tenn.: Tennessee Department of Mental Health.

Friesen, H., and Ashwood, E. B. (1965). Hormones of the anterior pituitary body—Medical Progress. New England Journal of Medicine, 272:1216, 1217, 1272, 1328.

Gallagher, J. R. (1955). Dysmenorrhea and menorrhagia in adolescence. Connecticut State Medical Journal, 19:469.

———, and Gallagher, C. D. (1953). Some comments on growth and development in adolescents. Yale Journal of Biology and Medicine, 25:335.

———, Heald, F. P., and Masland, R. P. (1958). Recent contributions to adolescent medicine, medical progress. New York Journal of Medicine, 259:24, 74, 123.

Gardner, L. I. (1960). Biochemical events at adolescence: Symposium on adolescence. Pediatric Clinics of North America, 7:15.

Gray, L. A. (1960). Gynecology in adolescence: Symposium on adolescence. Pediatric Clinics of North America, 7:43.

Greulich, W. W. (1938). A handbook of methods for the study of adolescent children. Monographs of the Society for Research in Child Development, vol. 3, No. 15.

Hampson, J. G. (1964). The case of management of somatic sexual disorders in children. Psychological considerations. In Human Reproduction and Sexual Behavior. New York: Lee and Febiger.

———, and Money, J. (1955). Idiopathic sexual precocity in the female. Psychosomatic Medicine, 17:16.

Heald, F. (1960). Obesity in the adolescent. Pediatric Clinics of North America, 7:207.

Inhelder, B., and Piaget, J. (1958). The growth of logical thinking from childhood to adolescence. New York: Basic Books.

Jacobson, C. B., and Aries-Bernal, L. (1967). Cytogenetic techniques in sexual anomalies. Journal of American Medical Women's Association, 22:875–885.

Jaeger, E. C. (1944). Source book of biological names and terms. Springfield, Ill.: Charles C Thomas.

Jones, M. C., and Bayley, N. (1950). Physical maturing among boys as related to behavior. Journal of Educational Psychology, 41:129.

Josselyn, I. M. (1959). Psychology of adolescents. In M. Levitt, ed., Readings in Psychoanalytical Psychology. New York: Appleton-Century-Croft.

Kallman, F. J., Schonfeld, W. A., and Barbara, S. E. (1944). Genetic aspects of primary eunuchoidism. American Journal of Mental Deficiencies, 48(3):203–236.

Kinsey, A. C., Pomeroy, W. B., and Martin, C. E. (1948). Sexual behavior in the human male. Philadelphia: Saunders.

Kolb, L. C. (1959a). Disturbance of the body image. In S. Arieti, ed., American Handbook of Psychiatry. New York: Basic Books.

———. (1959b). Body image in the schizophrenia reaction. In A. Auerback, ed., Schizophrenia. New York: Ronald Press.

Levy, D. M. (1929). Method of integrating physical and psychiatric examination with special studies of body interest, overt protection, response to growth and sex difference. American Journal of Psychiatry, 9:121.

———— (1932). Body interest in children and hypochondriasis. American Journal of Psychiatry, 12:295–315.

Keniston, K. (1965a). The uncommitted. New York: Harcourt, Brace & World.

————. (1965b). Young radicals. New York: Harcourt, Brace & World.

Montagu, M. F. A. (1946). Adolescent sterility. Springfield, Ill.: Charles C Thomas.

Mursen, P. E., and Jones, M. C. (1957). Self-conceptions, motivations and interpersonal attitudes of late and early maturing boys. Child Development, 28:243.

Newburgh, L. H. (1944). Obesity. Energy metabolism. Physiological Review, 24:18.

Offer, D. (1969). The psychological world of the teenager: New York: Basic Books.

Oxford Universal Dictionary. (1955). Oxford: Clarendon Press.

Papez, J. W. (1937). A proposed mechanism of emotion. American Medical Association Archives of Neurology and Psychiatry, 38:725.

Patton, R. G. (1962). Growth and psychological factors, Report of the 40th Ross Conference on Pediatric Research. Columbus, O.: Ross Laboratories.

Reynolds, E. L., and Wines, J. V. (1948). Individual differences in physical changes associated with adolescence in girls. American Journal of Diseases of Children, 75:329.

————. (1951). Physical changes associated with adolescence in boys. American Journal of Diseases of Children, 82:529.

Ross, G. T., and Tijo, J. H. (1965). Cytogenetics in clinical endocrinology. Journal of the American Medical Association, 192:977.

Schilder, P. (1935). The image and appearance of the human body. Studies in the constructive energies of the psyche. London.

Schonfeld, W. A. (1943a). Management of male pubescence. Journal of the American Medical Association, 121:177–182.

————. (1943b). Primary and secondary sexual characteristics. American Journal of Diseases of Children, 65:535–549.

————. (1950). Inadequate masculine physique as a factor in personality development of adolescent boys. Psychosomatic Medicine, 12:49–54.

————. (1951). Pediatrician's role in management of personality problems of adolescents. American Journal of Diseases of Children, 81:762–770.

————. (1961). Personality effects of gynecomastia in adolescence. Archives of General Psychiatry, 5:46–54.

————. (1962). Gynecomastia in adolescence: Effect on body-image and personality adaptation. Psychosomatic Medicine, 24:379–389.

————. (1963). Body-image in adolescents: A psychiatric concept for the pediatrician. Pediatrics, 31:845–855.

————. (1964). Body-image disturbances in adolescents with inappropriate sexual development. The American Journal of Orthopsychiatry, 35:493–502.

————. (1966). Body-image disturbances in adolescents: Influence of family attitudes and psychopathology. Archives of General Psychiatry, 15:16–21.

————. (1967). The adolescent crises today: Socioeconomic affluence as a factor. New York State Journal of Medicine, 67:1981–1990.

————. (1968a). The adolescent in contemporary American psychiatry: Critical evaluations by I. Josselyn, S. Lebovici, J. Masterson, Jr., H. Staples, and J. Boutourline Young. International Journal of Psychiatry, 5:470–496; 6:77–79.

————. (1968b). Depression and suicide in adolescents. Revista Brasileria de Psiquiatria, 2:89–96.

————. (1969a). The body and body image. In G. Caplan and S. Lebovici, eds., Adolescence: Psychosocial Perspective. New York: Basic Books. Pp. 27–53.

————. (1969b). Trends in adolescent psychiatry. In J. H. Masserman, ed., Current Psychiatric Therapies. Pp. 52–62.

————. (1970a). Comprehensive outpatient community mental health programs for adolescents. In J. Howell, ed., Modern Perspectives in Adolescent Psychiatry. Springfield, Ill.: Charles C Thomas.

————. (1970b). A practical approach to individual psychotherapy of the adolescent. Psychiatric Opinion, 7:6–15.

————. (1970c). Psychiatric sequelae of gynecomastia in adolescence. Medical Aspects of Human Sexuality.

————. (1971). Adolescent psychiatry: A challenge to all psychiatrists. In C. Koupernick, ed. Confrontations Psychiatrique. Paris.

————, and Beebe, G. W. (1942). Normal growth and variation in the male genitalia from birth to maturity. Journal of Urology, 48:759–779.

Schurter, M. A., and Letterman, G. (1967). Klinefelter's syndrome. Journal of the American Medical Women's Association, 22:855–864.

Schutt, A. J., and Hayles, A. B. (1964). Intersex. Mayo Clinic Proceedings, 39:363.

Shuttleworth, E. K. (1949). The adolescent period: A pictorial atlas. Monograph Society for Research in Child Development, vol. 14, series 50, no. 2.

Silverman, S. H., Migeon, C., Rosenberg, E., and Wilkins, L. (1952). Precocious growth of sexual hair without other secondary sexual development: Premature pubarche, a constitutional variation of adolescence. Pediatrics, 10:426.

Skeat, W. W. (1958). A concise etymological dictionary of the English language. London: Oxford University Press.

Sobel, H. (1962). Factors regulating growth. Report of the Fortieth Ross Conference on Pediatric Research. Columbus, O.: Ross Laboratory. Pp. 55 ff.

Stolz, H. R., and Stolz, L. M. (1951). Somatic development of adolescent boys. New York: Macmillan.

Stuart, C. (1946). Normal growth and development during adolescence. New England Journal of Medicine, 234-666, 693, 732. Vol. 239.

Tanner, J. M. (1962). Growth at adolescence. Springfield, Ill.: Charles C Thomas.

Wallace, W. M. (1964). Why and how are children fat. Pediatrics, 34:303.

Wilkins, L. (1948). Abnormalities and variations of sexual development during childhood and adolescence. Advances in Pediatrics, 3:159. New York: Interscience.

————. (1954). Tools and methods of diagnosis and new trends in the treatment of endocrine disorders. Pediatrics, 13:393.

————. (1965). The diagnosis and treatment of endocrine disorders in childhood and adolescence, 2d ed. Springfield, Ill.: Charles C Thomas.

Wylie, R. C. (1961). The self-concept. Lincoln: University of Nebraska Press.

PART III

EFFECTS OF EARLY OBJECT RELATIONS ON ADOLESCENT CHARACTER STRUCTURE

INTRODUCTION

The following essays focus on a similar theme: they illustrate psychopathological and defensive reactions to the disruptive aspects of early object relationships. The maternal relationship, in particular, is explored in a variety of contexts and its influence on subsequent personality development is emphasized. Each chapter deals with particular effects on various psychic structures and functions. For example, one chapter deals with the impact of the maternal introject on fantasy production, another on sexual development, and still another on the structure of the superego. The relationship between the outer world and various psychic systems becomes increasingly important as concepts of ego structure are viewed in a microscopic fashion, that is, in terms of ego subsystems.

The stimulus barrier is an integral part of the psyche, regulating and modulating external stimuli so that they can be integrated into the general psychic organization and adaptively utilized for emotional development. When such stimuli are disruptive, the psyche constructs characteristic defenses. These defenses, for example, precociousness, have features that are specific for the type of disruption. Other reactions, such as acting out, display a similar type of homogeneity.

The nature of the disruptive aspect of early object relationships is also examined. Impingement and assaultiveness seem to be the most damaging features, the ego feeling helpless and vulnerable insofar as it cannot master either the excitement or the frustration caused by the mother's ministrations. The usual concepts of deprivation or overindulgence, according to some of the authors, are artificial polarizations and not particularly useful. These disruptive early object relationships are always frustrating to the child because the mother is narcissistically gratifying her needs and not cognizant of the child's requirements. Too much or too little (giving) is meaningless: To not respond to an inner need or to respond when one is not needful is similarly frustrating.

These essays are interesting clinical studies and have many implications regarding both emotional development and therapeutic technique.

15] FANTASY FORMATION, EGO DEFECT, AND IDENTITY PROBLEMS

PETER L. GIOVACCHINI

Viewing the psychic apparatus in terms of a structural hierarchy from a physiological to a psychological-mentational frame enables one to raise the question as to what elements are involved in fantasy production. An inner need is experienced at all levels of the psychic apparatus. As physiological stimuli gain ascendency, drive representations are given shape as they interact with memory traces and reality. Various ego mechanisms are involved, and the cathecting of the appropriate executive apparatus determines how the need is met, that is, actual or fantasy gratification.

The role of fantasy can be considered in terms of its adaptive or disruptive aspects. Freud (1900) emphasized omnipotent wish fulfillment as corresponding to a magical-primitive developmental phase where reality and fantasy are not distinguished. He illustrates how both dreams and fantasies contain id elements striving for gratification, and if reality is too thwarting, the patient withdraws from it, seeking solace in fantasy.

Many patients, especially those suffering from severe psychopathology, are afraid of their fantasies. This is also true of many adolescents who do not permit themselves the freedom of fantasy production. In the consultation room these patients are often cryptic and concrete, unimaginative and incapable of free associating. The underlying id impulses that would become elaborated into a fantasy seem to be too disruptive for their loosely integrated egos, and they have to keep their inner excitement under control. Consequently, these patients are often con-

329

stricted, repressed persons who keep their feelings at a distance. Fantasy production is inhibited.

In contrast to frightening wish-fulfillment fantasies, one sometimes encounters fantasies that are primarily manifestations of defense. Many grandiose fantasies do not refer exclusively to the instantaneous gratification of all desires; often, they reflect an overcompensatory need for protection against the uncontrollable onslaught of destructive and self-destructive impulses. In other fantasies one can clearly discern vigilant and repressive qualities against the pressure of unacceptable strivings or parts of the self, whereas still other defensive fantasies are designed to make gratification less dangerous.

I shall present two brief vignettes to illustrate the subtle relationship among characterological pathology, fantasy, and the role of external objects in reestablishing equilibrium when the factors leading to fantasy production threaten psychic stability. These interactions also have relevance to the adolescent process in general.

Clinical Material

A homosexual senior college student constantly indulged himself in producing fantasies. He complained of his habit of living almost totally within himself to the point where he had only a minimal awareness of the surrounding world.

In his fantasies he constructed elaborate settings or dialogues in which he would try to master problems that usually took the form of a struggle with another person or situation. Instead of a strong or clever hero, he depicted himself as a bewildered, harassed, vulnerable person (this view of himself was an accurate reflection of his self-representation). He created fantasy situations where he would be in physical danger, ridiculed, or swindled. The activity around him would take place at an accelerated tempo. Objects and people would move at a rapid pace and cause him to feel dismayed and confused. He did not see himself as being able to preserve order or maintain equilibrium. This created further vulnerability and helplessness and made him less capable of coping with the threatening situation or problem that he was facing.

In spite of all these difficulties, he would overpower and outwit his opponent. His success was usually accomplished by his being able to anticipate his opponent's moves by reproducing the course of the latter's thinking and staying a step ahead of the situation.

When he had such fantasies in my office, he would spend lengthy periods of time constructing a situation between the two of us. For example, he would conjecture that I had been about to have intercourse with my previous patient but had to stop my advances because I knew that he was outside waiting for his appointment. I then would want to sadistically manipulate him by doing something unexpected. Perhaps I might act insane, and then he would be faced with the dilemma of determining whether this were genuine or simulated. If I faced him with my psychosis, then he would be completely discombobulated because this would represent a completely unforeseen reversal of roles. He would fantasy "You (the analyst) will think this, then if I say such and such, you will do this, so instead if I say————you will (do something different), but then I would————." After he had anticipated all my possible reactions and responses to his responses, he would then do something definite to counteract my attempt. The latter, after such a buildup, was usually a dull and crass anticlimax, such as simply calling the police. A telephone call would determine whether I were simulating because I would stop acting out if I were faking.

At other times the patient would create a dilemma of such magnitude that he could not find a solution. This occurred more frequently outside the analysis, though I had the opportunity to observe several episodes of such disruption. During one particularly memorable session, he had a sexual fantasy about a young lady he had recently met and who indicated that she was willing to become involved with him. He had never had a sexual relationship with a woman, though now he felt some desire and began anticipating the possibility of having heterosexual intercourse. This anticipation was the dominant theme of the fantasy, and he had tried to create a situation in which he would be making love to her. He tried to visualize a room, a bed, and her naked body, but he was unable to form a composite picture. He could only conjure fragmented bits which did not permit any cohesive action. In this abortive fantasy, he continued anticipating the sexual act, but he was unable to form a coherent picture. He stated that he did not have the "equipment," that is, "did not know how" to make love to a woman. Eventually these fragmented images began to whirl around in a "frenzy" and he felt he was losing control over them. He began feeling "bombarded" and "torn apart." His increasing anxiety reached panic-like proportions. When his discomfort reached such a peak that I began to feel it too, I stated that I was in the same room with him. I had learned from previous experiences that the acknowledgment of my presence would have an instantaneous calming effect. He was once again able to compose himself about

331

sex in an abstract sense, not referring to his fantasy again during the session.

Next, I would like to present another adolescent patient who demonstrated somewhat similar phenomena, which in this instance might have some relevance to the adolescent process, that is, ego mechanisms that might be characteristic of adolescence, and then to discuss both patients in terms of character structure and ego processes.

The patient, a nineteen-year-old male student had always thought of himself as precocious. He was academically ahead of his age group, had achieved adult social graces even before puberty, and had started having sexual relations at the age of fifteen (this was considered premature in his upper-class group). He sought treatment for the same vague, undefined reasons that older patients with characterological problems give. He found life unfulfilling in spite of his social and intellectual endowments. He did not know who and what he was, or the "purpose of his existence." He elicited all those symptoms that are often referred to as an existential crisis. He was moody and unhappy in spite of a seemingly sanguine demeanor, and was often depressed to the point of suicide. He felt his environment was "inordinately complex" and took drugs (marijuana and LSD) in order to withdraw.

Winnicott (1958) refers to the capacity to be alone and Borowitz (1967a) carries the theme into the sexual sphere when discussing the capacity to masturbate alone. This patient, in a sense, had not acquired the ability to have sexual intercourse "alone" with his girlfriend. He had to have other persons in the same house or apartment. He never had intercourse in anyone else's presence nor had he ever witnessed the sexual act. On the other hand, he had to have a friend or another couple nearby. The latter would also be having intercourse. If he just had male friends nearby, he would fantasy that they were masturbating. He had never had a sexual experience in any other circumstances.

During analysis he became aware of the fact that his mind was "always in the next room" when he was having intercourse. Though he did not completely exclude awareness of his partner, he almost did at the moment of ejaculation. During intercourse he would imagine conversations with his friends (there was nothing characteristic about the content) while they were either having intercourse or masturbating. He would shift his attention sporadically from his partner to these fantasies, but when ejaculating he would be completely immersed in his fantasy.

The patient went out of his way to create excitement, which often resulted in a painful aftermath. He had on several occasions been careless

with his drugs and suffered considerable fear that he would be appre-
hended by the police. On other occasions he would complicate his social
life to such an extent that he seemed to have created an intolerable morass. He would even invent competitive games and work himself into
frenzied excitement. He could not tolerate calm and peace.

This patient's background was similar to that of the first patient. Both
had highly excitable parents. Their mothers were overprotective but
also extremely stimulating and seductive. They described scenes in
childhood of seeing them naked and bathing with them, and in the first
case there is a possibility that he had actually witnessed the primal
scene. Both mothers were also extremely ambitious for their sons, and
pushed them to academic extremes. With the second patient the mother
needed to see him as a "little man" and cast him not only as a narcissistic show piece but also as a confidant. His father was a very successful
man but he remained aloof from his family. Both fathers were passively
uninvolved with their sons.

Discussion

Fantasy has been referred to as a substitute for action (Freud, 1900). In
some persons the content of the fantasy is a pleasurable anticipation of
a future satisfaction. These are wish-fulfillment fantasies that contribute
to a mood that will enhance ultimate gratification. In some respects this
is equivalent to forepleasure and raises the cathexis of the receptive
apparatus.

In some patients, particularly those suffering from ego defects, fantasies are not always or primarily pleasurable and usually do not lead to
constructive, goal-directed action. The first patient's fantasies, early in
the analysis, were elaborations of anticipated gratification, which continued being disruptively anticipated because the ego did not have the
resources to turn to external objects to achieve actual gratification.

Fantasy production is an intermediary step between the perceptions
of an inner need and the activation of the proper adjustive techniques to
gratify that need. In this patient and others suffering from characterological defects, the drives are imperfectly developed (Giovacchini,
1967). As physiological needs become elaborated (further structural-
ized) into a sophisticated desire such as a heterosexual one, the drive
becomes mentationally elaborated. Along with the defect in relating to

external objects, the first patient's mental elaboration of inner needs was also constricted, and this was reflected in the content of his fantasies. He had difficulty conjuring cohesive pictures, and often everything would become vague and jumbled, the various elements of the fantasy "coming apart" and resulting in chaos.

The occurrence of fantasy, as an intermediate step between the perception of an inner need and the activation of the proper techniques to gratify the need, raises the question as to whether during the process of gratifying an id impulse, a fantasy inevitably has to be interposed somewhere along the path from sensory stimulation to motoric activation. There are many activities that take place more or less automatically (reflexively) where there is no introspection, planning or fantasy elements that the person can recall. Still, in order to set the executive apparatus into motion so that the person relates to the outer world, higher ego systems, including consciousness, are involved. Some mentational activity takes place, though it may not have the organization of a fantasy.

Some psychoanalysts believe that the concept of unconscious fantasy is useful when considered in a psychodynamic context. Freud (Breuer and Freud, 1895), very early in his writings, describes patients having fantasies that led to ego disruption and then repressing these fantasies as defensive equilibriums were reestablished. The second patient illustrated this phenomenon, and as his defenses relaxed, previously repressed fantasies became conscious. Whether one refers to such repressed psychic elements as fantasies, when they are repressed, is a question of definition. Still, that which is repressed has the potential to be perceived as a fantasy if it can gain access to consciousness.

Arlow (1969) [1] discusses these questions thoroughly and by constructing a consistent conceptual system has succeeded in demonstrating not only how confusing questions can be resolved but also that many such questions are superfluous.

There are, of course, many differences between these two patients, but I feel that there are some important similarities that are relevent to the process of fantasy production. Both felt assaulted and impinged (Winnicott, 1958) upon by their early environment. The stimuli they received from their mothers, sexual and otherwise, were poorly integrated within their egos. The sexual overstimulation, in particular, was felt as assaultive and, because of emotional and physical immaturity, could not be smoothly incorporated within the psyche.

These patients described an inner excitement, vague and undefinable, but still related to this hyperstimulation which caused them to feel helpless and vulnerable. They felt unable to master their disruption.

As a reaction to his inner turmoil, the first patient would get himself "in trouble" because of homosexual behavior. Both patients frequently reacted to this turmoil during their analyses, though neither one acted out as intensely as some of Borowitz's (1967b) patients did. In my office, their inability to integrate the mother's hyperstimulation and precociously stimulated sexual feelings with various ego systems and with reality was reflected in their affects and fantasies.

The homosexual patient's behavior was practically all fantasy activity with very little action. He often emphasized how ignorant and hopeless he felt, indicating that he had never acquired the adaptive techniques necessary to cope with the complexities of the external world (Giovacchini, 1967). Similarly, he was unable to experience satisfactory gratification in any area, and even though he desired heterosexual relationships, he felt paralyzed and impotent with women.

With analytic progress he began to have fantasies of the wish-fulfillment variety. Though these fantasies also began by jousting with me, and anticipating my threatening maneuvers, he now saw himself being attacked because he was planning to seduce a girl. There was a gradual shift from his defense against me to the more exclusive preoccupation with the details of seduction.

Still, there was a curious reaction to what seemed to be a conversion of a relatively defensive fantasy to one where the elements seemed to become predominantly wish fulfilling. He became more and more anxious as he moved further in the direction of wish fulfillment.

For example, he could construct a situation in which he met a girl, took her out, and successfully went through a variety of social preliminaries. Once he brought her into the bedroom he began feeling confusion because he literally did not know what to do. Though repressive elements were evident in his associations, he emphasized that he had never learned how to proceed further. At this point what had started out as being somewhat pleasurable now became increasingly painful. Sometimes, as with previous fantasies, his anxiety would reach the point of mild panic. However, his affect would not become so disruptive as it had at the beginning of treatment, and I never found it necessary to intervene.

This patient suffered from two general but interrelated categories of difficulties. First, as the early fantasies demonstrated, he had to defend himself from an inner, disruptive excitement and agitation created by his inability to smoothly incorporate and amalgamate early maternal experiences. These experiences were perceived as threatening and assaultive, and their inner representations (introjects), which remained frag-

335

mented and encapsulated, were also threatening and disruptive. His initial fantasies reflected his need to be constantly vigilant and in control; there was considerable rumination and very little action. Second, he believed that he was unable to gratify inner needs (heterosexual) because he did not know how. The second group of fantasies indicated that not only had he found his infantile experiences disruptive but that they also did not form a base that would lead to the acquisition of techniques designed to relate to the outer world.

Because some of the stimuli (particularly sexual) he received from his mother were premature, the patient did not have the biological equipment necessary to respond to them. As an adult, he found himself in analogous (from a psychic viewpoint), though, of course, not identical, circumstances.

During infancy the patient's ego's executive apparatus was not capable of developing techniques that could respond to or master the mother's ministrations. So, in addition to having unintegrated introjects, there was a lack of executive techniques. His later fantasies demonstrated this lack, and in a sense, defined the ego defect. His characterological difficulties were based on a lack of integration and development of the executive apparatus to gratify biologically appropriate needs, in part because the needs were imposed on him when the psychic apparatus was too immature to deal with them. This led to constriction, and he found himself incapable of dealing with the disruptions of the inner world and unable to turn to the outer world for satisfaction.

The second patient's initial fantasies were obviously a defensive technique that helped him achieve orgasm. The fantasies also served as defenses against internal conflicts. The latter has to be understood in terms of his characterological difficulties, problems that I believe are fairly typical of a certain type of character disorder and of many adolescents.

The central psychopathology of this group of patients often involves the self-representation, that is, the identity system. The impact of assaultively perceived overstimulation has marked effects on the self-representation.

The maternal introject in these patients is perceived as dangerous and engulfing. The formation of the self-representation is a complicated process, one that at some stage involves incorporation or identification with external objects. When a precociously stimulating mother imago becomes part (an aspect) of the self-representation, the resulting identity is precarious and insecure.

The second adolescent patient often reported episodes when he felt he was being "eaten up inside" and his sense of existence felt threatened. The accompanying affect was painful panic, and he had all the symptoms that Erikson (1956) described as the identity diffusion syndrome. When capable of coherently describing his sensations, he had the feeling that something inside was pounding and hammering. He felt as if he would explode.

He could obtain relief from such an intolerable state by two maneuvers:

1. He could involve himself with friends and throw himself into frenetic social and sometimes sexual activity. He would give parties, attend meetings, take drug trips with a group; in other words, he did everything possible not to be alone. He indulged in many counterphobic activities in order to externalize inner excitement and then master it. While "high" on drugs, he and his companions would become tremendously excited watching candles burn. Each person would have his own candle. They would sit enraptured, watching them burn down. They reacted during these candle races with the same tension and excitement someone might experience at a horse race. His deliberate (though unconscious) creation of dilemmas in his daily life had a similar counterphobic defensive meaning. In these instances, however, he was not always successful and his dismay was a reenactment of the turmoil he experienced in childhood.

He might also become passionately involved with a girl and have frequent sexual relations with her. As mentioned, he was creating excitement in order to master and control his inner turmoil, but this behavior had the added meaning of turning to an external object for protection. In the transference this was clearly illustrated insofar as he turned to me as a rescuer from something inside of him that was "swallowing" his individuality. In dreams he was often pursued by engulfing monsters and found himself running toward a protective person. Thus, the external object was, as will be further discussed, an important factor in his fantasies.

2. This patient would sometimes go into a fugue state when his panic reached an intense pitch, and he was unable to reestablish his equilibrium by the activities just described. He would feel emotionally numb. His identity diffusion would occur when he believed that innumerable demands were made of him (school and family), that is, he felt unfairly imposed on. He felt as if he were in a "fog." He was not particularly uncomfortable, but he saw himself as apart from the rest of the world.

337

In the analysis it became apparent that he was also apart from the rest of himself. He saw everything in terms of extremes, and certain persons were either all good or all bad. This was true of his behavior and various roles. For example, being a student was bad insofar as students are dependent and useless. His involvement with various civil rights movements or even smoking marijuana was good. The transference also reflected this split, and my role shifted from being a nonthreatening, secure person who could protect him to a destructive manipulator, clearly a projection of the maternal introject.

He attempted to cope with this turmoil by withdrawal and drugs. Drugs represented an attempt to deny the existence of an arbitrary, rigid, and sadistic environment. While under the influence of drugs he felt he was in a "protected cage" and "nothing could get to him." He then felt peaceful and everything seemed to have a purpose and place.

The relationship between the identity sense, fantasy formation, and defenses, such as fragmentation and turning toward external objects, has relevance to our understanding of specific characterological pathology.

For this adolescent patient, inner impulses, particularly sexual impulses, were perceived as dangerous. This danger can be understood further from a characterological viewpoint. For example, when his self-representation was altered by a biological need—a sexual stimulus—he would experience tremendous anxiety. Insofar as sexuality and the maternal introject were closely fused, in that much of his maternal imago was constructed in the context of premature sexual stimulation, the maternal introject would be further cathected when he felt sexually excited. This made him feel vulnerable and helpless against the assaultive mother.

He once again faced a situation in which he feared being engulfed. The maternal introject is always instrumental in the formation of the self-representation. When this patient became sexually aroused, the maternal introject, in a sense, became fused with it. Sexual gratification, therefore, threatened to destroy him. This is perhaps an ego-psychological method of saying that he could not master his impulses, but, more precisely, emphasizes the vulnerability of the self-representation owing to the activation of the maternal introject.

He had to defend himself against such a disruptive situation. His defensive techniques against inner excitement and fear of assault generally have been discussed. He used similar techniques when facing specific sexual excitement and fear of assault.

As mentioned, he had to have someone near in addition to his partner while having sexual intercourse. This highlights the function of the external object. The presence of the external object made the self-representation feel less vulnerable.

One's weakness and helplessness is highlighted when alone; a group or a companion may help one to feel stronger and protected. Freud (1921) emphasized the role of the group in the formation of a collective superego. A group or a companion may also be instrumental in the formation of a collective self-representation. Groups assume an identity that transcends the individual's identity.

This patient introjected his companion to form an alliance against the assaultive maternal introject. The dyad helped him control his inner excitement. This does not constitute an actual relationship with an external object; the external object was a narcissistic extension of himself, an accretion so to speak, to the self-representation. The patient had to have someone, but it was the fantasy of a companion being engaged in similar sexual activity that enabled him to reach the climax of his excitement relatively safely.

The production of this fantasy was motivated by the need to get the "mother off his back." He would create a social environment by his fantasy which for the moment gave him the ephemeral security of having mastered the disruptive maternal introject. Though ephemeral, the fantasy created the illusion of strength, one that sustained him through a moment of danger. Once the sexual excitement subsided he could relax, because the maternal introject became relatively less threatening. Borowitz (1967a) presents similar clinical material; his patients had been assaultively and precociously sexually stimulated during childhood. They could not masturbate unless another person were present. The external object was required so that solitary masturbation could occur without being overwhelmingly disruptive.

The ego defects of these adolescent patients involve different systems, but now one can define the problem as resulting from a lack of development of the self-representation because the maternal introject is disruptive to an autonomous heterosexual orientation.

The sense of identity is the result of the operations of various ego systems (Giovacchini, 1965) and is also determined by the dominant psychosexual stage of the current ego state. For example, one feels alive because one experiences needs that are initially physiologic. They then become elaborated. First, one feels oneself in an oral fashion; for example, as a hungry mouth and then, with greater structure, there is a wider range of self-awareness up to seeing oneself as an aggressive, heterosexual, striving person with a variety of goals that promote self-esteem.

It is conceptually consistent to equate the self-image and the perceptual systems' self-observations with the identity sense. Even though one's self-observations may be defensive in nature and be reactions against other painful states of self-awareness, the identity sense is best defined by the way the person perceives himself at the moment.

What one observes about one's total integrations is the essence of how a person perceives himself. Though mechanisms do not have mental representations, their operations are associated with affects that do, and it is these affects that are felt and observed.

The identity sense of both these patients was characterized by a precociously stimulating and assaultive maternal introject. The acquisition of a heterosexual identity was thus inhibited, and the ego can be conceptualized as possessing a faulty integration of the identity sense with memories of satisfying heterosexual experiences. Consequently, the executive system cannot develop techniques for uninhibited and nonconflictual sexual expression. If the self-representation feels threatened by biological sexual arousal because of cathexis of a threatening maternal introject then the required integration between the perceptual and executive systems is traumatic and has to employ various defenses to cope with the situation as was demonstrated by the fantasies of these adolescents.

The adolescent process in the male may very well involve the task of shifting cathexis from the maternal introject to other females. The less the self-representation feels threatened by the maternal introject, the easier it is for the adolescent to incorporate satisfying experiences with girls in his introjects. These experiences then lead to the acquisition of executive techniques which are set in motion when the self-representation's heterosexual identification, not threatened by the maternal introject, becomes cathected through the activation of sexual feelings.

Patients suffering from characterological defects highlight pathological ego processes. Defective functioning and intrasystemic conflict are reflected in fantasies, which as these clinical examples indicate, may have specific defensive functions as well as representing wish fulfillment.

Summary

The production of fantasy is considered in an ego psychological context. Fantasies serve a variety of functions; in addition to wish fulfillment, the defensive meaning of fantasy is explored. The relationship between various ego systems and the relevance of fantasy as an element to maintain psychic harmony is emphasized.

Patients suffering from characterological defects demonstrate both disruptive and integrative aspects of fantasy. The ego defects of these patients can be generally described as an inability to integrate early disruptive introjects that do not lead to memory traces of satisfying experiences necessary to later activate the executive apparatus. Fantasy often represents anticipated gratification.

The impact of ego defects on the self-representation is specifically discussed. Fantasy production and the relationship to external objects is also explored in terms of their potential in protecting the self-representation from an assaultive maternal introject. The ego processes involved may have general relevance to the developing sexuality of the adolescent.

NOTE

1. Isaacs (1952) and Segal (1967) used the concept of unconscious fantasy in a somewhat different fashion, one that is tangential to the thesis here. See also Beres (1962).

REFERENCES

Arlow, J. A. (1969). Unconscious fantasy and disturbances of conscious experience. Psychoanalytic Quarterly, 38 (no.1):1–28.

———. (1969). Fantasy, memory and reality testing. Psychoanalytic Quarterly, 38 (no.1):28–52.

Beres, D. (1962). The unconscious fantasy. Psychoanalytic Quarterly, 31:309–328.

Borowitz, G. H. (1967a). The capacity to masturbate alone in adolescence. Paper presented to the Society for Adolescent Psychiatry, Chicago, Illinois.

———. (1967b). Premature sexual stimulation: Developmental aspects. Paper presented to the Illinois Psychiatric Society 1966 and the Jewish Hospital, St. Louis, Missouri.

Breuer, J. and Freud, S. (1895). Studies on hysteria. Standard Edition, Vol. 2. London: Hogarth Press, 1955.

Erikson, E. H. (1956). The problem of ego identity. Journal of the American Psychoanalytic Association, 4:56–121.

Freud, S. (1900). The interpretation of dreams. Standard Edition, Vols. 4 and 5. London: Hogarth Press, 1955.

———. (1921). Group psychology and analysis of the ego. Standard Edition, Vol. 18. London: Hogarth Press, 1955.

Giovacchini, P. L. (1965). Psychopathological aspects of the identity sense, Psychiatry Digest, 26:31–41.

———. (1967). Frustration and externalization. Psychoanalytic Quarterly, 36:571–583.

Isaacs, S. (1952). The nature and function of phantasy. In Miklein et al., ed., Developments in Psychoanalysis. London: Hogarth Press.

Segal, H. (1967). Melanie Klein's technique. Psychoanalytic Forum, 2 (no. 3): 197–241.

Winnicott, D. W. (1958). The capacity to be alone. International Journal of Psycho-Analysis, 39:416–440.

16] CHARACTER DISORDERS IN CHILDHOOD AND ADOLESCENCE: SOME CONSIDERATION OF THE EFFECTS OF SEXUAL STIMULATION IN INFANCY AND CHILDHOOD

GENE H. BOROWITZ

Through the study of transference phenomena in patients suffering from character disorders, inferences regarding normal and pathologic early ego development have been postulated, preoedipal features have been highlighted, and the importance of the early mother-child interactions emphasized. There have been few reports of direct observations of children suffering from character disorders, though longitudinal studies show great promise in testing and corroborating the hypotheses derived from reconstructive studies.

Presented here is material on two boys with character disorders. Both boys, from their infancy, were used by their mothers to provide them with sensual stimulation. As the boys grew older they developed an exclusive relationship with their mothers centering around mutual sensual stimulation. When the relationships with their mothers were interrupted, the boys attempted to re-create the same kind of relationships in each new setting, and with each new meaningful person.

The clinical material presented is derived from observations of the boys while they were enrolled at a residential treatment school. Particular attention is paid to the boys' visits with their mothers and the boys' subsequent reactions. In addition, both boys and their families had repeated contact with social agencies. Both mothers were known to social

343

agencies from the time they themselves were children and almost continuous longitudinal records were available.

Case 1

John, an eleven-year-old boy, had been placed at a residential treatment school because of marked behavior problems in school. On admission, John was an obese, prepubertal, hyperactive boy with a short attention span who was aggressive with smaller children. He was preoccupied with sexual matters and his vocabulary consisted almost exclusively of four-letter monosyllabic words. Psychological tests showed him to be of at least upper average intelligence. All the test results were interpreted as showing no evidence of thought disorder characteristic of schizophrenia, nor any evidence of organicity.

His parents had been married after a two-week courtship when his mother was fifteen and his father twenty. The marriage was hectic with frequent fights and physical battles. The patient, a cranky, hard-to-please baby, slept with his mother. He was breast-fed for his first three or four months but did not seem satisfied so he was started on supplementary feedings. He remained a poor eater, however. At six months he spent much of his time rocking and head banging. Inconsistent toilet training began at seven months. Between nine months and two years he frequently engaged in fecal play, taking feces from his diaper, putting them in his mouth, and smearing. When approximately two years old he developed daytime bladder control, but he had persistent soiling and nocturnal enuresis until his placement away from home. He began speaking at about six or seven months and walked when twelve months old.

When John was one, his mother became pregnant with his sister. At the same time his father was arrested on a charge of armed robbery, convicted, and sentenced to twenty-one years in prison and his maternal grandmother was killed in an automobile accident. His mother was extremely upset by all these events—crying constantly and feeling helpless—and she moved in with the paternal grandparents. John during this period cried almost constantly, smeared feces, and continued incessant rocking and head banging. Unable to pacify him, the mother's frustration reached such a frenzy on one occasion that she attempted to smother him but was restrained by the paternal grandmother.

344

Through the next few years John continued to be a difficult child to manage. During this time he and his sister were cared for by others— grandparents and then foster parents. At four and one-half years, John was described as hyperactive, with constant nightmares, nocturnal enuresis, and soiling. He was again living with his paternal grandmother when he started kindergarten at five years. From the beginning he was a behavior problem: he received multiple school suspensions because of the school's inability to cope with his behavior. When he was eight and one-half years his mother returned to live with her children, though they were still cared for by others during the day. At night John usually slept with his mother, if not in her bed still in the same room. As his mother had been markedly promiscuous since her adolescence, John had been witness to her many sexual encounters from his birth.

John, now eight and one-half, was increasingly difficult to handle for his mother—he was disobedient, stubborn, extremely restless, unable to concentrate, and destructive. She commented that he was "too much boy who didn't realize how strong he was and seemed to destroy everything he touched without realizing what he was doing." He continued soiling and being enuretic; he had frequent night terrors and an even more marked school problem. After frequent recommendations from the school, the mother applied to a child guidance center for help. She turned down numerous placement suggestions but finally agreed to place John at a residential treatment school.

After several months he stopped soiling or being enuretic and started to masturbate openly. He then settled into a fairly stable pattern of behavior during the next several months. His sexually provocative language and his masturbation provoked considerable anger in his cottage mother who was infuriated and wished to get rid of him; she was afraid of what he might do if he lost control. Because of his hyperactivity, poor attention span, and clowning behavior he did poorly in school. He continued to bully smaller children while at the same time he became the goat for older boys—the butt of their jokes and frequently beaten. Gradually he formed close relationships with several males on campus to whom he would run for protection against his cottage mother and other women on campus who he was afraid were going to kill him.

Following is a description of a typical visit between John and his mother. She arrived at the school dressed in a most sexually provocative manner and greeted him with passionate kisses and embraces. They fondled and petted each other as if they were lovers engaged in foreplay. They seemed totally unaware of the effect their behavior had on the

345

other people in the cottage. Almost all the onlookers became very embarrassed and frightened by the seemingly sexual nature of the interaction, and withdrew. The kissing and fondling between John and his mother continued for the entire visit, and they parted with passionate embraces.

He had a characteristic reaction following his mother's visits—"he went crazy." His hyperactivity markedly increased; he would jabber incessantly, and the speed of his verbal productions made it virtually impossible to understand him. He was obsessed with sexual matters; he gave a sexual meaning to everything he did. He ate voraciously and constantly and was nicknamed "Piggy." Unable to sleep, the fitful sleep he did manage was disturbed by night terrors. In an eminently successful and characteristic way he also provoked beatings from older boys. He would describe his mother's anatomy in vivid detail, pointing out the size and contour of her breasts, the shapeliness of her hips and legs, and would suggest how delightful it would be to "screw her" or to "suck on her tits." This would arouse tremendous anxiety in the older boys and they would beat him. During these crazy episodes he seemed to lose his concept of time; he would frequently be unable to recognize people he knew, and would have trouble knowing where he was. He was phenomenologically psychotic.

Following his mother's visits it took a week or two for John to gradually settle down. When the disruptive effects of his mother's visits were clearly recognized, they were curtailed and his crazy episodes gradually disappeared. They returned later when he lost his therapist to whom he had become markedly attached.

Case 2

Stanley, a twelve-year-old boy, was placed at the residential school because of stealing, but many aspects of his history are similar to John's. Like John, Stanley was the older of two children, having a younger sister, and was the product of an extremely unstable marriage. His father was an alcoholic who frequently deserted their home for long periods of time. His mother was promiscuous and, as happened to John, exposed him repeatedly to her sexual experiences as well as abandoning him to the care of others for long periods of time. Stanley also soiled and was enuretic. At the residential school, Stanley, a handsome, pubertal boy,

346

was ingratiating and a hard worker with perfectionistic standards. He earned considerable money, but instead of spending it, he sent all of his savings to his mother. As time passed it became clear that Stanley did not relate to anyone on campus; he maintained a pleasant but marked distance from adults and peers. Psychological testing revealed him to be of at least high average intelligence with no indications of schizophrenia or organicity.

His mother's visits also were grossly sexual. He was greeted as mother's little man. One specific incident dramatically portrays the interaction. While they were embracing and playfully wrestling, his mother wrapped her legs around him and held him tightly. Suddenly she screamed, "Rape!" Stanley was terrified and burst out of the room. About one half hour later, he sheepishly returned. When asked about her behavior, his mother laughingly replied that she often teased Stanley in this way and did not understand why he got upset about it.

Following his mother's visits to him, Stanley engaged in homosexual activity for several weeks. He would aggressively and openly seduce younger boys to perform fellatio and pederasty. During each of the episodes he contacted an older homosexual man he knew and was paid for performing fellatio. Within weeks, this behavior largely would disappear, and Stanley would return to his superficial façade of pleasantness, his hard-working habits, and his general isolation. His psychological state during these periods of gross, overt, homosexual behavior is best described as "driven." He was unable to concentrate, and he had no time to talk to anyone; even superficial amenities were dropped. He had a harsh and nasty word for everyone; the slightest intervention would lead to a rain of curses. Suffering from nightmares, he was unable to eat or sleep.

Stanley was seen in psychotherapy during this time. Early in the therapy he related in a hostile, depreciating manner, trying to maintain a grown-up, wise-guy attitude. As time went on, he began to relate as a young, helpless child. He experienced the therapist both in and outside the therapy sessions as a savior who would protect him against his cottage mother whom he felt hated him and wanted to destroy him. His play frequently showed destructive rage toward women and at the same time, he talked about his tremendous need to grow up and to take care of his mother. He reported how his mother frequently would tell him that his father was not at home and that she needed her "little man" to come home and take care of her. Stanley worked hard to earn money; he spoke of the time before he had come to the school and how he had

347

felt driven to steal in order to provide for his mother. It became evident to the therapist that Stanley felt he was his mother's husband and had to fulfill a role his father had been unable to. Though at first it appeared there was a good deal of pleasure in this seemingly oedipal triumph, he became more and more anxious. Following a telephone call from his mother, in which she told him that she was going to divorce his father and wanted him to come home, he had a period of intense, overt homosexual behavior. He appealed to his therapist to help him curb his disturbing and frightening homosexual behavior. Terrified, he talked about how he had to go home to take care of his mother and asked if that meant he would have to have intercourse with her. He went on to elaborate fantasies of her devouring him during intercourse. He then began dealing with feelings about his father toward whom he had always expressed a good deal of rage and contempt. He was disappointed because his father had seemed ineffectual and weak, unlike his therapist. Could not his therapist come home and live with him and his mother; could not the therapist marry his mother, he asked. He was certain that the therapist could take care of and satisfy her in a manner that his father had been unable to.

Discussion

The clinical material presented is of two boys who suffered from severe character disorders that sharply limited their adaptive capacities and necessitated their placement in a residential treatment school. At the school both boys attempted, and were partially successful, in re-creating many of the factors, both intrapsychic and interpersonal, that contributed to their difficulties. One characteristic pattern common to each boy is that when each was upset he became increasingly sexually preoccupied. A characteristic stimulus for the upset was a visit with the mother which involved a great deal of seemingly sexual interaction. It is quite apparent from the long history and severity of each boy's disturbance that any attempt to draw simple and direct correlations between the apparently sexual interaction with the mother and the subsequent sexual preoccupation each boy evidenced would be simplistic. However, focusing on the area of mother-child interaction might provide insights into some aspects of the boys' characters and some aspects of their pathologies.

348

In reviewing the childhood experiences of both boys one is struck by the gross inconsistencies in their care, the lack of stability in their environment, and the seeming lack of orderly progression of their experiences. Many authors have highlighted these factors in reconstructing the development of patients with character disorders. In these boys another factor is highlighted; from infancy each boy was present while his mother engaged in a wide variety of sexual activities, and from early in childhood each boy was treated by his mother, not primarily as a child, but as a sexual partner. There is more than sufficient corroborating evidence to show that the mother's sexuality was far from object-related genitality, however; the interaction between mother and child took on the currency of mutual sensual stimulation.

The nature and fate of early childhood sexual experiences has been a central core of psychoanalytic concern since its beginning. Freud's seduction hypothesis was a critical way station in the development of the theory of infantile sexuality, and though emphasis shifted markedly when Freud realized the crucial importance for personality development of phase-specific infantile sexual fantasies, he never lost interest in the importance and effects of early sexual experiences. Freud (1905) suggests some of the effects of early sexual experiences when he states,

we find the effects of seduction, which treats a child as a sexual object prematurely and teaches him, in highly emotional circumstances, how to obtain satisfaction from his genital zones, a satisfaction which he is then usually obliged to repeat again and again by masturbation. . . . It is an instructive fact that under the influence of seduction children can become polymorphous perverse, and can be led into all possible kinds of sexual irregularities. . . . [T]he effects of seduction do not help to reveal the early history of the sexual instinct; they rather confuse our view of it by presenting children prematurely with a sexual object for which the infantile sexual instinct at first shows no need. . . . If children at this early age witness sexual intercourse between adults . . . they [the children] inevitably regard the sexual act as a sort of ill treatment or act of subjugation: they view it, that is, in a sadistic sense. Psychoanalysis also shows us that an impression of this kind in early childhood contributes a great deal towards a predisposition to a subsequent sadistic displacement of the sexual aim.

Though Freud called attention to a variety of effects of sexual stimulation in childhood, in his later writings he concentrated on the child's perception, auditory and visual, of parental intercourse, the "primal scene." This particularly is elaborated in the wolf man (Freud, 1918).

What is the impact of viewing parental intercourse? The particular effect depends on the child's developmental level, though Freud (1918)

349

has noted that this complex stimulus is always meaningfully recorded. The effect of observing parental intercourse in prephallic phases is suggested in the case of the wolf man.

Before the phallic-oedipal phase, the experience focuses the child's feelings and fantasies on his mother; the child, in a situation that he finds exciting, feels abandoned, or left out. He attempts to integrate the exciting scene with his phase-specific fantasies and autoerotic activities but is unable to resolve his excitement. Depending on his stage of drive development and the nature of his representational world, he attempts to master the situation with autoerotic behavior. Spitz (1949) has demonstrated that there is a hierarchy of autoerotic behaviors that progresses from body rocking and head banging through fecal play to genital masturbation. However, the scene is so stimulating that the child is usually not able to soothe himself and remains highly excited after the parental intercourse has ceased and the parents have gone to sleep. Tantrums, screaming fits, crying, loss of urinary and bowel control, and vomiting are frequent sequelae. Freud (1918) reconstructs that the wolf man's response to observing parental intercourse at one and one-half years was to pass a stool and then cry.

There are many other varieties of sexual stimulation in childhood. From our analytic work we are most familiar with the visual percepts of the anatomical differences between the sexes and the parental sexual activity as well as the auditory percepts of the primal scene. Clearly, the range of possible sexual stimulation in childhood is much greater. Freud (1900, 1940) called attention to the practice of sexual arousal of the child by the mother during routine hygienic care as well as commenting on the practice of certain nursemaids who attempted to sedate children in their care by genital manipulation. In the cases presented here both mothers repeatedly attempted to soothe their infant sons by manipulating the boys' genitals. John's mother, while drunk on several occasions, poured milk on her vagina and attempted to have John, then an infant, lick it up. Both mothers repeatedly masturbated by rubbing their infants against their (the mothers') genitals. This behavior, suggestive of how the mothers viewed and dealt with their infants, is presented here to elaborate some of the many forms of sexual stimulation children may experience.

What are some of the effects of sexual stimulation in childhood? Freud suggested that the whole panoply of polymorphous perverse activity is fostered by disrupting the integration of component instincts into phallic, and later genital, sexuality. John's masochism and Stanley's homosexuality clearly illustrate this.

350

Though it is suggested that sexual stimulation in childhood may have specific personality effects, particularly in regard to later sexual development, it appears that in infancy the particular modality of stimulation may be less crucial. The question of the maintenance of levels of stimuli in infancy leads to a consideration of the concept of the stimulus barrier. Benjamin (1965) draws a distinction between a passive and an active stimulus barrier. A passive stimulus barrier is a function of a lack of neural maturation and is present from birth until the three- to four-week maturational crisis. The latter distinction, the active stimulus barrier, is dependent on neural maturation and is manifested in behavior at eight to ten weeks, or later. He suggests that in the period between the active and passive the infant is extremely vulnerable and that

the resultant enhanced vulnerability of this period, in turn, makes greater demands upon the mother or mother substitutes. Usually these are well met, with or without conscious awareness on the mother's part, that the infant has become more sensitive to stimuli. Sometimes these needs for additional protection against stimulation are less well handled . . . I have hypothesized that failure to meet these needs of the infant is one important factor out of many that may lead to a heightened *predisposition* to anxiety.

Bergman and Escalona (1949) suggested

that the infant who is not protected from stimuli either because of a "thin protective barrier," or because of a failure of maternal protection, may have to resort for such protection to premature formation of an ego. When the premature ego breaks down, possibly as a consequence of trauma, the psychotic manifestations are thought to set in.

Boyer (1956) commented, "Infants, whose maternal protective barriers are deficient, develop ego weakness and inadequate differentiation of ego and id. If the stimulus barrier or maternal protective barrier is deficient, or if the drive strength of the child is unusually increased, ego development may be disturbed." Benjamin, Bergman and Escalona, and Boyer call our attention to some of the possible sequelae of hyperstimulation in infancy—a predisposition to anxiety, premature but fragile ego development with a high liability toward severe character disorders, or psychosis.

In considering the psychic mechanisms involved, many have utilized Freud's (1900) model of the mind which suggested that the nervous system, as a whole, strives to keep itself free from stimuli. This model of the mind has been criticized by Holt (1965) and Benjamin (1965), who each point out that most of the findings of modern neuroanatomy and neurophysiology contradict this conception of the function of the nervous system. White (1963) suggests another mechanism, that much ego growth occurs in "free time," when the drives are not aroused. He postulates that when drives are aroused the ego apparatus is directed to instinctual aims and that ego growth occurs not solely or even primarily because of the arousal-gratification cycle, but because gratification of drives leads to increasing periods of free time in which play and exploration lead to important aspects of ego growth. He suggests that when an infant is hyperstimulated his instinctual drives are in a heightened and prolonged state of arousal thus giving the infant considerably less free time for play, exploration, and growth. These ideas parallel those proposed by Piaget (1954) as to when in the daily life cycle major cognitive growth occurs.

It is not clear at what point in the child's development he is able to discriminate the sensual from other stimuli. Klein (1970) calls attention to the hierarchical cognitive organization of sensual stimuli, particularly as they relate to the unfolding of erotogenic zones. At some stage in early infancy sensory discrimination becomes possible. Early hyperstimulation tends to delay and distort the development of sensory discrimination. With the discrimination, though perhaps with distortions, sexual stimuli begin to carry more and more importance. Kramer (1954) describes persons who are

characterized by driving restlessness and seemingly boundless energy. Uneasy when alone, though not always aware of it, they sleep little, constantly seek companionship, and are clamorous and obtrusive in their social relationships and work habits. Impulsive and unrestrained in most areas of their lives, they eat and drink rapidly and excessively, often gamble and engage in risky enterprises, and always undertake more than one thing at a time. They also take unnecessary physical risks, often to the point of serious danger to life—obviously patience is not one of their virtues, and their apparent endurance and tirelessness are forced and artificial.

On the basis of analytic material Kramer explains the patient's behavior as a never-ending attempt to re-create and master childhood sexual hyperstimulation.

The chronic stimulation, coupled with the helplessness in his attempts to discharge the tension, produced, in effect, a traumatic condition never since relieved. The character traits and behavior patterns represented an elaboration and endless repetition of his unsuccessful attempts to master the state of unrelieved tension experienced at that early age. The seemingly insatiable search for stimuli and the inability to hear, much less enjoy, a state of rest appeared to be a defense mechanism closely related to the well-known counterphobic defense described by Fenichel. The frantic struggle for stimulation is in reality a desperate attempt to find relief and rest through denial of the painful nature of the overstimulated condition.

Though Kramer's patients demonstrated considerably more psychic organization than John or Stanley, the description of the re-creation of conditions of excitement in an attempt to master the old hyperstimulation are directly applicable.

In considering the effects of sexual stimulation on children it is postulated that knowledge of the epigenetic unfolding of drives and hierarchical elaboration of ego structures suggests that the child has a differential sensitivity to perceptions. Some perceptions are considerably more meaningful and may have profound effects with even minimal exposure. When perceptions fit phase-specific fantasies important psychic organization occurs.

Winnicott (1955, 1960) has repeatedly called attention to the function of the environment in ordering stimuli (experiences) for the growing child. This is an important part of his concept of the "holding environment." In usual development, the environment, as embodied by the mother first and later by others, intuitively orders the child's environment, that is, the intensity and variety of stimuli to which he is exposed. As in the cases of John and Stanley, this ordering of the environment was out of phase with their level of development. As infants, their environment was chaotic; this was later reflected in the way they saw and attempted to structure themselves and their universe. Though clearly there was some order to their environment, and their mothers had relatively predictable patterns of behavior, the predictability was apparent only to a highly organized individual observing them over a period of time. From the vantage point of the infant and the child, the boys' environments were almost totally unpredictable. In the face of this situation, John and Stanley attempted to organize their universe around specific relationships to their mothers. Winnicott (1965) has described this mechanism as one element of the development of the false self. It is quite apparent neither mother viewed her son appropriately. They dealt with their sons inconsistently; the common thread was around sensual arousal. The boys, in turn, seemed to maintain some organization and to develop some sense of their own existence and worth by complying with what they perceived to be their mothers' expectations. The relationships with their mothers, in the boys' minds, kept them alive. Without these relationships, they feared dissolution, and would suffer marked regression. In every new situation they attempted to re-create their views of the relationships with the mothers. When the environment did not comply, their anxieties reached panic proportions; they became sexually preoccupied and increasingly psychotic.

The direct observations of the mother-child interaction revealed that these two mothers were unable to appropriately perceive their children. They perceived the boys as objects for their own sensual arousal. They slept with their sons whenever no other man was in the house and frequently masturbated with them when the boys were infants. In both cases the father was either entirely or frequently absent from the home. The mothers also were similar in many other respects. Each had a traumatic background and a long history of difficulty in relating meaningfully to people. Each married impulsively and had stormy and unsuccessful marriages to unstable men. Each exposed her child to her promiscuous behavior. The sexuality was pregenital and seemed to reflect an attempt to gain lost security through physical closeness and nurturing.

Clearly they were markedly ambivalent to their sons. In the first case the mother treated her son, John, like a treasured sexual object, on the one hand and, on the other, saw him as a destructive male who broke everything he touched. Her unbridled aggression was clearly demonstrated when she tried to kill him when he was two years old. In the second case, the mother's ambivalence was expressed in her constant expression of what a wonderful little man she had, and then frequently turning him over to the police because she could not handle him because he was "rotten just like his father." Even more striking was the rape scene during her visit.

Though the ambivalent nature of the mothers' reactions to their children is obvious, another factor warrants consideration, namely, their inability to perceive their children as discrete entities (seemingly since their births) and to act appropriately toward them. This was dramatically highlighted during the visits with their sons.

Each mother's poorly synthesized undifferentiated ego caused her to view the child as a narcissistic extension. Giovacchini (1965), in a discussion of the analysis of a woman with a character disorder, focused on this woman's inability to perceive her child's needs. From reconstructive analytic data he postulated the importance of a functional maternal introject in order to be a good mother. He suggests that if a woman had had inadequate mothering, the presence of the hostile maternal introject prevents the ego's structuralizing to the high level of ego functioning that mothering requires. He believes the absence of functional introjects is clearly revealed by the mother's perceptual distortion of the child's needs.

What appears to be of utmost importance in causing developmental ego defect is the mother's inability to correctly view the child as a separate entity, to perceive his individual needs, and to act on them appropriately. Lomas (1962) has expressed a similar view when he states, "A necessary feature of a parental attitude is an accurate perception of the child's particularity and a parent who lacks this perception is being dangerously unrealistic."

Need gratification is viewed in the form of an hierarchical continuum (Giovacchini, 1964). At first the infant only perceives sensations associated with physiologic disequilibrium; through the mother's perception of this disequilibrium and her intervention equilibrium is reestablished. Constant repetition of this cycle leads to the structuralization of both needs and techniques of gratification. This continuum progresses from disequilibrium-equilibrium to the child's awareness of the satisfying substance that is fused with the object that provides it. The child's ability to distinguish the satisfying substance from the need gratifier parallels the progression from part object to whole object. The development of the feelings of confidence (Benedek, 1950) depends largely on having during early phases of development an external environment that perceives needs and satisfies them appropriately.

The effect of inappropriate need gratification depends on the child's level of development. In the earliest phase it leads to continuing physiologic disequilibrium and frequently death. With higher levels of structuralization, this disequilibrium is experienced as rage, and if psychic structuralization proceeds to a sufficient degree it is internalized in terms of a hostile introject. Physiologic disequilibrium, rage, and hostile introjects prevent further psychic structuralization; the earlier the level of maximum frustration or inappropriate need gratification, the greater will be the level of disruption to the developing ego.

Very simply, good mothering may be defined as the mother's ability to perceive and act appropriately to satisfy the child's needs thus enhancing and permitting further ego structuralization. This definition presumes that through appropriate gratification, needs at one phase of development are not necessarily identical with needs at an earlier phase of development (Pine, 1970). The adequate mother is one who has sufficient ego structuralization to perceive empathically her child's needs and to satisfy them.

Inadequate mothers are mothers who cannot correctly perceive or ap-

355

propriately satisfy their child's needs. A number of factors may be involved, including the mother's own mother's presence, her own physical capabilities, and from our point of view, the somewhat more pertinent factor of her psychological capabilities. I am referring to mothers, similar to the two described in this chapter, who do not have the perceptual and/or executive skills necessary to either perceive or respond to the child's needs. Giovacchini (1965) has pointed to two conditions leading to this situation, conditions usually seen in admixture rather than pure culture. The first situation is where the mother, because of her own lack of adequate mothering, has not internalized a satisfactory maternal experience. The second situation is one in which the mother, because of a particular conflict, has repressed specific segments of her personality that are necessary for adequate mothering.

I would like to focus on the first group, mothers who have ego defects owing to their own lack of adequate mothering. As in cases of all ego defects, the object related to is seen in the light of projections of archaic imagos which are primarily destructive. The mother views the child as a hated part of herself. The need to care for the child highlights the mother's ego defect; the mother, unable to perceive the child's needs, is frequently unable to pacify the child. The child is cranky and irritable and the mother feels even more intensely her own feelings of worthlessness and helplessness (Bendek, 1959). This frequently arouses rage and may lead to an attempt to kill the child. This was illustrated in the first case when the mother tried to smother her son and is also dramatically illustrated in the battered baby syndrome.

The mother who is poorly structured because of the inadequate mothering she's received has largely repressed or not experienced early positive infantile experiences. Her negative infantile experiences (subjective) were many, poorly integrated, and repressed. When she is unable to satisfy her own upset child, her own negative infantile experiences are stimulated and recalled. She begins to lose differentiation between herself in the present and herself as an unsatisfied infant/child, and also to lose differentiation between herself and her upset child. With loss of differentiation, she begins to reexperience the rage that was the concomitant of her unsatisfied infantile needs and the destructive fantasies that accompanied the rage. She projects her old rage and destructive fantasies onto her upset child and, in her regression, with loss of reality testing, may begin to believe that the child can act on her projected fantasies. Within the mother's mind, she is now locked in a life and death struggle with the upset child whom she believes wants to, and has the capacity to, destroy her. Feeling so threatened, she may then attack and attempt to kill the child out of self-defense. An interesting aspect of the interplay between defect and repression is the observation that when one of these women regresses while attempting to handle her upset infant, she is unable to perceive the infant as an infant, but instead sees him as an older child, a child of two and one-half years or older, one who is old enough to have conscious recall. She attributes to the infant mentation and capacities of an older child, which involves her own angry childhood memories. She perceives her infant as feeling and having fantasies toward her as she remembers feeling and having fantasies toward her own mother when she had felt (and most times was) mistreated.[1]

More frequently, however, the mother is able to mobilize defenses that permit her to control her rage and afford the child some need gratification. The defenses frequently take the form of compulsive rituals, which, though not in any way recognizing the child's individuality, seem adequate to permit further growth. I believe this type of need gratification inhibits the development of the child's individuality and fosters a particular type of symbiotic fusion with the mother. This is illustrated by a recurrent nightmare that the first patient, John, had before and while attending the school: He is running away from something frightening but does not know what it is. He runs to the ocean, which is stormy and also frightening, and dives in. As he dives deeper he finds that it becomes calm and he passes schools of fish. He keeps going down and down, the calm and quiet increasing. Then he drowns. John awakened terrified. The dream shows marked regression and ends with his death, no segment of his ego remaining available to observe the death.

An important aspect of ego development is the child's drive toward autonomy (Mahler, 1965; White, 1963). The healthy mother perceives this need and aids in its development. The narcissistic mother has great difficulty in dealing with this phase. She cannot separate herself from her child because she needs him in order to project her self-hatred. When threatened by his autonomy, she reacts. She either clings to the child and attempts to keep him tied to her, retaining a part of herself by projection, or she may react to the other side of her ambivalence and reject the child (and the hated part of herself) completely. Both sides of the mother's ambivalence are seen in her reactions to the child.

If sufficient need gratification has occurred to permit some structuralization, the child becomes aware that his needs are not met at times appropriate to him but at times appropriate to some object in the external environment. The child, overwhelmed with rage at the external environment, is afraid of losing the object completely. This fear of object loss is frequently the dominant force in the personality and rage is repressed in an attempt to maintain object constancy.

What mechanisms does the child utilize to ensure survival? Gitelson (1958) offers a valuable suggestion while discussing a patient with a character disorder. "The question arises whether the patient's impaired sense of identity in reality might stem from his mother's unreal attitude. Did they [the mechanisms used] serve him as a means of 'fading into' the false picture of the severely disturbed family situation which the mother had tried to maintain?" Lomas (1962) elaborates this point in another discussion of a patient, also with a character disorder.

I wish to suggest that the original trauma to which such patients have been subjected can be usefully described as a failure on the part of the mother (or environment) to recognize and respond appropriately to the patient's real individuality—thus fostering a craving for recognition—and a seduction by the mother to satisfy that craving to a special and exclusive relationship with her in which he (the patient) feels valuable *only* because of this relationship. Thus, in his search for identity, he is dependent not on his capacity to form relationships, but on his capacity to form one particular relationship, and the quality which would lead him to have confidence in himself are not his real qualities but only those which happen to have importance in one person's eyes.

This special role is similar to the concept of the false self elaborated by Winnicott (1965).

I believe the cases presented here clearly illustrate this phenomena. Both boys were their mothers' sexual partners and felt that they had to maintain this position in order to have their needs gratified. Once this pattern has become fixed, the presence of the external object is no longer essential for the continuance of the behavior; he will play the role utilizing anyone else in the external environment.

The special role is well illustrated by each boy's behavior during his mother's visits. Each responded as if he was his mother's lover and played the part with facile skill. He fit right into what he perceived as his mother's expectations of him. The behavior of each boy after the visits demonstrates some of the consequences of this role adoption. Each boy was disruptively sexually stimulated but maintained his integration during the visit. When his mother left his behavior became markedly regressed and fragmented.

358

Each boy's ego was unable to integrate the intense affect-laden sexuality stimulated by the mother during her visit. Though the special role of "mother's little man" was the only way the young boy felt he could relate to his mother, the task of maintaining such a relationship in the face of overwhelming stimulation was too great for his poorly structured ego without his mother's actual presence. When the mother left and the relationship was temporarily discontinued signs of ego disintegration and fragmentation became manifest. The behavior of each boy showed signs of massive regression with some attempts at restitution. The restitutive mechanisms were primitive and only barely object related. In John's case the attempt at restitution was a masochistic involvement with older boys. His provocation of beatings represented partly an attempt to reassure himself of the possibility of control of his overwhelming rage at his mother. Stanley's homosexuality represented, in part, a flight from his fear of his mother—fear largely determined by his projected rage—as well as an attempt to maintain contact with external reality through intimate contact with an external object, thus affording a focus for external perception as a means for avoiding conscious, disturbing fantasy (Borowitz, 1967a).

The adoption of the special role presents multiple problems for the child. There is the child's fear that his mother will abandon him when he cannot fulfill what he believes are her expectations of him. Also, there is tremendous ambivalence, which may be manifested by feelings of power versus helplessness, heterosexuality versus homosexuality, activity versus passivity, and possessing versus being possessed.

Illustrative of this point of ambivalence is the story John told describing a picture he had drawn. The picture was of a caveman holding a club and a large bird with a huge wingspread. The bird was much larger than the man. John explained that "these are the last two creatures on earth. The bird is an ancient creature that eats flesh. Both are starving, one will have to kill the other in order to survive." John's associations made it obvious that he was the man and the bird was his mother. Rage, fear, and concern about object loss could not be more graphically illustrated.

Both these boys developed more positive attachments to men than to women. While at the school they evoked strong, positive, protective feelings in many of the men while generally the women hated them. In therapy the boys made their male therapists protectors against the perceived hostile, devouring women. Whenever either boy felt that any male had let him down, he reacted with violent and vehement rage. Gi-

359

telson (1958) suggested that, "The distorted oedipus complex is a psychological foothold which these patients strive to maintain as a defense against the regressive plunge by which they feel threatened." I would like to suggest that these patients, during crucial developmental phases, turned to their fathers to (1) be the person who could adequately satisfy their needs when they realized that their mothers could not, (2) protect them against their own overwhelming and devouring mothers, and (3) protect them against their own overwhelming and devouring rage at their mothers. Each boy conceptualized his father as a powerful, omnipotent, protecting object. The father, in reality, was unable to become involved and satisfied few of his child's direct needs. Because the child's expectation of his father as an omnipotent protecting object was unfulfilled, the child's disappointment led to intense rage. Studies of adult cases indicate that this mechanism is not uncommon. On the other hand, if a father has been able to provide gratification for some of the child's needs, the rage for not fulfilling megalomanic needs is frequently object related, one of the few object-related affects a child experiences. The relationship with the father was the source of many of the strengths of these boys.

Summary

A major factor leading to the development of character disorder is the result of the environment's inability to correctly perceive and gratify the child's phase-appropriate needs. The earlier any grossly inappropriate need gratification occurs the greater will be the degree and extent of ego distortion. If the amount of need gratification is only partial—a factor determined by the needs of the gratifying object, that is, the mother—the result can be a situation in which the mother and child develop a special and exclusive relationship that serves as the child's main mode of defense and adaptation. Once this relationship is internalized the child needs it, or one like it, to maintain himself. He resists any change in the relationship and he attempts to maintain it and/or to recreate such a relationship in each new setting with each new meaningful person. When the relationship is disrupted the child undergoes marked regression and fragmentation and utilizes more primitive global mechanisms of defense against his rage and fears of dissolution.

In the cases presented such an exclusive relationship with the mother was present. The most important interaction in each relationship, originally primarily determined by the mother's needs, was mutual sensual stimulation. The effect of sensual stimulation on the child depends on the timing, frequency, nature, extent, and content of the stimulation. The persistent early sensual stimulation led to premature and persistent patterning of dyssynchronous modes of sensual drives development and characterologic patterns of discharge. In the male, these distortions of perception and integration can lead the individual to structure his life so as to constantly experience situations in which he is highly excited but has limited capacities for mastery.

NOTE

1. These ideas were developed in a seminar with Dr. G. Lage and Dr. J. Loesch.

REFERENCES

Benedek, T. (1950). Adaptation to reality in early infancy. Psychoanalytic Quarterly, 7:200–214.
———. (1959). Parenthood as a developmental phase. Journal of the American Psychoanalytic Association, 7:389–417.
Benjamin, J. D. (1965). Developmental biology and psychoanalysis. In N. S. Greenfield and W. C. Lewis, eds., Psychoanalysis and Current Biological Thought. Madison: University of Wisconsin Press. Pp. 57–80.
Bergman, P., and Escalona, S. R. (1949). Unusual sensitivities in very young children. Psychoanalytic Study of the Child, 3/4:333–352.
Borowitz, G. H. (1967a). The capacity to masturbate alone in adolescence. Paper presented to the Society for Adolescent Psychiatry, Chicago, Illinois.
Boyer, L. B. (1956). On maternal overstimulation and ego defects. Psychoanalytic Study of the Child, 11:236–256.
Freud, S. (1900). The interpretation of dreams. Standard Edition. London: Hogarth Press, 1953. Vols. 4 and 5.
———. (1905). Three essays on the theory of sexuality. Standard Edition. London: Hogarth Press, 1953. Vol. 7, pp. 125–243.
———. (1918). History of an infantile neurosis. Standard Edition. London: Hogarth Press, 1955. Vol. 17, pp. 7–122.
———. (1940). An outline of psychoanalysis. Standard Edition. London: Hogarth Press, 1964. Vol. 23, pp. 141–208.
Giovacchini, P. L. (1964). The submerged ego. Journal of the American Academy of Child Psychiatry, 3:430–442.
——— (1965). Maternal introjection and ego defect. Journal of the American Academy of Child Psychiatry, 4:279–292.
Gitelson, M. (1958). On ego distortion. International Journal of Psycho-Analysis, 39:245–257.
Holt, R. R. (1965). A review of some of Freud's biological assumptions and their influence on his theories. In N. S. Greenfield and W. C. Lewis, eds., Psychoanalysis and Current Biological Thought. Madison: University of Wisconsin Press. Pp. 93–124.

Klein, G. S. (1970). Freud's two theories of sexuality. Paper presented to the Chicago Psychoanalytic Society, March 24.

Kramer, P. (1954). Early capacity for orgastic discharge and character formation. Psychoanalytic Study of the Child, 9:128–141.

Lomas, P. (1954). The concept of maternal love. Psychiatry, 25:256–262.

———. (1962). The origin of the need to be special. British Journal of Medical Psychology, 35:399–346.

Mahler, M. S. (1965). On the significance of the normal separation-individuation phase: With reference to research in symbiotic child psychosis. In M. Schur, ed., Drive, Affects, and Behavior. New York: International Universities Press. Vol. 2, pp. 161–169.

Piaget, J. (1954). The construction of reality in the child. New York: Basic Books.

Pine, F. (1970). On the structuralization of drive-defense relationships. Psychoanalytic Quarterly, 39:17–37.

Spitz, R. A. (1949). Autoerotism. Psychoanalytic Study of the Child, 3/4:85–120.

White, R. W. (1963). Ego and reality in psychoanalytic theory. Psychological Issues, 11:71–94.

Winnicott, D. W. (1955). Metaphysical and clinical aspects of regression within the psycho-analytical set up. International Journal of Psycho-Analysis, 36:16–26.

———. (1960). The theory of the parent-infant relationship. International Journal of Psycho-Analysis, 41:585–595.

——— (1965). Ego distortion in terms of true and false self. In The Maturational Processes and the Facilitating Environment. New York: International Universities Press. Pp. 140–157.

17] INTERACTIONS AMONG STIMULUS BARRIER, MATERNAL PROTECTIVE BARRIER, INNATE DRIVE TENSIONS, AND MATERNAL OVERSTIMULATION

L. BRYCE BOYER

It is assumed generally that there is a continuum of psychopathological states that spans from an hypothetical state of psychic health to one of total psychosis (Boyer and Giovacchini, 1967). The states that lie progressively nearer the psychotic pole of the continuum include the schizophrenias, schizoid states, and those conditions that have come recently to be included in the controversial diagnostic category, borderline states or conditions. In this chapter, states customarily designated by any of these three names will be referred to as schizophrenoid conditions.

The schizophrenoid conditions are considered generally to have more causative constitutional factors than those states that lie nearer psychic health, the neuroses. Modern studies have led to the conclusion that the role of genetic factors in the development of schizophrenic and schizoid conditions has been well established (Heston, 1970), and various observers have supposed that the same holds for the alleged borderline conditions (Rangell, 1955; Boyer, 1970), though the present diagnostic confusion obviates their study by geneticists. Psychoanalysts (Greenacre, 1952; Rascovsky, de Ferrer, Garma, de Mendes, Plata, Borrero, Rascovsky, Tomás, and Wencelbalt, 1960) and other observers have focussed attention on the constitutional effects of intrauterine experiences. The psychoanalysts have stressed that scientists of other disciplines must supply relevant data which can be but presumed by psychoanalytic theorizing.

Modern biologists maintain that the mutual influences of nature and nurture are so complex that any attempt to separate them into clearly delineated categories is fruitless (Dubos, 1968). This chapter deals with an example of the interactions between one constitutional factor, variability in the stimulus barrier and innate drive tensions, and early object relationships.

A general theory of the schizophrenoid conditions does not yet exist. Research proceeds from many viewpoints, including genetic, chemical, neurological, and psychological. The consensus is that there are probably inborn predispositions to mental illness that leave the infant ready to develop schizophrenoid conditions if requirements for emergence are present to some unknown critical degree. According to psychoanalytic thinking, such requirements lie ultimately in disordered relations between babies and their mothering figures. Psychoanalytic conceptualizations have resulted from reconstruction of continuous and precipitating causes of such psychopathological states from the case studies of infants, children, adolescents and adults, and extensive empirical longitudinal studies of normal and pathological personality development by many students, including Anna Freud (1965), Mahler and her coworker (Mahler, 1963, 1966; Mahler and Furer, 1960, 1963), Provence (1966), Ritvo and Solnit (1958), Spitz (1945, 1947, 1950, 1955, 1957), and Spitz and Wolf (1946).

The literature is replete with references to deleterious effects on children of parental neglect and rejection. However, it is clear that the situation is much more complex. Schizophrenics are not necessarily the product of unloving mothers (Searles, 1958, 1961). Though gross rejection may be a crucial factor in the development of some infantile psychoses, more subtle, continuous traumata are responsible to a great extent for the genesis of schizophrenoid states that flower later in life.

Because of incompleteness of myelinization and other factors that as yet are not sufficiently known to be clearly stated, the infant is born with a physical and physiological status that makes the perception of stimuli less efficient than subsequent growth will potentiate. Freud (1955) called the high perceptive threshold a stimulus barrier. He wrote "the mass of excitations coming up against it will take effect only on a reduced scale; towards that which is within, no protection against stimuli is possible." Concerning inner excitations, he continued, "There will be a tendency to treat them as though they were acting not from within but from without, in order for it to be possible to apply against them the defensive measures of the barrier against stimuli." He defined traumas as "such external excitations as are strong enough to break through the barrier against stimuli" and added "an external trauma will undoubtedly provoke a very extensive disturbance in the working of the energy against the new organism." That an accumulation of internal stimuli will similarly produce trauma is implicit. He wrote further "The flooding of the psychic apparatus with large masses of stimuli can no longer be prevented: to the contrary, another task presents itself—to bring the stimuli under control, to bind in the psyche the stimulus mass that has broken its way in, so as to bring about a discharge of it."

Following Freud (1961), neurosis is thought to result from a conflict between the ego and the id and psychosis from disturbances between the ego and its environment (Jacobson, 1967). Freud (1939) thought that the conflict with and subsequent break from reality could be traced either to features of reality itself or to increased drive pressure, and that an ego that reacted in such a manner to the rivalizing demands of id and reality on the ego must have been disturbed previously. Hartmann, Kris, and Loewenstein have assumed that such disturbances have the origins ultimately in the nature of the earliest mother-infant interactions and outlined possible steps in and requirements of the process of neutralization or binding of drives (Hartmann, 1939, 1950, 1952; Hartmann and Kris, 1945; Hartmann, Kris, and Loewenstein, 1946, 1949). Klein (1932, 1945, 1946, 1948, 1952, 1957) was particularly impressed with the importance of the aggressive drive in the development of ego disturbances. Hartmann (1953) suggested that a third possibility is that the ego's role as a mediator between the drives is impaired, stating "either the defensive counter-cathexis of the ego, or those ego functions that maintain contact with reality, may be incompletely developed or weakened. Thus, while a break with reality could ensue in all these situations, 'conflict with reality' can, as to its causative impact, only be evaluated in relating outer frustration not only to the instinctual, but also to the ego aspects of the situation." Thus, there is an increasing tendency to conflict, and the ego is unable to cope through its usual methods (Rapaport, 1967).

Bergman and Escalona (1949) described five children, four of whom had congenital abnormalities, who were markedly hypersensitive to external stimuli in the visual, auditory, gustatory, equilibratory, and temperature spheres. Their mothers strove to protect them from external excitations, assuming a role that Boyer (1956b) labeled the maternal protective barrier. Nevertheless, the children became psychotic. Bergman and Escalona suggested that "the infant who is not protected sufficiently from stimuli either because of a 'thin protective barrier' (the stimulus barrier), or because of the failure of maternal protection, may have to resort for such protection to premature formation of an ego. When this premature ego breaks down, possibly as a consequence of trauma, the psychotic mechanisms are thought to set in." Ego defects would result also if mothering care were inadequate to reduce satisfactorily internal stimuli in children with unusual drive potentials. The concept of maternal deprivation must be defined in terms that suit not only the great individual variability in the stimulus barriers of newborns but also of their differing levels of drive tension. Another possibility suggests itself: that the mothering figure may add excessive, traumatizing stimuli to the precarious balance, thus adding maternal overstimulation.

Spitz considered the stimulus barrier to serve as a model for certain ego functions as defenses, especially those patterned similar to repression. He wrote (Spitz, 1950), "But before that can come to pass, the threshold must be progressively reduced and finally disappear, to be replaced by ego functions." His observations of hospitalism (Spitz, 1945, 1947) can be interpreted to mean not only that the stimulus barrier begins to recede in its effectiveness during the third month of life but that inadequate maternal protection from injurious stimuli during the period when biological protection ebbs results in a lack of maturation and development.

In the schizophrenoid conditions, the ego's role as mediator between id and reality is impaired. The defensive countercathexes or those ego functions that maintain contact with reality are incompletely developed or weakened. What is most obviously deficient is the organized, integrated stability of the defenses as compared to what is found in normals and neurotics. Primitive defensive mechanisms are more characteristic, such as turning against the self, splitting, reversal into the opposite, and the detachment of libido. Such defenses do not involve large quantities of bound aggression in countercathexis (Hartmann, 1953). Unneutralized or deneutralized agression is used by the superego and either turned toward the individual or directed externally.

Defenses against potentially traumatic quantities of stimuli, whether of internal or external origin, develop in close interconnection with object relations. A circular dysfunction may exist in which a deficiency of the development of object relations and of defenses are mutually stultifying. More summarily stated, distorted object relations, adding to whatever constitutional factors may prevail, predispose to those ego defects found in the schizophrenoid conditions. A decisive factor on the side of the ego is the level of binding or neutralization. Differentiated object relations can no longer be maintained when dedifferentiation of the ego exists. Self-object and ego-id relations run parallel. Withdrawal of object cathexis leads to loosening of ties with reality (Freud, 1911, 1959). The dedifferentiation of reality testing may well be related to de-neutralization; cathexis of object representations as well as outer reality become distorted.

The development of object relations depends heavily on the capacity of the infant to perceive, make associations and to begin to think (Rapaport, 1951b). Despite the presence of the stimulus barrier, even the intrauterine baby is significantly influenced by external stimuli. Sontag and Wallace (1935) demonstrated that responsiveness to sound, whether perceived auditorily or somesthetically, begins during the thirty-first week of intrauterine life and increases as the fetus nears term. The fetus reacts to disturbances with the means at its disposal, such as sucking, swallowing, heartbeat, squirming and kicking. The emotional life of the mother affects the fetus. Her excitement is transmitted by known means: chemical, such as the effects of adrenaline, and physical, such as those of uterine contraction. The fetus' manifestations of discomfort that occur when the mother is near or engaged in a shouting argument may result from either chemical or physical means on the part of the mother of the baby's presumed auditory perceptive capacities. Infants are born at times with swollen thumbs (Greenacre, 1952) and newborns occasionally put their hands directly to their mouths. Is this the result of fortuitous contact which has then served some function? Has the fetus begun already the first steps of thinking? Greenacre (1952) postulates that the fetus may be evincing primordial anxiety. The importance of the relationship between the mothering figure and the infant in the complex process involved in introjection of mental representations and learning appears to be constant in many animal species. Two examples follow.

In birds and animals there appears to be an early specificity of cathexis associated with babies' observations of mothering figures with whom they have close relationships. The acquisition of song in the zebra finch is a case in point. Its learning is adapted to that species' social behavior in its naturally irregular breeding season.

Zebra finches not only get their "templates" very early but also terminate song development at only three months of age. They hear and acquire song elements before they begin singing, then fix sequence, length and rhythm while singing between their 40th and 80th days. They tend to imitate the song elements only of tutors with which they have a strong personal bond —and this is important, since the species breeds in mixed-species colonies (Smith, 1970).

Various investigators have suggested that infant mammals may learn specific skills, such as the acquisition of food, primarily from their mothers and from their elders. Recently Chesler (1969) has studied the phenomenon experimentally. She found that kittens that observed their mothers perform a stimulus-controlled response (lever pressing to a visual stimulus for food) acquired and discriminated that response sooner than kittens who observed a strange cat's performance, even though the kittens were on good terms with her. Kittens exposed to trial and error never learned the response. Initial differences in attentiveness to demonstrator performances disappeared by the second day. Food-sharing and other "altruistic" forms of social behavior were exhibited by both mother and stranger demonstrators.

Fascinating examples of interaction between human infants and their mothers illustrate that very young babies perceive, record however vaguely, physically or psychologically, and are influenced by maternal communications.

Escalona (1953) reported an instance in which an eager baby was unable to suck. His thoughtful mother cupped the infant's face in her hand, adapted herself to his breathing and took over the task of moving his jaws. After six weeks, this survival-supporting technique could be abandoned. In this case, we can assume that the continuing physical development of the infant was reinforced by the mother's assumption of a supplementary physical role. Whether learning played a role is moot but hypothetically possible.

Seitz (1950) reported the case of a girl of two and one-half years who pulled hair from her head and held it near her lips as she nursed from a bottle while held in her mother's arms. Such behavior had begun during rather strict toilet training at the age of eighteen months. She had been weaned before she was three weeks old. Seitz suspected that her mother's areolae were hirsute, which proved to be true. A nipple was constructed with human hairs projecting from its base. When the nipple and the hairs were brushed against her mouth, the girl stopped plucking her hair.

Freedman and his coworkers (Freedman, Fox-Kolenda, Margileth, and Miller, 1969) observed a congenitally blind infant of ten weeks who had learned to discriminate his mother's voice from all other stimuli.

When he was upset, only the sound of her voice would have a calming effect.

Fraiberg and Freedman (1964) reported the occurrence of a smiling response in a blind infant of five months. In contrast to the response described by Spitz and Wolf (1946), the smile was highly discriminatory and could be evoked only by the mother's voice and no other stimulus.

The importance of the nature of the nursing relationship is highlighted by Escalona's case. There, a delicate mutual interaction was required, mediated by bodily processes in mother and child. On the side of the baby must be considered the capacity of his regulatory mechanisms to cope with a myriad of stimuli that arise from inside his body or from the externum and the level of his relative sensitivities to those stimuli. Disturbing sensations from inside the body include those occasioned by gas bubbles, hunger pangs, respiratory difficulties, and bowel cramps. Active assistance is required from the mother in the alleviation of at least the first three discomforts, though after a few months, the infant will have developed the capacity to handle unaided, problems of eructation. On the side of the mothers again exists a wider range of variable behavior. Some will avoid supplying the baby with physical contact and others will be so unable to leave their infants alone that the infants will have difficulty in experiencing discomforts long enough to differentiate among them. The reasons for both types of maternal behavior and the varying intergradations are legion in the psychic structures of the mothers. When we recall only the countless degrees of skin sensitivity that exist among newborn infants, the potential problems of interactions and adjustments become readily apparent. The mother can control which kinds of infantile behavior she will accept and/or encourage. She will communicate her conscious and unconscious demands to the baby in many ways: through her muscular tensions, the qualities of her vocal utterances, the smoothness or jerkiness of her movements, her facial expressions, her overt or covert messages of approval or disapprobation. Among the child's first memory traces will be the communicated attitudes of the mother. Spitz and Wolf (1946) have indicated that muscular tensions and degrees of smoothness of motion of the mother will probably be more significant during the phase when the ego has not yet developed to the stage of the smiling response. We know from the examples cited by Seitz and Freedman and his colleagues that memory traces can be established firmly during the period when the stimulus barrier still plays a major physiological role.

The psychology of the mother maintains continuity, despite the advent of changes, throughout the life of the child. If she were unable to let the child perform acts for himself and if she repeatedly told him by actions or words when he was a toddler and older that his discomfort should be attributed to hunger or bowel fullness, regardless of its actual source, it is most likely that she was one of those who deprived him of infantile experiences that would permit him to make connections between disturbing stimuli and the means to alleviate them. Some adult patients who suffer from schizophrenoid conditions are unable to distinguish among the origins of various kinds of discomforts and seek to relieve them by inappropriate means. Some do not know whether they are hungry or cold or whether they are experiencing sexual excitement or excretory urgency (Bruch, 1959; Giovacchini, 1964). Patients with schizophrenoid conditions who could not distinguish between causes of discomfort have usually maintained that their mothers were most reluctant to let them make unassisted efforts to alleviate their distresses even when they were of grammar school age. It seems probable that such mothers interfered with their infants' development of the ability to connect discomforts with their origins.

Two women whose case fragments have been published serve as illustrations. One (Boyer, 1965a) responded at times to sexual stimulation that resulted from masturbation or intercourse with urination and thought she had never experienced orgasm though her descriptions of her sexual responses revealed them to have been orgastic. In one interview, she delightedly reported she had experienced her first orgasm. In fact, she had acute, severe cystitis. The other, Mrs. K. (Boyer, 1960) responded to hunger, cold, and even constipation with sexual excitement and desperately sought to relieve such discomforts through sexual intercourse. When the original distress was not alleviated through intercourse, her sexual behavior became more and more violent and at times she became panicky and regressed into transient, florid psychotic states.

Clearly, internal levels of stimuli and thresholds of perceptive sensibility in infants will interact in diverse ways with excitations from the environment. A child with a low threshold to perception who has an average inborn level of drive tension (Fries, 1944; Wolf, 1953) will perceive his mother's tensions more acutely through his various perceptors, be they tactile, auditory, visual, proprioceptive, or, at least theoretically, gustatory. Against visual stimuli he can shut his eyes. He lacks the means of diminishing the intensity of stimuli that impinge on his other receptors. If the mother fails to reduce the intensity of external stimuli, his levels of frustration will be heightened. The child born with an efficient stimulus barrier and average impulse tensions will be less perceptive to excitations, whether they arise from his interior or the externum. He will be able to tolerate relative neglect or rough handling. It would be redundant to elaborate further the possibilities. Even this imperfect description of means through which mothers can communicate their demands to even tiny infants suffices to indicate the complexities of what might be required for the baby to begin to develop the sense of basic trust to which Erikson refers (1950) and on which so much depends for the development of object relations and optimal ego differentiation.

Clinicians are able sometimes to guess what had transpired in the earliest mother-child interactions as a result of extrapolation backwards from the behavior of patients in treatment, through understanding the transferential meanings of all kinds of behavior. A case fragment of a schizophrenic woman has been presented previously (Boyer, 1956b). So far as could be determined, she was born with an average degree of sensitivity to stimuli. However, her mother was one of those who can not let their children learn to experience hunger and other such needs. It appeared also that the schizophrenic woman had been overstimulated continuously from birth onward in many ways. Of greatest importance was the impact of auditory stimuli. Studies of family interactions have revealed that parents' unconscious desires exert great influence on the personality development of children (Jackson, 1954; Johnson, 1953; Szurek, 1954). Continuing observational studies, combined with retrospective extrapolation from clinical phenomena and investigations of family interactions will eventually reduce the uncertainties of our understanding.

Let us recapitulate. The physical and physiological constitution of the newborn defends against the effects of excitations. He can be considered to have an inborn stimulus barrier. The range of the efficiency of the stimulus barrier is great, varying in gradations of effectiveness from infant to infant. At the same time, newborns have wide ranges of internal drive pressures. During the first months of extrauterine life, changes in the organic constitution of the infant reduce the efficiency of the stimulus barrier. Simultaneously, object relations with the mothering figure begin to develop. During this period, she can be thought of as serving the role of an external stimulus barrier, a maternal protective barrier. Ego differentiation proceeds in conjunction with and is shaped by object relations. Infants whose mothers fail to defend them against too-great sensory input or add to that input to a traumatic degree develop ego

371

weaknesses and the development of id and ego differentiation lags. We can use a mathematical analogy. Stimulus barrier plus maternal protective barrier plus optimally unfolding psyche produce normal psychological development. Ego development will be hampered if either the stimulus barrier or the maternal protective barrier is deficient or if the strength of the baby's drives is unusually increased. It follows that if the child has a normal stimulus barrier and average drive tensions, if the mother's behavior results in added traumatic sensory input, ego differentiation will be similarly hampered.

It appears to be established that there is an inherited genetic tendency toward the development of the schizophrenoid conditions and that emergence depends on the presence of variable undesirable socialization factors. We can, then, postulate that one of those factors may be the presence of an inadequate stimulus barrier, a deficient maternal protective barrier, maternal overstimulation, or any combination of the three. Theoretically, at least, if the infant's drive potential be unusually high, a less than optimal interaction between nature and nurture at this period of life will heighten the likelihood of emergence.

Though it is not the purpose of this essay to enter into a discussion of the relative theoretical merits of viewing these phenomena from an alternate standpoint, one should be indicated.

The formulations used in this communication follow from Freud's conceptualizing the relative incapacity of the newborn to perceive stimuli as a barrier against those stimuli. Spitz, who formerly had used Freud's formulation, wrote (1955): "The newborn is incapable of perceiving the outer world . . . the sensorium is not yet functioning, in terms of the dynamic viewpoint, the newborn has not yet cathected it . . . the stimulus barrier is not to be understood as an obstacle in the path of the reception of stimulation originating in the environment. It is to be understood as the uncathected condition of the sensorium."

Wangh (1955), in his discussion of Boyer (1956b), raised the question of whether conceptualization of the stimulus barrier is useful when we seek to formulate intrapsychic hypotheses. Following Spitz's suggestion, he asked whether we cannot assume that parallel with the gradual cathexis of the infant's sensorium, countercathexis, too, develops in the same way under normal circumstances, perhaps with a temporal lag. Viewed thus, we could think of a gradual transition from the uncathected to the cathected and then to the countercathected state of the sensorium. The mother who excessively stimulates her infant would be then considered to have interfered with the establishment of countercathexis. Hartmann (1953) said that countercathectic energy distributions are essential for the acceptance of external reality and that without them, the separation of inner and outer world cannot transpire. Wangh (1955) added the separation of self from not-self.

Spitz (1955) traced the common pathway of orality and the visual sensorium. Lewin (1946, 1948, 1950, 1953, 1953b, 1968) had deduced that if a regression occurs from the visual imagery level at which the dream functions, then there should be memory traces older than the pictures. Such memory traces have similarities to pure emotion and are made up of deeper tactile, thermal, and protopathic qualities which are in their way memory traces of early dim consciousness of the breast, the nursing experience, or the half-sleep state. Spitz considered that the regression of the dream screen goes to the mnemic traces laid down somewhere between the ages toward the end of the first half year and reaching to the end of the first year. He considered that in the Isakower (1938, 1954) phenomenon, the regression reaches traces of earlier experiences.

Spitz (1955) suggested that the sensations of three organs of perception—hand, labyrinth, and skin cover—unite with intraoral sensations to a unified situational experience in which no part is distinguishable from another. The example of Seitz (1950) appears to validate Spitz's suggestion of a common pathway between orality and the tactile sensory modality.

It is known that schizophrenics are frequently hypersensitive to auditory stimuli. In the case of the women reported previously (Boyer, 1956b), whose mother had overstimulated her in many ways but especially auditorily, there appeared to have been a common pathway between orality and the auditory sensorium. It is theoretically possible that common pathways exist between orality and other sensory modalities, though they may be difficult to validate.

Continuing to view these phenomena from the standpoint of countercathexis, let us now return to the examples of the common pathways of orality and the visual and auditory modalities. In defense against visual hyperstimulation, the baby's reflex eye closure will serve at first. Later, after some ego development has occurred, he will voluntarily close his eyes or avert his gaze. Such actions will suffice or reinforce countercathexis. In the case of auditory hyperstimulation, no such physical defenses exist, with the exception of such devices as ear plugs or deafness itself. We know that people who listen to very loud music develop progressive deafness, which may be transitory or permanent, as in the case of audiences of some kinds of modern music. Except for such deafness, which

373

could be thought of as a reinforcement of the stimulus barrier in Freud's sense, only countercathexis will serve as a defensive measure. To cite Wangh (1955): "Is it not possible that in the case of auditory overstimulation we need an extraordinary amount of countercathectic energy to avoid traumatization? The infant cannot plug its ears. Hence the great vulnerability of this perceptive route and therefore the frequent finding of auditory hypersensitivity of schizophrenics?"

In this chapter no attempt has been made to explain a phenomenon that is well known, namely that some children have deficiencies in some areas of ego functioning and precocities in others. If we seek to understand the origins of this discrepancy of levels of ego development and assume that they may be found also in the earliest months of life and to result from specific kinds of mother-infant interaction, it seems likely that the countercathectic hypothesis will be more useful than that of the stimulus barrier. However, I am unaware of any studies that have been directed to this point.

Conclusion

Constitutional factors are thought to be of importance in the development of the schizophrenoid conditions. Studies of heredity seem to indicate that there is a genetic tendency, at least in the schizophrenic and schizoid states. However, socialization factors can mitigate against or enhance the emergence of a tendency toward such disorders, whether it result from a genetic or from other constitutional factors. The infant is born with a physical status that makes perception of stimuli less efficient than it will later become. Freud thought of the high perceptive threshold as a stimulus barrier. As physical changes proceed during the first months of life, object relations develop. The primary figure of importance in this earliest phase of socialization is the mothering figure. Before the nursling can adequately perceive or defend himself against excessive excitation, the ideal mother serves as a supplementary protective barrier against traumatic external and internal stimuli. Infants whose maternal protective barriers are deficient develop ego weaknesses and inadequate differentiation of ego and id. If the stimulus barrier or the material protective barrier be deficient or the drive strength of the child be stronger than usual, disturbances in ego development result. It follows that if the stimulus barrier and the drive strength fall within the

374

average range and the mother hyperstimulates the child to a traumatizing degree, ego development might be abnormal.

One necessary factor for the emergence of the schizophrenoid conditions, given a genetic tendency, would be an unfavorable interaction of nature and nurture during this earliest period of socialization. Inadequate complementarity of the above-mentioned elements may constitute such an unfavorable interaction between the infant's constitution and his environment.

Attention is called to an alternative viewpoint. Spitz views the deficiency of perceptive sensibility of the newborn as the uncathected condition of the sensorium rather than as an obstacle in the path of the reception of stimuli originating in the environment. Wangh has raised the question of whether Freud's conceptualization of the stimulus barrier is useful when we seek to formulate intrapsychic hypotheses. Viewed thus, we could think of a gradual transition from the uncathected to the cathected and then to the countercathected state of the sensorium. Unsuitable care by the mother would then be seen as hampering the development of the capacity to countercathect.

REFERENCES

Bergman, P., and Escalona, S. (1949). Unusual sensitivities in very young children. Psychoanalytic Study of the Child, 3/4:333–352.
Boyer, L. B. (1956a). "Ambulatory schizophrenia": Some remarks concerning the diagnosis. Kaiser Foundation Medical Bulletin, 4:457–459.
———. (1956b). On maternal overstimulation and ego defects. Psychoanalytic Study of the Child, 11:236–256.
———. (1960). A hypothesis concerning the time of appearance of the dream screen. International Journal of Psycho-Analysis, 41:114–122.
———. (1970). Borderline states: A review of the concept and its applications. Report of the Proceedings of the Fall Symposium, 1968, of the San Francisco Psychoanalytic Institute Extension Division.
———, Giovacchini, P. L. (1967). Psychoanalytic treatment of schizophrenic and characterological disorders. New York: Science House.
Bruch, H. (1959). Studies in schizophrenia. Acta Psychiatrica Neurologica Scandinavia, 34: suppl. 130.
Bruch, H. (n.d.). Falsification of bodily needs and body concept. Proceedings of the Third World Congress of Psychiatry, pp. 1117–1120.
Chesler, P. (1969). Maternal influence in learning by observation in kittens. Science, 168:901–903.
Dubos, R. (1968). So Human an Animal. New York: Scribners.
Erikson, E. H. (1950). Childhood and Society. New York: Norton.
Escalona, S. (1953). Emotional development in the first year of life. In M. J. E. Senn, ed., Problems of Infancy and Childhood. New York: Josiah Macy, Jr., Foundation.

375

Fraiberg, S., and Freedman, D. A. (1964). Studies in the ego development of the congenitally blind child. Psychoanalytic Study of the Child, 19:113–169.

Freedman, D. A., Fox-Kolenda, B. J., Margileth, D. A., and Miller, D. H. (1969). The development of the use of sound as a guide to affective and cognitive behavior—A two-phase process. Child Development, 40:1099–1105.

Freud, Anna (1965). Normality and pathology in childhood. New York: International Universities Press.

Freud, S. (1911). Psychoanalytical notes on the autobiographical account of a case of paranoia (Dementia Paranoides). Standard Edition. London: Hogarth Press, 1958. Vol. 12.

———. (1914). On narcissism: an introduction. Standard Edition. London: Hogarth Press, 1957. Vol. 14.

———. (1920). Beyond the pleasure principle. Standard Edition. London: Hogarth Press, 1955. Vol. 18.

———. (1924). The loss of reality in neurosis and psychosis. Standard Edition. London: Hogarth Press, 1961. Vol. 19.

Freud, Sigmund (1939). An outline of psychoanalysis. New York: Norton.

Fries, Margaret E. (1944). Some basic differences in newborn infants during the lying-in period. Teaching film with guide. New York University Film Library.

Giovacchini, P. L. (1964). The submerged ego. Journal of the Academy for Child Psychology, 13 (no. 3):430–442.

———. (1953). Contribution to the metapsychology of schizophrenia. Psychoanalytic Study of the Child, 8:177–198.

———, and Kris, E. (1945). The genetic approach in psychoanalysis. Psychoanalytic Study of the Child, 1:11–30.

———, Kris, E., and Loewenstein, R. M. (1946). Comments on the formation of psychic structure. Psychoanalytic Study of the Child, 2:11–38.

———, Kris E., and Loewenstein, R. M. (1949). Notes on the theory of aggression. Psychoanalytic Study of the Child, 3/4:9–36.

Greenacre, P. (1941). The predisposition to anxiety. In Trauma, Growth and Personality. New York: Norton. Chap. 2.

Hartmann, H. (1939). Ich-Psychologie und Anpassungsproblem. Int. Ztschr. Psa. & Imago, 24. Organization and Pathology of Thought. (Translated in part in D. Rapaport, ed., New York: Columbia University Press, 1951.)

———. (1950). Psychoanalysis and developmental psychology. Psychoanalytic Study of the Child, 5:7–17.

———. (1952). The mutual influences in the development of ego and id. Psychoanalytic Study of the Child, 7:9–30.

Heston, L. L. (1970). The genetics of schizophrenia and schizoid disease. Science, 167:249–256.

Isakower, O. (1938). A contribution to the psychopathology of phenomena associated with falling asleep. International Journal of Psycho-Analysis, 19:331–345.

———. (1954). Spoken words in dreams. Psychoanalytic Quarterly, 23:1–6.

Jackson, D. D. (1954). Some factors influencing the oedipus complex. Psychoanalytic Quarterly, 23:566–581.

Jacobson, E. (1967). Psychotic thought and reality. New York: International Universities Press.

Johnson, A. M. (1953). Factors in the etiology of fixations and symptom choice. Psychoanalytic Quarterly, 22:475–496.

Klein, M. (1932). The Psycho-analysis of children. London: Hogarth Press.

———. (1945). The oedipus complex in the light of early Anxieties. In Contributions to Psycho-analysis. London: Hogarth Press, 1950.

———. (1946). Notes on some schizoid mechanisms. International Journal of Psycho-Analysis, Vol. 27.

———. (1948). On the theory of anxiety and guilt. International Journal of Psycho-Analysis, 29:114–123.

————. (1952). Some theoretical conclusions regarding the emotional life of the infant. In J. Riviers, ed., Developments in Psycho-Analysis. London: Hogarth Press.

————. (1957). Envy and gratitude: A study of unconscious sources. New York: Basic Books.

Lewin, B. D. (1946). Sleep, the mouth and the dream screen. Psychoanalytic Quarterly, 15:419–434.

————. (1948). Inferences from the dream screen. International Journal of Psycho-Analysis, 29:224–231.

————. (1950). The Psychoanalysis of elation. New York: Norton.

————. (1953). The forgetting of dreams. In R. M. Loewenstein, ed., Drives, Affects, Behavior. New York: International Universities Press.

————. (1953b). Reconsideration of the dream screen. Psychoanalytic Quarterly, 22:174–199.

————. (1968). The image and the past. New York: International Universities Press.

Mahler, M. S. (1963). Thoughts about development and individuation. Psychoanalytic Study of the Child, 18:307–324.

————. (1966). Notes on the development of basic moods. The depressive affect. In R. M. Loewenstein, L. M. Newman, M. Schur, and A. J. Solnit, eds., Psychoanalysis —A General Psychology: Essays in Honor of Heinz Hartmann. New York: International Universities Press. Pp. 152–168.

————, and Furer, M. (1960). Observations on research regarding the "symbiotic syndrome." Psychoanalytic Quarterly, 29:317–327.

————, and Furer, M. (1963). Certain aspects of the separation-individuation phase. Psychoanalytic Quarterly, 32:1–14.

Provence, S. (1966). Some aspects of early ego development: Data from a longitudinal study. In R. M. Loewenstein, L. M. Newman, M. Schur, and A. J. Solnit, eds., Psychoanalysis—A General Psychology: Essays in Honor of Heinz Hartmann. New York: International Universities Press. Pp. 107–122.

Rangell, L. (1955). The borderline case. Panel of the American Psychoanalytic Association, St. Louis, May 1954. Journal of the American Psychoanalytic Association, 3:285–298.

Rapaport, D. (1967). The conceptual model of psychoanalysis. Collected papers of David Rapaport, pp. 405–431. New York: Basic Books.

Rapaport, D. ed. (1951). Organization and pathology of thought. New York: Columbia University Press.

Rascovsky, A. de Ferrer, S. L. Garma, A., de Mendes, S. A., Plata, C. M., Borrero, H. P., de Rascovsky, M. I. W., Tomás, J., and Wencelblat, S. (1960). El psiquismo fetal: Investigationes psicoanalíticas sobre el desenvolvimiento primitivo del individuo. Bueonos Aires: Editorial Paidos.

Ritvo, S. and Solnit, A. J. (1958). Influence of early mother-child interaction on identification processes. Psychoanalytic Study of the Child, 13:64–85.

Searles, H. F. (1958). Positive feelings in the relationship between the schizophrenic and his mother. International Journal of Psycho-Analysis, 39:569–586.

————. (1961). The evolution of the mother transference in psychotherapy with the schizophrenic. In A. Burton, ed., Psychotherapy of the Psychoses. New York: Basic Books. Pp. 256–284.

Seitz, P. F. D. (1950). Psychocutaneous conditioning during the first two weeks of life. Psychosomatic Medicine, 12.

Smith, W. J. (1970). The acquisition and functions of vocal behavior: A review of R. A. Hinde, ed., Bird vocalizations, their relations to current problems in biology and psychology: Essays presented to W. H. Thorpe. Science, 167:39–41.

Sontag, L. W., and Wallace, R. F. (1935). The response of the human foetus to sound stimuli. Child Development, 6:253–258.

Spitz, R. A. (1945). Hospitalism: An inquiry into the genesis of psychiatric conditions in early childhood. Psychoanalytic Study of the Child, 1:53–74.

————. (1947). Hospitalism: A follow-up report. Psychoanalytic Study of the Child, 2:113–117.

————. (1950). Anxiety in infancy: A study of its manifestations in the first year of life. International Journal of Psycho-Analysis, 31:138–143.

————. (1955). The primal cavity: A contribution to the genesis of perception and its role for psychoanalytic theory. Psychoanalytic Study of the Child, 10:215–240.

————. (1957). No and yes: On the genesis of human communication. New York: International Universities Press.

————, and Wolf, K. M. (1946). The smiling response: A contribution to the ontogenesis of social relations. Genetic Psychological Monographs, 34:57–125.

Szurek, S. (1954). Concerning the sexual disorders of parents and their children. Journal of Nervous and Mental Disease, 120.

Wolf, K. M. (1953). Observations of individual tendencies in the first year of life. In M. J. E. Senn, ed., Problems of Infancy and Childhood. New York: Josiah Macy, Jr., Foundation.

Wangh, (1955). Discussion of L. B. Boyer, "On maternal overstimulation and ego defects." Paper presented to the Fall Meeting of the American Psychoanalytic Association, New York, N.Y.

18] MATERNAL CONTROL, SUPEREGO FORMATION, AND IDENTITY

GILBERT J. ROSE

Narcissistic identity disorders are conditions in which the sense of identity depends on the persistence of unconscious fantasies of fusion with objects (Rose, 1966). These individuals are preoedipally fixated and have hazy boundaries between self and object representations within the ego (Jacobson, 1964). They may conceive of themselves as phallic extensions, anal products, breasts, or mouths, and the view of the world may bear corresponding part-object imprints; sense of self and of reality may be proportionately impaired. The extent to which they use external objects and reality for ego and superego functions may be one indicator as to whether they are primarily neurotic or psychotic.

In the following case mother substituted in part for the patient's own superego structure. Mother's superego was such that it did not grant the patient's reality testing equipment full permission to operate apart from mother's values. Mother's approval or disapproval could confer or deny recognition of something's existence and, therefore, of its reality.[1] Some of the effects of this on the patient's ego functioning, character development, and sense of identity are traced.

Case Report

Ariel was an attractive but carelessly groomed art student in her early twenties. Her manner conveyed something tentative, unsubstantial, and vaguely bewildered. The fleeting expressiveness of her face, as well as her tip-toeing gait, made her seem like a young Alice lost in a wonderland. She sought treatment because, just as her formal training was approaching its completion she developed a work inhibition. She had black depressions, often felt suicidal, and could sleep for sixteen hours.

"Mommy" knew better than anyone, including Ariel, what Ariel was going through. She had never kept secrets from mother, yet she would often follow mother around tearfully beseeching, "Why won't you believe me?" Sometimes she had the feeling of mother looking over her shoulder, and Ariel would deliberately try to hate mother or pick a fight to hold her off, or she would try to make her mind blank so mother would not be able to read it. In childhood, Ariel had invented code words and a secret language to refer to the things that frightened her; if mother would guess correctly, Ariel would panic. She would jump "in pain" if mother did her hair, but could tolerate others doing it. If a comment were made that came too close for comfort, Ariel would cough; laughing or retching would be further degrees of holding something at a distance. Compulsive yawning was a way of expressing the wish for greater closeness.

Ariel was closer to her mother than to anyone. She had the same feelings that mother had, and would feel responsible if mother had pain. Mother would tell Ariel what Ariel was really thinking and what Ariel really meant and felt. When mother said, "You don't want to," it meant "You can't." Thus when Ariel did not want to do something she acted as if she could not, and when she did want to do something she felt and often acted as if she must, and immediately. This could become elaborated into a paralyzing degree of procrastination or an alarming impulsivity. For example, the feeling of "I don't want to," would be expressed as "I cannot do it on time." Often, too, when Ariel became interested in something, mother would become depressed and would tell Ariel how immature she was. This could make Ariel go to sleep for sixteen hours.

Where a perception led to the awareness of something mother considered negative, the perception would be repressed and reality denied. For example, Ariel thought she saw misery, hatred, and dishonesty in the world, but mother said this was being negative. When the new car would not start in the morning, mother dismissed as beneath discussion Ariel's pointing to the corroded battery terminals to suggest that the local mechanic might have substituted an old battery for the new one.

Mother systematically erased clues to external reality to keep Ariel bound to her. She refused to have the speedometer of the car or the gas gauge fixed; thus, the gas gauge and the speedometer always registered zero. Not being able to rely on these customary instruments, Ariel had to discover other visual or auditory cues to estimate the car's speed and whether the tank needed gas: A special vibration told her the gas level was within five miles of being empty.

A dream indicated to what extent mother could dominate Ariel's perception: "There was an eerie, blue, beautiful but threatening luminescence over the landscape at night. It was vast, cold and distant. When mother looked out to see this light on the horizon, she said it must be wrong and not real, and to put it out. When she said that, it became pitch black again and I lost the desire to look because she made me feel it was awfully evil." There could be light only to the extent that mother controlled the switch.

An important part of mother's superego must have included an ego ideal striving to be a male. From the beginning, mother had wanted Ariel to be the boy she herself had wanted to be, dressed her as one, and told her she was like mother's own dead brother. Before the age of two, Ariel developed an infection of the external genitalia. On medical advice the inflamed and adherent labia would be repeatedly separated and hot compresses applied. Perhaps not surprisingly, Ariel in adolescence developed the secret delusion of not having a vagina. This undoubtedly accorded with mother's own ego ideal and one might speculate further that Ariel unconsciously represented, for the mother, the wished-for phallus.

In any event, there was an urgent need for forms, in the sense of formative experience, to reinforce ego boundaries and mold reality into systematic experience. These forms and the experience they shaped would have to be consonant with her psychological existence as a creature of mother's mind. Psychopathology provided such neurotic forms; tastes and sublimations provided normal and socially valuable ones.

One of the most generalized forms was that of deaggressivizing and desexualizing fantasy. In adolescence, Ariel had experienced a mystical, ecstatic illumination after reading Thomas Mann's Dr. Faustus. Her love affair with the hero, the gifted but insane musician, Adrian Leverkühn, obsessed her. Almost everything came to her filtered through it, and it condensed much of her sexual and aggressive impulses into sadomasochistic themes. The obsession channeled and focused her life and provided a defense against unneutralized aggression and sexuality. Without such a fanatical obsession she said she felt gelatinous, like a jellyfish.

Fantasies not only channelized feeling, they also provided a passport

381

to reality. Whatever could not be embroidered into a fantasy with self-reference, simply did not exist for her; reality could be accorded recognition only via a personal fantasy. Thus, fantasy acted as a connection to reality but also as a buffer from it. Any strong direct impingement of stimulation might be experienced as a sexualized assault which she feared might destroy her. This included the morning sunlight from which she would attempt to escape through sleeping until well into the afternoon. Various qualities of light stimulated her sexually. She would try to transform it into an aesthetic response, diffuse it over the whole inanimate world, and fragment it into fantasies lest her feelings become so strong that she might not be able to stop them and remain forever in an orgastic trance-like state.

Sexual and aggressive instincts that could not be managed by desexualizing and deaggressivizing fantasy could be projected in the form of paranoid fears and avoided or counterphobically confronted. These phobic externalizations of instinct also helped protect fragile ego boundaries from dissolving into fantasies of fusing with her surroundings. For example, without phobias to keep people at a distance she felt in danger of becoming the passive instrument of their wishes, unable to resist them. Ariel was compulsively permissive and hyperempathic. If she hit her sister, she would weep; if she stepped on someone else's toes, she would herself say "ouch." If she had an intense conversation with a friend and then looked into the mirror she would be surprised to see her own face instead of her friend's.

Her fears protected her somewhat from dangerous action by keeping her at a distance from people. But counterphobic acting out would also erupt. Sometimes she would wander off in the early morning hours and strike up conversations with strange men. Her air of unearthly innocence disarmed them of sexual and hostile intent, and she was able to reduce them to tearful confessions of their own unhappiness. Her conviction that artificial divisions between people must be abolished led to a small amount of pleasureless sexual acting out.

The urge to return to some undifferentiated state of fusion was rationalized into various sociopolitical convictions with a sadomasochistic coloration. The chief of these was the civil rights movement. She left treatment for several months and worked in this cause at considerable sacrifice. She felt almost constant fear, but was able to act with courage and even heroism as long as she felt she was contributing to a real reconciliation between polarities. The intact part of her sense of reality showed her in time that there were many villains on both sides of the

382

civil rights struggle. This insight, born of hard first-hand experience, prevented her from further projecting sadomasochism in this framework.[2] It was reintrojected and she returned to treatment disillusioned and depressed. The last dream before she left treatment had to do with a perilous flight and rescue with mother and baby sister, a theme suggestive of a birth fantasy. In the light of this it is interesting that she returned to treatment nine months and six days from the time she had first come into treatment (Rose, 1969b).

Some of Ariel's tastes and sublimations helped provide external form for feelings. When her ego boundaries felt particularly fragile, she would make an effort to walk stiffly, comb her hair straight, keep her throat tight, and adopt an aloof manner and an implacable expression. She loved winter because its strong, clearly outlined forms of snow and ice seemed to provide structure and thus be full of life. Contrary to the usual connotation, spring represented death because melting and rooting led to the loss of rigid forms.[3] Her preference in music depended on the current state of fragility of her ego boundaries. When she felt reasonably secure she could enjoy classical music because it offered a wide range of possibilities for her to let herself feel. At such times, rock 'n roll was merely a bore. On the other hand, when she was upset she would use rock 'n roll as a tranquilizer. She said it "centered" her. Its very predictability and repetitiveness seemed to signify reliability, consistency, security, like the sound of a radio compass to a pilot in the fog. When she was especially upset she would keep rock 'n roll on constantly. It suggested to me that she let herself be enveloped within its embrace like that of the good mother whose verbal language is not yet understood, but whose unchanging formal characteristics are recognized and trusted. It may also be that its noisiness helped create new anticathectic barriers adding to the differentiation of self from not-self.

Picture-drawing was Ariel's most highly developed skill. When she drew she felt "most really real." Her first serious drawing, like so much of her activity, was oriented toward mother. It was an act of love and an attempt at apology and reconciliation. Aside from their content meanings, Ariel's drawings also had an important formal meaning: They represented the packaging of an intense emotion into an aesthetic form.

When Ariel suddenly took a massive dose of LSD, all the various forms that helped to constitute her reality in accordance with mother's requirements were fragmented or destroyed. She was flooded with repressed libidinal stimulation, and her integrative and reality-testing functions were swept up in a regressive tide. At first she felt she had been reborn, seeing the world without the protective filters and restrictive blinders of obsessive fantasies and paranoid fears. The world seemed new with fresh and luminous color, and she was aware of a wide range of libidinal and aggressive feelings. She felt freed and euphorically eager to sample the world that had magically been opened to her in this LSD "cure."

But every night for months the LSD psychosis returned and brought recurrent terror. She would feel sexually aroused and would masturbate, but the excitement would not subside. She was terrified to fall asleep and further lower the defenses of consciousness. Chronic sleeplessness increased her anxiety and fear of falling asleep, lest the LSD experience persist and she lose her mind permanently. Though she feared it, it never recurred during daylight or without prior masturbation.

Ariel would never lose the awareness that what she was experiencing were the illusions and hallucinations of a waking dream. She could not be sure whether she was touching herself or being touched. Objects appeared variable and imbued with shifting and fluid qualities. At the same time she knew them to be real and solid. These states could alternate or oscillate rapidly with normal perception.

The nocturnally recurring LSD psychosis was characterized by an instinctualization of perception. All orifices appeared vaginal and undulating; all projections were phallic. While lying awake she would see vivid sexual images of gigantic genitalia of both sexes, sometimes condensed into a bisexual symbol like a crocodile. Oral features, such as cannibalistic biting, sucking, or being devoured, would be prominent. Size, shape, and distance had no reliability. Forms fell apart. As the elements of a visual *Gestalt* would disintegrate into sexual fragments, these appeared to fuse and copulate with one another.

These abnormal perceptions served multiple functions, defensive and self-punitive; they may have also represented partial reactivations of the infantile traumata of having her adherent labia repeatedly separated and hot compresses applied to the genitalia. Aside from such content meanings, they represented the toxic dissolution of relatively autonomous forms of perception.

In an effort to protect herself from the intense anxiety of these experiences, she developed vivid fantasies of fusing with her surroundings. She imagined she was part of the walls and of everything else, and she would hallucinate these fusions taking place. The hallucinations would add to her terror but would also reassure her. She explained that if ev-

384

erything were really herself, she could, by fusing with it, control the amount of hurt she administered or received. Merging with the walls was thus an attempt to defend herself against the massive aggressivization and sexualization of her visual field. The aggressivization paralleled the fragmentation of percepts, and the sexualization, in the form of seeming copulation, paralleled the refusion of the fragments.

Ariel believed that, if she invested herself in everything, she had control and need not be afraid of assaulting and being assaulted. Real meant separate, and this meant loss of control. Therefore, she had to obliterate any distance or separation from herself, sacrifice reality, and retreat to the preobject forms of narcissistic fusion.

In Ariel's treatment the interpretive work was, of course, important. It is more important to emphasize, however, that the quality of the treatment relationship was essential. It was this primarily that enabled her to get through the difficult period of recurrent LSD psychosis without the aid of drugs or hospitalization.

The spirit of treatment was to see her as a person who had not been experienced as a whole person by her parents and thus had not experienced her own identity and that of others. The therapeutic alliance offered more realistic superego standards than mother's and directly confronted and opposed pathogenic superego elements. Mother's superego had withheld permission to recognize the hostile and sexual aspects of reality as well as her own female identity. Without mother's imprimatur, Ariel's sexual identity had not been accorded the sanction of being real, and her drives were largely split off and always threatening to destroy the tenuous differentiation from mother and the world.

In treatment, on the other hand, the right to exist extended to all thoughts and feelings; superego criticism would not destroy the recognition of their reality. The doctor-patient relationship could sustain mutual criticism and affection. Criticism of her destructive acting out did not impugn her integrity or compromise her right to her own behavior within the law. All of this helped to free her reality-testing from the restrictions imposed on it by her mother's superego distortions. Humor (Rose, 1969a) helped to usher thoughts and feelings into awareness and moderate self-criticism; it helped to maintain the affective tone of the treatment at an optimal balance between distance and closeness. It neither merged into hyperempathy nor became isolated by excessive aloofness.[4]

As Ariel became more tolerant of her thoughts and feelings, her actual behavior became less lax. She learned that disapproval and affection could coexist and that reality continued apart from either one. Because she could have both an affective relationship and reliable ties to reality in the treatment relationship, perhaps she could exist in reality with or without her mother's approval. She might not have to exist apart from reality or fused to mother, attempting to recapture the form of a narcissistically "perfect" earlier union.

In one of her final sessions she recalled that as a little girl she had walked unsteadily for years. It had been only after mother finally consented to Ariel's demands to be dressed in girl's clothes that Ariel suddenly began to walk steadily. Having won from mother some grudging recognition, if not approval, of her sexual identity, she could assume some greater bodily and psychological separateness from mother. She left treatment knowing that there was much growth to be accomplished but that, being less one with mother, she was herself more real, as was the ground she walked on; it might perhaps be relied on to support the growing weight of her own identity.

Summary

Patients with disorders of narcissistic identity depend for their sense of identity on the persistence of unconscious fantasies of fusion with objects and have various body-ego deformations. Some, in addition, make use of external objects and reality to substitute or reinforce their own psychic structure. A case is described in which the mother represented the patient's superego. This helped achieve drive control, but superego distortions undermined ego functioning, especially the perception of reality. The perception of reality came to be molded as well as reflected by the various forms which her psychopathology provided: fantasies, phobias, and counterphobic acting out. An LSD episode was followed by months of recurrent, nocturnal states of perceptual regression. Superego elements in the therapeutic relationship were especially helpful in freeing reality-testing from restrictions imposed upon it by mother's superego. This resulted in improvement of ego functioning and strengthening of the sense of identity.

NOTES

1. See Stein (1966): "The superego not only affects the sense of reality; it plays an essential role in giving permission to know."
2. Later she was able to remark with characteristic humor that if treatment changed her from being an ardent political integrationist to an arch segregationist, the cure might be worse than the disease.
3. "April's the cruellest month, breeding
    Lilacs out of the dead land, mixing
    Memory and desire, stirring
    Dull roots with spring rain.
    Winter kept us warm, covering
    Earth in forgetful snow, feeding
    A little life with dried tubers" (Eliot, 1930).
4. "But let there be spaces in your togetherness,
    And let the winds of the heavens dance between you" (Gibran, 1923).

REFERENCES

Eliot, T. S. (1930). The burial of the dead. In Collected poems. New York: Harcourt, Brace. P. 69.
Gibran, K. (1923). The Prophet. New York: Knopf. Pp. 19–20.
Jacobson, E. (1964). The self and the object world. New York: International Universities Press.
Rose, G. J. (1966). Body-ego and reality. International Journal of Psycho-Analysis, 47:501–509.
———. (1969a). "King Lear" and the use of humor in treatment. Journal of the American Psychoanalytic Association, p. 3.
———. (1969b). Transference birth fantasies and narcissism. Journal of the American Psychoanalytic Association, p. 4.
Stein, M. H. (1966). Self-observation, reality, and the superego. In Psychoanalysis—A General Psychology, New York: International Universities Press. P. 290.

19] SOME PSYCHIC DETERMINANTS

OF ORGASTIC DYSFUNCTION

PAUL H. TOLPIN

This chapter is an investigation of the development of what are considered to be two related types of orgastic pathology occurring in the same patient. The first, which I have called aberrant orgasm, was an orgastic discharge occurring in situations of intense anxiety; it began in latency and continued in a modified form into the patient's adult life. The second began in adolescence and was a severe form of premature ejaculation, *ejaculatio praecox ante portes*. For a time the two types coexisted, each initiated by its own unique emotional circumstances, though from the empirical data it was thought that the former influenced the development of the latter and that both arose from common characterological defects. However, the purpose of this essay is not simply to describe an unusual clinical entity or its pathological variations, but, rather, to present the formulations arrived at concerning the development, psychological organization, and mechanisms of that entity in order to point up what is considered to be a useful direction of thought regarding the understanding of the pathology of premature ejaculation in a way that has not been emphasized before.

An examination of the literature on premature ejaculation reveals that most of the formulations about the disorder have been conceptualized according to the classical model of symptom formation, the symptom developing as a result of the operation of transferences across a repression barrier; that is, the disorder has been considered to be the result of a dynamic structural conflict arising within the framework of a relatively well-organized, well-developed psychic apparatus with an ego

This essay was presented to the Chicago Psychoanalytic Society in October 1969.

capable of complex defensive actions and compromise formations. Implicit in these formulations is the use of the tripartite, structural model of the mind presented by Freud in "The Ego and the Id" (1923).

The disorder in its various manifestations did not appear to be primarily the result of classical transference phenomena or of defensive activities of the psychic apparatus in the usual sense; rather, it appeared to be the consequence of a relative weakness of the psychic apparatus owing to the inadequate development of certain of its regulatory structures and buffering functions so that it was incapable under certain circumstances of effecting adequate absorption, control, or discharge of intense degrees of drive, or of affect, or of the more primitive, somatized anxiety that accompanied the experiencing of such tensions. A model of the mind that was useful in understanding the conceptualizations to be presented here is one that, though implicit in Freud's structural model, has recently been made more explicit by Heinz Kohut (1961) and by Kohut and Seitz (1963). This model points out particularly a functional sector of the mind, the "area of progressive neutralization," in addition to the more usually described functional area of transferences. It is the maldevelopment and malfunctioning of this former area (of progressive neutralization) which is considered to be critical in the types of orgastic disorder to be presented here. From a clinical standpoint, the inadequate development of this area of progressive neutralization results in states of imbalance of drive and defense against drive which may be experienced or manifested as instinctual anxiety, phobias of the preoedipal type, hypochondriasis, some kinds of psychosomatic disorders, and so on. This is in contrast to the consequences of structural conflict of the transference neurotic type in which classical symptom formation or defensive inhibition occurs.

The clinical material on which this chapter is based is largely derived from the over ten years, on the average, once-a-week psychoanalytically oriented psychotherapy of one patient.[1] As mentioned, the sexual disorder that will be the main difficulty focused on here began when he was eight years old as aberrant orgasm; a closely related symptom, an extreme form of premature ejaculation (*ejaculatio praecox ante portes*), had its onset in his later adolescent years with the beginning of heterosexual erotic activities and continued relatively unabated during some seven years of treatment until the day he was married. At that time that symptom ended abruptly and never recurred. The related symptom, aberrant orgasm, which, as mentioned, antedated the later ejaculatory disturbance, persisted for a longer period of time, though in a modified form in dreams; however, it decreased greatly in frequency of occurrence.

The patient, seventeen years old when treatment began, was about to graduate from high school and was suffering from the exacerbation of yet another, apparently unrelated symptom, vomiting and fear of vomiting, for which he sought psychiatric help. He had had this symptom recurrently from the time he was four years old. As he recalled it, the vomiting symptom began one night when his parents were about to leave for the movies and he was to remain at home with his four-year-older sister, and his grandparents with whom the family lived. He became terribly upset at the idea of his parents going out together without him and he began to carry on, screaming and rushing to the door to prevent their departure until finally he had to be restrained by his grandfather. The tantrum continued for about an hour after his parents were gone. It ended abruptly when in the midst of his crying and yelling, he vomited. He immediately felt relaxed and quieted down. He was unable to go to sleep, however, until his parents returned home. The next day he was still upset and sulked for a while but then he got over it.

So far as he recalls there was no recurrence of vomiting until he began school when he was nearly six. He did not stay home from school though he would have liked to, but he became very anxious before leaving the house each morning, and sometimes he vomited spontaneously —then he felt less scared. Later his anxiety about leaving home was compounded by the idea that he might vomit on the way to or in school and that he would embarrass himself in front of the other children. He then began purposely to force himself to vomit each morning after breakfast because then his anxiety about leaving home and his fear about shaming himself in the presence of the other children was dispelled. However, on many days, forced vomiting once in the morning was not sufficient to remove the threat of renewed anxiety or the danger of involuntary vomiting during the day, and he would, therefore, force himself to vomit in private at school several times a day. This maneuver was only partially successful and as might be expected, his fear of vomiting began to spread to include other situations that were frightening to him such as going to the park to play with other children, having to take an examination at school, and so on. The essence of these fears seemed to be that he would lose touch with his mother or that he would lose a highly important feeling of satisfaction with himself which was sustained or reinforced by his mother's attitude toward him or by his own achievements.

His self-induced vomiting and his fear of vomiting continued with more or less severity throughout his childhood and for the first year or so of treatment. As mentioned, an exacerbation of this vomiting along with a weight loss of ten pounds in the last semester of high school led to his decision to get psychiatric treatment. He thought that the exacerbation was in part owing to his anxiety about graduation from high school and his going on to college, even though he planned to attend a college in the city and to continue to live at home.

Because of his intense turmoil, dependent needfulness, and his fairly trustful nature, he quickly became involved in treatment and surprisingly, despite his constricted personality, was able to talk about himself in a rather open if somewhat cautious way.

The patient was of superior intelligence though he was not an "intellectual," nor was he particularly interested in intellectual pursuits except for certain hobbies which did not require communication with anyone; these he pursued with a dry, detached passion. They will be described in more detail below. Though he was a fairly isolated person, he felt close to some male relatives his own age, and his social life was maintained through their greater outgoingness and social ability. Despite his shyness he did not like to be alone and made serious efforts to be "one of the boys," to go out on dates, and to participate in sports.

The onset of his manifestly sexual disorder occurred when he was about eight; he found the new symptom to be as disturbing and as relief-providing as was the vomiting, which continued concurrently with the new difficulty. It began as follows: One day while taking an examination at school, he found himself unable to answer some of the questions. He passed them by, planning to try them again later on. However, before he knew it, it was announced that the allotted time was almost up; with a growing panic he returned to the unanswered problems to try to complete them. The more he tried to work on them, the less he accomplished and the more anxious he got; his panic became utterly unbearable. Suddenly, he had what he later knew to be an orgasm. Though he had no ejaculation then or until puberty, the sensations were clearly orgastic ones. The effect was as dramatic as the effect of vomiting had been; his panic disappeared and he felt blissfully calm. Further, he could think clearly and was able to finish some of the unanswered examination questions.[2] Experiences of the same sort reoccurred a number of times from then on, though not with great frequency. With puberty, ejaculations began to accompany the orgasms, but the progression of events remained essentially the same: sudden fear of failure, or recognition of the inability to accomplish a task highly invested in by him, increasing anxiety leading to a near-panic state, orgasm, reduction of anxiety, and renewed ability to think clearly.

The patient was not sure how often this occurred during his grade and high school years. He thought not more than a few times a year, and by the age of sixteen or seventeen (which was shortly before treatment began), it did not occur again as such except in an abortive form in waking life. However, at some time in adolescence, the patient began to have nightmares in which a similar sequence of events occurred. These seemed to be a continuation in sleep of the waking life orgastic disorder. In those dreams he would begin to feel increasingly anxious and powerless to control his fear; the near-panic that would ensue would be terminated by an orgasm with or without ejaculation. The remembered manifest dream content, whether imagery or feeling, was not at all overtly erotic. It appeared as though the dreaming orgasm, like the waking orgasm, like the vomiting, was activated by extreme anxiety.

During treatment the patient began to report frightening orgastic dreams which he thought were similar to those earlier nightmares just mentioned and which can, I think, be considered an example of them. Two of them are as follows: The patient dreamed that he was riding a train which was to take him toward his home. As he glanced out of the window he saw that the scenery was unfamiliar, and he suddenly realized that he had mistakenly taken a train that had a different destination from the one that passed through his neighborhood; it had already branched off and was heading into a part of the city that was unfamiliar to him. He thought, how would he get back? The people in this strange part of town might be dangerous; he might be robbed! His anxiety mounted rapidly until the onset of the erotic sensations of an impending orgasm diverted his attention, and the dream ended abruptly with an ejaculation. In another dream the patient was on a lurching, speeding train, going somewhere, perhaps to school; he began to walk from one car to the next in preparation for getting off the train when suddenly he remembered that he had left his notebook and some textbooks on a seat in another car; turning quickly to go back to retrieve them, he saw that the train was beginning to split into two sections, one of which he was on and the other of which held his books; his anxiety increased rapidly as he hurried to get to the separating section before the distance between the cars became too great for him to leap across the widening gap; near panic seized him, and the final blow came when he realized that it would be impossible to jump the distance between the cars. Then a mixture of feelings boiled up in him, the most prominent of which was unendurable terror; this was combined with a sense of terrible loss, of futility, hopelessness, disaster—he felt overwhelmed. At that moment he began to be aware that he was about to have an orgasm and that it was already beyond the point of control; ejaculation occurred and he woke up.[3] The sensations of that last moment were not essentially different from those he experienced with his usually highly pleasurable masturbatory orgasms, and they also gave him a sense of great relief.

Early in treatment, the patient's vomiting and fear of vomiting disappeared; however, these were replaced by a series of phobic symptoms which seemed to signify a fear of being on his own, of being too far from symbolic representations of reassuring security. For a time he particularly feared crossing the Michigan Avenue Bridge because there was no sense of safe enclosure there with the river opening out abruptly on both sides, and the street suddenly widening into an exposed, open plaza. He did not quite believe, but had the obsessive thought, that passersby were contemptuous of him. He became concerned that he might be a homosexual and had a number of frightening dreams in which homosexual situations were hinted at. These agoraphobic symptoms, homosexual dreams, and near-ideas of reference disappeared within a relatively short period of time. However, I shall omit the details of the relevant therapeutic work since that is not the primary focus of this essay, except to say that as a result of treatment, the patient continued to improve symptomatically. By the age of twenty-six he had without any serious setbacks, though not without considerable struggle, completed college and six months of military service. He had made a major change in the course of his professional career and had done quite well in his new field despite considerable anxiety. He had married a girl he had known for about a year and the two were happy and apparently well matched. She was a calm, attentive, affectionate person who liked to please him, and who could not bear his being angry with her for more than a few hours.

The patient's later orgastic pathology, premature ejaculation, will now be further described. During the courtship of his wife to be, the patient continued to suffer from an extreme form of premature ejaculation, which, as he disclosed shortly after starting treatment, began with his first attempt at sexual intercourse when he was about seventeen years old. This event antedated the commencement of treatment by about four months though, as already stated, its unfortunate consequences per se were not the initiating causes for his decision to seek psychiatric help. The liaison was arranged by his more adventurous friends. His partner to be was an unattractive, apparently feeble-minded girl. The patient, though eager to try, was petrified by what he was doing. In his fear he scarcely knew if he was sexually aroused or not, and before he had touched the girl, he had an orgasm, probably with ejaculation. He felt terribly ashamed by his failure and later endlessly ruminated about it, despairing of ever being capable of normal coitus. In treatment, once his vomiting and fear of vomiting and other symptoms had subsided, this fear about his sexual adequacy became his most prominent concern. Despite his anxiety about this symptom and his moderately severe social anxiety, he began to date girls regularly and became very unhappy if they did not reciprocate his usually quickly developing, intense involvement with them. His sexual experiences with several girls with whom he developed a relationship lasting for a half-year or so was plagued by the already mentioned severe form of premature ejaculation. Unlike one of the more common forms of the disorder where sensual excitement is intentionally and enjoyably stimulated by increasingly active erotic play until orgasm and ejaculation occur or are achieved, this patient (whose sexual activity was relatively cautious except much later in his sexual experiences with his fiancee) was usually not at all aware that he had become sufficiently aroused for an orgasm to be precipitated. Under these circumstances orgasm and ejaculation always came as an almost complete surprise. That is, though he was aware of some degree of pleasurable sensual excitement, it was usually felt as of only moderate intensity or even, at other times, of rather minimal intensity; often he felt rather detached from the sexual experience altogether. It was not until the orgastic sensations were on him that a sudden rush of sensual pleasure was unambiguously recognized. The precipitant of the orgasm was often altogether unknown or was some apparently minimal action or tentative sexual thought on his part which he did not consciously consider (nor would it ordinarily be considered by others) to be sufficient to cause an orgasm. Nor was the patient usually consciously aware of any increased degree of direct penile stimulation caused by his own actions which would lead to orgasm, and direct genital stimulation by his partner never did occur until much later in his sexual life. It was his conscious intention during his sexual play with his girlfriends not to ejaculate, and he tried to regulate this by whatever physical or mental tricks he could think of, but with practically no success.

Though the patient did not experience the same kind of numbing fear he had experienced with his first attempt at coitus he did remain fearful of a number of aspects of his sexual activity, among which was his conscious concern about prematurity. There were other conscious fears too, such as the morality of his actions and his fear of being discovered. (I do not mean to imply that these conscious fears were all that interfered with his freedom of sexual expression.) The patient felt that these and other unknown fears interfered with his really ever being able to enjoy his own sensual excitement to its fullest, and he was unhappily aware that his erotic play with women did not reach that degree of sensual excitement he was able to achieve with masturbation.

The patient's experiences with his wife-to-be recapitulated the sexual difficulty just described. Throughout his premarital sexual life, he continued to suffer from *ejaculatio praecox ante portes*. There were a few times in the last weeks before his wedding when he was able to enjoy considerable sexual intimacy and excitement nearly to the point of intercourse without having an orgasm. He began to feel more confident about the possibility of coitus during marriage without premature ejaculation, but because of the vagaries of his performance he remained quite anxious about the outcome. It was a surprise to me (as it had been to him) when on returning to treatment after a two-week honeymoon, he announced that he had had intercourse regularly since his marriage and had not had a premature ejaculation at any time. In fact, he had had to learn to delay his climax in order to accommodate his wife, and he was able to do that with increasing success. In the several years that have passed since his marriage, the patient has led an apparently normal and for him quite satisfying sexual life and has not once suffered from premature ejaculation. It seemed to me that this unexpected, sudden, and apparently stable shift in the patient's ability more fully to experience and yet to "manage" his sexual excitement following his marriage was a clue to a useful direction of thought about his aberrant orgasm as well as his type of premature ejaculation—though the abruptness of the cessation of the latter was not later considered essential to the formulations.

It should be noted here that two related though different sexual disorders in this patient have been described. The first which has been called aberrant orgasm began when the patient was eight and continued in a modified form in dreams after the cessation of the second symptom, a type of severe premature ejaculation. The symptom aberrant orgasm seemed to be the consequence of the unmanageable quantities of anxiety, of a panic state occurring in a nonerotic situation. The second, *ejaculatio praecox ante portes,* did not seem manifestly to be the consequence only of such a severe degree of anxiety but seemed to be owing also to other more complex causes, including an unawareness of the degree of his own sexual arousal during erotically stimulating situations. However, I believe that the manifest differences are more apparent than otherwise, and I shall attempt to demonstrate this later.

I would like to turn now to some other information about the patient which will broaden an understanding of his sexual difficulties and of the organization of his personality in general. There was another kind of sexual dream that began to be remembered while the patient was in treatment. These were frankly sexual dreams, but they did not lead to orgasm. These dreams, though primarily erotic in content, also had affective components of anxiety; however, at no time did this anxiety reach the proportions of, or take on the quality of disabling dread that he experienced with the manifestly noneIfotic anxiety dreams that were terminated by orgasm. At first his sexual partner in these dreams was an unknown, not clearly discerned girl who was soon seen to be unattractive and therefore of no interest to him. Later the girls became more defined and more attractive, but then the setting was unacceptable because of the proximity of other people; later these unknown, interfering, hovering people merged into one person who was clearly recognized as the patient's mother; rarely the person was a man. In still later dreams the female partner turned out to be his sister, and a few times there were overtly affectionate though not manifestly genital erotic dreams about his mother.[4]

The patient and his mother were bound to each other in a close, narcissistic symbiotic tie. Even in his adolescent years she almost slavishly catered to his whims. Usually he was irritable and annoyed with her and bitterly criticized her for her inadequacies as a cook and housekeeper. He often felt that she purposely tried to be depriving or vindictive with him. At the same time he became unbearably lonely if his parents went away for even a brief, weekend vacation. The patient spoke relatively little about his father, and in contrast to patient's mother, he was rarely dreamed of. He was a very retiring man who with the help of his energetic wife made a meager living as a small businessman. He was perceived by the patient as passive and inhibited, with few of the masculine attributes he hoped to develop in himself and which he greatly admired and coveted in certain other men, such as the powerful and victorious generals of some of the famous battles of history. Some of the patient's earlier mentioned homosexual preoccupations were based on a primitivization of his desire for idealized masculine strength. He felt that he had always considered his father to be a weak, ineffectual disappointment.

The patient's relationship to his fiancee repeated much that had existed with his mother. Even before his wife-to-be had made any real commitment to him, he was jealously possessive of her and became intensely depressed and angry if she mentioned past boyfriends or interests she shared with girl friends.

Notwithstanding his intense longing for physical and emotional intimacy, the patient was very cautious in the open expression of positive emotions toward anyone. He wanted emotional closeness but seemed to require a considerable degree of emotional isolation as well. The isolating distance, however, was often in danger of becoming too great, causing him to feel too far removed from his relationship to his object. Relevant to this and to his characterology, of which his sexual symptoms were a circumscribed phenomenological manifestation, is a hobby that he had become interested in during late latency and that continued through his early adolescence: He was fascinated with the use of binoculars and telescopes; he liked to be able to look at things that were a great distance away, people or inanimate objects; he wanted to be able to see them at the point where the resolving power of the lenses would be still just capable of allowing him to distinguish what the object was. At puberty occasionally, an erotic component—to observe women who were a great distance away—was added to the already existing motives for his behavior, but the essential meaning of his activity as ascertained in treatment was unchanged. It was a wish to maintain or regain contact with an object felt to be almost beyond reach and about to slip out of his grasp, a wish to reassure himself that it was still possible to recapture the object before it disappeared forever.

Two further clinical vignettes (one of these is related to the danger of the loss of symbolic representations of objects as described above though here conceived of as a place) will illustrate some characteristics of the organization of his personality relating to his struggle to manage rapidly increasing feelings of anxiety that threatened to become overwhelming and lead to the aberrant orgastic discharge. These occurred during the time he was in treatment and to some extent reflect its effects.

In the several months preceding his marriage when the date of the wedding had been set, the patient and his fiancee would take long automobile rides into the suburbs with no particular destination in mind. The patient enjoyed these as long as he could keep available for instant recall a clear diagram of the route that led from the part of the city he knew to the relatively unknown area through which he was driving. So long as he could envision a link via a known roadway from his present position to his home, he felt comfortable. However, should he take a new turn and get his directions confused so that the route from the un-known place to the known was no longer certain, he would become in-creasingly confused and unable to think clearly; the dreaded panic would begin and he half expected and half feared that he would have an orgasm. This never did occur but on several occasions he had brief twinges (*frissons*) of erotic feeling in his penis which were like abortive orgasms; he is not sure if these helped to reduce his anxiety or to think more lucidly. What he learned to do to calm himself down was to stop the car, park, and have a cigarette. He could then begin to pull himself together by thinking through what the possibilities were of retracing his steps, returning to a familiar street, and so on.

Something similar would occur at his place of employment. The pa-tient was most comfortable there as long as he could remain isolated at his desk planning future purchase requests, going over his inventory, or calling the stock room for supplies. His compulsive character traits and his narcissistic pleasure in solitary thinking and planning for the future served him well in this aspect of his job and were reminiscent of an-other one of his adolescent hobbies—an endless preoccupation and fas-cination with the great battles of the Napoleonic wars. There were many determinants to his absorption with those campaigns, including, as men-tioned earlier, an important, attempted identification with the aggressive, powerful, and victorious generals, but in addition, the detailed logis-tics of supplying the troops and of massing armies for attack, of making order out of possible chaos, that is, of being able to regulate the rapidly gathering, cumulative force of enormous, ineluctable events provided him with hours of exciting, creative pleasure. In his job, how-ever, he could not control things as well; so, for example, when some of his employees were absent and he was required to deal directly with his customers, he often became perturbed; the old sense of panic would re-turn as he added up the bill for one customer while several more stood waiting for him with requests, complaints, demands. He felt that he could not satisfy himself or them. He thought, how could the sales-women have left him there to manage on his own, why did they not come back to help him as they had promised they would? As his inner call for help and his anger rose and fused with the pain of fear, the pos-sibility and even the transient sensations of an orgasm came to mind,

398

though again it never did occur. Instead, at the height of a sense of impending disaster and with the seeming inevitability of an orgasm, he would think of how, as soon as he had finished with one customer, he could retreat to the men's room where he would have a cigarette and just be alone with his own thoughts for a few minutes. This fantasy allowed him to finish his immediate task after which he would leave to carry out his daydream; that he would return to the floor and attend to those he had left waiting, his feeling of panic, abandonment, and rage having subsided.

I would like now to turn to some theoretical conceptualizations of the preceding clinical material that will, I think, provide a basis for an understanding of the patient's pathology and for its partial resolution.

Several considerations appear to me to be particularly germane to the understanding of these problems. The first is the malfunctioning of the patient's ability to tolerate delay of gratification; the second is the malfunctioning of his ability to calm himself down. Though these are closely related and, no doubt, developmentally mutually influencing, they deserve individual mention. A third and most important consideration is the measure that, I suggest, was at times taken by or, better, that occurred in this patient's psychic apparatus as a result of the severe stresses to which it was exposed as a consequence of the inadequate operation of the two above-mentioned functions. This measure, hallucinatory wish fulfillment, is considered to be crucial for the development of the patient's sexual disturbances. It will be discussed at a later point in this chapter.

The two developmental weaknesses are, of course, general ones and probably play an important contributory role in many kinds of pathology, but their role in this patient's pathology seemed to be of particular significance and was less than usually disguised by mere superficial character defenses. In this patient, the disappearance of what was for him his most overtly troublesome symptom, premature ejaculation, can, I think, begin to be explained on the basis of a gradual modification of both these weaknesses, that is, on the basis of an increase of the strength of his ego in these areas.[5] (The same modification is of relevance also in the reduction of his other symptom, aberrant orgasm.) One can find indications in the clinical material that, as the result of treatment, he had developed an increased sense of confidence that his need-gratifying object [6] would not be lost at the moment when the desire for it was most highly stimulated, and that there had been developed an increase in his ability to calm himself down in the face of rising psychic tension (whether it be anxiety or erotic excitement) which might have become overwhelmingly intense. The effect of the strengthening of both these capacities (which was a consequence of increased structural development, particularly neutralization) was that his anxiety was more adequately controlled and that he could allow himself the pleasurable luxury of heightened wishes and of the delayed gratification of them without the experience being felt as an increasingly dangerous one that would revive a traumatic state from which there was no hope of recovery. A paradigm of such a traumatic state seems to have been his experience that evening when his mother left for the movies. This does not mean to imply, however, that the separation from her at that time need be considered the genetic core of the later symptom, but given the proper predisposing factors, it could well have been. However, even if it were not itself the traumatogenic moment (after which some essential emotional development took a new direction), it may well have served as a time-condensed memory, an amalgamation of a number of prior and future events of greater and lesser psychic complexity which became incorporated into and were signified by that particular separation.

In relation to the postulated weaknesses, it should be noted that the patient's tantrum was terminated by the automatic physiologic act of vomiting. Apparently during that tantrum, no amount of involvement or support by substitute objects (the grandparents) served as sufficient emergency ego-bolstering to enable the patient to calm down. Only the apparently adventitious physiological discharge, the act of vomiting, with its complex interplay among peripheral autonomic innervations, central nervous system excitation, and the psychological reaction to these events was effective in altering the unrelenting, psychophysiologic experiences of longing, rage, and fear which are comprised by the term "tantrum." I would like to suggest that the later development of premature orgasm in this patient was markedly influenced by the fact that an earlier emotional crisis had been resolved by a primarily physiological means, vomiting, which led to psychological tension reduction; this reflected a tendency and set a pattern for the resolution of other emotional crises.

To put this in another way, for this patient the continued use in later life of somatic discharge processes induced by psychological stress does not seem unexpected because the somatic discharges were so effective in reducing tension during childhood and, also, the elaboration of psychological controls over more archaic tension reduction methods does not seem to have been adequately developed (see Grinker, 1953). And further, the alternation and then the substitution of the genital for the gastrointestinal apparatus at an age when the former has become physiologically available (even though precociously so in this case) seems to be a not unexpected eventuation in that the somatic experience of orgasm is inherently so superior to that of vomiting or to any other physiological process for the production of the psychological experience of pleasure and for the relief of unpleasurable tensions.

I would like to turn now to the third consideration mentioned earlier as significant for the formation of the patient's sexual symptoms. It was suggested that a particular psychic operation, hallucinatory wish fulfillment, had been evoked by the stringencies imposed upon the psychic apparatus by the double weakness of his ability to delay gratification and to calm down. This third process is considered a highly important (but not alone sufficient) one for the induction of the orgastic disorders from which this patient suffered.

The process, hallucinatory wish fulfillment, is the earliest psychological operation activated by the development of intolerable or dangerous emotional pain (unpleasure). It begins with the oral frustrations of infancy, and though in later years with the onrush of complex psychical developments it is covered over by defensive operations and developmental transformations of increasing subtlety and refinement, it is probably never done away with even in normal waking life, but continues to operate as the briefly recalled, revitalizing recollection of the reality of past gratifications; these are available forever to be turned to, to renew the hope and the expectation of future gratifications.[7]

One can trace various developmental line transformations of hallucinatory wish fulfillment as the psychic apparatus develops greater ability for delay and modulation. One of the most important of these, conscious fantasy (manifest regression), is well known and readily observable by introspection. I shall omit mention of other such transformations here except to make the commonplace observation that numerous magical wishes and mechanisms of thought persist throughout our adult lives.

However, I would like to suggest that in certain kinds of nonpsychotic adult personalities the unaltered process of hallucinatory wish fulfillment is reexperienced in a very circumscribed but archaically intense form and that with the occurrence of this process, the development of dangerous amounts of excitation within the psychic apparatus is circumvented.[8] Though this cannot be considered a manifestation of the operation of defense in the sense in which the term is used in the context of a dynamic structural point of view, it is an autonomous response of the human psychic apparatus that has value in protecting the apparatus from overwhelmingly painful excitement and as such might be considered a primal defense. However, it is mobilized, or set into operation, in its most massive, primitive form, not because the psychic apparatus actively endeavors to evoke it, but rather because the apparatus is too weak under the circumstances to prevent its occurrence. Under most circumstances its operation with a more optimally developed psychic apparatus would be limited to a signal memory or experience that would itself be sufficiently satisfying to reduce painful tension, or it would serve only to spur reality-oriented thought or action which would hopefully lead to current appropriate reality gratification.

With the patient whose case has been described here, it is suggested that the lack of adequate modifying or defensive structuralization, at least or particularly within a specific context, permitted the process of hallucinatory wish fulfillment to operate through the vehicle of the genital apparatus. This served to eliminate the danger to the psychic apparatus brought on by what was for it unbearable amounts of excitation. When this patient's ego was exposed to traumatic intensities of stimulation, the always available, archaic process of hallucinatory wish fulfillment was actuated in a full-blown fashion without adequate regulation by defensive structures. The consequences were of some advantage to him. Just as the hungry infant is buffered against the dangers of frustration by the revival of (or intensification of) memories of earlier oral gratification, so the danger of disintegrating panic in later life was avoided by memories of sensual gratification that, by inducing an orgasm, were preeminently suited to the reduction of anxiety. That these hallucinations resulted in an actual orgastic discharge and not in just the hallucinatory ideation of one, that a real consummation of the psychophysiologic act occurred that was not just imaginary as is the oral hallucination (of course, no food is really ingested) is, it seems to me, a function of differences in the physiology of the organ systems stimulated by, and mediating the psychophysiological response rather than an essential difference in the psychological processes that lead to a termination of the sense of danger.[9]

In relation to the idea of the danger to which the patient was exposed, the two train dreams reported in the clinical section of the chapter may be more fully explored at this time. It was suggested earlier regarding these dreams that a sudden experience of danger created a feeling of panic that led to and was terminated by an orgasm just as the terror of the possibility of failing his school examination at age eight had led to an orgasm at that time. In both dreams the sequence of danger, anxiety, orgasm is at least superficially clear. However, the reason for the experience of danger seems to arise from two sources. In the separating train dream, in particular, one of the dangers seems to be the reaction to the imminent orgasm itself, that is, the lost books representing the loss of higher, more neutralized controlling functions of the psychic apparatus that would have been able to modulate the overwhelming, libidinal surge (see Kohut, 1969). (The first dream of the wrong train route might be interpreted in a like manner, the foreign danger being that of the imminent but not yet recognized or acknowledged orgasm.) It would follow then that the source of the anxiety experienced in the above instances is owing to the observing ego's reaction to the awareness of the collapse of its regulatory abilities and the massive overwhelming of those higher controlling agencies by forces of primary-process intensity.

It is my contention, however, that the initiating danger is not that of the sexual process itself or of the ego's reactions to it, but rather that both dreams can be understood as a two-part process, both parts of which are the consequence of the same psychic defect, the lack of adequately developed defensive or modulating ego structures, the absence of which leaves the psychic apparatus vulnerable to the repeated exposure to traumatic states of (unmanageable) excitement. The first step is the precipitating or initiating danger. It is this event which may not be adequately characterized in the two presented dreams. However, the anxiety implied in the first dream (going away from home into dangerous territory) is reminiscent of the dread of loss of important, sustaining object relationships in childhood and is also a reflection of similar deprivations in his current life, including some aspects of the relationship to the therapist. (The details of the more current, precipitating events would require considerable elaboration to be reasonably convincing and so will have to be omitted here.) These precipitating events were experienced, however, with the same traumatic intensity as, for example, the failure of his self-sustaining abilities at the time of the school examination at age eight and as the separation from his parents at age five had been. Because of the weakness of his psychic apparatus these particular frustrations could not be adequately defended against or modulated but were experienced as overwhelming dangers.[10] That there was some modifying structure that did attempt to ameliorate the traumatic experience is probably attested to by the very presence of the reported dream, that is, some psychic elaboration did occur. However, within the dream itself the traumatic danger can only be surmised. As already indicated the second step in the process is probably better demonstrated by the second dream (of the separating cars and the loss of his books), though it too contains elements of the content of the initiating danger: The train ride for the patient could mean both a return to the security of home or the loss of that possibility, as in his fears about unknown automobile routes. Again, the lost books seem to represent the patient's horrified reaction to the failure and collapse of his higher, neutralizing functions. These functions fail to modify both the experience of danger that initiated the dream or to elaborate an erotically pleasurable fantasy that might offset the danger, or to prevent the apparatus itself from losing control over its own operations. The result in both dreams is relatively unelaborated, physiological orgastic discharge which does bring relief just as an oral hallucinatory wish fulfillment does.

To recapitulate, if the danger in the first step of the process is the consequence of the primitive evaluation of the reality situation which causes terror and a search for escape from pain, so the danger in the second step of the process is the recognition of the unwanted, sudden collapse of the psychic apparatus to a more primitive state in which physiological discharge dominates over psychic processes. As indicated before, both dangers are owing to the maldevelopment of the psychic apparatus in the two general ways that were suggested earlier.

I would like to enlarge here on what within the framework of the concept of inadequate structuralization I have considered the meaning of the achieved orgastic gratification to have been to this patient. I have not meant to imply that a genital erotic fantasy as it might be elaborated in an imagery dominated dream or daydream, was what was hallucinated by the patient, albeit here at an unconscious level. Rather I have thought of it in terms of an isolated, infantile, autoerotic experience, only loosely integrated into the rest of the personality, yet capable of affecting other operations of the apparatus by the reaffirmation of an essential, positive self-experience.[11] Though an orgastic discharge is by definition (in part at least) a genital experience, it is not here considered genital in the sense of a stage of libidinal development with the important structural and object-love attainments that that implies. It was thought to be primarily a sensorimotor experience of intensely satisfying, genital erotic quality on the border of physiological and psychological. Like the oral hallucinatory wish fulfillment before it (and probably integrated into it) this genital hallucinatory wish fulfillment is considered capable of reducing tension arising from numerous conflicts or frustrations which are not necessarily genital.[12] For example, in this patient the dangers that flooded his ego had a number of excitatory sources such as the loss of the availability of objects whose presence was essential to the functioning of his emotional economy, or the collapse of a vulnerable and highly cherished sense of self-esteem, and so on. These events were considered to have had the same disintegrating effect as the early paradigmatic traumatogenic experience he had had. At those times when it was genital sexual activities that led to a premature ejaculation, it was not (primarily, at least) because genital conflicts per se were aroused but because the conflicts or frustrations produced by genital sexual excitement were experienced by the same deficient apparatus as frustrations from other sources had been, and so could not be any more absorbed or diffused by that apparatus than had the others.

Regarding this, the following formulation seems helpful. In this patient, despite strong schizoid, narcissistic tendencies, the desire for need gratification from an external object (as indicated earlier, the complex issue of the quality of the development of the patient's object relations will not be further dealt with here) remained highly cathected. However, the recognition of the desire for gratification in relation to an object when raised to a certain level of intensity, a level that approximated childhood intensities, was most often experienced as frustrating and enraging; this level of desire was usually avoided or kept from consciousness. It was this denial or splitting that prevented him from consciously experiencing the sexual stimulation as more than moderately pleasant. Further, when he became sexually aroused, the wish for gratification in relation to the stimulating object began to approach the degree of intensity that must have existed in infancy in relation to the providing mother. Under the hypnotic, driven, all-encompassing state of erotic excitement, there was revived the obligatory quality of peremptory craving that characterized his unneutralized impulses in relation to his childhood, need-gratifying object; at such moments delay or relative indifference by the object meant utter disaster. Here then was the obliteration of the vision of pleasure that had just emerged, the slipping out of focus of the image in the telescopic lens, the realization of the impossibility of creating order out of chaos, and the emergence of unmanageable intensities of archaic rage. With the concurrently mobilized desire to escape from the danger of such a potentially traumatic experience, there was set in motion a regression from a desire for gratification in the present-day object relations to increasingly cathected memories of past, more narcissistically conceived of memories of erotic gratification. At such a moment the merest increase of erotic stimulation in reality added an amount of intensity to the already overburdened psychic apparatus that was beyond its capacity to modulate or to contain; higher level, neutralizing abilities collapsed; the hallucinatory image of erotic gratification was abruptly intensified, and premature ejaculation was precipitated.

I would like now to present a reconstruction of some of the effects of treatment and of the meaning and effect of the patient's marriage which appeared to me to have contributed significantly to the considerable reduction of his symptom of aberrant orgasm and to the cessation of his symptom of premature ejaculation. It was suggested earlier that the cooperative role of his wife was a crucial determinant in the remission of the latter disorder. Perhaps this can now be more fully explained and understood.

With his marriage and because of his wife's cooperative alliance with him, both in the weeks before but especially after the marriage ceremony, several psychological events of considerable importance to him are reconstructively assumed to have occurred. He became sufficiently reassured that it was not his wife's intention to frustrate him, that is, confidence in the availability and willingness of his object to replenish him became more secure as the reality events of the pre- and postnuptial period convinced him, at last, that his aroused desire for sexual gratification would not be interfered with, betrayed, or ignored. There was no need now for him to expect that a resurgence of the anguish of frustration of his aroused erotic needs might lead to the same kind of psychoeconomic balance that had so endangered him during latency as, for example, when his examination questions were too difficult to answer and which failure had caused the collapse of his system of positive evaluation of himself. The memory of need-satisfying experiences of his childhood had become more firmly reestablished in his mind in relation to the person of his wife who now could reassure him of his worthwhileness by her positively toned responses to him. She would not ignore him when he was most stimulated to need her attention.

I would like now to illustrate by way of a dream some of the changes that have been indicated above in connection with his sexual behavior with his wife, and which is empirical evidence of the increased, neutralizing capabilities of his psychic apparatus, that is, evidence of the internalization of optimally frustrating experiences that led to increased development of the area of progressive neutralization. Though the evidence to be presented in the dream that follows emphasizes an alteration of his ability to deal with reactive rage in relation to frustration, I believe it implies as well an alteration in the degree of libidinal frustration experienced and the ability of his psychic apparatus to handle both.

This dream occurred a number of times with minor variations throughout the course of treatment. The modification of the original dream sheds light on the shift of the balance of forces and the structural change that occurred as a result of treatment as well as of marriage and the increasingly satisfying relationship to his wife. I have called the dream "the dream of the crazy little boy" after the patient's name for it. The original dream is essentially as follows: The patient is shopping in a grocery store. Suddenly a crazy little boy appears out of nowhere and begins to attack him physically. Though the boy is only five to ten or so years of age, the patient is terrified of him. He tries to restrain the boy but he becomes wilder and more savage; he bites, hits, kicks, screams and spits, and each time the patient thinks that he has the boy under control or has gotten rid of him, the boy wriggles free or returns and the battle starts all over again. The patient calls for help but no one does anything; he thinks of calling the police, and so on. The dream ends in various ways: Sometimes the patient wakes up; sometimes the boy is gotten rid of or leaves; or he is held rigidly still by the patient; or the police do come. In any case, the patient is left with a sense of fearful alienation from the boy's deranged and incomprehensible behavior. A dream much later in treatment about the crazy little boy began in the same way but for the first time that the patient could recall, it ended differently. This time, in the midst of his struggles with the boy, his wife appeared out of the surrounding crowd of people; she said that the boy's parents were nearby and that she would take him to them; they would teach him to behave differently; the patient, greatly relieved, watched as the boy went off to his parents. They looked like his, the patient's, parents.

The connections between the crazy boy and the patient's recurrent childhood and adult tantrums (whether acted out or only inwardly experienced), the reassuring supportive role of his wife, and the beginning hope or evidence that the boy will be able to get over being so angry is, I think, clear. So far as the effects of therapy are concerned, only brief comment will be made here. It has been inferred that in this patient one of the important processes initiated in treatment was that of an increased ability for the neutralization of archaic impulses, particularly reactive rage. One of the important agents leading to that development was the feeling of being correctly understood by the therapist whose ego strength the patient was able to borrow at critical periods. Some evidence for this "feeling of being correctly understood" may be found in this recent dream, in the roles of the patient's wife and of his parents: his wife by being able to recognize and empathize with his fear of being overwhelmed by his rage and by her being available for the loan of her affectionate reasonableness, his parents by being conceived of as capable of, and interested in teaching the child to restrain himself. Both roles, I think, are, in turn, reflections of his experiences in the transference or transference-like relationship to the therapist.

One last issue, the relation of this patient's sexual dysfunctions to the kinds of premature orgasm that are more often encountered clinically, remains to be discussed.

It has been postulated here that the patient's symptoms were the consequence of a psychoeconomic imbalance in which unpleasurable states of tension were discharged by a primal precursor of defense, hallucinatory wish fulfillment. This defense was considered to have been set into operation not from a position of relative strength in the more usual manner of defenses, that is, as an active attempt by the psychic apparatus to protect itself from danger, but from a position of weakness, the apparatus being unable to absorb the influx of energies impinging on it (from other functional units of the apparatus) and being unable to prevent this occurrence of a passively experienced, emergency-like automatic discharge in which its later developed functions participated very little.

The material of the case presented here illustrates particularly in the earliest historical example (the patient's first orgasm) an archaic response to a situation of danger—the overwhelming of the psychic apparatus with intense anxiety, which the apparatus was incapable of dealing with in other than a most primitive, unmodified way. It has been suggested that there was no adequate calming structure to reduce his dread and no mechanisms available to absorb and to elaborate and thereby to prevent other than the most primal response. It was also suggested that the somatic, genital discharge that occurred at this time had been predisposed to by the earlier somatic, gastrointestinal discharge that, beginning in his earlier years, had proven effective in reducing psychological tensions and that had also arisen under conditions of extreme danger.

Though it has not been pointed out in the presentation here, there is, of course, both implicit and explicit evidence in the case material that considerable, advanced, structural development had occurred in this patient and that some of the material can be quite well understood using the (tripartite) structural point of view. However, as explained above, it seemed to me that the patient's symptom could not be adequately understood on the basis of a dynamic structural conflict, though it was recognized that there was some contribution of those struggles to the psychoeconomic imbalance which led to the symptom. For example, it was considered that though some superego strictures (implied above) added to his sense of danger as a nonspecific stress, their effect then was not based on castration anxiety per se but because any interference with intense wishes led to an increase of the danger of a dissolution of the psychic apparatus as a consequence of its being overwhelmed by too intense stimuli of reactive unpleasure that its relatively weak, defensive structure could not accommodate.

The more familiar formulation of the disorder premature ejaculation was suggested by Freud in "Inhibitions Symptoms and Anxiety" (1926). His initial conceptualizations have not been basically changed by later authors though a number of important, elaborative contributions have been made, such as those regarding the role of early stages of libidinal development, those of chronic character defenses, traits of masculinity and femininity, and activity and passivity, the symbolic meaning of various aspects of the sexual act that must be defended against, and so on. In essence, the classical formulation is that in the course of the act of coitus or in the foreplay preceding it, severe castration fear is remobilized, and this increasingly intense danger is diminished or avoided by an abrogation of the duration of the sexual act. The disorder can be understood as a symptom formation if the result (the prematurity) is conceived of as a new phenomenon or a function that has undergone an unusual change and that is both the expression of the impulse (the oedipally tainted, erotic gratification achieved) and a defense against it (the curtailment of the pleasure), or as an inhibition if the abrogation is conceived of as a partial avoidance of the possibility of a full consummation, which is unconsciously equated with a forbidden, incestuous pleasure.[13] In either case the disorder is considered to be the outcome of a dynamic, defensive struggle within the framework of a tripartite organization of the mind, and the effects of the psychic apparatus' defensive abilities in relation to the impulses are its hallmark. In contrast, the type of aberrant orgasm and the related type of premature ejaculation described in this chapter have been considered to be the consequence of

409

a defect or weakness in structure so that defensive activities or buffering actions of the mind are unable to prevent archaic discharges from occurring.

I would like to suggest that the conceptualizations arrived at in this essay can be applied to the more precise understanding of other disorders of orgasm. In some cases, the disorder premature ejaculation as a product of stress within certain types of psychic organization or under certain transient conditions that alter the usual organization of the personality can be better formulated or understood using the conceptualizations suggested for the particular case presented here, that is, on the basis of a maldevelopment of defensive or binding structure, or a transient, situational weakening of usually more adequately functioning structural organization. Aside from the more accurate conceptualization that such a formulation may allow, the therapeutic task may be considered in a different light. Whereas interpretation is probably the main therapeutic tool in the treatment of transference neurotic symptoms, other methods of treatment may be of more use in conveying to the patient what it is he suffers from in disorders in which there is inadequate structural development. In the treatment of my patient, for example, the conveyed understanding of the overstimulating effect of his impulses and the implicit loan of the analyst's strength in dealing with this were, among other things, quite effective in altering his own ability to tolerate the excitement. (It may be that for some patients, various content transference interpretations which though effective are used by them for purposes other than what the analyst had intended; so, for example, the reassuring tone of the analyst's voice or the patient's imagined omnipotence of the analyst with which he allies himself are more important in leading to an abatement of symptoms and for the, at least, temporary building up of structure than the accuracy of the interpretation.)

For other types of premature ejaculation the formulations and treatment based on the effectiveness of the defensive activities of the mind would remain the correct approach to the disorder, and transference content interpretations the primary therapeutic tool. In still other mixed types one or the other formulation and therapeutic approach might be more useful at different times depending on the changing internal problems with which the patient is confronted.

In conclusion, I have presented some clinical material from the long-term psychotherapy of a patient who suffered from two kinds of orgastic pathology. Because of the precocious onset and the unusual, exciting stimuli effecting one of these, it was designated "aberrant orgasm." Postpubertally a severe form of premature ejaculation also developed. It was considered that both the patient's disorders were related to characterological defects and were the outcome not of a defense against unacceptable (incestuous) sexual impulses as premature ejaculation has been classically formulated, but the consequence of a psychoeconomic imbalance owing to a lack of adequate development of defensive or modulatory psychic structure, a deficiency disorder that permitted the relatively unrestricted discharge of an inherent, automatic, archaic psychic reaction—hallucinatory wish fulfillment—to occur under specific circumstances. It was suggested that some other cases of premature ejaculation might be better understood using the formulations arrived at for this case. Clinical material from the case was used to illustrate how the presented formulations were arrived at and to indicate how treatment and its interrelationship with the patient's changing life circumstances may have effected an alteration of a chronic psychic response.

NOTES

1. Despite the fact that this patient was not psychoanalyzed and that the formulations that are developed here did not arise from the systematic analysis of a cohesive transference situation, and to some extent, therefore, are derived from material "beyond the bounds of the basic rule," I feel that a useful level of understanding was reached by the prolonged observation of the patient during treatment (perhaps enhanced by the relative lack of concealing defensive structure such as may obtain in the analytically sophisticated observations of children), and that these formulations can be of value then as an orienting framework for, or as a precursor to the understanding of phenomena occurring in a strictly psychoanalytic situation.

2. Another patient with quite different presenting complaints described an almost identical occurrence when he was eight. His first orgasm was precipitated by the sudden, horrifying realization that he could not correctly answer some school examination questions. The overpowering panic he experienced was terminated by what he described as one of "the most pleasurable, passive" orgastic discharges he has ever known. In fact, following puberty, this sensation became the model for actively induced, erotic excitement in which, through elaborate masturbatory fantasies and activities, he attempted to recapture the tension-reducing bliss of that earlier orgastic experience. In this patient also, following the orgasm he felt quite calm and was able to return to and answer correctly some of the questions which had set the anxiety-orgasm complex in motion to begin with.

3. The sequence of emotional events leading to the orgasm in either dream reported here cannot be precisely determined. The first dream appears, superficially at least, to illustrate the thesis of anxiety (in this instance, intense "separation" anxiety) leading to orgasm; the second dream may also illustrate that sequence, but it also illustrates more clearly the incapacity of the patient's ego to tolerate the loss of control by higher functions (his books) to the sensual intensities of the imminent orgasm. There were other

411

dreams not reported here in which intense "anxiety" stimulated by various frightening events did seem to initiate and terminate in orgasm. This issue will be discussed more fully in the theoretical section of this chapter.

4. Though the meaning of these dreams and material relating to some aspects of their latent content will not be dealt with or further elaborated in this chapter, I would like to note that there was evidence of the patient's having arrived at and experienced a form of an oedipal conflict. It may be, for example, that the more circumscribed fear in these dreams was the outgrowth of incestuous phallic impulses which were inhibited by superego prohibitions. A discussion of the interrelationship of the preoedipal stage of ego and libidinal development, the pathology of the transformations of narcissism touched on regarding this patient, and the psychoeconomic point of view as stressed in this essay on the one hand. and on the other hand, the parallel operation of the oedipus complex and the structural developments (the triadic relationships) that the former implies as they appeared in this patient have purposely been avoided in order to maintain a particular line of thought and to elucidate it in a relatively unencumbered way. However, it is my opinion that narcissistic vicissitudes and the developmental line of the self and the developmental line related to objects and object love, though separate to a considerable degree, do mutually influence each other in important ways. But that complex subject is one that I have less clinical evidence for and a further investigation of it would be out of place and too difficult as well as too distracting here.

5. Except where it is specifically mentioned in relation to the structural point of view, the use of the term ego in this essay follows Freud's earlier use of the term in the sense of "self" and not in the sense of its later use as one of the three major agencies of the mind.

6. A fuller discussion of the nature of the need and of the object cannot be entered into here. However, I would like to indicate that an affirmation of his relatively unmodified, childhood narcissistic self-experiences reflected by the necessary response to him of the object played a particularly important role in this patient's emotional economy and was necessary for the maintenance of a sense of cohesiveness of his self (see Kohut, 1966).

7. The recent work of Pinchas Noy (1969) on the psychoanalytic theory of the primary process is of interest here, particularly his suggestions about the integration of coexistence and simultaneity ot operation of the primary and secondary processes as opposed to the more usual concept of a distinct and usually constant separateness of the two processes.

8. The work of Stuart Miller (1962), which precedes that of Noy (1909), on persons in isolation or under great stress is pertinent here. It implicitly contains some of the theoretical assumptions Noy arrives at, but of equal importance for this essay, Miller attempts with a number of illustrations to document in considerable clinical detail a point similar to the one I have just made.

9. The mechanisms by which the unconscious psychological and physiological may interact has been postulated by Dorpat (1968).

10. Though a psychoeconomic point of view has been stressed in the discussion of this patient's pathology, I have not meant thereby to overlook other dimensions of his psychic organization that contributed to or were the basis of the economic experience of overwhelming anxiety. I have mentioned, for example, the needed narcissistic supplies from childhood objects, and the necessary experience of a superior intellectual self, and the effects of their disruption respectively by separations from his mother, and by failures at school. His narcissistic vulnerability was indeed considered to be one of the important sources of his intense anxiety reactions. For a pertinent discussion of the conjunctive use of psychoanalytic constructs in the understanding of normal mental functioning and in psychopathology, see Gedo and Goldberg (1969).

11. In Dr. John Gedo's discussion of this essay he suggested that the self-induced vomiting "reinforced a sense of unity of the self-experience" which counteracted a "vulnerability to fragmentation into auto-erotic self-nuclei." The patient's orgastic ex-

perience may be presumed to have had a similar effect and to have enabled his disintegrating psychic apparatus to reintegrate itself. It would be interesting to know whether the orgastic experience of normal adults may contribute to the reinforcement of a sense of essential positiveness about the "self" which is in part related to a reintegration of not a fragmented but an at least loosened cohesiveness of the unity of the self. [Chicago Psychoanalytic Society, Oct. 1969.]

12. Freud's early comments on the transmutability of any unusually intense psychic experience (even that of pain) into an erotic one is implicit in this idea.

13. Why premature ejaculation (as symptom or inhibition) occurs in some personalities rather than other types of impotence, for example, decreased pleasure in the act (psychical impotence) has not been much explored. It may be related, however, to the retained ability in some personality types to maintain, at least in the genital sexual area of functioning, a greater integration of the primary and secondary processes as suggested by Noy (1969) in relation to particular personality types owing to constitutional capacities or unique environmental stimulation.

REFERENCES

Dorpat, T. L. (1968). Regulatory mechanisms of the perceptual apparatus on involuntary physiological actions. Journal of the American Psychoanalytic Association, 16.

Fenichel, O. (1945). The psychoanalytic theory of neurosis. New York: Norton.

Freud, S. (1924). The economic problem of masochism. Standard Edition, 19. London: Hogarth Press, 1961.

———. (1924). The ego and the id, Standard Edition. 19. London: Hogarth Press, 1961.

Gedo, J., and Goldberg, A. (1969). Systems of psychic functioning and their psychoanalytic conceptualization. Unpublished manuscript.

Gedo, J. (1969). Discussion at meeting of Chicago Psychoanalytic Society—October.

Grinker, R. R. (1953). The effect of infantile disease on ego patterns. American Journal of Psychiatry, 110.

Kinsey, A. C., Pomeroy, W. B., and Martin, C. E. (1948). Sexual behavior in the human male. Philadelphia: Saunders.

Kohut, H. (1961). Discussion of "The unconscious fantasy" by David Beres. Paper presented to the Chicago Psychoanalytic Society, September 26.

———. (1966). Forms and transformations of narcissism. Journal of the American Psychoanalytic Association, 14.

———. (1968). The psychoanalytic treatment of narcissistic personality disorders. Psychoanalytic Study of the Child, 23. New York: International Universities Press.

———. (1969). Personal communication.

———, and Seitz, P. F. D. (1963). Concepts and theories of psychoanalysis. In Wepman and Heine, eds., Concepts of Personality. Chicago: Aldine.

Miller, S. C. (1962). Ego autonomy in sensory deprivation, isolation and stress. International Journal of Psycho-Analysis, 43.

Noy, Pinchas (1969). A revision of the theory of the primary process. International Journal of Psycho-Analysis, 50.

PART IV

*TRAINING IN
ADOLESCENT
PSYCHIATRY*

INTRODUCTION

The following position statement on training in adolescent psychiatry was derived from a conference cosponsored by the American Society for Adolescent Psychiatry and the University of Chicago Student Mental Health Department held at the University of Chicago, November 14 and 15, 1969.* From a series of papers relating to experiences in training psychiatrists to work with adolescents, college youth and families, the Committee on Training of the American Society for Adolescent Psychiatry drafted this statement which has been adopted by the society as its official position.

The variety of approaches and groups dealt with in the papers eventually fell into an over-all biopsychosocial conceptualization (Roy R. Grinker, Sr.). Salvador Minuchin stressed the different laws of regulation in each system from the biological through the social, economic, and cultural. Merton J. Kahne presented a working model of social psychiatry in a college setting and James F. Masterson, Willard J. Hendrickson, Robert Gould, Robert L. Arnstein, and J. P. Plunkett presented models for training in various settings. Harold Hodgkinson presented an educator's overview of the sociological role of psychiatry in institutions and how the psychiatrist might best function.

The Committee on the Position Statement on Training consisted of William A. Schonfeld, Chairman, Daniel Offer, Bertram Slaff, and Sherman C. Feinstein.

* Daniel Offer and James F. Masterson, eds., Teaching and Learning Adolescent Psychiatry. (Springfield, Ill.: Charles C Thomas, 1971).

417

20] POSITION STATEMENT ON TRAINING
IN ADOLESCENT PSYCHIATRY

AMERICAN SOCIETY FOR ADOLESCENT PSYCHIATRY

The need for more services and trained manpower to deal with the psychiatric needs of adolescents is clear. The National Institute of Mental Health reports that more than one fourth of all psychiatric clinic patients are adolescents. The recent increase in the inpatient adolescent population is overwhelming, with a 500 percent increase among boys and 150 percent increase among girls in the past fifteen years. It is urgent that additional psychiatrists receive training in how to meet these needs.

The American Society for Adolescent Psychiatry recommends that training in adolescent psychiatry be made available within the present residency structure as authorized by the Joint Residency Review Council of the American Board of Psychiatry and Neurology and the American Medical Association's Council of Medical Education. Five training levels are delineated: the psychiatry resident, the resident with a special interest in adolescence, the fellow in child psychiatry, the career adolescent psychiatrist, and the psychiatrist in practice.

All psychiatric residents should have supervised training and experience with adolescents during their three years of training. Trainees who wish more extensive involvement in this area should have the opportunity to take, as their third year of residency, an elective in adolescent psychiatry. Child psychiatry fellows with an interest in adolescents should have the same opportunity for a full year's elective in adolescent psychiatry; this, with a year's additional training in child psychiatry, would satisfy the residency requirements for certification in the subspecialty of child psychiatry. Those interested in college psychiatry should be offered the opportunity to study at a college psychiatric training facility. The existing one- and two-year fellowships in adolescent psychiatry currently being funded by the National Institute of Mental Health on the fourth- and fifth-year levels should be continued for those who plan to become career adolescent psychiatrists.

Competence in diagnosis and treatment is the core aim of general psychiatric training. The technical problems of working with adolescents requires knowledge of the physical, cognitive, and affective aspects of growth and development, the dynamics of family involvement and interaction, the significance of peers, the impact of school and recreational activities, and the total spectrum of adolescent behavior.

The resident must learn, under supervision, the techniques of individual interviewing and psychotherapy with adolescents and with their parents, psychopharmacotherapy, group therapy, conjoint family therapy, and crisis intervention techniques. He must be informed about various sociotherapeutic approaches, community psychiatry, the varied concepts of educational disabilities and their remedies, and psychological tests and their significance. The concepts of milieu therapy must become familiar.

He must learn how to collaborate effectively as a teacher and consultant with all the disciplines working with youth.

The college psychiatrist needs awareness of the sociological structure of the total college community. He may be working with administrative, faculty, and dormitory staffs as well as the students.

Involvement in specific research projects involving adolescents is to be encouraged.

A combination of adolescent inpatient and outpatient services provides the basic components of an effective training facility. In residency programs that lack these services the trainees should be rotated through affiliate organizations that can provide them. These could include hospitals, clinics, residential treatment centers or schools, day hospitals, group homes, half-way houses or residence clubs for adolescents, and the psychiatric services of courts and probation departments. Additional opportunities exist in the adolescent clinics designed to care for general medical needs. Schools, both public and private, the emergency services of general hospitals, aftercare clinics, neighborhood health centers, drug-abuse clinics, and special settings, such as homes for unwed mothers, also provide valuable opportunities for study.

What is required is actual and extensive experience with adolescents, under the supervision of psychiatrists trained and experienced in working with the age group.

The American Psychiatric Association's Task Force on Continued

Education has stressed the need for continued education. The task force may recommend that each district branch undertake to give refresher courses to its members. Adolescent psychiatry may be one area requiring such instruction. The local affiliate society of the American Society for Adolescent Psychiatry could foster such clinical seminars in collaboration with the district branch.

Recommendations

The purpose of the American Society for Adolescent Psychiatry's position statement on training in adolescent psychiatry is to suggest the means by which training in adolescent psychiatry could be implemented into graduate psychiatric training. These recommendations will be submitted to the American Psychiatric Association and the American Board of Psychiatry and Neurology for their support, review, and reactions.

The responsibility for establishing what the required residency training should be, lies with the Joint Residency Review Council of the American Board of Psychiatry and Neurology and the American Medical Association's Council of Medical Education. It is to this council that these recommendations are directed.

1. There is no need for a special certifying board in adolescent psychiatry. Psychiatrists with special interest in adolescents should come from both general psychiatry and child psychiatry.

2. There is an urgent need to include training in adolescent psychiatry for all psychiatric residents:

    a. The council should strongly recommend to the approved residency training centers that they give all trainees supervised experience with adolescents during the three years of the general psychiatric residency in those clinical facilities for training available in the community in which the training center is located. No resident is expected to involve himself with all the facilities for training, but all residents should be involved with some of the facilities.

    b. The council should urge the training centers to broaden their existing programs to cover adolescents by including questions on adolescent psychiatry on both the written and oral examinations of the American Board of Psychiatry and Neurology in general psychiatry;

3. Opportunities should be provided for special training in adolescent psychiatry for all residents who desire this in their third year of psychiatric residency.

4. The third year could also serve as the first year of the child psychiatry residency for those who wish to go on to child psychiatry.

5. The National Institute of Mental Health should also be encouraged to support more special career adolescent psychiatry fellowship training programs.

6. Special training programs for college psychiatry should be available.

7. The affiliated societies of the American Society for Adolescent Psychiatry should make available to the district branches of the American Psychiatric Association and to hospitals requesting assistance personnel to organize training seminars in adolescent psychiatry for extended psychiatric education of the practicing psychiatrist, and staff psychiatrists, both as long-range part-time and concentrated full-time programs.

PART V

PSYCHOTHERAPY OF ADOLESCENCE

INTRODUCTION

Though controversial, many psychiatrists believe that the therapeutic tasks with adolescents require special techniques that differentiate adolescent therapy from child and adult treatment. Gitelson in 1948 noted that the adolescent frequently reacted to the current situation (vis-à-vis the therapist) and aroused much anxiety. In contrast the role of the therapist with the child or adult is clearly defined as the adult helper or parent.

Therapy with adolescents requires dependability, controls through the intelligent use of authority, and the providing of an ego ideal. Gitelson saw the goal of therapy with adolescents as facilitating a character synthesis rather than analysis. Special therapeutic skills required are the ability to tolerate mistrust, the capacity to develop empathy and the making of narcissistic contact, especially in crisis situations. Adolescents require help with the establishment of identification and the reformation of the ego ideal leading to final consolidation of the superego. All this must be carried out at an optimum ego distance which allows the therapist to support and encourage the patient during his explorations.

Some of the most difficult aspects of adolescent therapy are the problems about the handling of aggression. Testing and acting out create serious therapeutic dilemmas and frequently lead to negative transference and countertransference reactions. Unfortunately, aggression in adolescence is often seen and dealt with as a regression to a drive level and therefore spontaneous and destructive. If in the treatment of adolescents the use of aggression in the sadistic and masochistic form is seen as a defense against their feelings of loss and a plea for help, then a great deal of their behavior becomes clear, and essential countertransference

425

problems may be avoided or dealt with. The aggression is not a regression to an old repressed conflict, but the utilization of aggression in the immediate present is in the service of mastery, not destruction.

The psychotherapeutic parameters required in adolescent therapy cannot be learned as an interpolation of either child or adult therapeutic techniques, but demand a curriculum and experience in depth based on direct contact with the adolescent and his institutions. The following chapters explore the therapy of adolescence in the individual setting, the group through network therapy and in the hospital by means of mileu therapy. Future papers will explore therapy through the family as well as other modalities.

Alfred Flarsheim presents the treatment techniques used with a psychotic adolescent locked in a symbiotic relationship with his mother. His handling of the transference-countertransference issues is crucial and explores the problems presented by the needs of the mother and her son to sustain the symbiosis and the dangers inherent when the therapist intrudes into this relationship. Bruno Bettelheim presents his ideas about the role of parents in the treatment process and the essential role of the therapist with the patient in regards to dealing with the current transaction, "Because only after we have a present can we acquire a conception of our past, and begin to gain a feeling for the reality of a future."

Max Sugar deals with newer concepts of group psychotherapy and presents a case report of an adolescent who could be engaged only through the use of the social network with which he was related. This technique shows some promise for dealing with severely disturbed youths who cannot be dyadically engaged and "underscores the need for flexible treatment to suit the individual patient's needs at the appropriate time when he is motivated."

Donald B. Ringsley reviews the basic elements of residential treatment of adolescents and deals with the important elements of the determination and preparation of the adolescent and his family for hospitalization, the postadmission reactions, the natural history of an adolescent in the program, and his eventual discharge. His discussion of the resistance maneuvers gives deep insight into the developing ego structure of the maturing adolescent.

The remainder of this section is the report of a panel held at the First Annual Scientific Meeting of the American Society for Adolescent Psychiatry, May 4, 1969 in Miami Beach, Florida. The panel with Malvina W. Kremer, Chairman, consisted of Robert Porter, Peter L. Giovacchini, Laurence Loeb, Julian I. Barish and Max Sugar. The essays presented in the discussion of the treatment of an adolescent boy deal with the themes of engaging the adolescent in therapy, the therapeutic alliance, the problem of permissiveness and restrictions, transference and the nontransference aspects of the patient-therapist relationship, characterological factors, and interpretative and noninterpretative approaches.

21] RESOLUTION OF THE

MOTHER-CHILD SYMBIOSIS

IN A PSYCHOTIC ADOLESCENT

ALFRED FLARSHEIM

Certain problems in the psychotherapy of the dependent psychotic adolescent patient are similar to those encountered in the treatment of children, and result from the fact that in both the psychotic and the child, the therapist is confronted with a symbiotic patient-family unit rather than with a separate autonomous individual.

I will describe a treatment situation in order to discuss the rationale of certain technical procedures. These procedures are patterned after the classical psychoanalytic setting and are designed to construct an environment within which we can utilize potentially disruptive forces for therapeutic benefit, particularly those that arose from the patient's relationship with his family who supported him financially. Replacement of the psychotic symbiosis between the patient and his family by a psychotic delusional transference reaction was important in this case, and seems to occur regularly in the treatment of patients with psychotic character structure.

I will discuss the theoretical implications of each technical procedure as it arises during the description of the psychotherapy. This method leads to interspersing clinical description and theoretical discussion, rather than separating these altogether into different sections of the chapter. I hope that this method will help to tie the theoretical considerations closely to the clinical data. The editors have graciously allowed this form to stand despite their preference for more consistent separation of clinical and theoretical sections.

The patient is a severely disturbed young man, and from the standpoint of life adjustment, the treatment was not a simple success story, but it offers us the opportunity to discuss very important questions.

First I will describe the delineation of the therapeutic setting. Then I will describe the way in which a paranoid patient made use of this setting. The following sequence was observed, and will be detailed: (1) He localized and controlled his paranoid expectations as a result of the treatment alliance. (2) He actively staged an assault by his mother on his therapy—the kind of assault he had previously had to undergo alone. (3) He regressed to an organized dependent state, after his therapy survived the assault. During this regression he developed a symbiotic transference relationship characterized by delusions that his union with me provided magical protection and assistance. I only recognized the existence of the transference delusions after the magical expectations were thwarted by reality. At that point he developed a painful somatic illness. In addition to being painful, his symptoms were characterized by greater vividness of sensory experience than he had known previously. During this illness he accepted and utilized physical care in a nurturing, sustaining relationship with his mother which represented a new achievement for him as well as for his mother. (4) He emerged from the regression, with retention of some of the vividness of perception and feeling that he had first experienced in the painful somatic symptoms.

Psychotic Symbiosis between the Patient and His Mother

Before treatment, a chronically incapacitated seventeen-year-old paranoid adolescent and his mother were unhappy in their relationship, being scarcely able to control murderous impulses toward each other. Still, they were inseparable. The mother had previously signed him out of hospitals against advice, at the same time insisting that she could not have him at home. The patient felt seductively tantalized, tortured, and poisoned by his mother and considered killing her, whereas she felt burdened, depleted, and threatened by him. Though the symbiosis enabled them to survive despite the ego defects of each, it was destructive in the sense that it blocked continued maturation of the patient, and also perhaps of the mother (Giovacchini, 1965).

When she telephoned to ask for treatment for him, the patient's mother described her son as very disturbed and at the same time as conforming and capable. As so often in the late adolescent, both were true, that is, he could at times adjust to the outer world despite severe inner disturbance (Arnstein, 1958). She stressed that she wanted her son "to get a good job," and therefore wanted the "best treatment" for him. Then she asked: "What if he won't come in to see you?"

In working with children and adolescents in private practice I had become sensitized to that question. As the later treatment confirmed, it was important that I not become involved in this question. I simply answered that if he did not come in to see me I would not see him and would respect his judgment by assuming that it was best for him not to see me.

At this point I want to mention a familiar argument against this way of handling the mother's question, and then some reasons why I chose to react as I did.

The reason often given for guidance and counseling of the psychotic, for manipulation of his environment, and for advice given to the patient's family as to how to manage him, is as follows: The psychotic patient is psychically incomplete as an individual, and complete only when we include those persons with whom he has a symbiotic relationship. If the symbiotic relation with the family hinders the patient's development, both by meeting his pathological needs and by forcing him to meet pathological needs of others, the therapist could be considered to be doing an incomplete job if he sees the patient alone. On the basis of such considerations it can be argued that for the psychotic, one must either provide conjoint or concurrent family therapy, or insist that the patient leave home and live independently of his family, or, if he cannot do this, remove the patient from his family and provide residential milieu therapy.

Now I want to summarize my reasons for *not* advising the mother about getting the patient to come to see me: For the therapist to give such advice is to offer omnipotence that he does not actually possess. Initiation and maintenance of therapy depends not only on the wishes of the patient alone, but on the total symbiotic patient-family unit. Two main categories of motivation lead parents to seek treatment for their psychotic child: The first is hope that therapy will make the child more submissive and compliant, and will bind him more closely in a pathological symbiosis with the parents. Even though this motive may be very prominent, it is conflict-laden, and we can assume that there is also at least potentially a second motive, on which successful treatment depends. The second is hope that treatment will foster the child's maturation and emancipation from the pathological parent-child symbiosis. Ambivalence toward psychotherapy is associated with the parents' ambivalence regarding the maturation and emancipation of the child.

If the therapist advises the parents how to handle the child at home the parents become the agents of the therapist in their management of the child. The therapist becomes responsible for the results of the parents' discipline of their child. The child feels controlled by the therapist as a parent, and if the parents' discipline fails, the therapy is, from their point of view, proved to be worthless, destroyed. If on the other hand the therapist limits himself to controlling things over which he actually has control, that is, the circumstances in the consulting room, he can more easily protect the treatment from confusion with parental handling of the patient, and the treatment is less vulnerable to destruction by the parents' behavior. The child may not come into treatment, or may not be allowed to continue it, but the treatment will be available, undestroyed, for him to use later if he should so decide.

Insofar as the treatment setting is invulnerable to destruction by the parents' ambivalence, it implements the parents' beneficial impulses toward the child and cannot be used as an instrument of destructive impulses toward their child. The parents may be very critical of the therapist, as was true in this case, but their guilt toward the patient is nonetheless reduced by their awareness that the therapist will not permit them to destroy the treatment.

Similar considerations apply to the patient. But by not directing the patient's life, the therapist avoids burdening him with the need to protect his treatment by compliance with the therapist's instructions. On the other hand when the patient is given guidance as to his behavior outside of the treatment room, guidance which is often called support, his failure to comply with the guidance (failure which may be represented by trivial symptomatic acts) can become a reason for guilt and fear of his therapist. When this guilt and fear is added to that which arises spontaneously as transference, disintegration often occurs. This series of events can lead to such severe anxiety that hospital confinement is required, and in some case reports this sequence has been used to confirm the need for "supportive" manipulation which in fact may have caused the disintegration.

If I had advised the mother about influencing her son I would implicitly be taking sides in her conflict. Though by advice I would have been trying to support the mother's wish for her son's treatment, I would have been ignoring her opposite feelings. Complying with a request to support one side of the mother's ambivalence would have the effect of showing her that the therapist does not appreciate and respect all of her feelings. This can lead her to feel competitive with the child who is to have treatment in which all of his feelings are valued.

Even the most benign advice given under these circumstances increases a splitting whereby the mother is allied with the therapist against the patient (and, incidentally, often against the father). The mother, for the moment, has positive feelings about the child coming into therapy. The patient, from the mother's viewpoint and to some degree from his own, is left with the opposite feelings. If the patient later develops hope and positive transference in the therapy, this balance is likely to be reversed. The mother then becomes aware of her own negative feelings which were initially projected onto the patient, and she will then need to try to sabotage the treatment.

In psychotherapy the patient has an opportunity to achieve autonomy, and to learn to what extent and in what ways he influences his family, rather than to see himself as either a passive victim of manipulation or as a possessor of omnipotent power. To some degree the mother is the patient's agent when she introduces obstacles against the initiation or continuation of the psychotherapy. To keep the field clear for the patient's understanding that to a significant degree the mother is his agent is an important reason for the therapist not to make the mother the therapist's agent by becoming involved in such management decisions. We hope to avoid obscuring the patient's ambivalence, whether this conflict is expressed directly by the patient or indirectly by a relative asking the therapist about manipulating the patient.

The patient may feel that he comes of his own volition, or he may feel pushed toward treatment by others. We do not have to dictate the kind of motivation that our patient uses to come to us. When the patient lives in a symbiotic relation with someone else, effective motivation for treatment must be that of the symbiotic unit, and cannot yet be the motivation of the patient alone. It is meaningless to tell the mother of such a patient to let the patient make his own decision about treatment. There is not a separate person to decide.

In summary, by asking how to get the patient to come to see me, the mother was inviting me to intrude into the symbiotic relationship between herself and her son. In addition, she was also unconsciously expressing her own ambivalence about treatment for her son. The symbiosis is needed by both patient and mother; if the therapist intrudes into it he threatens both of them. If he stays out of it, he can work with the patient while the symbiosis continues, providing an opportunity for the patient and the mother to achieve separation without violent disruption of their lives.

In this case, at the time of the mother's call I did not know that the kind of strain that the family situation would put on the treatment was being foreshadowed when she said she wanted to pay for her son's treatment. This turned out to fit in with the mother's pattern of tantalizing her son by promising something and then withdrawing it. Insofar as the patient contributes to or provokes the family's reactions, we expect these reactions of the family to become particularly useful in the treatment, as I hope this case will illustrate. When we cannot use the family's reaction to the treatment for therapeutic purposes it becomes one variety of what is sometimes called "sabotage of the treatment by the parents." In reconstructing the beginning of treatment in instances in which parents intruded into their child's treatment in ways that sabotage the treatment, I have found that I had intruded into the autonomy of the patient-family unit earlier by advising how to get the patient to come into treatment. In such cases it has turned out later that after such advice the patient and the parents lost the feeling that the treatment was being undertaken and maintained on their own voluntary initiative. Instead, they felt that I was trying to coerce the child into treatment, and they banded loyally together against the intruding therapy and the therapist.

I told the mother that whether the patient lived in a hospital or elsewhere while coming to see me was not for me to say; I did not dictate where he should live. The purpose of all this was to demarcate treatment from management. There are many psychiatric facilities in Chicago. I was therefore able to assure the mother that they could get other psychiatric help if the kind of therapeutic setting which I offered was not acceptable. I want to stress again that this is an application to an interdependent family unit of a way of beginning treatment which is routine when the patient is functioning as a separate independent individual and retains the initiative in his treatment. Just as with an individual, we hope that this will accomplish two purposes: first, that it will contribute to a definition of the therapeutic setting; and second, that it will help to identify patients who need casework to sustain them between sessions.

In summary, the mother's question provided an opportunity to define and delineate the therapeutic setting which I considered necessary in order to work with this type of patient. The patient was seen alone, and

433

no effort was made to direct his life outside of the consulting room, or to advise the family.

First Session with Patient

A week after his mother's phone call the patient called for an appointment. When he arrived, he looked around the office suspiciously. He said that he knew "they" were around somewhere. I followed his glance, but when I was not successful in seeing "them," I shrugged and looked back at him questioningly. He pointed toward the coat closet, and started to open it. I motioned him toward the exit door. I preferred that he leave rather than search for material things. A search of the room would have diverted our attention from psychological processes to material objects. I assumed from the start that I would either work with his mental representations of objects, or would need to provide residential care; I believed that there was no middle ground. I told him that it was because my only interest was in how his mind operated that I suggested that he leave if he did not share my interest (that is, if there were not a minimum self-observing function). This was a rejection of the patient's initial approach, but it was not only a rejection, because at the same time I was able to point out the value of his psychological processes, as adaptations, in that he had the ability to think of his enemies as behind a door, in the closet, kept hidden by me.

This put the patient in an interesting dilemma: The enemies were not visible in the office. Should he go out, and perhaps join them, or stay with me? He had expected the fifty-minute hour to be a requirement of mine, as though he would be a prisoner for the duration of each session. But inasmuch as I had already made my autonomous decision to work within the psychological frame of reference rather than in a material one, I was bound to respect the patient's autonomous decision to stay or to leave, and I told him so.

For the moment, anyway, he decided to stay. It was then that I learned that he lived in a world of persecuting monsters that in childhood had been largely limited to threatening to "touch" him in nightmares, but that in recent years had taken over most of his waking life as well, in the form of frightening visual and auditory hallucinations. He did not want to say more than this about them. (Later I learned that he and his mother were both ill during his infancy and early childhood and that

434

nightmares of childhood changed to halluncinations at puberty, age fourteen, when his parents separated. He felt sexually tantalized by his mother and was afraid of killing her or of being killed by her.)

He had heard of "free association" and of "resistance," and expected me to try to get him to speak openly and freely. In this way he gave me an opportunity to link what he called resistances against speaking with the doors he had been able to place between us and the enemies. I tried to maintain a consistent position despite his repeated invitation to coerce him to express himself freely. I tried to be consistent with him in my attitude that I had no reason to think that free association would be helpful to him, and that, far from resisting, by concealing thoughts from me he was succeeding in carrying out a decision that was important to him.

Despite several previous brushes with psychotherapists, the patient experienced this as something new. I learned later that he was used to making regular searches of therapists' offices, while the therapists tried, as he remembered it, to get him to tell his "secrets."

I took no formal history. One thing lost as a result of this was that I did not know whether there had been a good period during childhood to which the patient could be expected to be able to regress if necessary. The patient's ability to organize a paranoid structure in which he could hide secrets was, however, prognostically favorable. As we shall see later, during a period of regression that followed, both the patient and his mother achieved brief periods of more integrated mother-child relationship than had been reached at any time during his actual infancy. The main advantage of not taking a formal history was that the patient was left in control of speaking or not speaking, and deciding what to say and what to conceal.

In addition to leaving the initiative with the patient, this method of starting treatment enabled us to observe directly whether treatment would be helpful for him, rather than attempting to infer from historical data whether treatment would be possible.

As long as the patient comes in without any element of coercion by the therapist, and as long as the therapist consistently serves as an intermediary between parts of the patient's personality rather than as an intermediary between the patient and his outer world, we can be sure that the therapy will be helpful. We cannot, however, be sure that it will be sufficiently helpful for the patient. Only clinical trial can tell us whether treatment will be sufficiently helpful in any particular patient-therapist combination.

In this case, the patient's belief that I wanted to find out about him and also to change him contributed to his determination to resist what he saw as my impulse to trick him into free association. This could have been viewed as a negative prognostic sign. On the other hand, neither verbal free association nor resistance against it had any necessary place in his treatment. I told the patient what conditions I considered essential: the fee, the scheduling, and that he use the couch. All of those were for me. They enabled me to be honest when I told him that my needs in our relationship were already met. Within this framework, persuading him to talk was no more necessary than would be trying to dictate the manifest content of someone's dream. The arrangements of the treatment setting were to enable me to be comfortable in the roles he put me in: someone who hid persecutors in closets, and someone from whom to keep secrets, for as long as he needed me for this purpose. The setting enabled us to recognize his reticence as an achievement, rather than as a resistance against some goal of mine, a goal that I was trying to impose on him. The role of secrecy, the secret, and privacy in development have been stressed by many authors (see especially Bettelheim, 1950, 1967; Khan, 1963; and Winnicott, 1964). His reticence implied that he had not only someone from whom secrets were worth hiding, but also secrets worth protecting, and "some place to keep them," within himself.

To summarize, the patient began treatment with a paranoid transference reaction. I assumed that hallucinated dangerous objects (causing him to surround himself with guns) represented split-off aspects of his perception of me. By keeping the dangerous objects in this psychic location, that is, split off and separated from his perception of me, he was able to maintain his relationship with me and to control and modulate his anxieties during the therapeutic sessions. In this way we were able to regard the existence of the hallucinated objects, and the affects attached to and directed toward them, as successful adaptations rather than as pathological failures of adaptation (Sandler and Joffe, 1968). The patient's identification with this way of perceiving and valuing his hallucinatory experiences made it unnecessary for him to shoot guns at them in reality.

Symbiotic Transference

There followed a partial fusion with me, in which he regarded our thoughts and opinions as identical, while at the same time mutually dangerous to one another. Clear delineation of the limits and boundaries of the therapeutic setting made it safe and worthwhile for him to maintain delusions of fusion and mutual persecution, limited to the therapeutic relationship and replacing other persecutory delusions. A transference psychosis with a paranoid adaptation characterized by delusions of mutual persecution between himself and me temporarily replaced the symbiosis with his mother. This occurred in the following way:

He entered a two-year period of scornful triumph over me during his hours, and of combat with an hallucinated image of me between the hours. A major advantage of coming to see me at all turned out to be that he found me powerless and eligible for scorn and contempt during his hours. His relationship with my hallucinated image when he was not with me, however, was very different. He could by no means be so confident of triumph in the combat between us in his hallucinations when he was not in the office. For one thing, in the office we did nothing but talk to each other. On the outside our hallucinated contacts had a tendency to end in interminable bloody mortal combat; killing and being killed had to be repeated over and over again while an hallucinated image of me interfered grievously in every area of his life, both day and night.

Before coming in to see me, his life had been made miserable by jungle beasts and by the weapons of hordes of barbaric savage warriors. Within a very few weeks I had replaced all these, and my evil destructive intent was implemented by a wide variety of techniques by which he believed that I attempted to foil and to destroy him. A frequent method of torture used by my hallucinated image was to tantalize him. Repeatedly he saw me try to lead him to expect something good, and then ruin it or block his access to it, and then laugh triumphantly at his discomfort. He reproached me for masturbating him for hours on end in his bed at night. He could then frustrate me by not reacting. (Later he associated this with memories of his mother's "tickling" him as a small child.)

One day he ran on the beach in a distraught and dishevelled state, and when stopped by the police, told them that I was "after him." On the days of his appointments he would start off for my office in this dishevelled condition. He would begin to feel confident of his powers and before he came into the office would stop off in the washroom and tidy up. By the time I saw him he would come strolling into my office in a scornful and condescending way. While in the office, he would spend most of his time ridiculing me as someone who thought himself

437

to have great powers and could learn his secrets, but from whom it was pathetically easy to hide. In contrast to the power of my hallucinated image when he was away from me, while he was actually with me he saw me as someone with delusions of omniscience and omnipotence, to be regarded at best with the indulgence due a helpless and irresponsible child.

He preserved the belief that he was tantalizing me by not telling me things of importance about himself. Hiding secrets from me also meant, of course, protecting me from his dangerous thoughts, against which I would be helpless and vulnerable. I exposed myself to them anyway, despite his efforts to protect me from them, because he also talked of my omniscience that enabled me to know everything in his mind.

For the first year he regularly arrived ten to thirty minutes after the scheduled beginning of appointments. He called this "coming late." When I called it coming at the time he decided was correct to come, we found that he was trying to show me how it felt to be kept waiting, to share this feeling with me. We decided this might have some connection with childhood feelings of having been kept waiting. Coming late was both an attempt at communication, and an attempt at mastery by reversal, making me wait. He hated to be kept waiting and we assumed that this derived originally from the infantile feeding situation. It was as though his own rage at having been kept helplessly waiting could very concretely be transferred to me. This, of course, made me all the more dangerous, and made triumph over me all the more valuable and reassuring.

Later we found another meaning for coming late. The beginnings of the hours stood for his own beginnings, the infantile impulses he both needed and feared to reach. By coming late he omitted the beginning of the session, standing for his own beginning. In this way he revealed that he felt incomplete while he needed to exclude his beginnings, his infantile longings, from his treatment. I will describe how, during a subsequent period, he used coming late to exert magical influence to prevent me from leaving him.

During the paranoid phase, I did not want to reject the role of persecutor. I acknowledged it was an achievement on his part in that he could put both his tormentors and his desires into me, and we traced in detail the ways in which he was using me for this purpose.

This was repeated over and over in many different ways for about two years. For example, on one occasion he went into a restaurant. He thought that the waitress was pretty and looked at him lovingly and

438

would give him good food. Simultaneously, he saw me alongside of her, ugly, hated, and hateful. He was horrified to see that I gradually moved into the path between him and the waitress; and I became transparent. At that point the waitress became as ugly and hateful as I, and the food poisonous. He ran out of the restaurant in terror.

About a week later, he went to another restaurant, where things went more successfully. Again the waitress looked lovely; the food looked good. Again I appeared beside her, ugly, hated, and hateful. This time, however, he was able to move me all the way out of the restaurant onto the sidewalk, where he kept close watch on me through the window, while making threatening gestures that kept me from returning into the restaurant. As long as he did not lose sight of me for a moment he could prevent the waitress and the food from becoming horrible. He succeeded in keeping watch on me and was able to enjoy his dinner.

We can understand that he was considered strange and bizarre in the community, but in the therapy he and I could recognize the achievement of successfully excluding my image and the feelings associated with it, which earlier had poisoned his food.

The patient continually questioned and tested our relationship. "What was for whom?" became his continual preoccupation. Of all possible kinds of motivation that he thought I might have for seeing him, there were two, and only two, which did not threaten him. One was my wish to be paid the regular hourly fee, and the other was my interest in the currently manifest sources of his anxiety and in his currently manifest defenses against it. We could share recognition and appreciation of his achievements whenever we recognized the operation of current adaptive and defensive techniques, such as his victory in the second restaurant. Paranoid suspiciousness was regularly increased, however, whenever I showed any interest in increased understanding, or in learning more than was currently manifest. Paranoid suspiciousness was also increased whenever I showed any interest in his changing in any way, even when the changes were improvements in his life that he said he wanted. Any expression of interest in deeper understanding, or in his changing, indicated to him that I was dissatisfied with the way things were in our relationship at that particular moment and that I wished to change it. In addition, they both indicated my involvement with a future moment in his life, rather than the present one.

The future time was when I would understand more about him or when he would change in some way that he thought I wanted. While he was in the office, however, only present time could be controlled. Fu-

439

ture time and past time were joined and meant the same thing. They meant our relationship in the intervals between his appointments. He assumed that any evidence of my being dissatisfied with our relationship at a given moment meant enormously powerful dissatisfaction of an oral aggressive kind. There were at this time only two alternatives that he could envisage: safety from oral aggressive destructive devouring impulses or being torn to pieces by them. Any expression of my interest in understanding more about him was viewed as an indication that I was not merely unsatisfied with our relationship at any given moment, but overwhelmed by and consumed with oral sadistic impulses to penetrate and devour him.

Repeatedly he would come into the office expecting me to be displeased that he was not meeting some fantastic demands that he had projected onto me. (Much later the displeasure that he expected me to experience became attached to potentially realistic expectations such as academic and career goals. The substitution of these potentially realistic expectations for the megalomanic and omnipotent ones indicated a reduction of latent anxiety.)

In commenting on this case, Giovacchini observed that the ideal setting for the psychotherapy of schizophrenia permits the therapist to "be" with the patient for a treatment of indeterminate duration, without feeling required to "wait" for any changes in the patient's condition. Giovacchini described a case of his own in which even his satisfaction with his patient's present status threatened the patient, because it meant being consumed by the therapist. Freud (1910) illustrated "wild" psychoanalysis by describing various ways in which a doctor misused psychodynamic principles to direct a patient's activities.

Our treatment arrangement was such that I had no contact with his parents and was not involved in management decisions about him. The patient lived first in a hospital, then at home, and then alone in a rented room. He and his family were able to make these arrangements, thus freeing my attention for understanding the adaptive value of his behavior. As a result of my isolation I was relatively free from anxiety about his functioning outside the office, and I was able to be quite genuinely pleased by the understanding of whatever current adaptive mechanisms he was able to use. If I had assumed responsibility for his adjustment in the community it would have been necessary for me to share anxiety and criticism regarding his bizarre behavior in public. Had this been true the patient would have been burdened with the requirement that he regulate his behavior while away from me in order to protect his treatment from the disruptive effects of my anxiety and criticism if he failed to meet my requirements. My requirements within our treatment setting were simpler than regulation of his whole life.

The patient's mother paid his treatment fee unreliably. In this way she tantalized me as well as the patient. After I insisted that the fee be paid regularly, delusions of persecution disappeared, and he basked in comfort, based on the delusion that I provided magical omnipotent care and protection. The inevitable disappointment of these magical expectations led to murderous hatred of me, and he regressed to a very painful helpless infantile state, and recovered from the regression. I will now give some details of this sequence.

Family's Assault on the Patient-Therapist Unit

The patient became more comfortable after I had reliably replaced his former persecutors. At this time he began proclaiming independence to his mother. She blamed the treatment for his defiance, refused to continue paying for it, and we interrupted the treatment. He became increasingly anxious, desperate, and distraught until his mother again agreed that he should resume his treatment. This cycle was repeated several times. During this time he was able to tell me that in his own thoughts he had adopted his parent's title for me, "the greedy Jew." We found that this was not only a reflection of his family's values. It was also far more than the projection of his oral aggressive impulses, with ridicule of me and of the pious fundamentalist religiosity of his parents. More important, it was a request. By provoking his mother to pay for his treatment intermittently, he was repeating the kind of tantalizing that he felt had been done to him all his life. This time, however, the feeling was that the therapy, he and I, rather than he alone, were tantalized by his mother. The wish expressed in the term "greedy Jew" was that I would not put up with her laggard and intermittent payment of his fee. The patient had succeeded in arranging things so that something that previously had been his problem—that is, his mother's tantalizing —had now really and actually become my problem (Shields, 1962).

Finally I became displeased with partial payments and told him that I wanted to have the complete bill paid every month. He immediately took on this decisive attitude as his own, as though he and I were one. I believe that this is the same mechanism described by Silber (1962). He

441

reports that this kind of identification marked the turning point in his treatment of an adolescent. Khan (1963) described the treatment of an eighteen-year-old boy who reenacted a childhood experience by him as the patient felt he had been treated by his mother. Khan's reaction to being treated as his patient's infant self provided a focus for identification for the patient. Neither Silber's nor Khan's case involved their families to the extent that my patient did.

The patient came back the next day and said that his mother and stepfather "couldn't understand" and wanted to know why I made such a stipulation. I told him that if the bill were not paid I would not want to continue working with him. The patient was at first afraid that his mother would refuse to pay the bill and we would have to interrupt his treatment or to terminate it; but though she was "shocked" she decided to pay the fee on a regular basis.

At this point the patient felt a "new confidence in his treatment," as he put it, and entered a new phase.

Regression

The patient now had a new term for me—"whore." This, we discovered, had a very important meaning. He thought of a whore as a person who provides what the customer requests, is always available, cannot tantalize or keep one waiting. The demands that a whore can make are strictly limited. There is the money and a few clearly defined conditions. Having met these simple requirements, one need have no special consideration for her, or feel guilty about how one has treated her.

The patient's behavior showed marked changes. Nightmares and the hallucinations disappeared, and he began sleeping well at night and resting during the days. Where previously he had been aware of his body as a victim of illness or of external attack, or as strong enough to defeat powerful enemies, he now sunned himself on the beach, swam, and was generally quite conscious of caring for his body. Where previously his food had been chosen because it might give magical powers, or because there was some reassurance against its being poisoned, he now ate full regular meals, and enjoyed them.

I do not believe that he had worked or studied in any organized purposeful way since I had known him, but he had at times posed as a college student or graduate, and had talked of plans and expectations for great achievement without effort or preparation. Now he acknowledged, without flaunting it, that he was doing "nothing" and had no immediate plans. Weaknesses and strengths were not mentioned, where before I heard only of total helplessness and omnipotence. He spoke of expecting "some day" to return to school, and could imagine working toward a goal rather than needing to believe he had already accomplished it. For example, he began to notice students and could consider being one himself some day rather than needing to pose as a graduate of a university.

His attitude toward me was no longer one of contempt and scorn. He looked to me for clarification of what was happening, and for this he felt "totally dependent" on me, and what he mainly wanted from me was that I acknowledge that important processes were occurring within him.

It is interesting that openly acknowledging that he was resting was more disturbing to the patient's family and to their community than had been the overt paranoid symptoms of the past. It turned out that the family had consulted psychiatrists about the treatment before, when the patient was overtly delusional and hallucinating. Whatever they had been advised about psychotherapy then had been somewhat reassuring. At least, they had been told, proper psychotherapy, shock treatment, or drugs could always be used later. But now all this was changed. Now the family were warned the the patient's need for rest would be insatiable and that I should certainly be making him do at least some productive work. Before, the patient had been regarded as ill; now he and I were in collusion to foster the sin of sloth.

Indications of Structuralization during Regression

Several changes soon followed:

1. There was a reversal of the patient's attitude toward the treatment hours, and he became apprehensive on the way in to see me. He feared he might think of frightening things while he was in the office. Initially I recognized only the possible psychoeconomic advantages that this might hold for him, insofar as frightening things might be concentrated in the office and therefore contribute to his comfort elsewhere.

2. A week or two later, we discovered, however, that this change had

443

been associated with another one which at first the patient had not recognized. He realized that he had begun to dream with a sharper border between dreams and the waking state than he had ever known could exist (Klauber, 1967).

3. In addition, his dreams now included actual persons in his daily life rather than nightmare monsters. On several occasions, when a person would threaten him in a dream, the interchange between the patient and the dream figure included logical, reasonable argument rather than the previous more massive defenses. In the past he had partially awakened, or the dream was interrupted and replaced by an altogether different one, or there was combat between two enormous forces, or between one enormous and one powerless one, each represented usually by claws or body parts. Now, there was interaction in dreams between whole persons.

4. This change in the content of dreams, and the more clearcut distinction between dreams and waking life, such that the dreams no longer overflowed into his waking consciousness, were associated with the first new development which we had noted at that time (no. 1 above). It was then that he had become afraid of coming to my office, because he might think or say frightening things.

5. Within a few weeks another change followed. Whereas in the past he had gotten great pleasure in hiding his thoughts and feelings from me, now he said that it was a far greater pleasure to think that there were parts of himself that he did not know, and that he would never know. In the past he had thought of suicide as a protection against external enemies. Now he said: "There are parts of myself that I will never know about and therefore I will not have to kill myself to destroy them." I believe these developments indicate a capacity for internalization and repression, rather than the projection that had been evident earlier (Klein, 1946).

6. Not long after his new-found ability to forget, remembering came to have a new meaning. First he talked about many of the painful and unpleasant events of his childhood. I find it very interesting that all these events were already familiar to me. As far as the content goes, I believe that he had talked of each of them at one time or another in the past. In this sense he regained no new memories. At the same time there was a quality of newness and freshness in the way that he now talked about them. After these unhappy and painful memories, he began talking about some happy experiences that he could remember from childhood. Again these were events to which he had referred ear-

lier; none of them was new. As with the painful ones, though, there was something different about the feelings with which he talked about them, a tone of sincerity rather than of mocking. Certainly both of us recognized a new quality. It was only now that we came to realize in retrospect how limited had been his feelings in the past. Like and dislike were now expressed where earlier I had heard only about extremes, worship of perfection and loathing of evil.

He had a fantasy that I would produce a baby in him by using him as a woman. In connection with this, he mentioned that such fantasies had occurred occasionally around the age of fourteen, when his parents separated. I do not recall his having told me of these at any earlier time during his treatment. Instead, in the past he had boasted of enormous phallic superiority, especially compared to me. Now he talked about my giving him a baby by having intercourse with him as though he were a woman, with no evidence of any particular anxiety. One kind of relation between a homosexual fantasy and paranoid fears is illustrated by this fantasy. His sexual fantasies toward his mother had included mutual torture and murder. Now, he was equated sexually with a mother, and given an infant, his own infancy. The patient's own painful infant-mother relationship and painful infancy had been sources of suffering to him. Inclusion in his ego of identification with his mother, and of his own babyhood, were integrative steps, which were apparently beginning to be possible for him at a time during which the hateful and destructive impulses were lessened in intensity.

As mentioned earlier, he began to come on time for his appointments and no longer needed to come late to express scorn and condescension toward me when he could acknowledge infantile needs. Now that he had regained some feelings from his own beginnings he felt more complete, and could include the beginnings of his sessions.

Somatic Symptoms during Regression

After the pleasant childhood memories, he began to notice small children and their mothers, and to feel moments of "great sadness." He did not, however, sound particularly sad as he mentioned these.

Then one day he fell asleep while sunning himself on the beach, and got a moderately painful sunburn. This was painful only for a few days,

445

but it precipitated panic and physical symptoms that far outlasted the direct effects of the burn. He could hardly swallow, felt as though he "could not breathe," and as though he were "choking." "Sadness and grief" were "terrible," but there was no crying. As a matter of fact the idea of "crying" was mine; he did not think of it spontaneously. It was at this time he learned something from his mother that he had not known before, namely that he had not cried as a baby, while alone in the house, ill with respiratory infections. It was then that the nightmares had started, which became hallucinations in adolescence.

While watching a mother with a small infant one afternoon, the "choking" became so severe that he "expected to die." Crying seemed a frightening possibility, but did not occur. He said that if he were to start crying he "would never ever stop," and "no one would hear or understand."

His attitude to me during this time became clinging and dependent, and also reproachful. He said his "whole self became just pain, not just his thoughts and feelings." He told me that "if he had had any idea that treatment could lead to such suffering he would never have come" to me; he felt "incomparably worse than ever before."

Our Belated Discovery of His Magical Protective Expectations during Regression

Gradually over the succeeding weeks we discovered that he felt more than just reproach toward me. He also felt what he called "the kind of hatred that eats you up." For the moment anyway, the oral sadism was felt as his own, and was now directed toward an external and a separate object—me. At the time that he had felt this hatred with the most intensity he had not been able to tell me of it, nor had I recognized it. His hatred was justified because he considered me responsible for the illness that followed the sunburn. In the past he had hated me, because he felt that I was persecuting him in "magical and supernatural ways"; now his hatred was based on the failure of protective omnipotence which he had projected onto me.

We had already recognized that the term "whore" referred in part to the adaptation he needed from me, but it was only after the sunburn that we discovered the extent and the nature of this need. Only at this time did we recognize that it had included the belief that I was provid-

446

ing him with magical protection against the operation of the laws of nature. He believed that he should have been able to sleep in the sun without getting burned.

We can now understand that when the patient was in a regressed state, his expectations had necessarily included magic, and were inevitably doomed to disappointment in reality. In retrospect, therefore, the patient and I could see that I should have anticipated some such disappointment, even though I could not have anticipated the exact form it would take. It was only in the patient's reaction to the failure of the protection he believed I was providing that we discovered the delusional expectations. As long as he felt he had the protection, he took it for granted and had paid no more attention to it than to breathing.

As far as my own feelings were concerned, I had been so enamored of this particular method of handling a psychosis, without the usual "support," that I had failed to recognize the corollary of the paranoid organization—delusional trust. This latter had been manifested by the magical protective function with which the patient had imaginatively extended our therapeutic setting.

Within the first twenty minutes of the first session after the burn, he was able to recognize the self-created nature of his belief in "supernatural protection." The reason he gave for his ability to recognize this was that I did not provide, and in so many previous crises had not provided, actual guidance or assistance in his life outside the treatment room. (Such assistance is often called "support," but it might confirm a patient's delusional expectations. See James, 1964).

I believe that because of the demarcation of the treatment from the management and direction of the patient's affairs we were saved here from precipitation of a psychotic regression that could not have been handled in the treatment setting.

After the patient lost me as a "supernatural protector," his initial reactions were anxiety, helplessness, illness, and hatred of me. There were times during subsequent weeks when he felt that he had to have omnipotent "supernatural" powers because I had failed to provide them. This was followed by a feeling that neither of us needed supernatural powers. In this context he was able to begin to think more about using human powers. He became aware of grief and sadness about the years lost while needing to "be God" because of "ghost and other God-like enemies," in contrast to "human enemies, and friends."

It was springtime, and the patient knew that my summer vacation was approaching. He had feared that it would be impossible for him to survive while I was away, and that some stray angry thought might bring about my death while I was away on vacation, perhaps by causing an airplane to crash while I was in it. Along with this he wondered whether I might perhaps wish him harm in a way that would have magical destructive effects on him. He had not been able to talk about my actual vacation in concrete terms. He had tried to influence it magically. For example, he had imagined that every minute that he was late for an appointment would be substracted from my vacation. This was to occur automatically, not because of my wish to make up the time for him. At the end of an hour during which he had strongly experienced the "humanizing" of our relationship, he became able for the first time to ask me the actual dates of my vacation trip and to discuss his plans for that time.

There was other evidence of his increasingly realistic attitude toward me. His complaints about me and about his treatment became more realistic. Instead of feeling that I harmed him in magical ways as he had previously, he began to complain now about my interfering with his life through the mechanics of the appointments and scheduling. I think it is very important that at this point I began to feel definitely more irritated and "needled" by his complaints and attacks. Before, when he had expressed hostility toward me because of my "omnipotent powers" or "supernatural pretensions," I had never really felt that the hostility reached me. Now that his complaints were about more realistic things, the hostility reached me more realistically. For the patient, unpleasant somatic sensations, such as what he called "choking," continued to be the reference point for all vivid feelings (Szasz, 1957). I came to be represented in his life by the hated physical symptoms that he felt I caused and that tied him to me. Hatred of me became hatred of our relationship, that is, of his need for me. He thought of these physical sensations as the hold that I had on him. He wanted to lose the physical discomfort, and the relationship with me insofar as it stood for this discomfort, but he felt that this would include losing the vividness of feeling in all perceptual modalities, in his life in general, which he now saw as his only hope. In discussing this case at a seminar, Bettelheim compared the painful vividness of the patient's newly experienced feelings with the reactions of some concentration camp prisoners at the moment of release. He compared the external threat of the concentration camp to this patient's paranoid fears. While actually enduring the persecution, all attention was consumed by the task of survival. But when the external threat was suddenly removed, energy was freed from the preoccupation with survival.

448

Only then did some prisoners experience anxiety appropriate to the former threat.

Concrete Assistance during Regression

After the onset of the panic and the somatic symptoms, there were two things the patient said he needed from me. First, he was able to let me know that he valued my silence when he could depend on it. Anything I said was liable to be an intrusion, regardless of its content. Second, he was afraid that I would not recognize the seriousness and reality of his experiences, that I might think he was dramatizing, or pretending. This latter, he said, would be an "ultimate and crushing loss" and he was "horrified" to think about being "so let down." It kept recurring in his thoughts, however, along with moments of fear that the couch would let him drop to the floor. This fear recalled memories of being afraid during childhood, that his father would drop him while carrying him. In my office the fear was of being actually dropped. It was a real fear at certain moments, not only the memory of a fear. Therefore, at those moments, the couch had become equated with the supporting parent, and with me, rather than being a symbolic representative of support (Winnicott, 1958). From a subjective standpoint, at those moments the patient was receiving real, literal, and precarious support, which was subjectively equal to bodily support from me.

When his physical suffering and anxiety were at their height, he phoned for his first and only emergency appointment. Bettelheim (1950), Boyer (1961), Gitelson (1952), Little (1958), Searles (1963), Shields (1962), and Winnicott (1958), among others, have pointed out the need of the regressed patient to make some concrete demand on the therapist. From the baseline of the structured treatment setting, with its regular appointments, the emergency appointment constituted a significant departure from the regular routine. It may have been the context of regular routine that led the patient to feel that the emergency appointment was an important demand for him to make on me. In any case, he was reassured by it, and contrasted it with having been either alone in the house as a child, or afraid to call out or to go to his parents when he awoke from a nightmare. At his request we arranged more frequent regularly scheduled hours. He has not again had to call me between hours.

I am postulating that he was able to gain reassurance from something so minor as a phone call and a single unscheduled appointment because the baseline structure of the treatment was such that this constituted a significant departure, a significant addition, to what the patient regularly received from me. If what he needed was the significant addition, it was important for the arrangement to be such that the addition did not exceed what I wanted to give. If the patient had called me repeatedly for extra appointments, I would not have given them to him, because to have done so would have been to foster delusional expectations of magical rescue. A single additional appointment remained within the frame of the therapy and had symbolic value (Milner, 1952; Balint, 1958).

At that time the patient had been living alone in a rented room, which he had converted into an arsenal. He saw the emergency appointment with me as indicating that he could seek and accept realistic care and called his mother and returned to live with her. What he got from me and what he got from his mother were psychically linked, even though they were objectively so different (Little, 1966). What he sought from her was something that I could not possibly have given him. His attitude toward her was altogether different from what it had been earlier. He was now openly helpless and clinging, not wanting to be left alone even for a moment. At first his mother objected that he had already "drained her too much," had interfered with her life, that there was "nothing wrong with him," and that "all he needed was religion."

There was now, however, no really serious question of stopping payment for the treatment. In the past he had remained dependent on his mother while denying his need for her support. Now he told her that he was ill, that his treatment was a matter of survival, and stated flatly that he would kill himself if he could not continue. My impression, however, is that he not only blackmailed his mother into continuing payment for his treatment, but that he also made her recognize his needs as valid. He reported conversations in which she talked of his treatment, and of his resting, as important for his health and happiness rather than only as a means to push him to "get on with a career." His mother genuinely tried to cater to his needs, without seductive tantalizing. Both the patient and his mother seemed to recognize the possibility of using his regression as a second chance to correct something that had gone wrong earlier (Bettelheim, 1967).

At the time the patient returned to his mother's home it certainly was necessary that his mother should recognize and understand the importance and the meaning of what they were going through together. It would, of course, have been possible for me to explain this personally to the mother. My implicit contract with this patient would have been violated by my intrusion into his life outside the consulting room. But even beyond this there was another, perhaps more fundamental, reason for me not to advise her about her son's condition, even granting the importance of her being informed. Just as it was important for me to avoid intrusion into the destructive symbiosis that was so prominent at the time of the mother's initial call, now also their autonomy deserved respect.

For me to intrude might have disrupted a delicate process in the relationship, introduced a note of artificiality, and robbed them of the opportunity to find their own spontaneous feelings for each other. The mother's sincere efforts seemed to indicate that changes in the patient had in fact been reflected in a genuine change in her. She seemed to enjoy the opportunity to strive toward a maternal capacity that she had been unable to reach when the patient was a small child. It is as yet too early to know whether this "second chance" will be sufficient to permit belated resumption of maturational processes and sustained development toward health. Their efforts may fail. From the standpoint of the developing child, Winnicott (1965a) points out that the ability to retain the relationship with the actual mother makes increasing independence a part of growth instead of a disruption of the personality. Success for the patient must include a change in his subjective perception of his relationship with his mother. Because of the reality of the symbiotic attachment, this will require maturation of his mother also, as long as he chooses to use his actual mother for this therapeutic purpose. Success now means growing out of the need for one another while carrying the capacity for love into new relationships.

Recovery from Regression

PROGRESS NOTE—ONE YEAR AFTER RETURNING TO
HIS MOTHER

From one point of view he is, as he says, "sicker than ever before." Object relations are limited and tentative. He is living with his mother and stepfather, and without shame is accepting care appropriate to a very young child. His mother says he is more clinging than he was when actually a small child. He can, on the other hand, have "disagreements"

451

with his mother, rather than only the former "outbursts." Crying remains a "terrible danger" and has not occurred, though moments of "great sadness" persist.

He has experienced sexual urges toward a young woman, and there is evidence of the beginning of a relationship between them, complete with actual troubles and conflict. The following episode is illustrative: He tantalized this girl sexually and was tantalized by her. During the subsequent night he was concerned that she might come into his room and touch him because of her unsatisfied sexual wishes, which he was afraid he might not be able to satisfy. This stands in sharp contrast to his former fear of being touched in his sleep by frightening devouring monsters.

Familiar places such as streets and buildings, as well as familiar people, seem "painfully real and intense." He explores the neighborhood, "trying to expand the perimeter," and returns home when the new vividness becomes too intense. Recently he did some garden work, which was trivial in itself, but which the patient called significant, however, because he felt he was "acting voluntarily for the first time in his life."

His need to be able to depend on my silence is similar to what he calls "expanding the perimeter" of his physical world. In both instances the patient needs to maintain control over his feelings as he tentatively probes his newly cathected environment. Any response from the environment that is not clearly under the patient's control can be a reminder of the former vulnerability.

PROGRESS NOTE—ONE YEAR LATER

A year ago it was difficult to justify on pragmatic grounds the way I was treating the patient. The change from a paranoid adjustment to a regressed infantile state involved loss of structure, rather than the increase of structuralization, and increase of social responsibility, which are our usual criteria for successful treatment. I leaned heavily on the encouragement of colleagues, in order to sustain my confidence that spontaneous maturation from the regression would take place and that this would be reflected in improved functioning in relation to the outer world.

This in fact has now begun to be manifest. I will mention very briefly a few recent events. He began to feel constricted by his home and by me, and then expressed jealousy of what he regarded as my accomplishments. He linked this with the resentment of his need for me, and with the tendency to depreciate the very things he needed from me. We went through a stormy period during which dreams of precarious attachment to me alternated with repeated dreams of coming through glass barriers, from the inside of dark places into outside light, and of finding evidence of life among ashes and ruins. He said his mother originally, and now also I, were the "fault in his personality," while he became more tolerant and more casual with both of us. He anticipated freedom from us, without scornfulness. The patient had regressed from a paranoid organization to one in which he was dependent upon the therapy to enable him to make use of his mother's care during a breakdown: "A mental breakdown is often a 'healthy' sign in that it implies a capacity of the individual to use an environment that has become available, in order to re-establish an existence on a basis that feels real" (Winnicott, 1965b). When the patient emerged from the helpless dependent state he retained some of the vivid awareness of the reality of himself and of others. Such vivid feelings had previously been attached to the pain and discomfort of somatic symptoms and to hallucinated and nightmare objects.

He was "carried away" by an urge to work in an artistic, creative field, and his interest partially replaced his interest in dreams and fantasies (Coppolillo, 1967). He has become creative, and with decreasing effort, increasingly productive. I find it especially interesting that he has needed no education about dealing with the many practical problems involved in producing and marketing his work, despite the fact that he seemed so naïve about external reality during the previous paranoid and regressed states.

I felt sufficiently comfortable to doze occasionally during his hours. I do not believe that this was owing particularly to the symptomatic changes in his general life adjustment, with reduction of crises, nor to my withdrawal from obsessional defenses he developed. My increased comfort seemed rather because he took more responsibility for the course of each hour and needed less from me. For example, he spontaneously compared his feelings to those he had earlier during the same hour or during previous hours. He became more independent within the hours, but not yet independent of the treatment itself. I have not found out specific contents of "the secret" with which he began treatment; but the treatment became a "secret alliance" from which he drew confidence in dealing with the outer world. This confidence has not extended to intimate relations with women, which he wants but of which he is still afraid.

Infantile Symbiosis and Developmental Potential

In the regressed state, directing hatred toward me freed him to turn to his mother, to seek and to accept from her the kind of empathic nurturing care that she had not been able to give, nor he to accept, during his actual infancy. Though it was important for the mother to understand the patient's needs, only he could communicate them to her. The new symbiosis was characterized by empathic communication between the patient and his mother, and represented the infantile prototype of all exclusive relationships. My role was to help him understand his needs, for example, to link the disappointment and hatred toward me to the hatred that had disrupted his early relationship with his mother.

The mother did not seek advice at this time, and I believe this was an indication of potential health. She was able to achieve a modicum of belated success in functioning as a relatively mature mother. If we assume that the patient needed this kind of care from some mothering person, then he either had to get it from his mother or he would have required some kind of residential treatment. If I or someone else had intruded to tell her what to do, we might have taken away some of her pleasure in accomplishing something that was her own, and thus reduced her motivation to provide what was so urgently needed by the patient at that time.

The motivation of the successful mothering person (like the motivation of the psychotherapist) derives from the expansion of her own ego. This involves personal maturation with increasingly autonomous functioning, rather than the following of someone else's directions. For these reasons it was important for me not to intrude into the relationship between the patient and his mother when they were seeking a "second chance" to correct something that went wrong in his infancy. They had to make their own errors and to correct them in their own ways.

Discussion

COMPARISON OF THE MOTHER-CHILD AND THE THERAPIST-PATIENT RELATIONSHIP

Because the mother is the total environment of the unborn child, we equate her welfare with that of the child. Similarly in the relationship

454

between the mother and a newborn infant we recognize the necessity for the mother to maintain her own psychic organization in order that her adaptation to the infant will foster healthy development. We recognize the necessity for a setting that is protected from influences that are disruptive to the mutual adaptation between the mother and her infant and developing child. Mirsky (1953) describes a complementary series in this connection. The more efficient the inborn adaptive reflexes of the neonate, the less must be supplemented by the mother. The more unstable the inborn homeostatic ego processes of the infant, the more is required of the mother. The more that is required of the mother, the more support she needs from her own environment.

If the mother is frustrated in her efforts to provide for her infant, whether because of illness or because of impingement of the external environment, it becomes necessary for her to erect defenses in her relationship with the baby, to avoid assaultive behavior toward him. She might, for example, withdraw from the infant, in a personal way, even while continuing to function as a source of biological nurture. Further, to the degree that the mother achieves identification with her newborn infant and is subjectively undifferentiated from him, frustration by her baby and resultant hatred toward her baby is felt as hatred toward herself. This poses an additional burden against which psychological defenses must be erected. If, however, the degree of frustration in the relationship with her baby is of a lesser degree it can be sustained nondefensively by her ego. Under those circumstances, instead of arousing anxiety and defenses, it can contribute to her pleasure in seeing her infant develop autonomy and mature out of his need for her.

These same considerations apply also to the therapist's relationship with the patient. The therapeutic setting is designed to permit the patient maximum autonomy while the therapist maintains sufficient structure within his own ego to function in relation to the total ego of the patient. The alternative is a folie à deux in which the therapist participates in a mutual regression to a primitive level of functioning, for example to that of a nurturing part object for the patient (Bettelheim, 1950; Boyer and Giovacchini, 1967; Giovacchini, 1965; Hoedemaker, 1960; Rosenfeld, 1962).

Perhaps the question I asked myself most frequently about this case is whether he should have been treated in a hospital. I was encouraged to continue seeing him in the office by the composure with which he arrived and left the office, no matter how panicky he became during hours. Many times it was exactly when imminent danger of suicide, or when lack of evidence of positive functioning, had led me close to deciding to abandon treating him by respecting his autonomy that he came in the very next hour having mastered the problem that had discouraged me.

In residential treatment one hopes to be able to coordinate various aspects of the patient's life, such as his living quarters, eating and sleeping arrangements, and social interaction. If we can coordinate these interpretively as they appear in the material the patient presents in the office, we can assume that this coordination, in the patient's mind, will enable him to coordinate them in his life.

If the patient cannot come to the office and communicate with us in a way that enables us to coordinate and integrate the mental representations of the various parts of his personality, residential therapy may be needed (Bettelheim, 1967). The patient's ability to communicate in such a way that we can integrate his experiences as he presents them to us is not an absolute, but a matter of degree in each therapeutic situation. One thing is certain, however, and that is that our role as therapist would be radically changed if we were to take over parental functions in combination with our psychotherapeutic function.

[I]n the analysis . . . or in ordinary management of the more psychotic type of patient, a great strain is put on the (therapist) and it is important to study the ways in which anxiety of psychotic quality and also hate are produced in those who work with severely ill psychiatric patients. Only in this way can there be any hope of the avoidance of therapy that is adapted to the needs of the therapist rather than to the needs of the patient (Winnicott, 1958).

It is by arranging a therapeutic setting in which the personal needs of the therapist are clearly defined and already met in advance that we seek to free the therapist to consider the patient's needs, and thus to implement our intent to provide a therapy adapted to the needs of the patient. The therapist can enjoy working with the patient even during those times when the patient is suffering and is wanting to make his therapist suffer. In the ideal therapeutic relationship this can be distinguished from the sadism or masochism of the therapist. The therapist's enjoyment comes not from the fact that the patient suffers, or from being made to suffer by the patient, but from the fact that the therapist can utilize the patient's experiences, of whatever kind, as material for the exercise of the highest synthetic and integrative functions of the therapist's ego. Such functioning is pleasurable, so that the therapist can honestly and genuinely welcome the patient no matter how the patient may be feeling (Giovacchini, 1965). "Love in the countertransference" (Winnicott, 1958) seems an appropriate term for this pleasurable expansion of the ego of the therapist.

In order to free the therapist for this expansion of his own ego, his other needs in relation to the patient must already be met by the circumstances of the treatment relationship. Ultimately such expansion of the ego, our own and the patient's, is the therapeutic agent we hope to provide for our patient.

REFERENCES

Arnstein, R. L. (1958). The borderline patient in the college setting. In Wedge, ed., Psychosocial Problems of College Men. New Haven: Yale University Press.

Balint, M. (1958). The three areas of the mind. International Journal of Psycho-Analysis, 39:328–340.

Bettelheim, B. (1950). Love is not enough. Glencoe: The Free Press.

———. (1967). The empty fortress. Glencoe: The Free Press.

Boyer, L. B. (1961). Provisional evaluation of psychoanalysis with few parameters employed in the treatment of schizophrenia. International Journal Psycho-Analysis, 42: 389–403.

Boyer, L. B. and Giovacchini, P. L. (1967). Psychoanalytic treatment of characterological and schizophrenic disorders. New York: International Science Press.

Coppolillo, H. P. (1967). Maturational aspects of the transitional phenomenon. International Journal of Psycho-Analysis, 48:237.

Freud, S. (1910). 'Wild' psychoanalysis. Standard Edition. London: Hogarth. 1953. Vol. II.

Garma, A. (1966). The genesis of dream hallucination. In The Psychoanalysis of Dreams. Chicago: Quadrangle.

Giovacchini, P. L. (1965). Treatment of marital disharmonies. The classical approach. In B. Greene, ed., The Psychotherapies of Marital Disharmony. New York: The Free Press.

Gitelson, M. (1952). The emotional position of the analyst in the psychoanalytic situation. International Journal of Psycho-Analysis, 33: pt. 1.

Grinker, R. R. (1957). On identification. International Journal of Psycho-Analysis, 38: 378–390.

Group for the Advancement of Psychiatry. (1965). Sex and the college student.

Hoedemaker, E. D. (1960). Psychoanalytic techniques and ego modifications. International Journal of Psycho-Analysis, 41:34–46.

James, M. (1960). Premature ego development: Some observations on disturbances in the first three years of life. International Journal of Psycho-Analysis, 41:288–294.

———. (1964). Interpretation and management in the treatment of pre-adolescents. International Journal of Psycho-Analysis, 45:499–511.

Khan, M. M. R. (1963). Silence as communication. Bulletin of the Menninger Clinic, 27. Pp. 300–313.

Klauber, J. (1967). On the significance of reporting dreams in psychoanalysis. International Journal of Psycho-Analysis, 48:424–432.

Klein, M. (1946). Notes on some schizoid mechanisms. International Journal of Psycho-Analysis, 27:99–110.

Little, M. (1958). On delusional transference (transference psychosis). International Journal of Psycho-Analysis, 39:134–138.

————. (1966). Transference in borderline states. International Journal of Psycho-Analysis, 47:467–485.

Milner, M. (1952). Aspects of symbolism in the comprehension of the not-self. International Journal of Psycho-Analysis, 33:181–195.

Mirsky, I. A. (1953). Psychoanalysis and the biological sciences. In Alexander and Ross, eds., Twenty Years of Psychoanalysis. New York: Norton.

Rosenfeld, H. A. (1962). Review of psychotherapy of the psychoses. International Journal of Psycho-Analysis, 43:184–188.

Sandler, J. J., and Joffe, W. G. (1968). Comments on the psychoanalytic psychology of adaptation. International Journal of Psycho-Analysis, 49:445–454.

Searles, H. (1963). The place of neutral therapist-responses in psychotherapy with the schizophrenic patient. International Journal of Psycho-Analysis, 44:42–56.

Seton, P. H. (1965). Uses of affect observed in a histrionic patient. International Journal of Psycho-Analysis, 46:226–236.

Shields, R. (1962). A cure of delinquents. London: Heinemann.

————. (1964). Mutative confusion at adolescence. In Report of the Twentieth Guidance Interclinic Conference. London: National Association for Mental Health.

Silber, E. (1962). The analyst's participation in the treatment of an adolescent. Psychiatry, 25.

Szasz, T. S. (1957). Pain and pleasure. New York: Basic Books.

Winnicott, D. W. (1958). Collected papers: Through pediatrics to psycho-analysis. London: Tavistock.

————. (1964). Review of memories, dreams and reflections by Jung. International Journal of Psycho-Analysis, 45.

————. (1965a). The family and emotional maturity (1960). In The Family and Individual Development. London: Tavistock.

————. (1965b). The mentally ill in your caseload (1963). In The Maturational Processes and the Facilitating Environment. London: Hogarth.

22] DISCUSSION OF

ALFRED FLARSHEIM'S ESSAY

BRUNO BETTELHEIM

In his introductory remarks Dr. Flarsheim mentions that his chapter sheds light not only on the treatment of a schizophrenic adolescent, but also on the management of the therapist's relationship with the patient's family. I would like to address my first remarks to this problem, because what Dr. Flarsheim has to say on it is particularly pertinent in this day where the fashion seems to be to consider the entire family, if not an entire community, as the psychiatrist's patient. As you know, most child analysts, following the pattern set by Anna Freud, believe that psychoanalysis of children requires the cooperation of the parents in the treatment process. Cooperation is a high value and hence has a high price. The particular price such cooperation exacts is compromise; as likely as not, compromising the interests of the child to those of the parents. Dr. Flarsheim refused to engage in such compromising behavior. He made it clear that either the patient came on his own, out of his own free will, or not at all.

This the patient could not believe; as much as the children who come to the Orthogenic School, in terms of their past experience with their parents, society and their psychiatrists, are unwilling to believe that we mean it when we promise them that we shall not compromise their interests to those of their parents; that the treatment is strictly for them, with the only purpose to help them develop the type of personality they wish to develop, certainly not the one that the parents, who pay the bills, wish to see us develop. Like our children this young man also initially could not believe that the analyst really meant it. Therefore, in his first encounter with him, he had to test it out.

This takes me to the very beginning of the treatment, as it should, be-

459

cause in psychotherapy the beginning is not only half of the whole, as Plato taught, but rather, to quote Denham on prudence, "We may our ends by our beginnings know." This not only the patient knew well but, fortunately for him, also his therapist. All psychological phenomena are highly overdetermined, particularly all that happen in psychoanalysis. Therefore I hope Dr. Flarsheim will permit me, not to differ with him, but to add to his interpretations of the crucial event of the first session, when he motioned the patient to the exit door. I have no reason to doubt any of Dr. Flarsheim's interpretations, least of all the reasons he was conscious of for his pointing to the door. But I believe that even to this patient in his first session it was more important to find out what this therapy would be all about than to find out where the enemies were hidden, in the treatment room or elsewhere. The biggest worry of the patient is whether therapy is for his benefit, or for someone else's including that of his family, or his therapist. We must remember he had been placed in a mental hospital by his mother. She had arranged for treatment for him in the past. She still was paying for it. She was paying for a fifty minute hour. How obvious then that treatment was engaged in for her benefit. She wanted him to be in treatment with Dr. Flarsheim. But Dr. Flarsheim's motioning toward the exit door meant to the patient that as far as this therapist was concerned, he did not have to stay, for fifty minutes, or in this therapy, and more, that he was asked to leave if he wanted. He did not have to stay either in the treatment room or in treatment.

In putting this interpretation on the patient's reaction I might be overimpressed by my experience with schizophrenic youngsters who began to consider staying at the Orthogenic School worthwhile at the very moment they can believe us that all our doors are so constructed that even if we wanted, we could not lock anybody in, because all our locks can only lock people out of a room, but never lock anybody in. That they might physically or mentally become our captives is their greatest anxiety, as it was Dr. Flarsheim's patient's. Dr. Flarsheim's motioning the patient to the exit made it very clear to him that at least in one respect he was secure; Dr. Flarsheim would not make him captive to Dr. Flarsheim's or his mother's desires.

Of course Dr. Flarsheim's not letting him explore the closet on a deeper level also suggested to the patient that actually what needed exploration was not physical or external space, but the secret space of his mind. To this patient, as to all others like him, external reality is populated by persecutory monsters. No child is cured of his paranoia by his therapist engaging with him in shooting down the imaginary figures, because there is no end to the dangers of the external world. They can be mastered not by destroying them out there, but only by building up inner security. This, essentially, Dr. Flarsheim proceeded to do. He built up the patient's inner security, never mind how dangerous the external world may appear. Or to put it differently, there is no way to do away with the chaotic impact of the id; our only chance is to increase the strength of the ego, so that it may be able to control the pressures of the id.

On the basis of such beginning it was predictable that the patient would, from time to time, have to test out whether he really was in charge of his treatment. And this such patients typically test out by breaking appointments or coming late, very often the first signs of self-assertion. Unfortunately all too often the mistake is made to view this as resistance and try to analyze it as such. Nothing would be more erroneous. Dr. Flarsheim correctly interpreted it as meaning that the patient came at the time that was the correct time for him, namely the time that proved to him that he was not trapped but, on the contrary, in charge of his own treatment.

With this conviction firmly established, he then could move on to the other psychological determinants of his lateness, those Dr. Flarsheim specified, such as a reversal of roles by him: keeping others waiting as he had been kept waiting as a child.

Here I may add that nothing impresses the child more as to all-powerfulness of the parent, and his helpless bondage, than the parent's ability to keep the child waiting, starting with the very first helpless waiting of the crying infant to be fed. Thus, to be kept waiting means to be at the mercy of others. To keep waiting means to finally have become a somebody who, though he may still be in the power of others, also has powers of his own.

Dr. Flarsheim makes the point that what was of essence in the treatment of this patient was that in the treatment hour "only present time could be controlled." Much too much of the treatment of children and adolescents is directed toward the future. That is, parents get concerned because the youngsters do not work well in school, do not prepare themselves for a useful life. Erikson has pointed out to which degree the adolescent in our society needs a psychosocial moratorium, and this young man certainly needed such a moratorium very badly (Erikson, 1956). Even after he was convinced that treatment was for him, not to shape him in line with the desires of his mother, he still feared that the

461

analyst had certain plans for his future. Therefore it was of such great importance that Dr. Flarsheim was not at all interested what the patient would do in the future, or outside of therapy, but only in what he was doing when with the therapist. Because only after we have a present can we acquire a conception of our past, and begin to gain a feeling for the reality of a future. Exactly because the adolescent who needs our professional help is so terribly beholden to the images of the past must we avoid worrying him, or with him, about his future. Because as long as the past is not mastered in the present, no future is possible. Because no future can master the past, only the present can. If on the other hand we have mastered the past in the present, we automatically have a future. This the patient knew and that is why he refused to be concerned about his future.

Even before we can have a past, even before we can have a present, we must have a body. Witness the Draw-a-Man Test, which more than any other clearly shows how the schizophrenic neither possesses a body, nor a body image. Neither did this patient. As many other schizophrenics, he, too, in defense against his mortal anxiety that he is at all times threatened by utter destruction, believes, to the contrary, that his body is indestructible. As he got better, as he began to acquire a body, he had to test it out, dangerously. As the sunburn proved that he had a body, thereafter he suddenly was wracked by physical symptoms, including his choking and being hardly able to swallow. His sadness and grief of this moment were intolerable. As he had now gained a body that could be hurt, he realized what he lost, or never acquired, the feeling of having a body, namely in the nursing situation. That is why he could suddenly not swallow and was choking. As a baby he had not cried, probably because he had learned too early in life that his crying did not make any difference. As I pointed out in other context, the infant gives up crying if his crying is ineffective in gaining him satisfaction of his needs, because it is then only another unwarranted expenditure of energy of which such an infant possesses all too little.

Therefore it becomes understandable why his cry for help, namely the request for an emergency appointment, when it was met, had such great importance to him. Because it was the symbolic experience that proved that when he cried out for help now, it was available. This is why he did not need to abuse it.

Had Dr. Flarsheim permitted himself to be involved in the management of reality, then one, or a few, emergency appointments would have been relatively valueless and the patient would have asked for more and more. Because if we get involved in reality, then what counts is reality, and not the symbolic experiences. But since Dr. Flarsheim from the very beginning insisted that in psychotherapy we deal only with symbolic experiences, the symbol of one emergency appointment could go a very long way in demonstrating that now satisfaction of needs is available on demand.

REFERENCE

Erikson, E. H. (1956). The problem of ego identity. Journal of the American Psychoanalytic Association, 4:56–121.

23] NETWORK PSYCHOTHERAPY

OF AN ADOLESCENT

MAX SUGAR

An adolescent in therapy often brings in his "steady girl" or close friend(s) to meet the psychiatrist and sometimes asks that the friend be allowed to join the session with him. Is this an invitation to include the friend as a participant in the network of psychotherapy?

Speck (1965, 1967, 1968) has described his innovative use of the social network in therapy with schizophrenics and adolescents. His interest in and use of this approach stem from the common frustration of working with a psychotic who is the puppet or foil for someone who never appears on the scene. This experience led to his efforts at therapy in the home.

In his initial network therapy with young adult schizophrenics, the network consisted of multiple generations—a vertical network. Later he began horizontal networks for adolescents in which only their peer group is present. Networks, he stated, were indicated for psychotic and suicidal patients, involving friends and relatives with emphasis on treatment of the social field or network to avoid hospitalization. Speck's aim was "to tighten the bonds between people and as a corollary to loosen the binds."

This chapter will describe the use of the peer or horizontal network in the psychotherapy of an adolescent boy and will discuss some theoretical implications.

464

The Adolescent

At age fourteen years, while confined in a private mental hospital, Rodney was referred for extramural group therapy because he talked rarely in individual sessions and his therapist hoped that with group therapy he might progress further. This was to be in addition to individual psychotherapy, milieu and drug therapy, in which his progress was slow.

Rodney had been a chronic runaway and school truant, and as a result had had difficulty with his family, schools, and police. Because of his erratic behavior, the parents never knew whether he was sleeping at home or wandering around all night, whether he was in school or playing hooky for days or weeks at a time.

His family consisted of an aggressive, "no-nonsense" businessman father and a self-contained mother who was considered an inefficient housewife by her husband but who was creative in cooking and other hobbies.

Unlike Rodney, who could hardly make passing grades in school, his four siblings were considered brilliant. Parental memory was vague, but indicated that his birth and early months had not been unusual, nor had his early development in another city, except for enuresis. Major events in his life can be schematized as follows:

Sixteen months: sister's birth, for several months before and after which patient had hives; threw bottle across room when offered it on mother's return from hospital with sister.

Sixteen months to two years: father assumed rearing of Rodney while mother preoccupied with infant sister and other siblings.

Two years: family moved to New Orleans, Louisiana.

Three years: patient began running away from home; police called, considered "fey," "different from siblings," and "not long for this world" by mother.

Four years: family left New Orleans; patient fell down steps, fractured collarbone.

Five years: mother had miscarriage; patient never showed anger; when under stress cried or ran away.

Between ten to twelve years: patient laughed when punished with belt; enuresis stopped.

Eleven years: mother had hysterectomy.

Twelve years: family returned to New Orleans (father traveled a lot until then).

Thirteen years: patient attended public school for one year, having failed entrance for private school; patient refused tutor that sister had; sister then passed reexamination for entrance to same school where older brother was football star.

Fourteen years: patient entered another private school, where he was a truant and runaway; did not become a basketball star, as hoped by coach and father, but was a star runner; later expelled and entered public school, with further runaways and truancy; admitted to hospital; failed eighth grade; unable to make up mind; indecisive; many friends visited him in hospital, all disapproved of as "oddballs and wild" by parents.

Group Therapy

Rodney appeared to be a depressed schizophrenic, showing apathy, confusion, perplexity, extreme suspiciousness and negativism, and at times dissociation. He spoke in monosyllables, as if the weight of his words would collapse his lanky, thin, bent body. He seemed unable to make contact with the other group members and vice versa, though he attended fairly regularly for nine sessions over five months in spring and summer. He did not participate spontaneously, but he did seem to notice the others and at times reacted silently to various interactions and emotions with body movements, such as pushing his long hair out of his face. During this period he had some violent outbursts in the hospital, as well as some runaways from the hospital, both leading to intervals of seclusion, which kept him from several group sessions.

He was discharged from the hospital to return to school in September and continue therapy as an outpatient because he had shown some improvement during the summer: His behavior in the hospital had become manageable; he had taken a speed-reading course that improved his reading. His father, who had had some financial reverses, warned him that if he now played hooky from school he would be admitted to the state hospital. Rodney played hooky when he returned to school and went to the state hospital, which terminated his group therapy. His participation and responses in group therapy sessions had been remarkably unvarying and he had shown no change.

Rehospitalization

His state hospital stay of five months was marked by uninvolvement in therapy, noncomformity, battles with the staff at all levels, threats of and one actual runaway, and stays in seclusion. Treatment included tranquilizers, individual and group therapy, quasicounseling for the parents, and the threat of electroshock therapy. While on pass, he ran away for three days. His parents accused his friends of stealing during visits to his home. He complained about the public school and especially about the Negroes who picked fights with him.

No successful arrangements had been made for therapy or school when the mother called two months after discharge for him to return to group therapy. The parents seemed uninterested in Rodney's therapy; the father was aware of his lack of interest, and the mother was busy going in circles to avoid therapy for Rodney. Their passive aggressive sabotaging became very obvious. After further overnight absences from home, his parents had readmitted him to the state hospital two weeks before I saw him.

The Network of Psychotherapy

Because I did not feel that group or individual therapy were suitable for Rodney, I offered network psychotherapy to him, and he eagerly accepted it. His mother accepted the network, perhaps because she was caught off guard and because of the pressures of the situation. His father also acquiesced. But his mother managed to indicate her displeasure and indecisiveness on the day of the first scheduled session.

From the initial discussion of a therapeutic club for him, Rodney brightened up, became somewhat enthusiastic, and remained verbal and excited. He contrasted this proposed group with the previous one, which he said had not been satisfactory to him. He asked if he might bring in anybody that he wanted, and I agreed. He mentioned that his parents tried to dissuade him from going around with certain of his friends whom they considered unacceptable, and he expressed surprise that I would accept them in his group. I explained that he would be re-

467

sponsible for the attendance of the other people in the group as well as for his own attendance; that this group would be arranged on the basis of a therapeutic club for him, a special kind of group for him; that the arrangements about my confidentiality would be as before, but that there were no restrictions about confidentiality for him and his friends; and that whatever was discussed in the group by him and his friends would not be a secret for them; that there were no limitations about their meeting outside the sessions; and that they could continue their relationships. He seemed delighted with the possibility of arranging a club of his own in which his parents had no say-so.

At this time Rodney was still in the state hospital, but he was expected to be discharged shortly, and there would be no problem about his continuing with me unless he became restricted for infractions of the rules. He was attending school in the hospital and doing all right.

The forty-five-minute sessions were scheduled on Mondays after school hours, so that Rodney could arrange, during his weekend pass from the hospital, for his friends to come in on Monday. The fee for Rodney was on a regular basis for a forty-five-minute session.

Rodney's mother became much more noticeably vague, loose, and disorganized when I met with her to arrange the network, and I began wondering if she was not the psychotic person in the family for whom Rodney was acting out a psychosis.

For the first scheduled network meeting, his mother provided a barrier and indicated her resistance again. On the morning of the first session, she called to say that he could not be brought over because she had some other important plans for an anniversary luncheon with some of her schoolmates. The session was cancelled; the matter was not discussed as resistance, but another date was set for Rodney to be seen after school. The mother was told that she had to explain to Rodney why she cancelled the session that day.

For the first session Rodney came with Paul and Steve. They made the sign of universal acceptance of pot smoking—the V for victory sign —and greeted me profusely. Like Rodney, they were dressed like hippies—no shoes, leather wristbands, mandalas around their necks, long, unkempt hair, and dirty faces, hands, and feet. They commented that they were surprised to be accepted, and then sat down, smoked, and talked rather anxiously. I said that I did not care whether they wore shoes generally, since it was their feet, but that in my office I did not wish them to return without shoes simply because of the odor of their bare feet, which was not acceptable to me. They laughed about this and accepted it. Discussion centered on angry feelings about the hospital;

468

teachers; legal and parental authorities; sex ("booty"); civil rights; unfair treatment of Negroes and adolescents; use of LSD, pot, and other drugs. They also discussed Paul's being in psychotherapy and Steve's once having been to a psychiatrist. Steve was currently upset about the recent murder of his favorite uncle. Paul was the friend whom Rodney was concerned about bringing because of Rodney's parents' strenuous objections. Paul made suggestions and Rodney followed them. In this and the next two sessions, however, it was clarified that Rodney made suggestions or speculated about doing certain wild things and if Paul said, "Why not?" Rodney did them. It was as if he were testing out some of his impulsive notions on Paul. Paul was in good control, planning and promoting things, which he might abandon if they were too troublesome. If he gave the go-ahead signal, however, Rodney would follow through. The three of them were involved in the runaway escapade when they were picked up by the police.

For the second session Rodney came with Paul. There was some discussion about Rodney's leather wristband and the meaning of it. It was "related to a natural thing that you make yourself, nothing to do with machines and modern machine man who has no feelings, is not involved with other people." He discussed in great detail and with glee how it "smelled after a while and is never removed." "You play with it on, you sweat, you wash yourself whenever you wish, if you do, but the band stays on as a mark of real feelings, nature, natural man." This explanation seemed to be a response to my comments about their footwear in the first session. There was further discussion about Rod's acting out Paul's wishes, Rod's daring escapades over rooftops, encounters with cops, and the like. I pointed out how Steve and Paul were acting as parts of Rod's brain, particularly Paul, who was given the authority to approve things for Rod that he might not otherwise do and that gave Rod courage and an ideal to follow. Paul also provided a valuable superego, because he prodded Rod about doing better in schoool, the importance of education, using as an exmple his own continuing in high school, where he was a senior.

In the next session Rod was accompanied by Steve and Mark. In contrast to Paul and Steve, both of whom had had troubles with their families and had been to psychiatrists, Mark had no problems and did not know why Rod had asked him to come. He was merely doing Rod a favor. He had been smoking pot and had some fears about being caught, though he had never had any problems with police, in contrast to Rod, Paul, and Steve.

In the following session Rod came with Jerry, who was psychopathic in many ways. He complained about many things in society, especially about the way Rod had been treated and mistreated, and particularly about Rod's parents. Rod had told him a great deal, and he manipulated the details dramatically. Throughout the sessions there had been considerable testing of me, and each time Rod's suspiciousness, provocativeness, and efforts to test me were interpreted. His effort to malign me with the state hospital, his parents, and teachers with distortion of my powers was pointed out each time that the transference seemed potentially disruptive. Rod volunteered he had not told his parents of my cancelling the previous week's session, and he came to town on pass as usual. His parents did not check or ask about the lower bill that month.

In the fifth session Rod brought Paul, Steve, Jerry, Robert, and Mae, Robert's girlfriend. Robert was a psychotic youngster whom I had seen for evaluation some months before. Considerable time was taken up with Robert's hostile remarks about abuses by authority and especially about how Rod had been railroaded into the hospital. Robert was aware that he "was crazy, but Rod was not and should never have been in the hospital." There was a good deal of discussion about running away, traveling all summer, going to the Newport festival, to Detroit, and heading out West or other places, with a remarkable exchange of organized information about telephones, addresses of "pads" and friends in these different towns, and so on.

For the sixth session Rod brought Paul and Steve again. They discussed police brutality and authority, how and when to fight it, how to stand off, how not to get hurt, and so on. Paul was supposed to have been traveling out on the coast, but for some reason he did not go, and his plans were indefinite for the summer. Rod was interested in visiting his brother who, though married and in college, "was also hippy and cool, had a beard, understood" him, and he felt he would get along much better there than with his parents. This was further reinforced from the previous session, when Robert had indicated that he was going to move in with his own brother, who was also "hip, and not fuddy-duddy and a conformist" like his parents. It seemed to be a goal that would be helpful to him, and he was promoting the same thing for Rod.

In the seventh session Paul and Steve were with Rod. They displayed further paranoid suspiciousness of me in relation to Rod's presence in the hospital (even though he was on termination pass now), parental restrictions about school plans, and refusal to allow Rodney to visit his brother alone. They accused me of interfering with his discharge from the state hospital and visiting his brother.

470

In a session with the parents that same week, in response to their request to discuss school plans, it became apparent that father was very hostile, paranoid, and rigid. He was very antagonistic to psychiatry, did not accept his son's condition as an illness but felt that Rod simply "needed discipline, straightening out, sticking to the rules, and making more rules." He had no flexibility and denied awareness of emotions and emotional needs, particularly of the adolescent. He compared Rodney unfavorably with his other children. The parents wanted to return him to the private school from which he had been expelled or enter him in the school where he had been refused admission. They had denied Rod the school of his choice because they considered some of his friends who were going there undesirables. I pointed out that they could not really control this and that he might find undesirables at any school he attended.

On the morning of the seventh session, when Rodney was accompanied by Paul and Steve, Rodney's mother called to get further guidance. The school of Rod's choice was giving a test for admission that afternoon, at the time of his session, and she wondered if Rod should take the test though she had not talked with him about it. It was suggested that if the same test were being given at any other time, she schedule Rod for it, in the meantime discussing it with him at an opportune time. In this way she could allow Rod to attend his group session that afternoon. Rod's appearance at that session indicated that his mother had not tried to force him to take the test that afternoon. Many of their comments and complaints focused on trust, my involvement and commitment to my patients, and the comparison of their clothes with mine.

At this point it seemed that Rod was making good use of the group. He was relating well to me, though in line with his transference and with his suspicions. Many of his friends were as ill as he, but some were much better integrated. He was coping well on a peer level. He was against conformity, of which his father was an ardent example; he was against disorganization, of which his mother was an obvious example. His therapy seemed doomed to failure or abrupt termination unless the parents were brought into some treatment. An effort to have them come in regularly as a couple was sabotaged by the father who, at the end of their session, said, "There's nothing for us to talk about until we talk to the people at school and see where we can get Rod in. After that we will call you." I had previously mentioned to the parents that I thought that a couples' group might help them with some of their problems, not only with Rod, but also concerning the father's recent job change, the changing family fortunes, and the various stresses on them within the family of all the children. The father immediately refused vehemently and the mother was undecided. At this point the father was extremely negative toward me, whom he considered the devil's advocate, a view that made Rod's negativism and suspiciousness more understandable.

Rod was discharged from the hospital a week before his eighth session, which Steve and Don attended. The state hospital staff was very cooperative; they believed that Rod had been helped by the network psychotherapy, because his behavior had improved, he was giving no trouble to the staff, and had had no further runaways during his stay. Steve wished to continue the discussion of the previous session about trust, my commitment to treatment and them, my being different from them but respecting them, and my wearing the clothes that pleased me. Rod felt that he should discontinue therapy because he was no longer in the state hospital now. Rod refused to accept my interpretation that he was using me to get out of the hospital and maintained that he had not hurt me. I agreed that I had not been wronged, but pointed out his manipulation of me. Steve and Don agreed that he had used me and observed that "Rod is so busy screwing other people he feels everyone is going to screw him; he doesn't realize how distrustful he is all the time." When they gave examples of how Rod had screwed them and could not trust himself, he denied them. I pointed out that he felt he had been misled by people telling him bad things—Paul's telling him to "split out of town," which he did; Steve's telling him to jump into two feet of cold, muddy water, which he also did, but which Steve did not. There was some discussion about visiting his brother, choice of schools, and the feeling I was really in charge. I pointed out that his parents were in charge of him.

For the ninth session, Rod could not get any friends. He was planning to visit his brother for three or four weeks. There was a discussion of his not trusting me and his projection-displacement system. His family's plans were now changing the original agreement to provide continuity of therapy for Rod after discharge from the state hospital. I now felt that the mother and father were not reliable and manipulated and interfered with any close relation Rod had with me, other therapists, or any friends. I wondered about a possible strong homosexual tie between Rod and his father because the father took care of him in his infancy. The father manipulated, and Rod adapted to it and identified with the aggressor.

472

For the tenth session Rod brought Paul, Steve, Don, and Bill. Rod admitted that getting out of the state hospital was his goal in coming to see me and that he did not want to continue therapy thereafter. He was going to his brother's, where he wanted to continue school. To me he said, "I'm suspicious of you; you are going to interfere with me. I can't trust you." The group pointed out his using me to get out of the hospital and expecting me to be reciprocally suspicious and untrustworthy. The group was jolly, but also attacked me, perhaps because this was the last session before my vacation.

Rod had an appointment to continue therapy after my vacation, but his mother called to say he would have two or three visits with a psychiatrist while remaining at his brother's, to decide if he needed additional therapy. I suggested that they enroll him in school there or here and indicated that if he obtained therapy there, I would send a report, but questioned the advisability of his seeing a psychiatrist for only two or three visits unless necessary.

Follow-up six months later indicated a continuing acceptable adjustment in school with peers, brother's family (of wife and three children), and the parental home during school holidays.

At follow-up a year later Rodney stated that he had remained with his brother, failed the school year, was without plans or goals, except for returning to his brother's at the end of the summer or going to New York. He felt his parents were the same but were not on his back so much now. Though still psychotic, he was not in trouble now and was functioning to his satisfaction.

The network may also have prevented another immediate hospitalization (as had occurred twice previously), and possibly future hospitalizations, by allowing him to separate from his parents peacefully and move to his brother's home. If further contact is maintained, however, we may have his younger sister as a patient instead, because the family scapegoating has not been dealt with at all. Sufficient data were lacking to reconstruct his early years and the meaning of his first symptoms or the effect of his sister's birth on his tie with his mother.

Discussion

Adolescents in psychotherapy are known to be difficult for many reasons (Freud, 1958). The tendency to spontaneous gang formation has been used as a foundation and natural stimulus for group therapy (Sugar, 1967). One published report cites a "Spontaneous Request for Treatment by a Group of Adolescents" which was successful (Richmond, 1964). The authors referred to the grouping as "based on narcissistic identification with strong symbiotic components" and catalogued some similarities among the members of their group, some of which I observed in the network. Their "group had apparently developed a whole network of relationships"; they had frequent extragroup contact; motivation for treatment was minimal; and school was their worst enemy.

In offering Rod a network, I was asking him to ally part of his ego with me as I offered him "a friendly living room." I indicated that he could be more responsible to and for himself and his ego, to his friends and to me. This appeal to his healthy islands of ego may have raised his self-esteem as it put him in charge of himself and his friends and approved closer ties to peers, thereby eventually helping him with controls, increasing his autonomy, and reducing his confusion and ambivalence. I also offered him another type of symbiosis—a looser one with me and his peers, instead of with his parents.

In psychoanalysis, the protection of the psychoanalytic situation offers safety to regress and eventually to demonstrate in the transference neurosis a wide variety of impulses, defenses, and transferences. In the ordinary home, the inhabitants may blow off steam and behave briefly in a disturbing neurotic or psychotic manner to which the rest of the family accommodate themselves. The observing or participating family or friends accept the irrational act partially, and when the individual recovers, they may imitate, caricature, suppress, or deny the outburst and the individual may feel safe. In other social situations, however, such behavior is not acceptable to the organized self and ego, leading defenses to operate to control such behavior.

In network therapy these irrational or peculiar mementos are eventually brought in for clarification and sorting out by those with whom these interactions occur, and the individual has an opportunity to recognize the psychopathology and maladaptive responses. In the vertical network this may appear to be easily available, but in the peer network it may be more so because there is less entrenched hostility over lengthy periods than in the multigeneration networks.

The horizontal network brings in the absent important person(s)— who here were the designated central patient's alter egos and served partly as his observing ego—his friends Paul and Steve especially. In

474

the ordinary group each patient is a stranger to the others, and the hazards of exposure increase anxiety. But in the network the peers know him and each may spotlight a different area of interaction with him and his disturbances.

The comments about the initially absent footwear gave Rodney a chance to rebel against a particular small item but set limits in the sessions, and perhaps decreased the danger of breaking off treatment. If he chose to rebel he could come without shoes, but he would still be attending sessions. Perhaps their wearing shoes helped them express their angry rebellious feelings with words instead of using action. His friends illustrated his poor judgment, paranoid ideas and behavior, poor reality testing, and suggestibility. They confronted, interpreted, and supported him; they invited integration and better reality testing. Rodney was able to develop some insight. Ties remained between peers, and the tie to the therapist was diluted.

Peer relations, strengthened by continuing outside contacts, perhaps provided a potential opportunity for daily alternate sessions. The network provided a vehicle for Rodney to identify with me and his peers, increasing his peer bonds while loosening the parental binds, and for this he seemed to borrow some ego and superego from the therapist and peers (Sugar, 1967). But the network also helped him in differentiation of self from parents, peers, and me with his own values about school, clothes, and work.

Perhaps a loose symbiosis was formed with me. Rodney developed some trust of me, for he told me he came to town the week I was on vacation and that he had used me to get out of the state hospital; he brought his friends in; and he attended sessions even though he was no longer in the state hospital. Though afraid of mental hospitals, he returned to visit some of his friends who were in the private psychiatric hospital. He seemed to have cathected the network, with notable affect changes in him indicating some further ego development and growth. Ultimately, he achieved his goal of freedom from father and mother, that is, separation and some autonomy.

Rodney's history and development suggest that he was involved in a symbiosis with his mother and that he had not moved beyond the separation-individuation phase. Contributions to the disruption of this tie and the manifestation of symptoms at fourteen may be speculatively ascribed to: (1) adolescent development: adolescent changes in sexual and aggressive drives, ego, ego ideal, and superego (Freud, 1958, Jacobson, 1961), usual adolescent separation protest and disorganization (Sugar,

1968); (2) disruption of tie when oldest brother married and left home; (3) disruption of tie when patient did not meet father's academic or athletic standards.

Running away was perhaps the best adaptation effort available to separate from a probably psychotic mother and a feared, rigid, conforming, and confining father. The truancy and runaways were not to home, but to the streets and other cities with friends.

With traditional treatment, Rod became either more apathetic or more rebellious, and did not learn much except to try to avoid getting caught, to avoid the punishment of solitary, and to avoid excessive drugs, lest his passes be denied. The initial discussion of his own therapeutic club initiated a blossoming of affect and speech. He progressively demonstrated increased assertiveness, self-esteem, open verbal testing and challenging of authority, a sense of humor, paranoid ideation, and improved organization. At times he was considered not psychotic, but more likely a paranoid personality with severe dependency, immaturity, and a tendency to disorganize. After the network began, he was promoted to the ninth grade with good grades and had no runaways. When he terminated therapy, he had managed to leave home acceptably and to go to someone he wanted to be with, his brother, who was functioning satisfactorily.

The parents' decision to let Rod remain with his brother may have been the combined result of Rod's efforts to separate from parents and therapist, as well as the parents' wishes to keep him out of treatment, keep him under family surveillance, avoid the expense of treatment, and avoid the stigma they felt Rod caused by getting him out of town acceptably.

A fierce loyalty between Rod and his friends was evident from the beginning, in his visiting his hospitalized friends and having his friends appear with him for the network sessions without much explanation from him. The intensity of his friends' tie to Rod was reflected in Paul and Steve, each of whom attended six sessions with him, as well as in their separation reaction when Rod went on vacation.

Perhaps peer networks can best be used with a youngster in whom there is a pathologic symbiosis with his parents and where there is also present a somewhat healthier type of transformation or variant into a clinging or intense loyalty to friends. On the other hand, this type of network might not be suitable for an autistic psychotic patient. A beneficial effect might therefore depend on oscillation of the level of object relations between anaclitic and ambivalent, as it did with Rodney.

Summary

The use of a variety of therapeutic techniques for some or all diagnostic categories with variable results underscores the need for flexible treatment to suit the individual patient's needs at the appropriate time when he is motivated. This is particularly important in the presence of continuing situational, maturational, and developmental changes, as with adolescents, especially with disorganization in their internal (emotional, hormonal, physical) and external (home, culture, and school) environment. This chapter focuses on this principle in the application of network psychotherapy to an adolescent through a peer network.

After many unsuccessful therapeutic efforts, an outpatient peer network was initiated for a psychotic adolescent boy while he was still an inpatient in a state hospital. Earlier therapy had included inpatient and outpatient psychotherapy (individual and group), drugs, and threats of punitive, restrictive devices.

Beginning with the initial offer of this type of psychotherapy, there was a noticeable affective change in him. The ten network sessions were marked by considerable positive shifts, and progress was made toward better integration. The horizontal network allowed him to view his values, self, and overt and covert aspects of his pathology and history, and bring them into therapeutic focus. This came about by his peers' challenging, confronting, supporting, encouraging, and interpreting on the basis of what they knew from their associations with him, along with the observations and interpretations of the therapist. A variety of material was exposed and accepted by the peers and the patient more easily and readily than in group or individual therapy, where the patient has to bring it in. Here the network had the data and revealed them in association with particular stimuli in each session.

The patient was able to move out of a pathologic symbiosis with his parents and effect a separation from them in an efficient and constructive fashion without his usual symptom of running away. He was also spared repeated hospitalization, because though still psychotic, he was able to function outside.

Some of the factors contributing to his progress are discussed from the standpoint of his paranoid ideation, his ability to trust, his superego,

477

and his ego difficulties with organization, responsibility, judgment, and impulse control.

REFERENCES

Freud, A. (1958). Adolescence. Psychoanalytic Study of the Child, 13:225–278.
Frieman, A. S., Boszormenyi-Nagy, I., Jungreis, J. E., Lincoln, G., Mitchell, H. W., Sonne, J. C., Speck, R. V., and Spivack, G. (1965). Psychotherapy for the whole family. New York: Springer. Chaps. 12 and 22.
Jacobson, E. (1961). Adolescent moods and the remodeling of psychic structure in adolescence. Psychoanalytic Study of the Child, 16:164–183.
Richmond, A. H., and Schecter, S. (1964). A spontaneous request for treatment by a group of adolescents. International Journal of Group Psychotherapy, 14:97–106.
Speck, R. V. (1967). Psychotherapy of the social network of a schizophrenic family. Family Process, 6:208–214.
———. (1968). Personal communication.
———. (1968). Normal adolescent mourning. American Journal of Psychotherapy, 22:258–269.
Sugar, M. (1967). Group therapy for pubescent boys with absent fathers. Journal of the Academy for Child Psychiatry, 6:478–498.

24] THEORY AND PRACTICE
OF INTENSIVE RESIDENTIAL
TREATMENT OF ADOLESCENTS

DONALD B. RINSLEY

I am particularly pleased to address you under the auspices of the Institute of the Pennsylvania Hospital, first American hospital to open its doors to the sick. For I am by profession a hospital psychiatrist, a physician whose efforts are devoted to those whose mental sufferings are of such a nature and extent as to require the hospital ward in order to emerge from the dissembling limbo of their illness. It is not unfitting, moreover, that a hospital psychiatrist should address you at a particular point in the evolution of our discipline when we are beset with the polyglot claims of the so-called "third psychiatric revolution"—community mental health—some of whose advocates would assert that the proper goal of the mental hospital should be its own demise.[1]

I welcome further an opportunity to discuss with you my own special interest in the vast domain of psychiatry, the adolescent who needs residential treatment, a subject as timely as the steadily decreasing mean age of our population and the steadily burgeoning variety of problems that our adolescent youth have come to pose for the society in which we all hold membership. Finally, I bring to my discussion an admitted psychoanalytic bias, a point of view descended from Freud, vivified in the therapeutic contributions of the tradition of the so-called healing pedagogues, of Anna Freud (1935, 1946a, 1946b), Paul Federn (1952), August Aichorn (1935, 1964), Gertrude Schwing (1954), and Madame Sechehaye (1951, 1956), and theoretically deepened in the writings of

Revised from the Fifth Annual Edward A. Strecker Memorial Lecture, October 14, 1968. Reprinted with permission from the *Psychiatric Quarterly*.

the so-called British School of Object-Relations, most notably those of Melanie Klein (1950, 1961) and W. R. D. Fairbairn (1954) (Guntrip, 1961). The historical basis from which I shall take my departure includes the pioneering efforts of Ernst Simmel (1929) to apply the insights of psychoanalysis to the treatment of hospital patients, extended in turn by the Menninger brothers in Topeka (Menninger, 1936, 1937, 1939) and leavened by the development of the child guidance movement in the United States. Among the questions I propose to consider are: What characteristics determine an individual's need for residential, hospital, or inpatient treatment? What, in turn, are the characteristics of the residential milieu that are conducive to lasting reorganization of the personality, and not merely to those more superficial processes generally termed "sealing over," "transference cure," or, more banally, "symptomatic dissimulation"? What is the natural history of the hospital course of those patients who undergo the experience of significant intrapsychic reorganization, as compared with those who do not? Finally, what particular modifications of the hospital setting are essential for optimal psychiatric treatment of the adolescent with the more severe forms of psychopathology?

The "Weak" Ego

As Simmel noted some forty years ago (1929), individuals who by whatever route eventuate in the psychiatric hospital are regularly found to suffer from a variety of difficulties that together comprise the protean syndrome of ego weakness (Rinsley, 1968). We generally diagnose such persons as borderline or "as if" (Deutsch, 1965), or else append to them such labels as schizophrenic, psychotic, character neurotic ("psychopathic"), immature, impulse-neurotic, polymorphous-perverse, or infantile-narcissistic (Gralnick, 1966). Careful genetic-dynamic study of these individuals reveals a variety of characteristics of the weak ego, including:

1. Failure of normal repression;
2. Persistence of primitive mechanisms of defense, with reliance on projection, introjection, regression, and denial;
3. Impairment of the ego's synthetic function, leading to disruption

480

of self-environment relations and dissemblement of perceptual, cognitive-ideational, affective, and motoric functions;

4. Predominance of anxiety of the instinctual type;

5. Lack of "basic trust";

6. Pervasive impairment of object relations;

7. Failure of sublimation of "raw" instinctual impulses;

8. Persistence of primary-process thinking with reliance on transitivity, and gestural and word magic;

9. Persistence of primary narcissism, associated with which are varying degrees of infantile megalomania;

10. Serious difficulties with preoedipal and sexual identity.

The clinical manifestations of these underlying coping or defense mechanisms include pervasive inability to trust, depression, impaired tolerance for frustration, failure to interpose thought between instinctual need and direct action aimed at relieving it, hence undue access of instinctual drives to motility; or else the individual's behavior, if not excessively action oriented per se, seems otherwise peculiar, dissembled, or bizarre. As a result, there ensue various degrees of disruption of interpersonal communication and social disarticulation. As a consequence, in the majority of cases, others—the family, friends, and associates or representatives of the wider social community—bring the patient to the hospital. It is precisely in these cases in which one discovers the apparent lack of motivation for that nice cooperation between patient and therapeutic figure that classical psychoanalytic therapists put forth as a prime requisite for successful therapy, supposedly indicative of "lack of insight," hence illustrative of unsuitability for optimal reconstruction of the personality or "cure."

If reliance on the aforementioned coping mechanisms bespeaks the seriously ill adult, it more or less normally characterizes the intrapsychic organization of children, whence one calls it immature or puerile. Inasmuch as the clinical manifestations are in both instances similar, one refers to the seriously ill adult as immature or regressed, the latter from a presumably higher level of psychosexual function. Like the psychotic adult, the child, by virtue of the immaturity of his ego, will tend to act out. Deficient in self-objectification and in well-developed secondary process or categorical ideation, which Piaget (Inhelder and Piaget, 1958) tells us develops only by early adolescence, the child will prove incapable of conceptualizing his need for treatment and the motivation of his prospective therapist to help him. Hence, if judged by the stan-

481

dards of the dynamically oriented therapist of the neurotic adult, the child will give the appearance of lack of motivation. Like the psychotic adult, the child normally, and the sick child overwhelmingly, must depend on the auxiliary adult egos who would treat him in the same fashion as his parents whom he would otherwise depend on for love, including protection, support, instruction, and the proper application of external controls for his actions. Hence, the intensity of the sick child's labile, direct parentifying transference to the prospective helping adult.[2]

The nature of this direct transference to treatment figures requires further elucidation. First, the life of the preadolescent or adolescent child is organized around the child's dependency on parental figures, whether the latter are natural parents or surrogates; hence, their teachers, coaches, scout leaders, and older siblings and peers come to be invested with needs, wishes, urges, and fantasies displaced from the primary parental objects, or, more properly, from the mental representations of the latter. This major aspect of childish transference assumes even more cogent significance for adolescents, one of whose major struggles involves powerful strivings toward emancipation from parental surrogates, leading in turn into pervasively ambivalent needs both to devalue and, paradoxically, to remain dependent on them. Thus, the normally labile transference of children becomes the more so among adolescents, replete as it is with further decathexis of parents, multiple anxieties over psychobiological experiences and functions, and substitute object-seeking, leading to the shifting bipolarity of instinctual drives and their affective derivatives so characteristic for the adolescent (Blos, 1941; A. Freud, 1958).

Second, the seriously ill adolescent suffers from oedipal fixations based, in turn, on traumata of a major degree earlier suffered at the hands of parents or equivalent surrogates. Hence, to the normal coping and defense mechanisms and identity struggles of adolescence are added, in these cases, a welter of cognitive, affective, and behavioral difficulties that are derived from very early insults to the archaic ego of the child. These, in turn, contribute to the patient's transference an added measure of ambivalence and lability, such that his treatment figures come to be invested with an extra measure of unneutralized instinct, of expectations and fear that represent the externalized vicissitudes of the patient's own internal object relations.

Third, adolescence is a period of life characterized in part by the individual's search for intimacy, by his efforts to bring his reservoir of infantile partial aims and his seeking of partial objects under the hegemony of genital primacy. His need for peer and adult models for identification in part witnesses various degrees of dynamic-genetic regression, with circular defusions and refusions of instincts and notable tendencies to reinstinctualize (Spiegel, 1951). Thus, reaggressivization and resexualization of previously autonomous ego functions contribute to the kaleidoscopic quality of the adolescent's self-seeking and object seeking. Once again, these regressive tendencies are enormously accentuated among adolescents ill enough to require residential treatment, and they pose special problems for the adult treatment figures, whose countertransference is pulled hither and yon as a result of their needs both to enter and resist projective and introjective identifications with their young patients. These latter are wont to lead the adult figures into extremes of bipolar attitudes toward the management of the patient, which in turn reflect the bipolarity of the patient's own instinctual organization, namely, undue authoritarianism or undue permissiveness. In the former, one glimpses the elements of the new order therapies, exemplified in the writings of Szasz (1965), Glasser (1965), and Mowrer (1963a, 1963b), who emphasize behavioral conformity to accepted modes of conduct, or the assumption of responsibility by the patient, or who attempt to build in or strengthen the superego, as it were. In the latter, one glimpses a variety of antiauthoritarian reaction formations, which find expression in a congeries of laissez-faire, permissive approaches to the care of patients. These often involve the misapplication to adolescents of such varied modalities as classical psychoanalytic technique, therapeutic community, and child-centered methods based presumably on progressive educational views and organismic concepts that claim that, if left to themselves, children (including sick ones) will intuitively and spontaneously "actualize themselves," or will otherwise make the right decisions for themselves, much as laboratory rats will self-select appropriate diets.

The effect of overauthoritarianism is, of course, to preclude or forestall the patient's attempts to gain mastery by maintaining what amounts to an essentially megalomanic attitude toward the child and this, in turn, often reflects the adult's misguided efforts to defend against the infantile grandiose, narcissistic wishes that the child projects onto him. The effect of overpermissiveness is basically the same, for if the adult spuriously invests the child with adultomorphic powers, the child will inevitably misapply them, and hence will fail.

A fourth aspect of direct adolescent transference is of special importance in those cases in which the patient's fixations date from early infancy, prior to the inception of the normal mother-child symbiosis which ordinarily flowers during the latter half of the first year of life. These adolescents, developmentally deviant from the very earliest postnatal period, comprise a group of patients whom Fliess (1961) would classify as autistic-presymbiotic—including the classical autistic children first described by Kanner (1943, 1949)—and whom Bender (1947, 1953, 1956) would classify as pseudodefective. They are characterized by sweeping psychobiological deficiencies and dyssynchronies, and are not rarely mistakenly supposed to have no object relationships. Careful clinical study reveals, to the contrary, a pervasive, bizarre, fragmented autistic pseudocommunity, populated by a welter of magical hallucinatory internal objects, the majority of which are monstrous, terrifying, or "bad." The patient combines a congeries of self- and object perceptions characterized by a most intense fear and suspicion of others, and by a profound degree of infantile megalomania specific for the stage of primary narcissism; or else, one readily observes the persistence of the prenarcissistic condition to which S. Freud (1914) referred as autoerotic, during which the various erogenous zones pursue pleasure gain, as it were, mutually independently, without benefit of any degree of psychic organization.

Though individual psychotherapy is the cornerstone of the treatment of such adolescents, the ward staff must wrestle with the patient's exceedingly primitive introjective and projective defenses as the latter urgently seeks and yet is terrified by and must massively resist fusion with them. In these more primitive cases, the over-all treatment pivots about the need to build in, as it were, those "good objects," derived from the patient's identification with the psychotherapist, which will hopefully serve as nuclei about which the earliest, most archaic ego functions and representations will proceed to crystallize. Thus, the milieu supports the individual treatment process, beset as the latter often is with innumerable misunderstandings among the therapist and the other staff members, which reflect the variable extent to which staff members have become enmeshed in the patient's profuse use of splitting defenses.

A fifth aspect of adolescent transference concerns the child's defensive maneuvers with respect to the early object losses, which are regular features of the history of the residential patient of this age. By the term "object loss," I refer to those situations in which key surrogate figures died, were lost through parental separation or divorce, or were in effect psychologically unavailable to the young child as a result of their own psychopathology. Early object loss leads the child into the persistent use of splitting, wherein the object loss is simultaneously and ambivalently both affirmed and denied (or, better, disavowed) by the ego (S. Freud, 1927, 1940). The splitting is, in these cases, associated with longstanding depression; the latter manifests itself in a wide variety of regressive symptoms so peculiar to children (Rinsley, 1965), in contrast to the classical depression of adults, a subject to which I shall later refer. As a result, the residential patient perceives adult treatment figures in terms of this background of loss, ambivalence, and splitting, and shows enhanced degrees of alternating anaclitic clinging and negativistic pseudoindependence in respect to them. Thus, coupled with the patient's desperate need for objects is the fear that the objects he invests, hence on whom he comes to depend, will in the end desert him. Another way of viewing the patient's predicament would be to say that the patient despairs of object constancy, or is devoid of trust.

In such cases, the patient brings into play a congeries of restitutive efforts that center on a further regression to defenses of an introjective and projective nature, based, as is well known, on the mechanism of splitting. The lost object is reintrojected in order that its actual disappearance may be denied. But along with the reintrojected mental representation of the object are also reincorporated the welter of aggressive attributes that the child has previously projected into it, so that what is, as it were, taken in comprises in essence a hostile superego introject.[3] The clinical result is profound guilt. Thus the patient feels that he has brought about the death of a natural parent, or parental separation or divorce, or has visited on his siblings a wide variety of insults and injuries; he feels himself to be "bad," which may mean destructive, homicidal, "crazy," stupid, and the like.

Much of the labile, kaleidoscopic, manipulative behavior of adolescent inpatients stems from the above. Their provocative alloplasticity, often called "transference splitting" or "transference diffusion," in part represents ambivalent efforts to work through the traumata associated with early object loss. The patient's guilt leaves him poignantly susceptible to the recurrent fear that intimacy with a love object will repel the latter, that his love destroys, that there is no real prospect for object constancy, hence that he is foredoomed to rejection and psychological starvation (Fairbairn, 1954). As a result, one witnesses the adolescent patient's abiding suspicion of adults, coupled with his peculiarly transilient efforts to extract from them proof of their love for him while he counterphobically acts in a manner to ward them off (Rinsley and Inge, 1961).

485

Some Axioms of Residential Treatment

The aforementioned characteristics of the transference of the adolescent residential patient are essential for an understanding of the child's immediate postadmission behavior. In part because of his intense struggle over dependency needs, the adolescent, who is often sensitively aware of his need for help, nonetheless can admit it only in the most obscure, oblique ways. As a result, he often seems unmotivated or resistant. The form and variety of the adolescent's resistances are described in greater detail below (see Rinsley and Inge, 1961). But the basic issue concerns the salient fact that inasmuch as early resistance behavior is heavily loaded with transference, the forms it assumes provide notable insight into the manner in which the patient has dealt with and attempted to regulate his relationships with key figures from his past, generally parents or equivalent surrogates, as these come to be expressed within the residential setting. Some learning theorists would perhaps say that the patient will perseverate in the use of outmoded, maladaptive, insufficiently drive-reducing adjustive techniques and that his illness in part expresses the narrowness of his coping hierarchy.

A first axiom of residential treatment would therefore hold that, to the degree to which the treatment setting otherwise tolerates or abets the patient's ongoing use of early transference resistances, their underlying significance will remain obscure, hence uninterpretable, and, further, that the patient will remain unengaged with the staff members. The obvious corollary to this axiom holds, therefore, that the residential milieu must provide controls for the patient's behavior, in some cases stringent ones, to preclude direct drive discharge through motility, and to rechannel it via intercalated processes, namely, thought and verbal communication. To this end, the closed ward is essential, for it alone provides the security of carefully titrated behavioral restrictions which must operate to force the patient back on and within himself.

A second axiom concerns the matter of the patient's contacts, both vis-à-vis and via correspondence, with members of his family. Inasmuch as the child's psychopathology develops within and in part gives expression to a skewed, pathological familial constellation, interruption of the hierarchy of pathogenic interactions among the patient and other family

486

members must be effected as quickly as possible. In order to accomplish this with a minimum of serious trauma to all concerned, a concomitant psychiatric casework process is begun, within which the staff caseworker initiates the diagnostic study of the family, while simultaneously assisting the family to deal with the often profound anxieties that rapidly develop when a family member previously necessary for their repression or scotomatization has been removed. Often these anxieties propel the remaining parents and siblings into herculean, even bizarre efforts to undo their separation from the child, to so contaminate their contacts with him with double-binding communications as to decimate the patient's treatment by intimidating him into redoubling his resistance behavior. In some cases, the parents will attempt to bring attorneys, clergymen, interested friends, employers, public or political figures, other relatives, and a variety of other avuncular persons into the early diagnostic process, or may threaten litigation or even violence in eleventh-hour efforts to intimidate the staff into releasing the patient. Careful study of the family members' own early resistance maneuvers reveals that they both cover and convey a welter of terrifying fantasies, which become projected onto the treatment milieu in general and the figure of the caseworker in particular, and which they will attempt to communicate to the patient (Rinsley and Hall, 1962). Thus, the staff must have the necessary legal armamentarium with which to enforce, if need be, the parent-child separation and, during this early period of inception of treatment, must carefully regulate the patient's family visits and correspondence.

A third axiom of residential treatment concerns the use of specific restrictions of the patient's behavior, a matter of importance throughout the entire course of the patient's residence but of even greater significance during the early period of treatment. In connection with the matter of restrictions, I shall have recourse to the following relevant if oversimplified graphic representation (see Figure 24–1). *W* represents

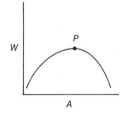

FIGURE 24–1.

what one could call "useful psychological work," a term notoriously difficult to define, roughly analogous to the thermodynamic concept of free energy and to the psychological concept of goal- or task-oriented secondary-process thought and action; a key component of W, from our point of view, turns out to be related to the patient's ability to respond to verbal restraint or control from the staff members and to comprehend the significance of the interpretations they offer him. A denotes anxiety, in our cases predominantly of the instinctual type, whereas P denotes a critical point of inflection. That portion of the curve to the left of P we shall call the ascending limb, whereas that portion of the curve to the right of P we shall call the descending limb.

For individuals situated somewhere on the ascending limb of the work-anxiety curve, each increment of anxiety leads to a corresponding increment of psychological work; put more succinctly, one may say that under such circumstances, anxiety motivates. Similarly, in the case of an individual situated on the descending limb of the curve, further increments of anxiety yield corresponding decrements of work; we say, therefore, that under such circumstances, anxiety disorganizes.

Now it may be said that the overwhelming majority of residential patients undergo referral for admission because the level of their instinctual anxiety has propelled them onto the descending limb of the work-anxiety curve, past the point of inflection, P. This level of anxiety has, in turn, induced the well-known traumatic state of the ego, with more or less paralysis of autonomous ego functions and regression to the use of those primitive defenses or coping mechanisms to which I have already referred. As the traumatic state is known to result from breakdown of the defense mechanisms of the ego in the wake of relatively excessive endopsychic and/or external stimulation, the immediate therapeutic task resolves itself into efforts to limit incident stimuli. For this general purpose, we may use judicious dosages of ataraxic medication, or limit the patient's overstimulating peer interactions by restricting him to the ward or to his room; in some cases in which the patient finds himself beset by panic of a degree that has led to dissolution of his defenses against anxiety, a period of seclusion may be indicated (Charney, 1963).

The psychoanalyst would view such a program as justifiably analogous to the function of the infant's maternal surrogate figure as a stimulus barrier against both excessive exogenous stimulation and endogenous affectomotor storms (Masterson, 1968; Bergman and Escalona, 1949). Concomitantly, it promotes the patient's investment in the staff figures, whose early function amounts to protecting him while allowing a comfortable degree of regression to proceed apace. Most important, however, is relocation of the patient to a point somewhere on the ascending limb of the work-anxiety curve. So situated, he begins to reassume an increasing degree of self-control, to communicate more coherently with the staff, and to experience relief from the terrifying feelings of loss of control which have characterized his pretreatment state.

The Resistance Phase of Residential Treatment

As many authors have noted, the family member who comes to be identified as the patient emerges from a longstanding pathogenic manifold of familial intercommunications; [4] indeed, Zentner and Aponte (1970) have termed it the "amorphous family nexus." Many of these families are dyssocial, alienated groups with varying degrees of effective social façade, whose membership is characterized by diffuse, shifting, interchangeable individual identities, multiple-binding communications, *pars pro toto* and *totum pro parte* roles, and superficially unpredictable lines of authority; thus they have been termed "skewed." Such families, or pseudofamilies, offer to their members a variety of protective gratifications, and the characteristic of the patient is his inability, for whatever reasons, to continue to use them; thus, the family appeals, with profound ambivalence, to the dreaded extrafamilial authorities or agencies for help, or else the patient is wrested from them despite their overt or covert protests. The purposes for which the help is sought are, of course, legion. The intricate if bizarre family nexus may be disintegrating, and the patient is selected out to communicate this. Or, one or more family members may perceive that the patient's continued presence in their midst threatens their composite existence; hence he must at least temporarily be expelled—though not rarely the patient may in fact be the least ill family member, and the burgeoning conflict between his own ineluctable urge for growth and the family's pathogenic pressures on him force him apart from them, by whatever means or route. Whatever the case, the family directly or otherwise carries its deviant member to the helping agency for its own purposes, which, in the case of families of severely ill adolescents, amount to a need either to get rid of him outright, or else to induce the agency to refurbish him so that he

489

may once again assume his usual place, basically unaltered, within the family nexus.

The profound dislocation of the family's and the agency's respective expectations of the latter's functions of treatment contribute heavily to the wide spectrum of patient and family members' behavior which subserve the function of resistance to treatment. In the case of adolescent residential patients, the various resistance maneuvers subserve the need to preserve ongoing fusion or symbiotic ties, based in turn on the preoedipal fixations to which I have already referred. A particularly subtle manner in which the patient and the family will unconsciously conspire to accomplish refusion, described in detail by Zentner and Aponte (1970), is to behave in such ways as to attempt to incorporate the treatment structure into the family's nexus, to render the former into an arm of the latter, so to speak. Thus, the generalization common to the aforementioned axioms becomes: the major purpose of identifying, interpreting, and precluding the patient's and the parents' early resistance behavior is to precede refusion among them, hence to detach the patient from the pathogenic family nexus and to promote his engagement with the treatment staff. As already noted, the treatment facility must have at its disposal for this purpose, and be prepared to use fully and definitively, whatever legal means are available for those cases in which the family's and the patient's efforts to refuse assume herculean proportions.

The spectrum of the adolescent residential patient's resistance maneuvers, which ordinarily occupy a period of from six months to a year following admission, and the metaphorical communications they convey have been described elsewhere (Rinsley and Inge, 1961). I shall now briefly recapitulate them:

1. Identification with the aggressor. The patient in various ways attempts to imitate the adults' behavior, in an as-if effort to ward off the latter. Included here are the well-known assistant doctor, assistant nurse, assistant aide, and related counterphobic efforts to scotomatize archaic instinctual urges which the patient has projected into the adult staff members.

2. Leveling. The patient attempts to make siblings or peers of the treatment figures. Leveling constitutes a rather more advanced variety of counterphobic maneuver than simple identification with the aggressor; certainly it displays a somewhat greater use of intellectualization. Included under leveling are the well-known buddy-buddy, pal, and we

girls phenomena; in addition, one notes the occasional adolescent inpatient whose otherwise smooth pseudoreasonableness covers massive attempts to isolate affect and cover profuse use of projection; thus, intellectualized admissions or confessions of illness (the famous adolescent cop-out), "Let's discuss things as equals," and related maneuvers often signify leveling, the more so during the resistance phase of treatment.

3. Flirtatiousness and seductiveness. The patient attempts to sexualize the relationship with treatment figures. Techniques of sexualization are legion, vary from the most subtle to the very crude, generally have notably aggressive significance, and allow notable insights into the adolescent's transference. These maneuvers pose some of the knottiest countertransference problems that staff members must face; they are particularly difficult in the case of the typical, all-American boy and the genuinely physically attractive adolescent girl, neither of whom, despite otherwise severe psychopathology, looks sick.

4. Oversubmissiveness. Oversubmissiveness, obsequiousness, or sycophantic behavior (including shuffling or the Uncle Tom phenomenon common among Negro adolescents) comprise yet another counterphobic maneuver.

5. Persistent avoidance. More frequent among the most seriously ill adolescents, persistent avoidance includes frank negativism, muteness, marked aboulia and apathy, seclusiveness, sleepiness, disruptive efforts to provoke isolation, various forms of seizure and dissociative phenomena (including self-induced seizures in patients with epilepsy), absorption in daydreaming fantasy, and stubborn or persistent refusal to eat (anorexia nervosa).

6. Scapegoatism includes such phenomena as denigration or vilification of ward peers ("He's stupid," "She's crazy," and so on), and efforts to manipulate wardmates into proxy roles by which the peer acts out for the subject (behind-the scenes manipulator phenomenon); the purpose is to draw staff attention to others, hence away from oneself. The inverse or passive form of scapegoatism is also not infrequent: the patient actively or passively provokes verbal and/or physical assault from others —the personification of the injustice-collecting masochist; such an adolescent is invariably found to harbor a paranoid world view, perceives both peers and staff as hostile predators, and assuages depression through flagellation.

7. Outright rebelliousness. The major function of wildly disruptive ward behavior in part subserves the need to ward off closeness to staff figures by attempting to force them into unremitting efforts to provide

simple and direct behavioral control; the underlying need for closeness is, however, glimpsed in the direct, physical staff-patient contact that the disruptive actions provoke. In many cases, outright rebelliousness represents a form of passive scapegoatism.

8. Transference diffusion. This is an exceedingly frequent and important resistance maneuver among hospitalized adolescents. It includes various forms of playing favorites, a wide spectrum of staff-splitting and manipulations of peers, gossiping and tale-carrying, aimed at keeping knowledge of oneself spread thinly enough to preclude any one of the treatment figures from obtaining a comprehensive view of oneself.

9. Somatization. Multiple bodily complaints serve to ward off staff attention to thoughts, feelings, fantasies, delusional preoccupations, and the like, as well as to communicate nonverbal material (body language). Careful analysis of the complaints will, however, often uncover the hidden (repressed) inner experiences.

10. Peer-Age Caricaturing. Also called "outtypifying oneself," this consists in a variety of actions that seem to convey the patient's need to be viewed as a typical adolescent. The behavior ever so slightly exaggerates such things as dietary fads, emotional lability, popular idealizations, and the general excesses adults are wont to associate with typical adolescent behavior.

11. Clique formation. Seriously ill adolescents are incapable of generating normal teenage peer groups; the normal-appearing small groups they are prone to form on the ward are usually found to serve the need to share data about themselves with one another that never reach the treatment staff. Needless to say, such groups require the most assiduous scrutiny and staff regulation, particularly during the resistance phase of treatment, lest peer-peer relationships dilute or eliminate peer-staff relationships, which are, of course, essential for the individualized treatment each patient requires.

12. "Craziness" and pseudostupidity. The defensive function of disorganized ("crazy") behavior is to arrest, enthrall, or paralyze, hence to ward off the treatment figures. Similarly, the pseudostupid patient conveys the message, "I'm so stupid that you can't expect much from me (hence I can remain unengaged)."

13. Artistic pursuits. Included here are such varied activities as unsupervised autobiographical novel, and short-story writing, solitary drawing and game-playing, and premature diary-keeping; of particular relevance are complex or bizarre drawing and painting, and pseudoscientific preoccupations, such as electronic circuitry, graphic anatomical

productions, and the like. Such pursuits have immense, if often autistic communicative significance; in many cases, they must be interrupted or interdicted, lest the patient remain immersed in them to the exclusion of consensual communication with treatment figures.

14. Elopement. Running away is a complex, overdetermined phenomenon, connected with all sorts of aggressive, erotic, rescue, and reunion fantasies. When it occurs, it obviously terminates therapeutic contact between the patient and the treatment staff.

Some Remarks on Parental Resistance Metaphors

As already noted, the patient's resistance behavior has enormous transference meaning; and, in addition, it expresses anguish over separation from his parents, or else from his fantasy constructs which serve as dereistic substitutes for them; at root, it conveys the expression of refusion or reunion fantasies. Concomitant with the flowering of the patient's resistances are those of the parents, whose fantasies are no less elaborate nor regressive than are the patient's. Careful study of the parents' fantasies during the resistance phase of their child's treatment discloses that they are, as expected, compounded of primitive aggressive and erotic wishes, that they are at root preoedipal, and that they are exceptionally prone toward displacement or projection onto the treatment staff and the physical characteristics of the hospital (transference to the hospital per se), in general, and onto the caseworker, in particular. The latter will in general develop only if the treatment structure precludes transmission of the parents' resistance messages to the patient.

Our own study of early parental resistance metaphors has led us to classify them according as they in turn express (1) the parents' narcissistic or self-preoccupations, (2) the parents' view of the family's endogenous efforts to maintain its precarious equilibrium, and (3) the parents' particular ways of depersonifying the child, hence of attempting to put him to psychological use in ways that violate his own juvenile identity (Rinsley and Hall, 1962).

Insofar as the family is in various degrees dyssocial, or in metastable equilibrium with extrafamilial objects and situations, revelation through whomever or by whatever means of the family members' idiosyncratic ways of maintaining the family group's pseudoequilibrium poses a severe threat to its perceived, ongoing integrity. Their overweening con-

493

cern is that the child will "tell the family secrets," hence both their conscious and less than conscious efforts to admonish the patient against the development of trusting ties with the treatment staff. Thus is derived the patient's dilemma: If he acts on his nascent perception that the staff members can somehow be trusted, he courts disaster to his family, including loss of the parental figures; if he successfully resists treatment, he remains ill. Thus does the apparent paradox transpire that, from the child's point of view, getting well is worse than being sick, and a notable measure of the secondary gain of his illness lies in the preservation of his relationship with the parents and other members of his disordered family.

Rapid control of the patient's immediate postadmission behavior, regulation of contacts between parents and child, judicious use of ataraxic medications when indicated, and carefully graduated increments of privileges lead the adolescent to a point at which the aforementioned resistance maneuvers come into full expression. As these develop, they are dealt with in turn by appropriate further control of the patient's behavior, coupled with interpretations directed at their underlying transference significance. The major purpose of the latter, which we may consider to represent the inception of the resistance work proper, is threefold: First, it has the effect of reassuring the patient that separation from his family, in particular from his primary parental objects, will not prove disastrous to him or to them; second, it serves to stimulate the patient's curiosity about himself, to get him thinking about his past history and current behavior; third, it aims to promote the patient's early identification with staff members, thereby further detaching him from his symbiotic ties with his parent figures.

The patient's early identifications with staff figures, which find their inception during the resistance phase of treatment, are different from those he will later make with them. During the resistance phase, they assume the qualities of primitive superego introjects, and hence signify to the patient the operations of external surrogate egos which, like the "good" maternal objects of infancy, protect the archaic ego by limiting incident stimuli, curb self-injurious actions and, in part through the discipline they inculcate, provide reassuring nurturance. The resultant reduction of the patient's instinctual anxiety moves him gradually toward the ascending limb of the work-anxiety curve, and hence makes possible increasing increments of responsive, interpretive work by the patient, done increasingly, now, in collaboration with the adult treatment figures, and in particular with the psychiatrist.

Provided that the analogous resistance work is accomplished in the parents' casework process, it transpires that, in most cases within six to twelve months, the patient has developed sufficient trust in the staff and the parents sufficient trust in their casework process, which represents the treatment structure to them, that the parents begin in earnest to relinquish the patient to the staff's care. Thus, the definitive resolution of the well-known loyalty problem begins to appear. Parents and child have come to perceive that they may indeed exist without each other, the former in various ways communicating to the patient that he may work with the staff without fear of injury to himself or to them or of reprisal from them.

Resistance Behavior as Protest

Ongoing clinical study of the adolescent patient's and the parents' resistance metaphors led us to the conclusion that these metaphors, expressed both verbally and nonverbally, could be viewed as more than crudely analogous to the behavior of prematurely separated infants, which Bowlby (1960a, 1960b, 1961, 1962) has termed, protest (Rinsley, 1965). Several factors seemed indeed to support the analogy. First, the adolescent's otherwise natural tendency to recapitulate, hence to work through earlier oedipal and preoedipal conflicts, appeared highly relevant; furthermore, such recapitulative working through is regressive, and fluctuating proneness to regression is a hallmark of the adolescent's struggle toward an eventually stable identity.

Second, as already noted, the patient's resistance metaphors seemed to convey a powerful need to undo the parent-child separation, hence to bring back the child's lost objects and to reinvolve them; thus, the resistance metaphors regularly tended to assume the quality of mourning.

Third, we recall that the persistent reliance on the defense mechanism of splitting regularly characterizes the mourning reactions of the child, as he ambivalently reaffirms and disavows the object loss he feels called on to mourn. Persistent use of splitting likewise affirms the child's ongoing fixation at, or regression to, the early predepressive (paranoid-schizoid) position of infancy (Klein 1950), which signals the use of part object relations. Thus, the adolescent's redoubtable tendency to split or manipulate represents the clinical emergence of his use of introjective and projective techniques for regulating his good and bad part

495

object relations. It comes as no surprise, therefore, that the fundamental psychological traumata on which the adolescent residential patient's illness is based occurred during the infantile years, in a majority of cases during the predepressive period prior to the inception of the second year of life, a fact that careful historical and psychodynamic study of our patients has almost invariably revealed.

Viewed from a genetic-dynamic standpoint, successful managment of the resistance phase of residential treatment precludes the patient's use of splitting and guides him ineluctably toward entrance into what must be considered as later manifestations of the original depressive position. As these changes occur, the resistance phase of treatment draws to a close, and the patient enters the next arena of his treatment, the phase of definitive treatment which I have chosen to call the phase of introject work.

The Definitive Phase of Residential Treatment: The Phase of Introject Work

As Aichorn (1935) originally taught us, successful treatment depends on the respective capacities of patient and therapist for mutual identification. Resolution of the resistance phase of residential treatment thus proceeds from the patient's ability to identify with the treatment figures who are charged with his care; in particular, it proceeds from the child's trusting ability to have internalized in significant measure the external controls for his behavior which the residential milieu has supplied to him. Thus is set in motion a complex congeries of processes of growth, common in the experience of the healthily developing child, but deficient in that of the child who reaches the adolescent years hobbled by psychopathology serious enough to prevent successful negotiation of the oral stage of psychosexual development ("I am"), and beginning entry into the anal stage ("I am separate and distinct; I can control and master"). It is my view, therefore, that an adequate, intensive residential treatment process comes to develop, within an admittedly compressed span of time, the basic attributes of a healthy child-rearing experience.

A major characteristic of all children is their early infantile omnipotence, a residue of middle to late orality. The healthily developing child comes normally to project his omnipotence into the figures of his parents, leading to a sweeping overestimation of his loved parental objects.[5] The seriously ill child, essentially devoid of parental object constancy early in life, has found the normal projection of omnipotence impossible, hence has, in effect, clung to it. As the young child's omnipotence is comprised of primitive (raw) aggressive and erotic instincts, their projection into the residential treatment figures evokes the patient's fear that they will retaliate, injure, destroy, or absorb him, a fear that also in part accounts for his resistance to them. Thus does resolution of the resistance phase of treatment imply the treatment figures' acceptance of the patient's megalomanic projections into them, without acting on the primitive wishes associated with the projections, a situation that cements strongly the bonds of mutual trust between the patient and themselves.

As the patient begins, now, to part with the nucleus of bad internal objects, which have long comprised the roots of his psychopathology, he parts as well with what have been basic components of his early, pathological identity. The loss of these parts of the self induces him to mourn for them; and the two major components of his mourning are the emergence of depression and the appearance of regression, both of which are, of course, inextricably interrelated.

Among adolescents, whether hospitalized or not, the emergence of depression heralds far more than the otherwise classical picture, combining as does the latter the subjectively felt loss of self-esteem, sadness, and various degrees of psychomotor retardation. Rather the depression in these cases is rife with splitting, and with denial or disavowal. Thus, the patient's mourning for the loss of his departing introjects conveys far more than the process of object removal (Katan, 1951), for the objects that proceed to be removed are, as it were, pejorative, and their loss is accompanied, in the case of residential patients, by the most profound ambivalence; thus, the mourning becomes pathological. Pathological mourning among adolescents is a protean process. It is accompanied by sweeping regression in all areas of psychological function—cognitive-ideational, affective, sensory-perceptual, and even motoric. The patient proceeds to assume a more primitive clinical appearance, which includes fluctuant clinging dependency, marked negativism, notable swings of mood, and unpredictability; of great importance are the experiences of depersonalization and estrangement (derealization); overt thought disorder may reappear, with classical associative loosening, tangentiality, syncretism, and concretism, and the occurrence of grandiose, self-referential, and nihilistic delusions. There

497

occurs regressive reinstinctualization of bodily parts and functions, with all manner of somatic difficulties and, in some cases, frank somatic delusions. The patient now begins to speak of his "badness" and "evilness"; he talks of destructive wishes, and he berates himself for his past misdeeds, and for the harm he feels he has visited on others. His terrifying experiences may indeed be likened to the drainage of pus from a long-concealed abscess, as a necessary step in the healing of tissue that the purulent matter had previously infiltrated and split apart.

Our extended observations of the behavior of the adolescent who has entered this phase of residential treatment have led to the conclusion that it is, at root, analogous to Bowlby's so-called second stage of infantile mourning, which he has termed the stage of despair. Common to both are the protean complexities of the "impure" depression of children. Indeed, the phenomena classically grouped about the concept of depression per se may be wholly or in largest measure overshadowed by the multiple regressive signs that portend the onset of a period of undoubted disorganization of the weak ego so characteristic of the residential patient of this age (Rinsley, 1965).

The emergence of bad internal part objects and the concomitant introjection of good ones are of basic importance for the successful treatment to which the residential milieu is oriented. First, it strongly reinforces the patient's beginning awareness, during the resistance phase, that he and his parents are indeed capable of separate existence. Second, it moves the patient progressively from a condition of primary narcissism toward increasing self-objectification, which means enhanced ability to sense and test reality, and to exert mastery over endopsychic and external events. Third, it signals the patient's entrance into the later, depressive position of infancy, during which he begins to perceive that his aggression, whether innate or derived from the aggressive cathexes associated with his bad introjects, is incapable of destroying what he comes increasingly to experience as whole objects; thus he moves from part to whole object relations. Underlying the above are the processes characteristic of this second, or later, form of the adolescent residential patient's identifications with his treatment figures, namely, the gradual metabolization and depersonification of his introjects as these become assimilated to his self-representations, and hence become a part of his ego (Jacobson, 1964; Kernberg, 1966). Fifth, the identifications on which these critical processes and experiences are based have sweeping effects on the economic dispositions within the child's ego. They lead to defusion of instincts, with ensuing liberation of both aggressive and erotic energies for subsumption under the ego's synthetic function; thus, neutralized aggression comes increasingly to drive the defensive functions of the unconscious part of the ego, whereas libido comes increasingly to drive the ego's synthetic and perceptual functions, leading the ego toward increasing use of sublimations and growth of secondary autonomy (Rinsley, 1967b, 1968; Hartmann, 1964).

It will be evident in what I have said that, from the standpoint of the residential patient, there are two exceptionally critical junctures in the residential treatment process, successful management of which has an important influence on the prognosis of the child's residential experience. The first is, of course, successful conclusion of the resistance phase, with subsequent entry into the definitive phase. The second critical juncture comprises the staff's capacity to withstand the protean, regressive turn of events in the definitive phase. A most important resistance with which all must deal is, as expected, staff countertransference resistances to the often exasperatingly difficult regressive behavior of the patient as the exchange of introjects sets in in earnest. Staff members' efforts to bring the latter to a halt, whether by efforts to suppress it or through their own regressive identifications with the patient, must be precluded in largest measure if the patient is to work through his painful experience of mourning.[6]

The processes of mourning of the hospitalized adolescent ordinarily require the better part of another year of residential treatment, if not rather longer. As they proceed, and as their associated regression begins to recede, the patient becomes ready for increasing reassociation with his family, the members of which he has begun to view as distinct from himself, as increasingly real objects, whose limitations he may allow himself to understand without remaining enmeshed in them. His enhanced internal controls, based on identification with the staff members who have signified his auxiliary egos, lead him to a gradual expansion of privileges; thus, with careful guidance, he assumes increasing responsibility for what he does. The time now approaches at which continued, full-time residential treatment becomes unnecessary and, depending on the circumstances of the individual case, the patient may be discharged to the day hospital, or to his own home, or to foster placement, in many instances to continue his psychiatric treatment on an outpatient basis for a variable future period of time.

Though my remarks have comprised but a bare outline of the natural history of the complex residential experience of the adolescent in full-time hospital treatment, they nonetheless permit several conclusions

499

concerning adolescent psychopathology and reconstructive as distinguished from symptomatic treatment in the residential setting (Rinsley, 1963, 1964).

I have reference, at the outset, to the important contributions of Masterson (1967, 1968) regarding the etiological significance of adolescent turmoil, with which I am in thorough agreement. He concludes that this omnibus term makes reference to a wide spectrum of personality difficulties of more ominous significance than is usually recognized. As a result, the more ominous psychopathological phenomena to which adolescent turmoil refers are commonly viewed as little more than manifestations of transient situational or adjustment problems, frequent enough among adolescents, of relatively superficial importance, and hence in need of superficial handling or management. I believe that this situational view of adolescent turmoil stems from several readily identifiable factors. First, from a diagnostic standpoint, the criteria for recognition of classical (schizophrenic) thought disturbance, set forth by Bleuler (1950) and developed by numerous careful students of categorical ideation, are as applicable to adolescents as to adults; failure to apply these criteria in the careful study of the formal processes of the adolescent's thinking regularly leads to an underestimation of the degree of the patient's psychopathology. A second factor involves failure to recognize the stereotypical characteristics of the pseudoamorphous, skewed, psychotogenic family to which I have already briefly referred, within which the adolescent residential patient is regularly discovered to have grown up and to which his illness in part gives graphic and tragic expression.

Yet a third factor, basic to the foregoing, concerns the adult's not inconsiderable difficulty in recognizing any sort of major psychopathology in children. Such a difficulty is in direct proportion to the extent to which any given adult must repress or even deny the variety of his own subjective difficulties during that age that is personified in the patient he may be called upon to study. The well-known adult countertransference to the presumably noisome adolescent finds expression in a variety of approaches to his problems; these appear with regularity in the psychiatric literature and tragically too frequently in the attitudes of professional workers (Rinsley, 1967a). Thus, one finds problems of underdiagnosis, to which I have already referred; one finds statements to the effect that "adolescents cannot be analyzed"; one finds well-meaning programs in which seriously ill adolescents are treated on adult hospital wards, motivated in part by the need to pare institutional budgets, which leads to the placement of sick children with sick adults, and results in endless prolongation of the adolescents' resistance maneuvers; one hears of short-term programs for adolescent treatment, in which little or no effort is made to help the patient and his parents to recognize and resolve the herculean problems of their mutual resistances toward separation. Finally, one hears the view, appropriate to the needs of the less seriously ill child, and thoroughly incorrect for the more seriously ill one, that it is better not to sunder a family by attempting to treat one of its members outside it. This view, in fact, represents a failure to appreciate the dereistic, dissocial pseudoorganization of those families who produce severely ill children. For the child, whether adolescent or younger, trapped within a profoundly disordered family unit, sanguine efforts at outpatient treatment are in many cases foredoomed to failure: The residual family members will exert powerful pressures on the child to resist the therapist's "dangerous" ministrations, and the pressures will succeed because the looser therapeutic structure is unable to cope with them. In such instances, the so-called community mental health approach, which advocates "bringing the treatment to the family in its own setting," in fact proceeds to transport the treatment to the very worst place for its inception and fruition.

Summary

We may summarize, now, the basic goals of intensive residential treatment for the two major groups of severely ill adolescents who require the full therapeutic services of the inpatient milieu.

As already noted, the autistic-presymbiotic ("nuclear," or process, schizophrenic) adolescent, who has failed to experience the normal mother-infant symbiosis, requires a therapeutic program oriented toward its inception. For such an adolescent, the full residential setting provides a highly concrete, compulsively styled, maximally predictable environment, as free as possible from peer-competitive experiences, and organized to provide comprehensive support for the 1:1 or individual therapeutic process that serves as its foundation. The goal of the latter process comprises catalysis for the crystallization of basic or archaic ego nuclei, and points toward establishment of the patient-therapist symbiosis which symbolizes the earlier symbiosis that the patient has failed to develop. Once established, the patient-therapist symbiosis requires extended efforts directed toward desymbiotization, which signals the inception of the patient's first genuine efforts at emancipation or individuation. (See Figure 24–2 for a diagram of the process.)

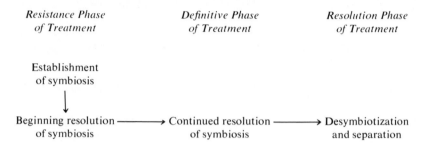

FIGURE 24–2.

In the case of the autistic-presymbiotic adolescent, establishment and beginning resolution of the patient-therapist symbiosis occur during the resistance phase of treatment. During that period, the patient comes to reexperience and to begin to work through the transference psychosis; hence the enormously archaic experiences consequent on very early object loss. Among the various factors contributory to the exceptional difficulty of this work with autistic-presymbiotic adolescents, two emerge with special clarity: First, the patient's early resistances assume herculean proportions, as a consequence of the terror that ensues whenever externalization of the bad internal objects threatens to occur; second, many such adolescents are products of thoroughly disorganized, fragmented pseudofamilies, or else have long since lost contact with parents or other family members. As a result, there is often little if anything in the way of concomitant casework treatment; hence the resistance phase of treatment is prolonged.

In the case of the symbiotic adolescent, essentially locked within a prolonged, unresolved mother-infant fusion relationship, the therapeutic goal comprises desymbiotization, with attendant emancipation and individuation. To this end, the predominant therapeutic work of the resistance phase of treatment is addressed to recognition, externalization, and interpretation of the adolescent's fantasies which center on reunion with and megalomanic control of family members, notably the parents, and especially the mother. As these occur, the residential program increasingly emphasizes progressive socialization, graduated expansion of privileges, peer-competitive participation, including residential school, occupational, and recreational therapy classes, and increased personal responsibility. Though individual psychotherapy may be prescribed, it is not considered essential for the symbiotic adolescent. (See Figure 24–3 for a diagram of the process.)

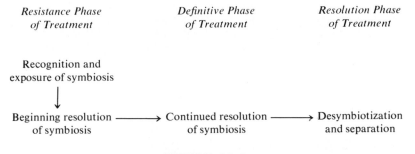

FIGURE 24–3.

In keeping with the view that the psychoneurotic adolescent is rarely admitted into, nor long remains within, a carefully supervised residential setting, brief reference to the widespread problem of underdiagnosis of the severely ill adolescent is justifiable. (See Table 24–1.)

Conclusion

From the foregoing, one may distill the following generalizations concerning the intensive residential treatment of adolescents who demonstrate the more severe forms of psychopathology:

1. In the majority of such cases, physical or geographical separation of the patient from the remainder of his family members, notably his parents, is mandatory.

2. The patient should be admitted into a closed ward or cottage, within which careful scrutiny of, and application of appropriate controls for, his behavior become immediately operative.

3. A concomitant, dynamically oriented casework process with the patient's parents or with his responsible guardian surrogates should begin with his admission into residence.

4. Intensive psychiatric and parallel casework study of the patient and his family should begin coincident with his admission, utilizing the services of the full diagnostic team, including the admitting and ward psychiatrists, the clinical psychologist, the psychiatric social worker, the teacher of special education, and the ward or cottage nurse and aides or

TABLE 24-1

RINSLEY'S TERMINOLOGY	EQUIVALENT DIAGNOSES	OFTEN MISDIAGNOSED
1. Autistic-presymbiotic psychosis of adolescence	Nuclear schizophrenia Process schizophrenia Childhood schizophrenia, pseudodefective type Schizophrenia, childhood type Schizophrenia, catatonic type (occasional) Schizophrenia, hebephrenic type (occasional) Kanner's syndrome (infantile autism) (rare) Atypicality	Mental retardation, moderate to severe Psychosis with: Organic cerebral impairment Mental retardation Chronic brain syndrome, owing to various causes Various syndromes of ego and developmental arrest
2. Symbiotic psychosis of adolescence	Reactive schizophrenia Childhood schizophrenia: Pseudoneurotic type Pseudopsychopathic type Schizophrenia, childhood type Schizophrenia, paranoid type Schizophrenia, chronic undifferentiated type Schizophrenia, catatonic type (occasional) Schizophrenia, hebephrenic type (occasional)	Adjustment reaction of adolescence Adolescent turmoil Neurosis (anxiety; phobic; hysterical; obsessive-compulsive; depressive, etc.) Various schizophreniform conditions Personality disorders, especially, schizoid, antisocial, dyssocial, delinquent inadequate School phobia (occasional) Various syndromes of ego and developmental arrest

child-care workers. Though in a few instances the patient needs to resist the immediate postadmission study, the deepening intra- and interpersonal processes into which he feels himself to be plunged in most cases will be found to reassure him that those who are in charge of him are extremely interested in and concerned about him; hence, the diagnostic process becomes at once an integral part of his treatment.

5. The intial therapeutic task that faces the treatment personnel of the ward or cottage comprises the identification, recognition, control, and interpretation to the patient of those segments of his behavior that serve as resistance of warding off devices, aimed at preserving the pathological symbiotic ties with his mental representations of parental surrogates. This early resistance work serves, in addition, to uncover the nexus of pathological communications and object ties characteristic for the patient's family, in which the patient has heretofore been immersed.[7]

6. Particular attention needs to be given to the adolescent's early communications, which convey a premature need to identify himself with staff members. Though one may discover much that augurs positively in such messages from the patient as "I like you," "I need your help," and "You are nice (handsome, beautiful, powerful)," naïve acceptance thereof as indicators of more profound ego identifications early in hospitalization is a grievous error. It bespeaks, in part, the adult's own difficulties in recognizing the patient's counterphobic use of the resistance aspect of early positive transference. It is significant that one recently reported inpatient program, in which much is allegedly made of such early positive communications, actually "treats" adolescents for a maximum of six weeks (Abend, Kachalsky, and Greenberg, 1968).

7. It follows that the closed ward, with its endogenous security devices, provides the optimal setting for the inception and at least part of the work of the resistance phase of treatment. The closed ward also serves well as the locale for the more regressive experiences associated with the definitive phase of treatment, during which the work of exchange of introjects comes to the fore.

8. The residential staff must be prepared to recognize and deal with the ineluctable regressive changes that accompany the patient's entry into the definitive phase of treatment. During this period, ward or cottage staff require considerable help with their countertransference, lest they proceed into a variety of maneuvers aimed unconsciously at warding off or terminating the patient's regression. If this occurs, the treatment quickly founders.

9. It is necessary to restate the fact that adolescents who require residential treatment are products of families, the pathology of which involves ill-defined, diffuse lines of authority and variable blurring and shifting of the roles and identities of their members. Hence, sick adolescents do not belong on adult mental hospital wards with sick adults whose psychopathology mirrors the disabilities of the adolescents' own parental surrogates, a locale that abets the adolescents' ongoing immersion in the same sort of pathogenic experiences that contributed so heavily to their illnesses in the first place. The sick adolescent needs healthy adults, not sick ones, until such time as his treatment will have led him to extricate himself from them.

10. It must be remembered that psychiatric treatment in the general sense should constitute a growth experience for both the patient and for those who essay to treat him. The residential treatment of the adolescent should point him toward the achievements of the latency period,

505

during which the child makes otherwise notable strides toward the attainment of self-objectification, mastery, sublimation, growth of secondary autonomy, the beginnings of categorical ideation, and peer identification, which symbolize the further development of his identity as a person. Once this has set in in earnest, the patient begins once again to move toward synchrony of his over-all level of psychological development and his chronological age. And with this, he reenters the arena of adolescence proper, to begin to struggle healthily with the numerous problems characteristic for this critical stage of his maturation.

NOTES

1. For recent, concise statements concerning the possible impact of the community mental health movement on the training and identity of the psychiatric clinician, see Kubie (1968), Kernberg (1968), and Wallerstein (1968).

2. A cogent formulation of the significance of magical and parentifying expectations of the therapist is set forth by Rado (1956, 1962).

3. I used the term "superego introject" to refer to notably punitive, underpersonified or "unmetabolized" introjects of an archaic nature which have not become assimilated into the unconscious defenses of the ego. See Jacobson (1964) and Kernberg (1966).

4. For a concise review of major contributions to this exceedingly important area of psychiatric research, see Mishler and Waxler (1966).

5. There is considerable evidence in support of the view that the origin of belief in an omnipotent deity is derived from the parents' further displacement of the child's megalomanic projections into them. This displacement is in turn seen to result from the parents' need to ward off (deny) the child's projections, which threaten to reawaken in the parents their own repressed infantile megalomania.

6. Hendrickson (1969), Hendrickson, Holmes, and Waggoner (1959), and Holmes (1964) have written cogently concerning transference-countertransference problems with adolescent inpatients.

7. In a recent book on adolescent residential treatment, Easson (1969) asserts that "open and direct staff interpretation" of the adolescent's nonverbal communications "would make the patient feel as if he had been stripped and his very integrity violated." Such a view stems from several misconceptions. (1) It fails to take account of the powerful resistance meanings of the adolescent inpatient's earlier postadmission nonverbal metaphors; (2) it therefore fails to conceptualize, and hence deal with, the innumerable phenomena common to adolescent's resistance phase of hospitalization; (3) it profoundly underestimates the severely ill adolescent's capacity, not only to withstand, but to respond therapeutically to early, vigorous interpretation of resistance behavior; (4) it confounds interpretation of resistance with violation of ego integrity, and hence tends actively to reinforce, through passivity, those very pathological defenses that most require interruption and rapid elimination; (5) it conveys a spurious respect for the adolescent inpatient's fragile ego through what is, in effect, a hands-off policy toward communications of a peculiarly disturbing or primitive nature, thereby reinforcing the patient's inference that staff members are fearful of—and hence unable to listen to—the archaic self-experiences that frighten him so much; (6) such a view retards the essential process by which the patient's archaic nexus of communications

may be translated into consensually valid ones, delays the formation of early identifications, and hence prolongs the resistance phase of treatment.

REFERENCES

Abend, S., Kachalsky, H., and Greenberg, H. R. (1968). Reactions of adolescents to short-term hospitalization. American Journal of Psychiatry, 124:949–954.
Aichorn, A. (1935). Wayward youth. New York: Viking.
———. (1964). In O. Fleischmann et al., eds., Delinquency and Child Guidance. New York: International Universities Press.
Bender, L. (1947). Childhood schizophrenia: Clinical study of 100 schizophrenic children. American Journal of Orthopsychiatry, 17:40–56.
———. (1953). Childhood schizophrenia. Psychiatric Quarterly, 27:663–681.
———. (1956). Schizophrenia in childhood: Its recognition, description and treatment. American Journal of Orthopsychiatry, 26:499–506.
Bergman, P., and Escalona, S. (1949). Unusual sensitivities in very young children. Psychoanalytic Study of the Child, 3/4:333–352.
Bleuler, E. (1950). Dementia praecox, or The group of schizophrenias. New York: International Universities Press.
Blos, P. (1941). The adolescent personality. New York: Appleton-Century-Crofts.
Bowlby, J. (1960a.). Grief and mourning in infancy and early childhood. Psychoanalytic Study of the Child, 15:9–52.
———. (1960b). Separation anxiety. International Journal of Psycho-Analysis, 41:89–113.
———. (1962). Childhood bereavement and psychiatric illness. In D. Richter et al., eds., Aspects of Psychiatric Research. London: Oxford.
———. (1961). Processes of mourning. International Journal of Psycho-Analysis, 42:317–340.
Charney, I. W. (1963). Regression and reorganization in the "isolation treatment" of children: A clinical contribution to sensory deprivation research. Journal of Child Psychology and Psychiatry, 4:47–60.
Deutsch, H. (1965). Some forms of emotional disturbance and their relationship to schizophrenia. In Neuroses and Character Types. New York: International Universities Press.
Easson, W. M. (1969). The severely disturbed adolescent: Inpatient, residential, and hospital treatment. New York: International Universities Press.
Fairbairn, W. R. D. (1954). An object-relations theory of the personality. New York: Basic Books.
Federn, P. (1952). Ego psychology and the psychoses. New York: Basic Books.
Fliess, R. (1961). Ego and body ego: Contributions to their psychoanalytic psychology. Psychoanalytic Series, vol. 2. New York: Schulte.
Freud, A. (1935). Introduction to psychoanalysis for teachers and parents. New York: Emerson Books.
———. (1946a). The ego and mechanisms of defence. New York: International Universities Press.
———. (1946b). The psychoanalytical treatment of children. London: Imago.
———. (1958). Adolescence. Psychoanalytic Study of the Child, 13:255–278.
Freud, S. (1914). On narcissism: an introduction. Standard Edition, Vol. 14. London: Hogarth Press.
———. (1927). Fetishism. Standard Edition, Vol. 21. London: Hogarth Press, 1961.
———. (1940). Splitting of the ego in the process of defence. Standard Edition, Vol. 23. London: Hogarth Press, 1964.
Glasser, W. (1965). Reality therapy. New York: Harper and Row.
Gralnick, A. (1966). Psychoanalysis and the treatment of adolescents in a private hospital. In J. H. Masserman, ed., Science and Psychoanalysis. New York: Grune & Stratton.

Guntrip, H. (1961). Personality structure and human interaction. New York: International Universities Press.

Hartmann, H. (1964). Comments on the psychoanalytic theory of the ego, and notes on the theory of sublimation. In Essays on Ego Psychology. New York: International Universities Press.

Hendrickson, W. J. (1969). Training in adolescent psychiatry: The role of experience with in-patients. Paper presented at the Conference on Training in Adolescent Psychiatry, University of Chicago, Chicago, Illinois, November.

———, Holmes, D. J., and Waggoner, R. W. (1959). Psychotherapy with hospitalized adolescents. American Journal of Psychiatry, 116:527–532.

Holmes, D. J. (1964). The adolescent in psychotherapy. Boston: Little, Brown.

Inhelder, B., and Piaget, J. (1958). The growth of logical thinking from childhood to adolescence. New York: Basic Books.

Jacobson, E. (1964). The self and the object world. New York: International Universities Press.

Kanner, L. (1943). Autistic disturbances of affective contact. Nervous Child, 2:217–250.

———. (1949). Problems of nosology and dynamics of early infantile autism. American Journal of Orthopsychiatry, 19:416–426.

Katan, A. (1951). The role of displacement in agoraphobia. International Journal of Psycho-Analysis, 32:41–50.

Kernberg, O. (1966). Structural derivatives of object relationships. International Journal of Psycho-Analysis, 47:236–253.

———. (1968). Some effects of social pressures on the psychiatrist as a clinician. Bulletin of the Menninger Clinic, 32:144–159.

Klein, M. (1950). The psycho-analysis of children. London: Hogarth.

Klein, M. (1961). Narrative of a child analysis. New York: Basic Books.

Kubie, L. S. (1968). Pitfalls of community psychiatry. Archives of General Psychiatry, 18:257–266.

Mahler, M. S. (1952). On child psychosis and schizophrenia: Autistic and symbiotic infantile psychoses. Psychoanalytic Study of the Child, 7:286–305.

Masterson, J. F., Jr. (1967). The psychiatric dilemma of adolescence. Boston: Little, Brown.

———. (1968). The psychiatric significance of adolescent turmoil. American Journal of Psychiatry, 124:1549–1554.

Menninger, W. C. (1936). Psychiatric hospital treatment designed to meet unconscious needs. American Journal of Psychiatry, 93:347–360.

———. (1937). Psychoanalytic principles applied to the treatment of hospitalized patients. Bulletin of the Menninger Clinic, 1:35–43.

———. (1939). Psychoanalytic principles in psychiatric hospital therapy. Southern Medical Journal, 32:348–354.

Mishler, E. G., and Waxler, N. E., eds. (1966). Family processes and schizophrenia. New York: Science House.

Mowrer, O. H. (1963a). The new group therapy. Princeton: Van Nostrand.

———. (1963b). Payment or repayment? The problem of private practice. American Psychologist, 18:577–580.

Rado, S. (1956). Psychoanalysis of behavior, New York: Grune & Stratton. Vol. 1.

———. (1962). Psychoanalysis of behavior, New York: Grune & Stratton. Vol. 2.

Rinsley, D. B. (1963). Psychiatric hospital treatment, with special reference to children. Archives of General Psychiatry, 9:489–496.

———. (1964). Psychiatric hospital treatment, with special reference to children. In J. H. Masserman, ed., Current Psychiatric therapies. Vol. 4. Pp. 69–73.

———. (1965). Intensive psychiatric hospital treatment of adolescents: An object-relations view. Psychiatric Quarterly, 39:405–429.

———. (1967a). The adolescent in residential treatment: some critical reflections. Adolescence, 2:83–95.

———. (1967b). Intensive residential treatment of the adolescent. Psychiatric Quarterly, 41:134–143.

———. (1968). Economic aspects of object relations. International Journal of Psycho-Analysis, 49:38–48.

———, and Hall, D. D. (1962). Psychiatric hospital treatment of adolescents: Parental resistances as expressed in casework metaphor. Archives of General Psychiatry, 7:286–294.

———, and Inge, G. P., III (1961). Psychiatric hospital treatment of adolescents: verbal and nonverbal resistance to treatment. Bulletin of the Menninger Clinic, 25:249–263.

Schwing, G. (1954). In R. Ekstein and B. H. Hall, eds., A way to the soul of the mentally ill. New York: International Universities Press.

Sechehaye, M. (1951). Symbolic realization. New York: International Universities Press.

———. (1956). A new psychotherapy in schizophrenia. New York: Grune & Stratton.

Segal, H. (1964). Introduction to the work of Melanie Klein. New York: Basic Books.

Simmel, E. (1929). Psycho-analytic treatment in a sanitarium. International Journal of Psycho-Analysis, 10:70–89.

Spiegel, L. A. (1951). A review of contributions to a psychoanalytic theory of adolescence. Psychoanalytic Study of the Child, 6:375–393.

Szasz, T. S., (1965). The ethics of psychoanalysis: The theory and method of autonomous psychotherapy. New York: Basic Books.

Wallerstein, R. S. (1968). The challenge of the community mental health movement to psychoanalysis. American Journal of Psychiatry, 124:1049–1056.

Zentner, E. B., and Aponte, H. J. (1970). The amorphous family nexus. Psychiatric Quarterly, 44:91–113.

25] TECHNIQUES OF PSYCHOTHERAPY

IN ADOLESCENCE:

A PANEL

MALVINA W. KREMER, ROBERT PORTER,
PETER L. GIOVACCHINI, LAURENCE LOEB,
MAX SUGAR, JULIAN I. BARISH

Robert Porter: Therapy of an Adolescent Boy

Kenny, an only child, asked his divorced parents for therapy just prior to his 11th birthday. The woman consultant (who saw the parents and the patient for 3 appointments) believed Kenny to be "in desperate need." He told her "I've got to have someone I can bring my problems about my parents—because I still need both of them."

The consultant observed that the father was very seductive with his son, even admitting how open he has been in disclosing his sex life to Kenny. The father appeared to be "quite sick—possible somatic delusions." He had dropped out of school before completing high school, and separated from mother when his own father died, when Kenny was eight. Despite his lack of formal schooling, father had held jobs requiring considerable intellectual skills. He has also had periods when he was without a job, and the consultant observed that money and the lack of it had been a principle mode of expression of conflict in the marriage. Father had long been highly critical of his wife in a way that apparently paralleled his complaints about his own mother; he quite openly encouraged Kenny to disregard his mother's discipline and

* This panel was presented at the Annual Meeting of the American Society for Adolescent Psychiatry, May 4, 1969, in Miami Beach, Florida.

wanted to "give" Kenny independence. He was still in therapy (Sullivanian).

Mother had just received her permanent appointment as a school guidance counselor. She had had two years of law school, but she didn't graduate. Later, she worked for her M.A. in counseling. She was eager for therapy for herself, and began treatment soon after Kenny started. Consultant observed that the mother, too, appeared unable to respond to the boy's cues, though both parents were clearly concerned and wanted him to have help, which they believed necessary. Although the mother didn't believe the father would be willing or able to pay for Kenny's treatment, he did for three years until he lost his job.

Prior to their separation, his parents had noted that Kenny seemed increasingly unhappy, and had many headaches. Mother had taken him to a hospital, where she was assigned to a mothers' group conducted by a male social worker, and where, the following fall, Kenny was assigned to a childrens' therapy group which met only sporadically with a young female social worker. A psychiatrist there saw Kenny three times when he was ten, and felt he needed to be in a group of his peers, but did not need therapy. Later, however, Kenny appeared more troubled and his school work (which had been very good; in keeping with his IQ of 135) became more uneven and he worried about whether he would be able to do new things "perfectly." His father, with whom he visited twice weekly, and his father's friends, noted "compulsive babyish behavior" extending to "baby-talk and crawling." He also openly showed jealousy of friends of either parent to whom they showed interest or attention.

Kenny began treatment with me, on a weekly basis when he was eleven years old and clearly approaching puberty. He was eager to have someone to whom he could talk, and was serious about his problems, but soon recognized that he really did not know how to define them very precisely beyond feeling caught in the conflict between his parents. At times he could and would discuss his feelings, but more often he would tend to "analyze" situations or people, tell highly witty jokes or be argumentative and intellectually competitive. His voice and manner of speech were a curious blend of assertive, masculine elements with seductive, childish elements. In the first two sessions Kenny revealed a conscious preference for his father, but also strongly felt that they did not have a good parent-child relationship. He described himself as being rebellious in his attitudes, especially with his mother. He was very aware of his father's similar attitudes, and the open support his father gave him in disregarding rules.

He spoke of difficulties he had in relationships with peers. He dated these from the time of parents' separation, and his moving with his mother to another area, and was inclined to explain his troubles by citing apparent differences in the popular street games. He felt he had been good at such games before, but was excluded in the new neighborhood because the games were unfamiliar to him.

After I had indicated my interest in dreams as sources of understanding problems, he brought a pre-treatment dream to the second session. It concerned plotting chess moves: "I just see the moves; I'm moving. I make up little chess pitfalls, like the one I really made on my father. One was beautiful. I moved my knight in front of his pawn. He could take it,—but if he did I'd move, he'd move (no matter where), I'd move: Mate, or he'd lose his queen. You know, it was a brilliant pitfall, but he didn't fall for it. I regained the piece, and finally beat him—with king against king."

In the next session, he brought the first treatment dream, which involved his catching flies (baseball) with a friend and a bunch of chimpanzees. First he may have been a monkey, then his left hand was like a chimpanzee's hand, only much larger—something like a baseball glove. It changed back forth and he could "make" the chimpanzee hand go away briefly, and did so long enough to cover his hand with a piece of cloth. This would prevent direct contact with his skin and thus keep him from turning entirely into a chimpanzee—but that happened anyway. He was briefly on an operating table and the surgeons were amazed to find the cloth under the chimpanzee skin of the hand.

He asked for my ideas, which I deferred till I had gotten him to elaborate on some of the details. I commented on the contrasting feelings, the size and hairiness of the hand, and the fear of turning into a chimpanzee might indicate some feelings about growing up. He argued this vigorously, even denying that chimpanzees are hairy all over. I dropped this line of exploration although I felt there were certainly indications of envy of his father which he could not acknowledge.

In discussing "operations," he revealed that he thought birth was always an operation. He recalled a comment from his father about how he felt at Kenny's birth, when he said, "What are you doing to that little boy"? He recalled another story of his father's of how, when Kenny was born, father looked at him and said "Where will we ever get enough bananas to feed that little monkey"?

Concerns about sexual matters came up repeatedly. If Kenny had had any latency period, it must have been extremely brief. On the one hand, intellectual knowledge of sex had had open approval from his father and at least some tolerance from his mother. On the other hand, he was so consciously preoccupied with the details of his parents' sexual relationships that he had obvious conflicts whenever he brought any sexual matters up in his sessions. Initially, he tested to see whether I would react to vulgarities, dirty jokes, etc. Later, dream material came up in which he himself recognized sexual elements—but tended to deal with this in terms of intellectual generalizations. Still later, he became consciously aware that hearing details of his father's premarital sex life while interesting, was upsetting, and he asked that I speak to his father to get him to stop. After letting the intensity of his conflict become quite clear to him, I pointed out that if he really wished not to continue this sort of conversation with his father, he was the one who could most strongly communicate this. He did discuss this with his father, who respected his explanation and apparently discontinued his sexual reminiscing.

Periodically, Kenny indicated some knowledge of theories of the oedipal relationship, and this idea frightened him very much. By and large, he maintained an outward façade of annoyance and rebelliousness with his mother which belied any of his more tender or dependent feelings; but increasingly material came to light, both in dreams and in patterns of physical symptoms such as diarrhea, stomachaches and headaches, which allowed some exploration of his dependent feelings. His mother would telephone me periodically to keep some two-way knowledge alive of how things were going, and she had become aware, partly through her training and experience in guidance work, and partly through her own therapy, that she might have been behaving toward Kenny in ways that would be too stimulating and seemed ready and able to modify this sort of behavior.

Many conflicts over authority and discipline, over sexual fantasies and the displaced elements of the family romance came out clearly in transference manifestations, about which he was able to speak quite directly. Initially, he expressed strong friendly feelings toward me, reacting with intense disappointment when he first missed an appointment because of sudden illness. His upset over missing the appointment was such that he and his mother phoned to say he had missed me.

He described a dream in which he had joined the Little League, even though he was afraid of hard ball baseball, and had done quite well largely through the errors of other players and was enjoying it so much he regretted awakening. He wanted my comment on the dream. I told him

513

that it sounded like a good dream since he had faced and overcome one of his fears in it. Thereafter, there were a series of dreams, about sports, dramatics in school, etc., in which he enjoyed successes and gained respect from schoolmates, including girls he admired. It was my impression that, among other meanings, these served as trial balloons to see whether I would really want to see him succeed in these areas. Later, there were clear and conscious expressions of strong beliefs that I could not possibly really want him to grow up and become capable of successful contention with me.

After about eight months of treatment, symptoms of headaches, stomachaches, diarrhea, and "one-day viruses" began to come up week after week, usually on the day of his appointment with me. Once he came 15 minutes late, saying urgently but cheerfully "help me—I've got terrible diarrhea." After emerging from the bathroom, he recounted a dream whose theme was of boys and girls his age at a summer camp, sharing the same bunk buildings, and without adult counselors, getting along "like brothers and sisters." He commented that "kids are purest before the age of 5; when they're younger, they don't know enough to be bitter and disappointed." He acknowledged some conscious regrets about growing up. The theme of upset-stomach, nausea, and diarrhea were very prominent and he recalled these had been frequent 3 years before, when his parents broke up. He became aware of great anger, especially at his mother recently. He described a "panic," when his mother went from the house to her psychiatrist on a day that was a school holiday, so that he was aware of the trip. He then told of a nightmare regarding the "awful" third grade teacher (previously described as "a sweetish old lady" whom he couldn't stand). In this dream, he was being cared for by her, because his parents were dead; he was trying to escape, but she successfully pursued him through mud, rivers and weeds and finally captured him in a store, where he realized she had a gun in her pocket. He became angry with me when I indicated possible repressed death wishes, claiming that I was trying to make him angry.

In the next few sessions, there was no regression nor any escape from the emerging awareness of anger in situations of dependency. He tended to be more argumentative, quibbling over words, frequently indicating a need to get across an idea which he strongly felt even though it could not be logically justified. Thus, he claimed "guility" meant just doing something, even if not prohibited or bad, with his conviction being that the "guiltiness" derived from the parents—"How could they feel guilty if someone didn't *make* them," he finally said, after looking up the word in the dictionary and indicating surprise that he could find no support there for his feeling about what it meant.

A few months later, he was aware of strong sexual anxiety when in the office with me. He had been standing very close to the desk many times as the end of sessions approached, and it was my feeling that he was being immensely seductive with an evident lack of awareness of doing so. Finally, when he began to describe his intense fear, he first indicated he feared I would kill him—and later that he felt I might seduce him homosexually. He immediately recognized both feelings to be like those he often had when at his father's apartment. While he spoke of this, and indicated by his voice and demeanor that he felt great anxiety, he did not lose his earlier positive relationship. Finally, he acted out an actual homosexual experience with a Negro classmate whom he had for an overnight guest by inducing the other boy to engage in mutual masturbation. The discussion of this episode indicated intense voyeuristic drives to make comparisons with someone his age whom he feared might be more developed than he (but turned out not to be). In any event, there was no repetition of this, nor any other overt homosexual activity thereafter. What did emerge in the following months were fantasies which revealed his reasons for fearing the active hostility he had fantasied from me and his father. Rather grandiose daydreams of being able to seduce and please any and all girls, then women, finally led to the frightening but pleasant idea that he would be able to seduce my "girlfriend" away from me even though he had no idea who she might be, how old, how attractive, etc.

He now seemed able to moderate his intense competitive pattern with boys his age, and began to form and sustain some friendships which provided companionship. He was maturing rapidly physically, and found reassurance in doing so. His excellent intelligence allowed him to proceed successfully in his school work, and he entered one of the academic public high schools, where he has continued to be an outstanding student.

A hiatus in treatment, although not discussed to any extent occurred which seemed meaningful in several ways. It followed a period of successful social adjustment (summer AYH trips, etc.), when he continued to move more actively into gratifying group experiences. It seemed to mark an unspoken recognition of the transition from early adolescence to late adolescence. Moreover, it appeared to by-pass a transference problem he had not yet been successful in working through, i.e., his tendency to expect me to share the attitudes he attributed to his parents. Thus, he took this "vacation" when he ventured into a trial of marijuana on his own, or at least, with the sanction of some of his friends and without any direct risk of inhibiting influences from me.

Since Kenny had from the beginning established a good working alliance, and had shown a consistent desire not to wreck his own important plans and hopes, I had never found it necessary or appropriate to offer parental-style warnings, but felt I could best provide a place for him to think through matters about which he recognized his own concern. This seemed to work well, and seems to be doing so still. I have made few transference interpretations of a direct sort, partly because he has often recognized such manifestations himself. He understood well the kinds of affectively loaded material which would be important to report, and brought up matters such as his parents' comments on my statements when they called me. Other areas where occasional "interpretations" were made were those designed to make him aware of his severe superego and restrictive defenses, as well as his tendency to continue to see his fears and blocks as still being actively instilled by his parents. At this point, he seems more ready to deal with deeper and more disturbing feelings in a persistent manner, with less defensiveness, and with the same capacity to bring his excellent intelligence to bear on understanding and coping with them. Whether this results from his first ventures with "pot" and LSD, which did indeed let him experience things intensely, or whether he tried the drugs because he felt ready to dip into these feelings, it appears he is working more seriously and meaningfully on his conflicts than he was able to as a younger adolescent.

Peter L. Giovacchini: Characterological Factors in the Psychotherapy of Adolescents

General therapeutic principles can be formulated only in the context of clinical material. Inasmuch as the interactions between therapist and patient are often subtle and consist of undemonstrable nuances, the presentation of clinical data may not always have the intended result. Frequently, discussions of case histories are punctuated by a variety of formulations that may or may not have some relevance to the clinical material. The discussant's theoretical orientation dominates, and whatever data are presented (which are, of necessity, always incomplete) can be made to fit a preconceived bias.

Thus, the question of the value of case discussions can be raised. In spite of the possible misunderstanding of the clinical material, there are valuable insights to be gained from a discussion of a specific patient. I find that I have very little to say about the given patient, but on the other hand, I am always reminded of one of my own patients who may or may not resemble the presented case. Still, this reexamination of one's own material in the presence of colleagues who are facing somewhat similar problems is always worthwhile and even if our formulations of the presented case are fanciful, one may achieve considerable conceptual clarification.

Here, one can focus on a group of patients who have some homogeneous factors, both in their background, that is, early object relations, and in the adaptive and defensive aspects of their character.

The role of early object relationships in character formation, whether relatively stable or psychopathologically distorted, is extremely important. An intrusive environment leads to characteristic defenses, though there are other variables besides early interactions that have to be considered. The quality of the intrusion also has to be specified.

The concept of hyperstimulation can be understood in terms of how an external stimulus is perceived. Winnicott (1954) writes of impingement in a similar fashion. If the mother, for example, ministers to a need that does not exist, the child's psyche experiences such an attempt as an intrusion.

Spitz (1945) wrote of deprivation and its opposite, a "psychotoxic" type of giving. In either case the effects on the neonate are deleterious. The child's basic requirements are not being met inasmuch as every need is associated with an optimal response that will achieve gratification. Too much or too little are similarly disruptive.

Quantitative aspects are not in themselves the most significant factors; rather, the disruptive effects of the interaction are the most crucial for future character formation.

Not to respond to a need or to respond to a need that is not felt are similarly frustrating. Returning to the clinical material, one can add that responding to needs that belong to later psychosexual stages and have not yet developed (for example, sexual feelings) is experienced as assaultive rather than gratificatory and will lead to the formation of defenses designed to dampen and to control the otherwise disruptive stimulations of such ministrations. Dr. Porter's patient has a psychologically oriented mother and a father who regaled him with anecdotes of his sexual adventures. Apparently both parents made demands of him that

517

were not appropriate to his chronological age and his stage of emotional development.

They treated him, more so than most parents, as narcissistic extensions of themselves. Perhaps because of their difficulties with each other, they sought him as an ally in order to justify themselves. The child is put in the not uncommon situation of being a pawn (note the chess game dream). He is not reacted to in terms of his own needs, but becomes a defensive adjunct or a repository of the parents' instinctual needs through whom they seek vicarious gratification. The latter is especially disruptively stimulating when it took a sexual form or when his father was encouraging him to smoke marijuana.

The parents' needs, which clashed, also clashed when they were projected into the patient. On the surface they emphasize the familiar question of loyalty to either parent. To some degree the patient is perplexed with choosing, choosing whom he belongs to or who belongs to him. He, himself, is shoved into the background and his individuation and needfulness in a fundamental sense are ignored.

Internally, the parents contradictory demands lead to conflicts that have profound and even devastating effects on various ego systems. For example, not knowing to whom you belong or should belong is reflected both in the identity system and the superego. Frequently, these children do not know who and what they are and they are further confused as to their moral standards and value systems. Both as children and adolescents, they have a more intense than usual identity problem and in adulthood this becomes an important aspect of their characterological pathology (Giovacchini, 1965). Regarding difficulties with moral standards owing to superego defects, they do not tend to act out in the usual antisocial fashion, though in some instances their behavior may be counterphobically self-destructive. Instead they commonly manifest confusion in their general orientation rather than through specific behavior.

Identity problems have a deterrent effect on emotional development. Insecurity in the present causes one to look on the future with fear and trepidation. I agree with the therapist that the monkey dream refers to the fear of growing up. The patient is faced with the dilemma of whether he wishes to grow up or maintain the status quo. Even though the present state is dominated by instability basically owing to a precariously constructed self-representation, he has, nevertheless, achieved some defensive balance. All the problems he now faces, in that they are in a sense adult problems, will be intensified once he is actually an adult. The weaknesses he now experiences and his defenses against

518

them not only will become accentuated, but what now serves in a defensive capacity will later have to be a fundamental modality, an intrinsic aspect of the adult character. A defensive pattern has to be converted into an adaptive mechanism to relate to the outer world in general rather than a specific mechanism to protect one from hyperstimulating disruptive external forces. It is especially difficult for this developmental conversion to take place because the foundations for later development are unsubstantial and constricted since they were harnessed for defensive purposes. As a characterological modality these early defenses were a thin veneer, a shaky façade, even though they were being manifested as precocious maturity.

More specifically the parents accentuated the dangers of adulthood by the specific ways they related to him, which led to the defenses just alluded to. For example, to a large measure they treated the patient as an adult. Most likely he was cast in the role of a confidant. Frequently, one finds the provider-dependency axis is reversed, and the child becomes the person on whom the parents are dependent and on whom they depend for reassurance and justification. This forces the child prematurely into an adult role.

This patient, and others similar to him, could accept this role because of superior intellectual endowment. A constitutional strength can now be used to effect a relationship that is a defensive response to what otherwise would have been a disruptive hyperstimulation. The premature assumption of adult responsibilities is, in response to both parental demands, a protection from being overwhelmed by them and leads to an enhancement of narcissism, a narcissism that would have been unattainable because of the parents' need to use him as a narcissistic extension.

This precocity leads to both narcissistic gratification and achieves some stability to the identity sense. It is a defensive identity but nevertheless it leads to some cohesion and stability to the personality. There is, therefore, an uneven progression and development between the hypercathected intellectual component and other aspects of his psyche. Physiologically, in terms of drive differentiation, he is immature, a sharp contrast to the role that has been thrust on him, one that I doubt he could have assumed without a better than average intellectual endowment.

This precocious role, however, does not represent a stable defense, because he is faced with the dilemma of considerable power and yet nothing to back it up. In spite of his premature sense of responsibility he is still vulnerable and dependent.

519

When such children are shielded from peer relationships, they can successfully maintain their omnipotent position for a long time, and in some rare cases indefinitely if, because of their brilliance, they can find parental surrogates in adult life who will be both dependent on them and protect them from the outside world.

During childhood and adolescence, peer groups are not particularly impressed by intellectual achievement. Thus, these children are confronted with being powerful at home and average or even mediocre with their peers. This discrepancy heightens the basic sense of inadequacy which is a fundamental aspect of the self-image even though it is relatively submerged by narcissistic defenses.

In this patient, it is quite likely that the parents' assaultiveness is displaced to the peer group as may have been depicted in the baseball dream.

Finally, regarding treatment these patients are, because of their brightness, superficially easy to relate to. The therapist finds himself attracted by the patient's precociousness which, as in this case, contains considerable charm. If the therapist responds as Dr. Porter did, that is, with his own intellect but not competitively, a strong rapport is established.

At first, one would believe that the patient in the transference reenacts the relationship with the parents and reinforces his intellectual defenses. This is, indeed, the case but the chief difference that eventually gets through to the patient is that the therapist is reacting with his mind but the rest of him is not making any demands. For once, the patient's mind is accepted for what it is without any ulterior motives. Even though this may be an intellectual harmony, it is, nevertheless, harmony. The trend is reversed; the patient is the recipient and the responsibility for the relationship is no longer his.

These patients, in contrast to other bright, verbal children and adolescents do not often use their intellect competitively. This has been one area that has been granted to them, and peers, perhaps because they know the futility of competing, simply devalue this area as a means of obtaining status. In treatment, I have found when there is a meeting of minds, the patient need not feel competitive, rather he idealizes the therapist for his intellect.

Rather than discouraging what begins as an intellectual defense, the development of such a relationship can lead to much therapeutic benefit. The patient gradually trusts the therapist because he neither demands nor intrudes in the intellectually charged atmosphere. This situation may lead to an idealization of the therapist generally. Undoubtedly such an idealization is associated with many magical expectations, but it can also lead to an incorporation of the therapist's observational viewpoint and nonintrusiveness.

The meeting of minds, initially an intellectual meeting, can become a much more elemental meeting where the patient, for the first time, can understand that someone values his talents for their own sake. To be made aware that something inside of him is valued is the beginning of a self-awareness that initiates the consolidation of a self-image that is not defensively constructed.

The details of the therapeutic interaction are endless in quantity and variable in quality. The understanding, however, of some basic principles of psychic structure and therapeutic interaction can be a rewarding experience for both the patient and therapist.

Laurence Loeb: Transference and the Adolescent

Though the topics of transference and countertransference have been widely discussed in the literature pertaining to the psychotherapy of adults, there has been remarkably little written concerning these topics as they relate to the treatment of adolescents.

Perhaps it is necessary to review our fundamental assumptions and to reiterate the known fact that adolescents are not adults; the reactions to which we are accustomed in our work with other patients do not necessarily apply to those in the adolescent groups. Those of us working with these groups have approached our fairly recent field using concepts of child therapy and adult analysis.

Certainly, the original concept of transference is derived from adult therapy, specifically, from those in classical analysis. "Transference," as originally applied, referred to the unconscious process whereby feelings, attitudes, and ideas formerly directed toward some significant person in the patient's environment became transferred to the person of the analyst, so that the analyst would unconsciously be seen by the patient as parent, sibling, nursemaid. Clearly, the transference response to the therapist, even in classical analysis, is not the only response of which the patient is capable; no therapist has yet succeeded in becoming a blank screen. If the adult patient's responses involve more than transference (as indeed they do), how much more complicated is the situation for the adolescent patient in office psychotherapy, for whom treatment is rarely the axis about which his total life revolves.

Pearson (1968) described other responses of the adolescent:

> Where an affect for one reason or another cannot be discharged directly on the appropriate parent object but instead is repressed or suppressed and finds expression in relation to the therapist, this is designated by the term "displacement," in contrast to transference . . . Rapport is used to refer to a relationship between patient and therapist of accord and empathy, where a feeling of mutual understanding and acceptance exists, such as would be conducive to a working relationship. The capacity within the patient for rapport may in itself very well be a kind of transference deriving from his early dependent relationships with a parent figure.

Transference and rapport by no means exhaust the possibilities in such a relationship. Pearson added that,

> The patient also experiences direct object relationships with the therapist, where his feelings toward the therapist are predominantly determined by the current reality of the relationship. As a part of his direct object relations with the therapist, the child will carry into the treatment certain behavioral patterns, which are really not a form of transference, but rather characteristic behavioral attitudes the child has adopted in the course of his development and continues to use, not only with the therapist but in his daily life as a means either of coping with the realistic demands of his environment or of defending against anxiety.

> Another relationship we see in the child patient is that of "identification." Here the child takes in all or part of the characteristics of the therapist and makes them a part of his own self without necessarily discriminating between the healthy and unhealthy aspects of the therapist.

Given these five factors, then, of transference, rapport, direct object relations, characterological responses, and identification, it is difficult for the therapist to know which predominates at any given moment in what well may be a confusing mixture of many. To the foregoing, it must be added the probability that people entering treatment, or seeing a psychiatrist for the first time, have a set of expectations of which they may or may not be aware. In the case of the adolescent, this may refer to attitudes toward the "shrink" common to his particular peer group, those psychiatrists he has seen on television, in films, and the like. It would be extremely unusual to find a patient who did not enter his initial contact experience with a psychiatrist with some expectations. For the most part, the adolescent's first meeting with the psychiatrist involves some measure of distrust. The psychiatrist is part of the adult world; he may be seen as an ally of the parents, or any number of fac-

522

tors may influence the adolescent's initial distrust. As Holmes (1964) puts it,

Because the standard circumstances of adult psychotherapy do not provide such covert protections for the adolescent, he must make his own. He is so desperately aware of his need for help that he dare not call it by that name. He must represent it to himself and to others as an abominable infringement upon his personal rights by a meddling adult. He doesn't understand about "transference." When he becomes angry with his therapist he really thinks he is angry at his therapist and he also acts like it. He seeks a great deal more than self-understanding.

It is unusual for a ten-year-old boy to ask for therapy, as the case presented by Dr. Porter did. He did not come to his initial session with the distrust, hesitancy, and general guardedness so often seen in this age. It is likely that his expectations were very different from those of the average late latency child. In this particular instance they seem to have been related to his mother's function as a guidance counselor, and the boy's knowledge that his father had been in treatment. At all events, the stage had been set for the establishment of a good working relationship from the time of the initial interview.

The potential for such a good relationship was evidenced in the first interview with the consulting psychiatrist.

Seeing adolescents for consultation purposes only is often very difficult for the patient, as most do have a tendency toward the establishment of rapidly developing relationships, this, in spite of the surface denial of the need for help or with the adult world. Often, no matter how well prepared for transfer to a treating psychiatrist, the need for transfer itself may be seen as rejection. The late latency child or adolescent, finding himself in rapport with an adult, is loathe to give this up for fear that the subsequent relationship may not offer the same emotional comfort. For indeed, it is this emotional comfort that is sought "a great deal more than self-understanding."

To return to the case at hand, we find that the patient's father was seductive toward the patient, and this warned of the possibility that the relationship with the therapist might be made more difficult by the patient's reaction to the curiosity of the therapist, particularly as regards sexual information.

The patient's pretreatment dream was of considerable interest for therapy, serving to warn the therapist of the pitfalls and traps that the patient was very likely to set for the therapist in the transference. To recall this dream concerning plotting chess moves, "I make up little chess pitfalls, like the one I really made on my father. That was beautiful. I moved my knight in front of his pawn. He could take it, but if he did, I'd move, he'd move (no matter where), I'd move: mate, or he'd lose his queen. You know, it was a brilliant pitfall, but he didn't fall for it. But I regained the piece and finally beat him with king against king."

As the transference develops and becomes an "oedipal game," as this patient clearly used chess, the therapist was well advised to avoid the traps and pitfalls that the patient did, in fact, devise as therapy went along. This was particularly clear at the time the question arose of discussing his father's sexual preoccupations, and later, when the question of drug use was raised.

As first dreams during treatment are apt to reveal a great deal about a patient's personality structure and difficulties, they also often give clues as well to the present and future state of transference. This patient's first dream apparently included not only his fear of growing up in general, but the animal-like aspects of masturbation, the penalty for which was that of ending up on an operating table. Sexual ideas came up repeatedly and were the more frightening as they encroached on the oedipus. The surgeon of the dream may well have represented the therapist, both liked and feared by the patient in the transference.

Where there is evidence of strong transference involvement on the part of the patient, one would expect that this would be intensified in the presence of severe separation anxiety. This, indeed, seems to have been the fact in this case. Separation played a major role in his life, his parents separating at the time of his grandfather's death. Coping with this paternal separation must have been made more difficult by the persistence of sexual drive resulting from the father's open sexual discussions. As Dr. Porter pointed out, his patient had a total absence of a latency period. This may have been responsible as well for his precocious adolescence, a case illustrating well the fact that adolescence, the psychological transition between childhood and adulthood, may precede physiological puberty. At any rate, that a strong transference relationship occurred very rapidly was evidenced by this patient's response to missing the fifth session. As treatment progressed, his therapist noted that the patient actually verbalized expressions of strong beliefs that he could not accept the fact that the therapist would allow him to grow.

Apparently this patient became increasingly comfortable with the therapist. Clearly, aspects of the transference having been worked through, he became more at home with the fact that the therapist did, indeed, approve of his growth and would neither seduce nor kill him.

He became more able to establish relationships with contemporaries and the interference with his school work, a presenting symptom, disappeared.

This patient has evidently progressed greatly, yet it seemed likely that treatment will have to continue. His dependency needs are still strong and could well interfere with his functioning as he moves toward college. It is likely that the past intensity of the transference might now be threatening to this midadolescent, who may need to keep treatment more superficial than had been the case in the past.

During the course of work with the adolescent, the therapist is many things. By virtue of being an adult he is much more of a reality figure than he is to the adult patient. It is often appropriate to help the adolescent with homework, if asked, or, to render an opinion when asked; ordinarily, with the adult, one would question why the patient has brought problems (of keeping his budget or deciding on a course of action, as examples) to the therapist. With adults who ask about our families, we ask "Why do you ask?" With the adolescent, we may, at times, answer his question directly and perhaps later ask why the question arose. The adolescent rarely profits from transference interpretations. As the schizophrenic or borderline patient may not understand the nature of the transference relationship, knowing himself to be angry at the therapist, and not the therapist as imago, so, too, the adolescent, whose ego structure may resemble that of the borderline or schizophrenic, cannot make such distinctions.

Anna Freud (1946) points out that the child does not form a transference neurosis, because

The child is not, like the adult, ready to produce a new edition of its love-relationships, because, as one might say, the old edition is not yet exhausted. Its original objects, the parents, are still real and present as love-objects— not only in fantasy as with the adult neurotic; between them and the child exist all the relations of everyday life, and all its gratifications and disappointments still in reality depend on them . . . there is no necessity for the child to exchange the parents for him [the analyst].

The adolescent, in his flight from his parental attachments, sometimes functions in the treatment relationship as does the child, sometimes as does the adult: Interpretation of the transference, when it does exist, is made more difficult by this flight. To express it otherwise, the adolescent will fight the inference that he is still involved in what he sees as a child-like relationship to parents and therapist. The task of maintaining a positive therapeutic relationship, necessary for continuing work with the adolescent as with the child, is thus made more difficult. The negative aspects of transference can often more easily be interpreted. To maintain the positive, frequently one can, without any attempt to play a role, emphasize the rapport and object-relation aspects of the relationship. As the adolescent moves into late adolescence, to an ego position closer to that of the adult, the transference proper may be worked through.

Max Sugar: The Family and the Adolescent in Treatment

I should like to begin by complimenting Dr. Porter for having made available the data about this adolescent boy and for his courage in attempting a condensation of approximately five years' work in a few pages.

The early history and the developmental data could have provided perhaps a firmer background for comments, but perhaps they are lacking for reasons of discretion, and therefore we will have to be more speculative than otherwise. My comments focus primarily on aspects of structural development and the therapy of the adolescent patient relative to the family situation.

An important aspect of the therapeutic endeavors with this adolescent was that the therapist was nonjudgmental and nonrestrictive. Initially the therapist was seen and used by Kenny as a narcissistic object choice. This inaugurated a current of positive development which has continued. The more recent sessions indicate that the therapist had been used for identifications of a major sort and for very important elements of his ego ideal as well as superego. The therapist made himself readily available and reliable. This was quite unlike Kenny's father, who was unreliable, unpredictable, undermining, and inappropriately stimulating, which made it even more difficult than usual for the patient to develop a more appropriate type of superego as well as ego and ego ideal.

Kenny was given the opportunity to improve his own judgment by being allowed to make his own choices, such as his request that the therapist help him stop his father's sexual talk, as well as Kenny's interest in continuing to take pot or acid, and the therapist's endeavors to be interpretive rather than restrictive. This, it seems, promoted further integration. It also facilitated some resolution of his conflict about fears of abandonment (noted in his early transference reactions to Dr. Porter when he went on a trip and his wish to abandon father).

Beginning with the superego, a harsh critical one (and the symptom of headache which may have been an expression of the conflict between the ego and superego), there was a gradual shift that has led to the current state where there is a varying degree of wavering about a set of values of his own and a somewhat less severe and less critical superego.

Working with adolescents or others who are realistically dependent, the cooperation of parents or guardians is of vital importance if the therapy is to be successful. In this case the cooperation of the parents apparently was quite readily available, and there was minimal interference throughout the therapy except by the ordinary maladaptiveness of the parents, particularly the father. The mother's sexually stimulating behavior was dealt with by the therapist and the mother apparently responded very readily to the guidance offered her. Dr. Porter's use of the mother as an ally underscores the much-needed cooperation of every family in treatment.

There is a question, however, of how the matter of the fees being paid by the father might work in other situations. It is not clear why the father was able to be brought in as a continual guarantor and provider of the fee, as he was not the domiciliary parent, he had sabotaging tendencies, and his lack of money had been used as the principal mode of expressing marital conflict. Frequently in such a situation, arrangements for the fee may be used for blackmail, bribery, or extorting certain advantages from the other parent or from the child. In my own experience, though it may work quite comfortably as it did here for Dr. Porter, frequently it seems to work more smoothly if the parent with whom the youngster is domiciled takes the responsibility for the fee whether the other parent pays for it indirectly or not.

Kenny's wish for therapy and feeling caught in a conflict between the parents may be a reflection of his being used as another target for their marital conflicts which aggravated his conflict about divided loyalties and guilt about wavering toward one or the other parent. Children of divorced parents often have the fantasy of reuniting the parents because of their guilt about their fantasied contribution to the divorce.

Dr. Porter indicates that he felt that if Kenny had a latency period at all it was very short. Perhaps the situation of Kenny's short latency period may be viewed from another viewpoint. Perhaps there was no latency period of the usual variety because there was never a satisfactory resolution of the oedipal phase. During initial phases of treatment Kenny first needed to develop an oedipus complex and then to resolve it. Essentially, this youngster was in a preoedipal phase when first seen,

527

which may have been reflected in his early obsessional behavior, particularly with school work. His early statements about needing both parents seem to indicate his fear of abandonment, which is more characteristic of the preoedipal child than the oedipal or latency child. His difficulty in forming an attachment with a female therapist indicates that perhaps there were some beginnings of an oedipal conflict, and his initial strong and immediate tie to a male therapist, Dr. Porter, may be a wish to remove himself from his attachments to his mother. However, such an attachment may be overdetermined. In any case, he formed a strong ambivalent tie to the therapist which has persisted throughout treatment.

It is especially significant and noteworthy that the paternal grandfather died when Kenny was eight. Apparently the father became disorganized at that time and the parents separated and divorced. The antecedent disturbances and father's reality testing are not detailed, but we have to assume such disturbances were interfering factors that, in some way, contributed to the lack of an oedipus complex and its resolution before the age of eight. Also, there is no material indicating that Kenny had the usual fantasies of the family romance, which by its absences indicates the lack of resolution of the oedipus complex.

The tasks of the latency period child are to change oral and anal drives into character traits and to develop defenses against pregenital drives. When there is severe trauma, especially loss through death or divorce of parents, this development is interfered with and leads to an excessive development of guilt. This, in turn, results in some defect in character structure and in the management of impulses. The subsequent defenses are usually directed exclusively toward the management of pregenital drives.

Kenny's father criticized both his wife and the paternal grandmother. He encouraged Kenny to emulate him and disregard mother's discipline. After his father left, Kenny may have believed his father was a misbehaving sibling who had been sent away to a boarding school. We do not know the extent of Kenny's involvement with his grandfather, nor the impact his death had. The loss of his grandfather and then his father may have activated fears of loss of his mother and loss of love. It would seem therefore, that he never developed a suitable superego appropriate for the ordinary latency period child. This would also tend to foster a clinging, symbiotic, compliant attitude to both his mother and father.

When his mother moved to a new neighborhood, Kenny's difficulties increased and were then projected onto the environment. He was not

528

able to talk about the loss of his father, but he was able to talk about the loss of his peers and play groups in the old neighborhood, as well as old school ties. This seems to have been the only way he could sum up any feelings about the loss of his home and his father. Being an only child with a single woman must certainly have increased his need to defend himself against sexual feelings and contributed to being fixated at a pregenital level. He may have done this in response to his own drives and the mother's needs. The situation of a mother living alone with a pubescent son is often fraught with danger for the boy in that the mother often unconsciously tends to direct many of her sexual and aggressive impulses toward him. She may disparage him unwittingly and cast aspersions at him that formerly were directed to the spouse. They activate and therefore arouse further defensive measures against incestuous feelings.

The need for the early adolescent to begin separating from the family psychologically is well known (Blos, 1962; Sugar, 1968), but Kenny's situation led him to feel he could not give up either parent. Perhaps one of the contributing factors to this need was the father's homosexual tie to him and vice versa, which interfered with his separating from the parents and also inhibited the development of sexual and aggressive drives. It also interfered with the consolidation of his genital drives and his defenses against pregenital impulses. The father's fragmented ego served as a poor model for identification and further ego and superego development.

The regression during the first year of therapy with oral and anal somatic symptoms, which usually occurred on appointment days, seems to relate to his feelings about his mother and demonstrates his need to be expulsive and keep distant as well as to be cared for and almost cuddled. The ambivalence about wishing to be cared for and at the same time getting rid of mother is further highlighted by his dream and angry response to the interpretation of his wish for her death.

As therapy progressed there was some separation from the mother, which led to Kenny's moving away. There was also some separation and differentiation from the father, and there was a transference shift of his need to be close to the therapist; this was evident when he described hanging around and brushing up close to the desk and to the therapist. The more recent therapeutic sessions indicate that the separation protest phase, or second individuation phase (Blos 1962), has developed. There has been some mourning for the parental objects, a sine qua non for the psychological development of the adolescent. It seems that at the present time there is a shift toward other females. Even the separation from Dr. Porter may be viewed as an effort at separation from the parents, Dr. Porter having assumed the mother's role in the transference.

Now there seems to be an overlapping of the maternal transference with the reworking of the oedipal conflict. An oedipus complex developed during treatment, one that is currently being worked on as well as separation from the parents. There are still many oral and anal derivatives interfering. There is evidence of mourning for object loss, that is, the mother, as well as for the unfulfilled ego ideal. There is some fear of his genital drives and superego components.

It would seem that this youngster is now well on his way and is very deeply involved in therapy. At this point he might embark on a much more intensive and deeper level of therapy. The question of diagnosis was not mentioned. I believe he is now compulsive. When he first entered treatment he might have been classified as a borderline patient.

Julian I. Barish: *Engaging the Adolescent in Psychotherapy*

Each patient in psychotherapy presents a different set of psychodynamic, biological, family, and social conditions; and each therapist uses a frame of reference and therapeutic techniques compatible with his own personality, training, and experience. Hence, psychotherapy is highly individualized, a unique event for patient and therapist; and psychotherapeutic techniques have an infinite variety that defies comprehensive description. Yet, it is possible to observe features held in common and in a limited way to abstract unifying concepts. My focus is on the intricate, spontaneous process of engaging adolescents in psychotherapy, describing two techniques of engagement derived from a frequently occurring emotional conflict.

THE PROCESS OF ENGAGEMENT

The first task in psychotherapy is to engage the patient. Engagement may be defined as the initial involvement of patient and therapist in an emotional relationship conducive to work toward therapeutic goals.

The case summary on Kenny reports that Kenny asked for treatment and that he was articulate and serious about his problems. Ostensibly, the therapist had little to do to engage him in treatment. But the apparent ease of engagement is deceptive. We can assume that Dr. Porter responded in facilitating ways to Kenny's self-presentation, guiding himself by his understanding of Kenny's need.

DEPENDENCY CONFLICT IN ADOLESCENCE

Kenny's statement to the consultant was, "I've got to have someone I can bring my problems about my parents—because I still need both of them." Kenny, who was not quite an adolescent when he began therapy, said clearly that he needed help from his parents and from the therapist. Kenny's open admission contrasts with adolescents' typical intolerance of their dependency needs. Adolescents are, at long last, "grown up," a fact in which considerable self-esteem is invested. But they are not ready for full responsibility, and their new status is challenging. At times they secretly yearn for the dependent role of childhood, and the temptation to regress is threatening. They battle with parents about freedom of action, and they act out the dependency conflict with characteristic zest and scope. Often enough, they cannot ask for help except by overvehement denial of their need or by behavior provocative enough to demand intervention. In treatment a popular opening gambit is, "If only parents and society would let us alone everything would be all right."

TECHNIQUE OF RESPONDING TO DEPENDENCY CONFLICT

The near-universal dependency conflict in adolescence furnishes the conceptual basis for a technique of engagement—an implicit response to both sides of the conflict. On the one hand the therapist gives help freely, saving the patient the embarrassment of asking and the humiliation of admitting that he is not so self-sufficient as he would like to be; on the other hand he reassures the fear of regressive dependency by insisting that the patient contribute his share.

Promptness seems to be a more important consideration in engaging adolescents than it is with children or adults. The critical time for engagement is often in the first session, sometimes in the first few minutes and almost invariably within the first few sessions. An adolescent who is not engaged early is likely to be off and running, or perhaps worse, to remain in body only. For adolescents in a hospital there is less urgency. As relatively captive subjects in psychotherapy, inpatients pose a special set of problems and opportunities.

The engagement process begins before the first session. Preinterview preparations may be helpful. The therapist orients himself and makes preliminary psychodynamic inferences from whatever information is available. Instructions to parents may be necessary on how to inform a rebellious, suspicious, or otherwise recalcitrant adolescent about the consultation. (As an example, "Explain the visit as an evaluation and a possible source of help. Do not use trickery or deception. Listen to but do not counter verbal protests; avoid threats, bribes, and arguments. Expect his compliance. At the appointed hour say 'It's time to go.' "). Arranging the first appointment directly with the adolescent is desirable but not often practical. The first session may include one or both parents, but the patient should be seen first, and alone.

The therapist's opening statement to the patient can structure the dual approach to the dependency conflict. It varies in style and content, but it might include a summary of what the therapist already knows about the patient, for example, "Your mother told me on the telephone that you're having trouble, you've flunked two courses, and you're having arguments at home about smoking marijuana. Perhaps I can help. I'm interested in knowing how you feel about this."

The technical principle of working with both sides of the dependency conflict can be applied repeatedly in the first interview. The therapist actively directs the inquiry, asking as many and as pointed questions as necessary to understand the problem and to elicit the patient's full response. He listens actively, offering occasional comments about the history as it unfolds, and he asks the patient for his comments in return.

The same technique of gratifying realistic dependency needs (realistic because the patient presumably has shown that he cannot resolve his problems alone) and of reassuring the fear of regressive dependency may be applied by defining the roles of therapist and patient. Suggesting continued visits for further exploration the therapist may say, "I know something about the meaning of such problems and I'll help you understand them. But you have an essential contribution to make; you are the expert on your own feelings. You will need to observe your reactions and bring them up for discussion."

With this technique the therapist uses his own emotional responses to satisfy the patient's dependency needs within realistic limits. In his therapeutic use of self, the therapist demonstrates that he cares and that he is responsive to the patient's needs. Equally important, the therapist shows respect for the adolescent's status; he does not infantilize him; he manifests age-appropriate expectations; he demonstrates that he will not exploit the patient for his own needs as parents often do. He encourages the patient to pursue self-understanding, to become aware of his feelings, and to be guided by those that are constructive. When realistic

532

help is thus offered and the fear of regression is reassured, the adolescent's characteristic intense interest in understanding himself and others can emerge.

TECHNIQUE OF INTERPRETATION

So far the discussion has concerned a technique of engagement based on an implicit understanding of a common trend in adolescents—a conflict about dependency. A second technique, complementing the first, is one of explicit interpretation. The therapist offers, as soon as is practical, a psychodynamic interpretation of some aspect of the presenting problem. Whereas the first technique of working with the dependency conflict fosters a therapeutic alliance, an interpretation strengthens it by beginning therapeutic work on a specific problem.

In the case summary, the first recorded interpretation was in the third session, following the initial dream of treatment. Of many possible inferences Dr. Porter selected for interpretation one dealing with Kenny's conflict about growing up. Dr. Porter developed the interpretation gradually in a dialogue with Kenny. It was couched in Kenny's everyday language and was offered tentatively. (Kenny argued vigorously against the interpretation, a sign of active engagement in the therapeutic process.)

Selection of an opening dynamic issue is highly individualized, determined not only by the presenting problem but by the therapist's frame of reference. In practice, the initial interpretation may focus on any facet of motivation, the main requirement being a sound therapeutic rationale. Similarly, the language, extent, and form of interpretation may vary widely. The point emphasized here is the value of early interpretation of a central dynamic issue.

CASE ILLUSTRATIONS

Two clinical vignettes will illustrate diverse applications of the techniques.

Case 1

Bob, a tall, obese seventeen-year-old high school senior was referred for therapy because a few months before graduation he had stopped attending classes. His mother arranged the first appointment and he accompanied her with skepticism, but without protest. Seen alone, he tried to answer questions about himself but could manage only brief responses. By dint of persistent questioning his story emerged. He had never liked school and had not done much homework but he was bright enough to pass without working in grammar school. As a freshman in high school he had avoided failure by dropping a course when he fell behind. Shortly before the end of his junior year he had stopped going to two courses and failed both. Early in his senior year he had again stopped attending classes but forced himself to return after a few weeks. Recently he had found it impossible to concentrate on homework and had cut classes rather than admit he had not done his assignments. His explanation of his behavior was that he did not care about school and would rather be doing something else. Moreover, he was too embarrassed now to confront the teachers. Still, he did want to graduate and to go on to college. Further questioning revealed that his father was a huge, authoritarian man who demanded instant obedience. His mother, less strict, tended to nag him about his homework. Before the end of the session an offer was made (and accepted) to intercede with the school about suspension, and to request his parents to ease the pressure so that he might work out the problem himself. In addition, his explanation of the problem was challenged and an alternative proposed that he was handicapped by a hidden emotional interference. Afterwards, his mother corroborated his history and added that he had been offered boarding school but that he had been reluctant to leave home.

Bob appeared alone for the second visit and was more voluble. His current circumstances and his background were reviewed at greater length. With prompting, he recognized his fear of expressing his anger directly at his father, and by the third session an interpretation was offered of the passive-aggressive intent of his school avoidance. Bob was visibly impressed with the new perspective about himself and corroborated the idea with enthusiasm. He returned to school, did not graduate, but arranged to repeat his senior year away from home.

This passive, skeptical, emotionally blocked boy was engaged in meaningful psychotherapy by virtue of a vigorous effort to get essential information, an active appreciation of his feelings and his needs, an insistence that he contribute to the therapeutic exploration and especially by direct interpretation. He rapidly became involved in a working relationship with awareness of feelings he had previously suppressed.

Case 2

Eve, a petite 14-year-old girl, who lived with her divorced mother, had become unmanageable at home and at school during the past year.

534

She had been in a boarding school since the age of four following the divorce and her mother's return to work. She had been visited weekly by the mother and had spent summers at camp. The father had disappeared until Eve was nine, and then he saw her sporadically. Around the same time she had returned home to live and to attend a day school. Problems had arisen, and Eve started in psychotherapy. During the past year she had again attended boarding school and she had been expelled for disciplinary reasons. Returning home, she refused to abide by any restrictions and was assaultive with her mother and maids. One day when she returned from an unauthorized all night outing she was met by ambulance attendants who gently but firmly escorted her to the closed ward of a psychiatric hospital.

On admission to the hospital Eve was in a state of stunned disbelief but soon accommodated herself to her new surroundings. She refused to leave the closed ward except for psychotherapy sessions. She willingly related her life story but would not accept any responsibility for her behavior. Her view was that she had no problems except her mother who did not trust her to take care of herself.

After a few days Eve began to request privileges and was given slightly more than she asked for. She was helped to get the belongings she wished. She was not pressed to attend activities until she asked to do so. She asked for more and longer therapy sessions, filling them with requests, complaints about her mother, and threats of running away. Invariably, she was righteously indignant when confronted with infractions of hospital rules. When angry she would storm out of the office, to return hours later in a friendly mood. On occasion, when she looked angry, forlorn, and friendless, she was hugged. She adopted a warm but wary manner with the therapist and there was a sense of increasing, if ambivalent, attachment. She derided the therapist's comments about her feelings and behavior, but at intervals brought out bits of "confidential" information, apparently testing the therapist's trustworthiness, and alluded to other information she would not yet divulge.

Eve's dependency conflict was a central problem, antedating, but accentuated by, her adolescence. Her fierce independence strongly denied her ambivalent ties to her mother. Alternately she wished to leave, to destroy, and to be reunited with the depriving, controlling mother.

Eve was engaged in a therapeutic relationship by means of demonstrative responses, within a hospital setting, to her dependency needs and to her conflicting wish for autonomy. The impact of the therapist's responses was increased by the degree of control over daily life that a

535

hospital provides. Interpretations of dynamic issues were less important in the engagement process.

SUMMARY

Two complementary techniques in the process of engaging adolescents in psychotherapy have been described. The first promotes engagement by implicit responses to both sides of the adolescent's dependency conflict; the second is an interpretative technique of cementing the engagement by beginning work on a specific dynamic issue. Both techniques require early and active involvement of the therapist.

Malvina W. Kremer: Summary Discussion

As moderator, I have the privilege of closing this workshop on techniques in the psychotherapy of adolescents by congratulating Dr. Porter for bringing us this very challenging case history. I take this opportunity also to thank Drs. Giovacchini, Loeb, Sugar, and Barish for their excellent discussions. I will not attempt to summarize all that has been said, but I will make some comments on the formal and floor discussions as well as on the case itself.

There was general agreement that Dr. Porter's patient was a very unusual adolescent in many respects. From the point of view of technique, the most remarkable feature was his continued earnest attempt to deal with his problems. As a result the process of engaging him in therapy, often a difficult task, proved to be a minor issue. As a rule the task is not a simple one, so that the therapist ordinarily must give a good deal of thought to his procedures. I liked Dr. Barish's suggestions for responding to the dependency conflict and making early, explicit interpretations. There is probably no general rule for engaging an adolescent. Engagement is often all a dynamic concept and consists of a series of steps. Some would say that a patient is not really "engaged" until he has brought in a dream or made a significant interpretation by himself.

In the course of the floor discussion Dr. Porter pointed out that he had not found it necessary to make many formal interpretations. He found it more useful to raise questions and allow his patient to arrive at the interpretations. This tactic proved satisfactory because of the patient's diligence in the therapeutic world. At the same time this tactic also served to highlight one aspect of the role of interpretation. It seemed as though this patient gradually became aware of problems,

536

grappled with them, gathered his strength, tested out ways of dealing with them, and then made the interpretation. He started with an obvious trend toward intellectualism and profound doubts about himself and his relations to the people around him. To me it seems that the therapy was a continuing series of tests, of the therapist, then of his parents, of his impulses, of his peers, all intertwined.

The early dream of the ball game with the chimpanzees in which he had to struggle to keep himself from turning entirely into a chimpanzee illustrates how he viewed himself at the outset. The self-representation evidently came from the father's remark, "Where will we get enough bananas to feed this little monkey?" The father must have told the boy this story, and he never did feed his child what he really needed. But the boy was also depicting his expectation that the surgeon would cure his troubles and be very surprised at what would be found was underneath the skin.

I do not feel so certain about the universality of the dependency conflict and fear of growing up to which several of the panalists referred. I think that Dr. Porter's patient was not afraid of dependency but rather that he felt he could not depend on his parents. As a consequence, he also felt that no one else would be dependable. Dr. Porter proved himself to be dependable, reasonable, and consistent. Above all, Dr. Porter conveyed his implicit respect and confidence in the patient by allowing him to find his own way at many crucial points. The patient was thus able to develop some sense of reliance on a significant figure on whom he was really more dependent than he realized, at the very same time that he was developing self-reliance and independence. The dream about boys and girls sharing a bunk at camp like brothers and sisters had an obvious sexual significance in the context of the then current situation. I would like to stress the other detail of the dream, namely, that there were no counselors and the boys and girls were managing by themselves. I take this to be an expression of his growing sense of strength and his capability. Dr. Porter mentioned that to his surprise the boy's own comment about the dream was that children under five "don't know enough to be bitter and disappointed." Disappointed in what? In the light of the history of this case the disappointment must have been in his parents for failing him and in himself for not being able to somehow overcome the lack. This dream came after one in which he was doing well in baseball mainly because of the errors of other players. Then there were a number of dreams in which he was succeeding in dramatics and various sports. He was by this time satisfied that Dr. Porter really wanted him to succeed. All this was necessary to enable him to see himself among his peers getting along well and without adult supervision, a condition imposed on him by the nature of the parents' personality problems. This dream provides an interesting contrast with the pretreatment dream about the chess game in which he tried to trap his father. The father avoided the trap but the patient won "king against king." As any chess player knows, and as the boy must have known, king against king is not a win but a stalemate. That must have been what the boy feared was happening to him, but in the dream he got around the problem by ignoring the rules.

Dr. Porter's willingness to let his patient make his own decisions on such important issues as marijuana and LSD was the subject of discussion from the floor. Several members of the audience raised questions about this apparent permissiveness. Dr. Giovacchini was of the opinion that the therapist must be permissive, but within limits. Dr. Barish pointed out that the therapist has varying degrees of responsibility in these matters depending to some extent on the situation, but a therapist in the hospital has both moral and legal responsibility for patients in his custody. Dr. Gaukler felt that as therapist he reflects cultural values but he cannot be the enforcer of these values. Dr. Sugar agreed that the therapist cannot be the prohibitor nor should he be the seducer. Summing up, Dr. Porter suggested that the therapist must fundamentally be a sanctioner not a prohibitor. He had firm confidence throughout that his patient would in the final outcome make constructive and satisfactory decisions.

I would add that this sense of confidence must have been conveyed to the patient and contributed a very important element to the boy's development. Adolescents, I believe, are remarkably sensitive to the therapist's expectations. The therapist's confidence that the patient will do well or his fears that he will make bad choices influence the choices that the patient actually makes. Perhaps the issue of permissiveness is really a question of what we anticipate our patients will do.

This workshop addressed itself to the problem of techniques. The case report posed many important questions. The discussions revealed many areas of agreement and some minor shades of difference in approach. This is in itself a matter of considerable interest. It points to a certain degree of convergence when therapists of varying background are confronted with specific clinical material. It points also to the sharpening delineation of techniques that are especially applicable in the therapy of patients in the adolescent age group.

REFERENCES

Blos, P. (1962). On adolescence. A psychoanalytic interpretation. Glencoe: The Free Press.

Freud, A. (1946). The psycho-analytical treatment of children. New York: International Universities Press.

Giovacchini, P. L. (1965). Psychopathological aspects of the identity sense. Psychiatry Digest, 26:31–41.

Holmes, D. J. (1964). The adolescent in psychotherapy. Boston: Little, Brown.

Pearson, G., ed. (1968). A handbook of child psychoanalysis. New York: Basic Books.

Spitz, R. A. (1945). Hospitalism. An inquiry into the genesis of psychiatric conditions in early childhood. Psychoanalytic Study of the Child, 1:53–74. New York: International Universities Press.

Sugar, M. (1968). Normal adolescent mourning. American Journal of Psychotherapy, 22:258–269.

Winnicott, D. W. (1954). Mind and its relation to the psyche soma. British Journal of Med., Psychol., 37.

INDEX

541

Index